S0-BKT-407

CARDIAC FUNCTION IN HEALTH AND DISEASE

ROBERT J. MARSHALL, M.D., F.R.C.P.I., M.R.C.P.

Professor of Medicine, West Virginia
University School of Medicine.

JOHN T. SHEPHERD, M.D., M.Ch., D.Sc.

Professor of Physiology, Mayo
Graduate School of Medicine,
and Chairman, Section of
Physiology and Biophysics,
Mayo Clinic.

W. B. SAUNDERS COMPANY / Philadelphia · London · Toronto / 1968

W. B. Saunders Company: West Washington Square
Philadelphia, Pa. 19105

12 Dyott Street
London W.C.1

1835 Yonge Street
Toronto 7, Ontario

Cardiac Function in Health and Disease

 Made in the United States of America. Press of W. B. Saunders Company. Library of Congress catalog card number 68-11637.

To our wives

PREFACE

The development of techniques for cardiac catheterization by Cournand and McMichael and their respective colleagues about 1941 provided a powerful and continuing stimulus for the study of the human circulation.

The ensuing quarter century has seen the application and validation of the direct Fick principle and the indicator-dilution method for the measurement of cardiac output, the refinement of catheter-manometer systems for the measurement of intracardiac and intravascular pressures, the introduction of oximetry, and the development of flowmeters. These and other techniques have permitted increasingly accurate measurement of physiological phenomena. As a consequence, we now understand the function of the intact human heart as well as that of the laboratory animal. Major advances have followed in cardiovascular pharmacology and in the diagnosis and surgical correction of structural defects of the heart.

The exponential rate of growth of knowledge has made it difficult for a newcomer to survey this increasingly complex field. We therefore felt it timely to review some of what is currently known. In our book we have chosen to discuss particularly the dynamics of the human heart; electrophysiological and biochemical aspects of cardiac function are considered only insofar as they are directly pertinent to our principal theme.

Detailed consideration of the theoretical basis and practical application of the various physiological techniques devised to study the cardiovascular system is beyond the scope of this book. The information has been published in such works as the *Handbook of Physiology*, Section 2: *Circulation*, Volumes 1–3 (American Physiological Society) and Glasser's *Medical Physics* (Year Book Publishers), to which the interested reader is referred.

In writing this book, we have had in mind several groups of people:

senior medical students; resident physicians and fellows, particularly those developing a special interest in cardiology or cardiovascular surgery; young investigators desirous of obtaining a broad understanding of cardiovascular function before selecting an area for special study; and established clinicians and investigators seeking an up-to-date survey of aspects of cardiac function with which they are not familiar.

Our thanks are due to Mrs. Mary Alice Bowers and Mrs. Carole Pitman for preparation of the manuscript, to Dr. Peter Viles for its appraisal and to the Editorial Staff of the W. B. Saunders Company for their encouragement and advice.

ROBERT J. MARSHALL
JOHN T. SHEPHERD

CONTENTS

Chapter 1

CARDIAC DYNAMICS AT REST

- Contractile Properties of Heart Muscle
- Cardiac Output in the Supine Position
- Cardiac Output in the Upright Position
- Oxygen Saturation of Blood in the Heart and Great Vessels
- Cardiac Volume
- Intracardiac and Intravascular Pressures

CONTRACTILE PROPERTIES OF HEART MUSCLE

The contractile proteins of heart muscle are arranged in the longitudinal myofibrils, each of which consists of repeating units, the sarcomeres. Sarcomeres are composed of myofilaments, which are macromolecular complexes of contractile proteins. There are two types of myofilaments (Fig. 1-1). The thicker type, limited to the A band in the center of the sarcomere, consists of myosin; the thinner type, presumably consisting mainly of actin, courses from the Z line to the A band (Huxley and Hanson, 1954).

The sarcoplasmic reticulum is the structural basis for the link between the electrical phenomenon at the cell membrane and the contraction and relaxation of the muscle protein within the cell (Spiro and Sonnenblick, 1964). This reticulum consists of a network of anastomosing, membrane lined intracellular channels which encircle the myofibrils and also approach the cell surface. The sarcoplasmic reticulum has two components. The first consists of communicating tubules that run longitudinally in close apposition to individual sarcomeres but do not penetrate the Z lines. The second consists of intermediary vesicles that are continuous with the cell membrane (sarcolemma) and penetrate the cell transversely at the level of the Z line. The two components approach each other closely but do not communicate. Continuity of the vesicles with the cell membrane may facilitate the spread of excitation from the sarcolemma to the individual sarcomeres. Ionized calcium links the electrical phenomena of the membrane to the mechanical events of contraction in the intact cell (Frank, 1964); it is released from the sarcoplasmic reticulum during excitation and is trapped by the reticulum to effect relaxation.

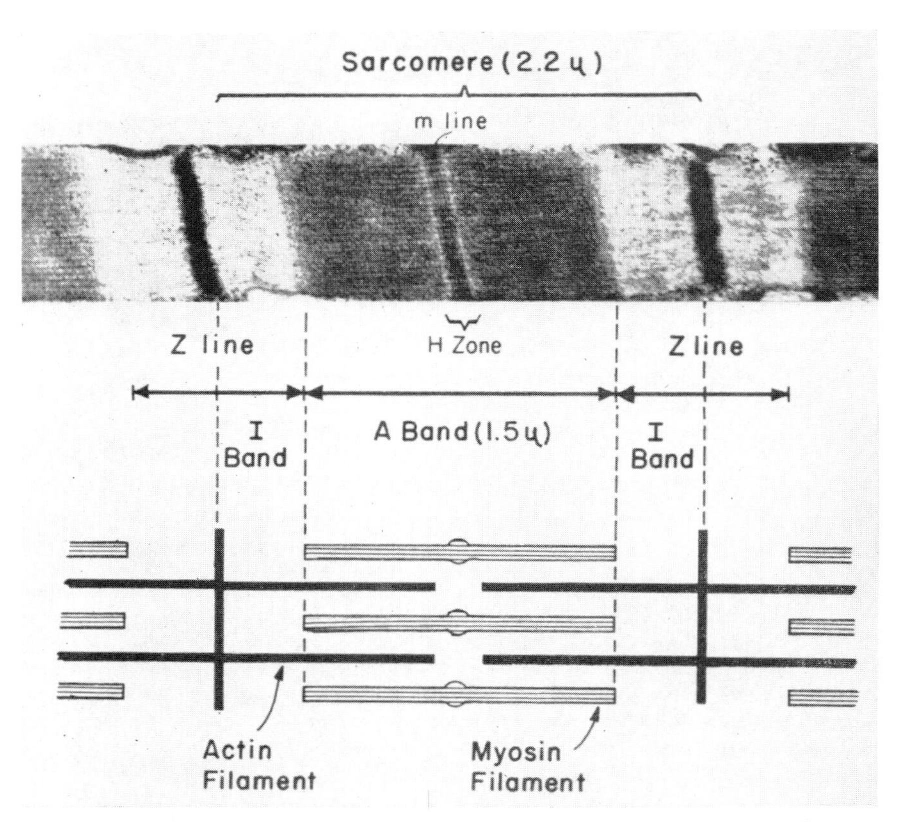

FIGURE 1-1. Diagram of filamentous fine structure of the sarcomere (*below*) in relation to the sarcomere band pattern (*above*). (From Sonnenblick, Spiro and Spotnitz, Am. Heart J., *68*:336, 1964.)

The most obvious difference in the structure of skeletal and cardiac muscle is the presence of large numbers of mitochondria in the latter; these are undoubtedly related to the capacity of myocardium for continual activity. Adenosine triphosphate (ATP), the immediate source of energy for muscle, is formed within the mitochondria during the oxidation of substrates by the process of oxidative phosphorylation. The completeness with which the process of phosphorylation is coupled with that of oxidation determines whether the energy liberated by the oxidation of substrates becomes available for useful mechanical work by the contractile apparatus (Chidsey et al., 1966).

The similarity of structure of the myofibrils in skeletal and cardiac muscle suggests that the sliding filament hypothesis (Huxley, 1961) accounts for the changes in length of heart muscle. This hypothesis involves an interaction between the two sets of filaments: the thin actin filaments slide past the thicker myosin filaments to shorten or lengthen the sarcomeres and, therefore, the muscle cell as a whole. The thick and thin filaments, which are said to remain constant in length (Huxley and Hanson, 1954), may interact by virtue of the specific force developing bridges formed between them (Huxley, 1957). In the resting state, the cross bridges, which are projecting parts of the myosin filaments, are not attached to the actin filaments, and they are free, therefore, to slide past them. When the muscle is active, the cross bridges become attached to specific sites on the actin filaments. This leads, in some unknown fashion, to the development of a force between the filaments and, if the muscle is allowed to shorten, to movement (Huxley, 1961). The bridges then become detached and, if movement has occurred, they are free to form other attachments farther along the actin filament. Each bridge undertakes a number of such cycles when the muscle is active, and different tensions can be developed depending upon the number of cross bridges that are active at the same time.

Hill (1949) regarded muscle as a system with two components—a contractile element arranged in series with an elastic component. The activated contractile element is capable of developing force and shortening, while the series elastic acts as a passive non-linear spring. Whereas the passive series elastic is characterized by its load-extension properties, the active contractile element may be defined in terms of four dimensions: force, velocity, instantaneous muscle length and time (Sonnenblick, 1965). The relation among the first three dimensions is unique for any given contractile state of the muscle. Thus, a change in the velocity coordinates of this relation may be used to define a change in the contractile state of the muscle.

Patterson et al. (1914), using the heart-lung preparation, found a direct relationship between the diastolic volume of the ventricles and the energy liberated during the subsequent systole. They concluded that "the law of the heart is, therefore, the same as that of the skeletal muscle: namely, that the mechanical energy set free on passage from the resting to the contracted state depends on the area of chemically active surfaces, i.e., on the length of the muscle fibers." This is now referred to as the Frank-Starling law of the heart. It is based on the relationship between the initial length of and the tension developed by cardiac muscle. The ultrastructural basis for this relationship may be the degree of overlap of thick and thin filaments (Sonnenblick et al., 1964). An increase in length over the physiological range appears to cause only an increase in the ability of the contractile element to develop force and not an increase in its intrinsic velocity (Sonnenblick, 1962).

Sonnenblick et al. (1965) examined the relationships between initial length and developed tension in papillary muscles excised from patients who were having their mitral valves replaced by prostheses. All length-tension curves were obtained at 30°C. and at a frequency of 12 contractions per minute. As the muscle was lengthened, both active and resting tensions

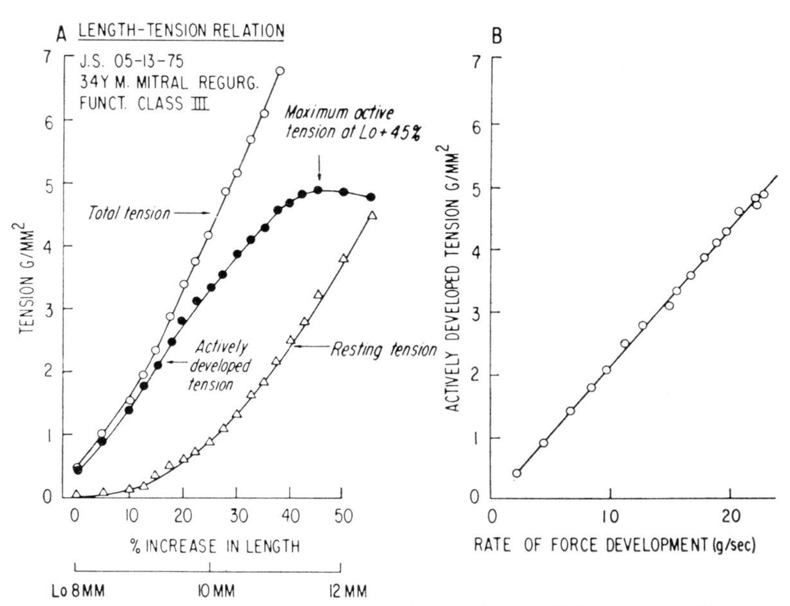

FIGURE 1-2. *A.* Length-tension relationships of excised human papillary muscle. Abscissa: muscle length (mm.), and per cent increase in length above Lo (length at which both resting and active tensions approach zero). Frequency of contractions: 12 per minute. Cross section of muscle: 3.6 $mm.^2$. *B.* Relationship between actively developed tension and maximal rate of development of isometric force. (From Sonnenblick, Braunwald and Morrow, J. Clin. Invest., *44*:966, 1965.)

increased (Fig. 1-2*A*). The peak of the curve relating length to activity was attained when the muscle was stretched to an average value of 151 per cent of that at which both resting and active tensions approached zero. With further increase in length, actively developed tension began to decline. The time from the onset of contraction to the instant at which peak tension was achieved was independent of muscle length. When muscle length was increased, the maximal rate of force development was found to be a linear function of actively developed tension (Fig. 1-2*B*). The large increases of tension that occurred in response to small increases in initial length illustrate the potential usefulness of the Frank-Starling mechanism when increases in the force of cardiac contraction are required. As the peak of the curve relating length to active tension was approached, the slope of the curve relating length to resting tension increased steeply (Fig. 1-2*A*).

In their studies of the force-velocity relationship, Sonnenblick et al. (1965) set the initial length of the muscle by a small preload, which was maintained constant for the entire curve. The effect on the velocity of shortening of progressive increases in the afterload was then determined from single contractions of the muscle. An inverse relation was observed between the afterload and both the initial velocity of shortening and the extent of shortening (Fig. 1-3). The time required from the application of the stimulus to the development of maximal shortening was independent of the magnitude of the afterload.

Thus, an increase in initial muscle length increases the maximal force of isometric contraction without altering the maximal velocity of shortening. It appears that alterations in initial muscle length change the total number of active contractile sites in the muscle without affecting the rate of their interaction (Sonnenblick, 1965).

The development of force by muscle requires the interaction of the contractile element with the series elastic component. As the former shortens, the latter is extended. If the external ends of the muscle are fixed (isometric contraction), the rate of force development by the muscle depends not only on the force-velocity relations of the contractile element, but also upon the stress-strain characteristics of the passive, spring-like series elastic. Hence, during the period of so-called isometric contraction of car-

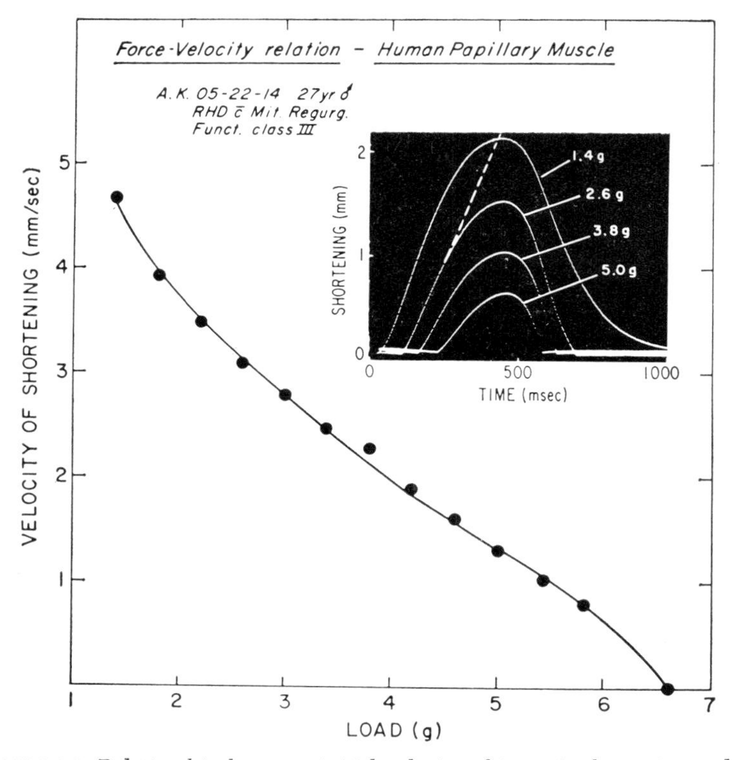

FIGURE 1-3. Relationship between initial velocity of isotonic shortening and afterload. Frequency of contractions: 12 per minute. Cross section of muscle: 3.6 mm.^{2}. Preload: 1.4 g. with a muscle length of 15 mm. *Inset:* oscillograms from which experimental points were calculated, with corresponding afterloads. (From Sonnenblick, Braunwald and Morrow, J. Clin. Invest., *44*:966, 1965.)

diac muscle, significant shortening of the contractile element occurs. This accounts for the apparent discrepancy between the actual work performed by the contractile element and the calculated external work performed by the isolated muscle or the intact heart (Britman and Levine, 1964). Thus, when the frequency of contraction was increased in the experiments of Sonnenblick et al. (1965), the duration of contraction diminished, but the velocity of shortening increased reciprocally. The resultant force developed, or the extent of shortening, remained relatively unchanged. Thus, at any given muscle length, the improved contractile state of the muscle resulting from an increase in the frequency of contraction was reflected by the augmented power developed by the muscle, but improvement was not evident in the external work performed.

It can be shown that the Starling mechanism is operative in normal subjects after the influence of the autonomic nervous system has been removed. Intravenous infusion of 1.5 liters of blood in normal subjects caused little or no change in cardiac output or stroke volume, although the filling pressure of the ventricles was increased. A similar infusion, following pharmacological blockade of the autonomic ganglia, increased the left ventricular end-diastolic pressure from 5 to about 22 cm. H_2O; cardiac output, stroke volume, left ventricular work, left ventricular power and tension-time index were increased; and the duration and mean rate of left ven-

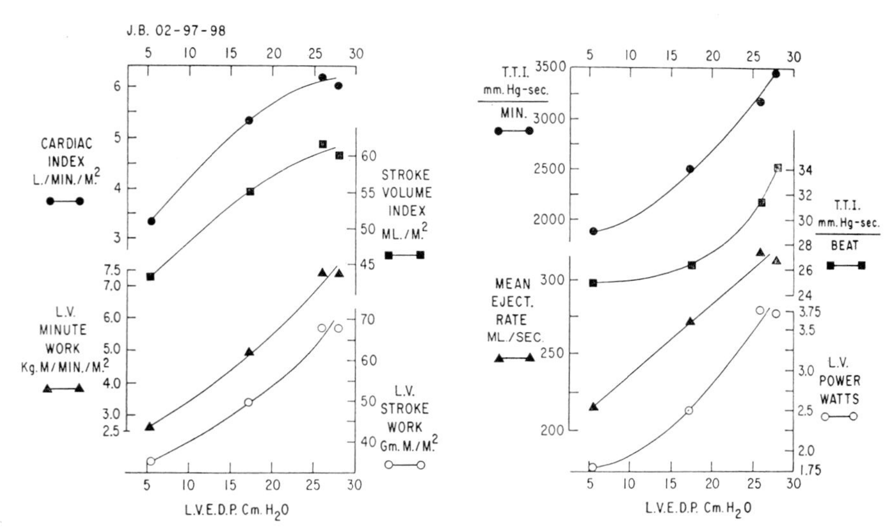

FIGURE 1-4. Relationships between LVEDP (difference between left ventricular and esophageal pressures at end-diastole) and various parameters of left ventricular performance in a normal subject in whom autonomic nervous activity had been suppressed with Arfonad. TTI (tension-time index) was calculated from the area under the systolic portion of the arterial pressure pulse. LV minute work was the product of mean arterial pressure (cm. H_2O) and cardiac output (liters per minute) divided by 1000. (From Braunwald, Frahm and Ross, J. Clin. Invest., *40*:1882, 1961.)

tricular ejection was augmented (Frye and Braunwald, 1960; Braunwald et al., 1960, 1961; Fig. 1-4).

The force of the atrial contraction is a function of the atrial pressure existing at the time of its onset (Braunwald and Frahm, 1961). This suggests that, in man, the atria as well as the ventricles behave in accordance with the Frank-Starling law of the heart.

In the living animal, the role of the Frank-Starling mechanism may be obscured by variations in myocardial contractility. Starling (1920) was well aware of this. Thus, the relationship between the initial length of the muscle fiber and the developed tension changes when the autonomic nervous system modifies the contractility of the heart (Sarnoff, 1955). For example, when the heart is driven at a constant rate, increased sympathetic stimulation results in more work at a lower filling pressure (Sarnoff et al., 1960 A and B). Thus, the heart may, from moment to moment, use a number of Frank-Starling curves relating cardiac output to ventricular volume. Since increased sympathetic activity alters the contractility of muscle in all chambers of the heart, it is the Starling mechanism which permits the stroke volume of each ventricle to be adjusted independently on a beat to beat basis, thereby ensuring optimal distribution of the total blood volume between the pulmonary and systemic vascular beds.

Although an increase in initial muscle length is capable of increasing the work and power at a given afterload as well as increasing the maximal work and power of the muscle, it does not alter the maximal velocity of contraction at zero load. A change in the velocity coordinates of the force-velocity-length relationship may be used to define a change in the contractile state of the muscle. The force-velocity curve can be shifted by increasing the frequency of contraction so that the maximal velocity of shortening can be increased without changing the initial fiber length. Sonnenblick et al. (1965) suggested that this type of shift in the force-velocity curve does represent a change in the contractile state of the myocardium, since it is believed that the increase in the maximal velocity of shortening results from an increase in the rate of interaction of the contractile sites, regardless of the number of sites involved. Stimulating the sympathetic nerves to the heart, or adding norepinephrine, increases the intensity of contraction, shortens its duration and hastens its decline. These by definition are examples of inotropic stimuli. The biochemical basis for inotropism is unknown, but changes in metabolism (Sutherland and Rall, 1960), excitation-contraction coupling (Kavaler and Morad, 1966) and soluble relaxing factor (Stam and Honig, 1965) must all be considered.

To study the force-velocity relationships of the ventricular myocardium in intact man, Glick et al. (1965) measured the velocity of movement of radiopaque markers, sutured to the external surface of the ventricles, simultaneously with the intraventricular pressures. One marker was placed on the right ventricle just beneath the pulmonary valve, and the other at the

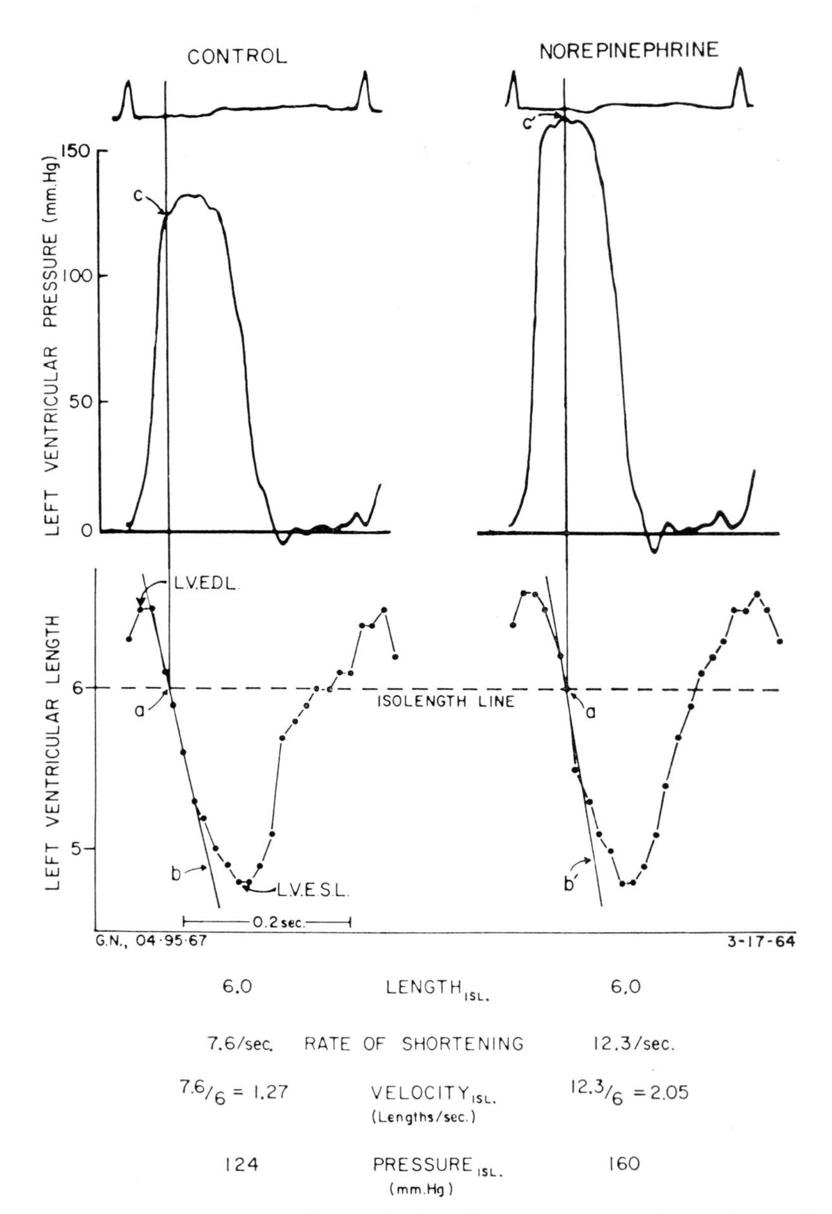

FIGURE 1-5. Instantaneous force-velocity relationships in an intact heart. From above down are the ECG, left ventricular pressure pulse and curve relating left ventricular dimension to time at intervals of 1/30 second. *Left:* control values. *Right:* during infusion of norepinephrine. Points a and a′ are isolength points at which both instantaneous velocity of shortening and intraventricular pressure are measured. Lines b and b′ are tangents at points a and a′, and represent the velocity of shortening at these points. The steeper slope of b′ as compared with b indicated increased velocity. Points c and c′ are the temporally related points on the ventricular pressure curve. LVEDL: left ventricular end-diastolic length. LVESL: left ventricular end-systolic length. (From Glick, Sonnenblick and Braunwald, J. Clin. Invest., *44*:978, 1965.)

most inferior portion of the anterior surface. Markers were placed along the lateral surface of the left ventricle, one near the apex and the other near the base. All observations were made with the patient in the supine position. To eliminate the effect of respiration on ventricular dimensions (Goldblatt et al., 1963), measurements were made only at end-expiration. Since the contractile state is defined by the curve relating velocity of shortening and force at any one muscle length, the force and velocity of a segment of the ventricular myocardium were measured as it passed through a specific length during its contraction (Fig. 1-5). Under these conditions, the position of the force-velocity curve for that particular muscle length is determined by the contractile state of the myocardium. Thus, the force-velocity relationship, which characterizes the active contractile elements of skeletal muscle (Hill, 1938), has a valid counterpart not only in isolated heart muscle (Sonnenblick et al., 1965), but also in the ventricles of man and dogs (Fry et al., 1964). A shift in the force-velocity curve is always characterized by an increase in the maximal velocity of shortening, whether or not a change in maximal force occurs; this serves to define the contractile state of the muscle (Fig. 1-6).

Another technique that has been used to assess myocardial function in man is to measure the rate at which ventricular pressure increases (the first derivative of the pressure pulse). To avoid the artifacts inherent in pressures measured by standard catheter manometer systems, Gleason and Braunwald (1962) used a catheter with a high fidelity micromanometer mounted at its tip, or a needle directly attached to a manometer. The peak of the first derivative (maximal rate of pressure rise) in patients without

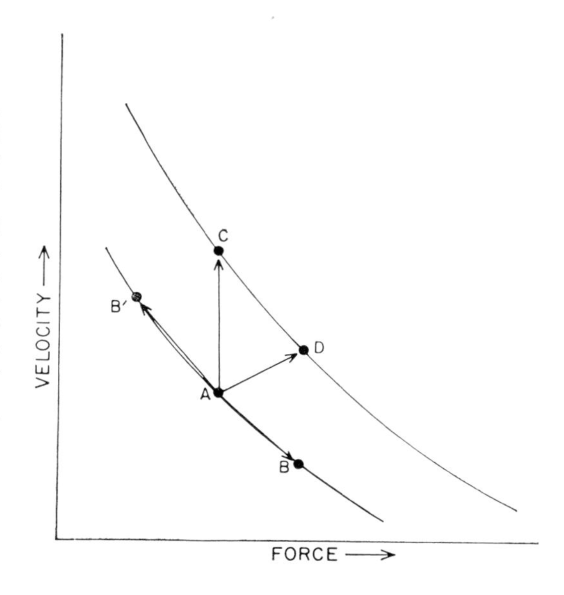

FIGURE 1-6. Effects of various stimuli on the myocardial force-velocity relationship. Point A indicates control values. An increase (B) or decrease (B′) in afterload causes a reciprocal change in velocity; the contractile state of the myocardium is unaltered. A pure inotropic stimulus shifts the relationship to point C, while an inotropic stimulus that also increases the afterload shifts it to point D. (From Glick, Sonnenblick and Braunwald, J. Clin. Invest., *44*:978, 1965.)

hemodynamic abnormalities ranged between 841 and 1696 mm. Hg per second in the left ventricle and between 223 and 296 mm. Hg per second in the right ventricle. Inotropic stimuli such as muscular exercise, isopropylnorepinephrine and norepinephrine resulted in increases in the peak of the derivative.

CARDIAC OUTPUT IN THE SUPINE POSITION

Since the time of Harvey (1628), physiologists have been interested in assessing the output of the heart. Although a variety of methods have been used in the past, the direct Fick and the indicator dilution techniques have become established as the standard methods.

To establish standards for the normal range of values for cardiac output, allowance has to be made for the fact that individual subjects are variable in size. It has become customary to adjust values for cardiac output (and for other measurements derived from this, such as stroke volume) in accordance with the equation of Dubois and Dubois (1916) relating height H and weight W to surface area SA:

$$SA = 71.84\, W^{0.425}\, H^{0.725}$$

in which SA, W and H are in units of $cm.^2$, Kg. and cm., respectively. Although the Dubois equation was based on direct measurement of the body surface area of only nine subjects, it has been widely accepted as reliable. More rapid methods of determining surface area are now available, such as the use of the Sendroy-Cecchini (1954) nomogram.

The expression of cardiac output as cardiac index (liters per $M.^2$ body surface area per minute) implies that cardiac output is proportionate to the surface area of the body (Taylor and Tiede, 1951). Although the validity of the assumption is open to question (Kleiber, 1947), there is no doubt that the use of values adjusted in this manner has been of great clinical value in separating the normal from the abnormal.

Many different ranges of values for the cardiac index of normal subjects resting in the supine position have been reported. The differences are due, in part, to variations in the conditions under which the measurements were made: for example, whether or not sedative drugs were used for premedication; whether the subjects were experienced or inexperienced (and possibly apprehensive); and whether or not the subjects had fasted previously. The differences are also due, in part, to the manner in which the results are expressed: for example, whether every single result is included; or whether the range given comprises the mean ± 2 S.D. Wade and Bishop (1962) stated that values below 2.0 and above 5.0 liters per $M.^2$ per minute are clearly abnormal. However, this range is too wide to be of much practical value. In most laboratories, 90 per cent of values in relaxed normal subjects are in the range of 3.0 to 4.0 liters per $M.^2$ per minute. Barratt-Boyes and

TABLE 1-1. Distribution of Systemic Blood Flow and Oxygen Consumption in a Normal Subject at Rest in a Comfortable Environment*

WEIGHT 70 KG.
SURFACE AREA 1.7M.²

CIRCULATION	BLOOD FLOW (ML./MIN.)	PER CENT OF TOTAL FLOW	A-V O_2 DIFFERENCE (ML./100 ML.)	O_2 CONSUMPTION (ML./MIN.)	PER CENT OF TOTAL CONSUMPTION
Splanchnic	1400	24	4.1	58	25
Renal	1100	19	1.3	16	7
Cerebral	750	13	6.3	46	20
Coronary	250	4	11.4	27	11
Skeletal muscle	1200	21	8.0	70	30
Skin	500	9	1.0	5	2
Other organs	600	10	3.0	12	5
Total	5800	100	4.0	234	100

* From Wade and Bishop, Cardiac Output and Regional Blood Flow. Oxford, Blackwell, 1962.

Wood (1958) found a mean value of 3.5 liters per $M.^2$ per minute in normal subjects who were familiar with the procedure for measuring output; 95 per cent of the individual values were within the range of 2.8 to 4.2 liters per $M.^2$ per minute. For most purposes, 2.5 and 4.5 liters per $M.^2$ per minute may be regarded as the lower and upper limits of normality. Consecutive determinations should be within 10 per cent, and preferably within five per cent, of each other.

The output of the left ventricle is mainly distributed in accordance with the metabolic needs of the body tissues. When the metabolic rate of a certain organ or tissue changes, the caliber of its precapillary resistance vessels is altered so that the rate of inflow of blood is adjusted to its new requirements. An estimate of the distribution of the output of the left ventricle in a normal subject resting supine in a comfortable environment is shown in Table 1-1.

The resting heart rate, like the cardiac output, is influenced by many factors: for example, apprehension, discomfort, prior sedation and the state of digestion. Normal young adults, when fasting and free from apprehension, have pulse rates in the range of 56 to 72 per minute during rest in the supine position. The stroke volume index is in the range of 45 to 55 ml. per $M.^2$.

CARDIAC OUTPUT IN THE UPRIGHT POSITION

When a normal person changes from the supine position to standing upright in a relaxed manner, it has been estimated that 300 to 800 ml. additional blood is contained in the lower limbs (Sjöstrand, 1952). The volume of blood in the heart and lungs decreases by about 20 per cent

(Wang et al., 1962). In 10 athletes aged 17 or 18 years, the cardiac volume while supine was 801 to 1160 ml. and while standing, 693 to 888 ml.; the mean difference was 241 ml. (Holmgren and Ovenfors, 1960).

The cardiac output is less during quiet standing than during rest in the supine position; the difference is 1.0 to 2.7 liters per minute (Nowy et al., 1957; Wang et al., 1960; Chapman et al., 1960; Reeves et al., 1961; Bevegård et al., 1963). The heart rate also increases, to a variable extent, so that the decrease in stroke volume may amount to 40 per cent or more of the value obtained in the supine position.

Since the oxygen consumption of the body is similar in the supine and upright positions (Wang et al., 1960; Reeves et al., 1961), more oxygen must be extracted by the tissues from each liter of circulating blood. This is reflected by an increased difference in oxygen content between aorta and pulmonary artery. For example, in the subjects studied by Reeves et al., this difference changed from 37 ml. per liter when supine to 63 ml. per liter when standing, an increase of 70 per cent. The arteriovenous difference for the lower limbs increased to a greater extent than that for the entire systemic circulation; the difference averaged 42 ml. per liter when supine, 120 ml. per liter when passively tilted to 70 degrees and 123 ml. per liter when standing. Thus, blood flow to the lower limbs is reduced by two thirds on changing from the supine to the upright position, whether or not the limbs are supporting the weight of the body. This finding of a disproportionate decrease in flow to the lower limbs has been confirmed by Pentecost et al. (1963), who used an indicator dilution technique to measure blood flow in the inferior vena cava.

The systemic arterial blood pressure is maintained through reflex constriction of resistance vessels in the kidneys (Kattus et al., 1949), splanchnic area (Culbertson et al., 1951) and skeletal muscles (Brigden et al., 1950). The constriction is mediated by increased activity in the adrenergic fibers to the resistance vessels and is initiated by activation of receptors that are responsive to shifts of blood volume. The site of these receptors is undetermined, but they may be in the thorax as well as in the carotid sinus (Roddie and Shepherd, 1963).

Passive tilting from the supine to the head up position is also accompanied by changes in cardiac output, heart rate and stroke volume. Tuckman and Shillingford (1966) found that the major decrease in cardiac output occurred between 10 degrees and 20 degrees of tilt, but the heart rate continued to increase and the stroke volume to decrease with additional tilting up to 60 degrees. There was no significant change in systemic arterial blood pressure.

Contrary to what is often taught, when gravitational changes are induced by tilting into the upright position, or simulated by applying subatmospheric pressure to the pelvis and lower limbs (Brown et al., 1966), there is no sustained reflex response of the capacitance veins to counter the hydrostatic shift of blood (Gauer and Thron, 1965; Samueloff et al., 1966). The transient increases in tone in the veins that occur on tilting are due, not to the shifts of blood, but to involuntary deep inspiration or to psychic effects associated with tilting or the application of suction. The dominant role in the maintenance of systemic arterial pressure is played by the resistance vessels; their sustained reflex constriction controls the rate at which blood accumulates in the dependent parts (Samueloff et al., 1966).

OXYGEN SATURATION OF BLOOD IN THE HEART AND GREAT VESSELS

There are differences in the oxygen saturation of the streams of venous blood entering the right atrium. Because of the high rate of extraction of oxygen in the coronary circulation, blood in the coronary sinus is markedly desaturated, in the range of 30 to 45 per cent. In the conscious subject resting in the supine position, the saturation of blood in the inferior vena cava is slightly higher than that in the superior vena cava (Barratt-Boyes and Wood, 1957). During anesthesia, this difference may be reversed, due to redistribution of systemic blood flow. The inferior vena cava, in turn, receives blood of widely different saturation from such areas as the liver, the kidneys and the lower limbs. Since there is laminar flow in the inferior vena cava, and since there is only a very short segment of vena cava above the entry of the hepatic veins, there is often difficulty in obtaining a truly representative or mixed sample of blood from this site.

Further, adequate mixing of the streams of venous blood does not occur in the right atrium. Blood sampled from the region of the coronary sinus is more desaturated than blood from other sites. In the fetus, maintenance of an effective circulation is dependent upon lack of mixing in the right atrium. Desaturated blood returning from the superior vena cava is deflected by the tubercle of Lower towards the tricuspid valve and thence to the pulmonary artery, ductus arteriosus and descending aorta, while highly saturated blood arriving from the placenta via the inferior vena cava is directed towards the foramen ovale and thence to the aortic arch and cerebral vessels. This streamlining persists in the adult heart, although it is less complete. Thus, Silver et al. (1956) showed that, in those cases of left to right shunt through an atrial septal defect in which a small right to left shunt was also present, a greater proportion of blood was shunted in the right to left direction from the inferior than from the superior vena cava.

Table 1-2 shows the variations in the oxygen saturation of blood samples obtained in rapid succession from various sites in the great veins and right heart chambers in a normal subject. In view of such variations, care must be exercised in determining the significance of an apparent slight increase in oxygen saturation in samples of blood drawn from the right atrium. Various authors (Dexter et al., 1947; Cournand et al., 1949;

TABLE 1-2. Variations in the Oxygen Saturation of Blood Samples Obtained in Rapid Succession from Various Sites in the Great Veins and Right Heart Chambers in a Patient with No Intracardiac Shunts

SITES	TIME	PER CENT SATURATION (CUVETTE OXIMETER)
IVC below renal veins	9.37	80
Right renal vein	9.38	89
Left renal vein	9.40	86
IVC above renal veins	9.40	83
Hepatic vein	9.41	73
IVC at diaphragm	9.42	83
Low right atrium	9.43	79
Mid right atrium	9.44	78
High right atrium	9.45	77
Superior vena cava	9.45	77
Coronary sinus	9.47	40

Storstein et al., 1952) have published figures for the variations which may occur in normal persons from one site to another in the right side of the heart, and Lurie et al. (1952) published probability tables for the significance of differences. Conclusions about the significance of differences can be drawn more readily when samples are obtained in rapid succession from different sites and when more than one series of samples is taken. Difficulties arise when the subject is in an unstable state: for example, wide swings in saturation occur if he is hyperventilating, crying or coughing.

Venous blood is more adequately mixed after it enters the right ventricle and pulmonary artery. Barrett-Boyes and Wood (1957) found values of −2.2, +3.2, +0.1 and +0.1 per cent for the means of the average differences in oxygen saturation between multiple paired samples of blood withdrawn from right atrium and superior vena cava, right atrium and inferior vena cava, right atrium and right ventricle (inflow tract) and right ventricle (outflow tract) and pulmonary artery, respectively.

Blood in the pulmonary capillaries and veins has a saturation of 97 to 99 per cent. During its passage through the left side of the heart, it becomes slightly desaturated through admixture with cardiac blood entering the cavities of the left atrium and ventricle via the venae cordis minimae (Thebesian veins). Thus, the saturation of arterial blood is in the range of 94 to 98 (mean 97) per cent.

One gram of hemoglobin combines with 1.33 ml. oxygen. Therefore, 100 ml. of blood that contains 15 g. hemoglobin carries 20.0 ml. oxygen when it is fully saturated, or 19.4 ml. when 97 per cent saturated. In addition, the plasma of 100 ml. blood contains 0.3 ml. oxygen in physical solution when the oxygen tension is at its usual level of 90 mm. Hg. Thus, the total content of oxygen in such a sample is 19.7 ml.

The mean difference in the content of oxygen between the systemic arteries and the pulmonary artery (mixed venous blood) in normal sub-

TABLE 1-3. Oxygen Content and Percentage Saturation of Arterial and Mixed Venous Blood in a Normal Subject Resting in the Supine Position *A* While Breathing Room Air and *B* While Breathing 100 Per Cent Oxygen [Blood Contains 15 g. Hemoglobin per 100 ml.]

CONDITION	BLOOD SAMPLE	SATURATION OF HEMOGLOBIN (%)	O_2 COMBINED WITH HEMOGLOBIN*	O_2 IN SOLUTION*	TOTAL O_2 CONTENT*
A Breathing air	Arterial	97	19.4	0.3	19.7
	Mixed Venous	79	15.8	0.1	15.9
	Difference	16	3.6	0.2	3.8
B Breathing 100% O_2	Arterial	100	20.0	1.6	21.6
	Mixed Venous	88	17.6	0.2	17.8
	Difference	12	2.4	1.4	3.8

* ml. per 100 ml. blood.

jects resting in the supine position is approximately 3.7 ml. per 100 ml. blood (Reeves et al., 1961). As was pointed out previously, this difference increases when the subject stands or is tilted towards a vertical position.

When 100 per cent oxygen is breathed, the arterial pO_2 increases to about 500 mm. Hg and approximately 1.5 ml. oxygen is carried in physical solution in the plasma. Since this is immediately available to the tissues, less oxygen is removed from the hemoglobin. Therefore, the arteriovenous difference in oxygen saturation is reduced (Table 1-3).

CARDIAC VOLUME

Several methods have been used to estimate the volume of the whole heart or of its individual chambers. Since the studies of Rohrer (1916), there has been interest in the application of ellipsoid approximation techniques for measurement of the total cardiac volume. The following measurements are made from the posteroanterior x-ray film: l, the long axis of the cardiac ellipsoid, from the junction of the aorta or superior vena cava with the right border of the heart to the left lower pole of the heart; and s, the short axis, from the right cardiophrenic angle to the junction of the pulmonary artery with the left ventricle or the left atrial appendix. The diameter of the heart, d, is obtained from the lateral x-ray film. The formula for cardiac volume is:

$$V\ (\text{ml.}) = K \times l\ (\text{cm.}) \times s\ (\text{cm.}) \times d\ (\text{cm.})$$

where K is a factor taking into account a correction for x-ray magnification.

Despite many theoretical objections, including the facts that the heart only remotely resembles an ellipsoid, that the two axes in the anterior plane are rarely precisely at right angles, and that pulsatile changes are not always taken into account, the method has been considered by several workers to give results that are of acceptable accuracy for clinical purposes. Evidence at autopsy has confirmed that the volumes are usually, but not always valid (Friedman, 1951). The greatest potential error is observer variation in measuring the axes. This diminishes with practice, but there remain differences between successive determinations on the same person of up to 12 per cent (Kjellberg et al., 1951). Evans and Carpenter (1965) concluded that measured differences of 160 ml. or more in sequential studies signified a real change in volume in an individual heart, and that measured differences of 210 ml. or more signified genuine differences in the volume of two different hearts. They found the method unsuitable for hearts with unusual silhouettes and for those in which the relevant parts of the contours could not be seen clearly.

To eliminate uncertainties due to variations in the heart volume during the respiratory and cardiac cycles, Holmgren and Ovenfors (1960) exposed x-ray films during maximal inspiration and triggered the exposures from the *R* wave of the electrocardiogram. They found a mean value of 918 ml. in normal men resting in the prone position. König et al. (1962) reported a mean value of 819 ml. in 40 apparently healthy older men, aged 60 to 75 years. Musshoff (1964) gave additional details of the techniques of measurement and of the ranges of values encountered in health and disease.

ANGIOCARDIOGRAPHY AND CINÉANGIOCARDIOGRAPHY. Knowledge of the total volume of the heart is of limited application, since it provides no information relating to the size of individual chambers, or to the extent to which they fill and empty during the cardiac cycle. Angiocardiography can, however, be used for the estimation of the volumes of the cavities of the left atrium and ventricle. Because of their irregular shapes, the right atrium and ventricle are unsuitable for direct measurement. Of the two available techniques, cinéangiocardiography has the advantage of providing many more frames per second; the film changer provides much clearer resolution of contours.

The cavity of the left ventricle approximates a three dimensional ellipsoid, and calculations of its volume are based on this (Arvidsson, 1961). With the use of a rapid film changer, volume curves can be constructed incorporating data from successive cardiac cycles (Fig. 1-7). From these curves, values for end-diastolic volume (EDV), stroke volume (SV) and end-systolic volume (ESV) are available. Arvidsson (1961) found that, in 14 of 16 patients, values for stroke volume obtained by the angiocardiographic and direct Fick methods did not differ by more than 20 per cent, even though the measurements were not simultaneous.

Dodge et al. (1960) distended left ventricular cavities at autopsy with known volumes of radiopaque material and derived the volumes, using different mathematical formulae, from x-ray films of the same hearts. The radiographic method gave overestimates of the true volumes, probably, in

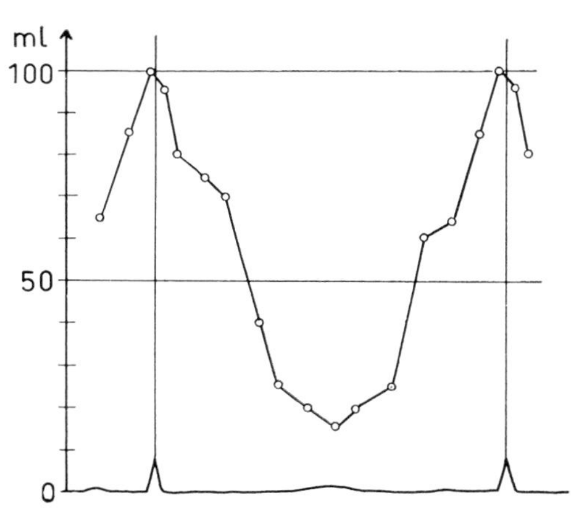

FIGURE 1-7. Left ventricular volume curve constructed by plotting volumes determined from successive cardiac cycles. The maximal volume is at the time of the *QRS* complex, and the minimal volume, at the end of the *T* wave. (From Arvidsson, Acta Radiol. Scand., *56*:321, 1961.)

part, because it did not discriminate between the radiopaque medium and the trabecula and papillary muscles within the cavity. Chapman et al. (1958) also obtained larger values by the indirect method. More recently, Carleton et al. (1966) found differences of up to 13 per cent between known volumes and radiographically derived volumes of spheres and ellipsoids.

Miller et al. (1964) used a simplification of Arvidsson's method in order to avoid elaborate calculations and to facilitate its application to clinical problems. They found that calculations of left ventricular volume based on measurements of four films were almost identical with those derived from composite curves.

Angiocardiography is unsuited for repetitive studies of left ventricular volume in man. In addition, radiopaque media, which are strongly hypertonic, produce immediate and profound effects on the circulation: for example, hypotension, tachycardia and an increase in end-diastolic pressure in the left ventricle (Friesinger et al., 1962; Rahimtoola et al., 1966). Therefore, the volumes obtained may be different from those preceding the injection.

DYE DILUTION AND THERMODILUTION TECHNIQUES. The indicator dilution technique may also be used to measure ventricular volumes provided the injection of indicator is made rapidly, adequate mixing occurs and the resultant time-concentration curve in the vessel leading from the ventricle (aorta or pulmonary artery) is recorded faithfully. Earlier attempts to measure the volume of the right ventricle in man were unsatisfactory because sampling of blood through a long catheter imposed such slurring on the curve that step functions corresponding to successive systolic ejections could not be distinguished clearly (Bing et al., 1951). The advent of fiberoptic catheters promises to solve this particular problem (Hugenholtz et al., 1965; Fig. 1-8).

When washout curves are obtained sufficiently free from distortion

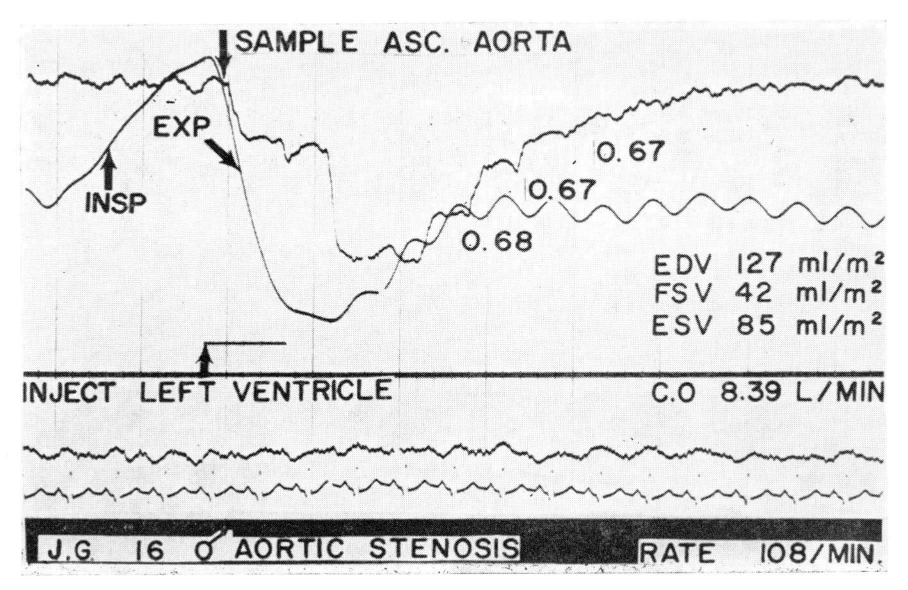

FIGURE 1-8. Dilution curve obtained by a fiberoptic catheter in the ascending aorta following injection of indicator dye into the left ventricle in a patient with a minor deformity of the aortic valve. Step functions are clearly seen in the washout slope of the curve, and successive estimates of the ESV/EDV ratio were 0.68, 0.67 and 0.67. Since cardiac output was also derived from the curve, the fractions of the left ventricular volume could be derived in absolute terms, and are shown in the figure. FSV: forward stroke volume. (The dilution curve is crossed by the pneumogram.) (From Hugenholtz, Gamble, Monroe and Polanyi, Circulation, *31*:344, 1965.)

to permit recognition of successive step functions, the end-diastolic volume of the ventricle into which the injection was made is calculated from the equation:

$$\mathrm{EDV} = \frac{\mathrm{SV}}{\left(1 - \frac{\mathrm{Cn} + 1}{\mathrm{Cn}}\right)}$$

where *Cn* and *Cn + 1* are the concentrations of indicator in the aorta or pulmonary artery corresponding with successive cardiac cycles. The stroke volume is derived from the cardiac output and the heart rate, and the end-systolic volume, by subtracting the stroke volume from the end-diastolic volume (Bristow et al., 1964).

Rapaport et al. (1965, 1966) used the thermodilution method for measurement of right ventricular volumes (Figs. 1-9 and 1-10). In normal subjects resting in the supine position, average values for EDV, SV and ESV were 98, 42 and 56 ml. per M.^{2}, and the ESV/EDV ratio was 58 per cent. When the subjects were tilted to the 60 degrees head up position, the average values for EDV, SV and ESV were 82, 28 and 54 ml. per M.^{2}, and

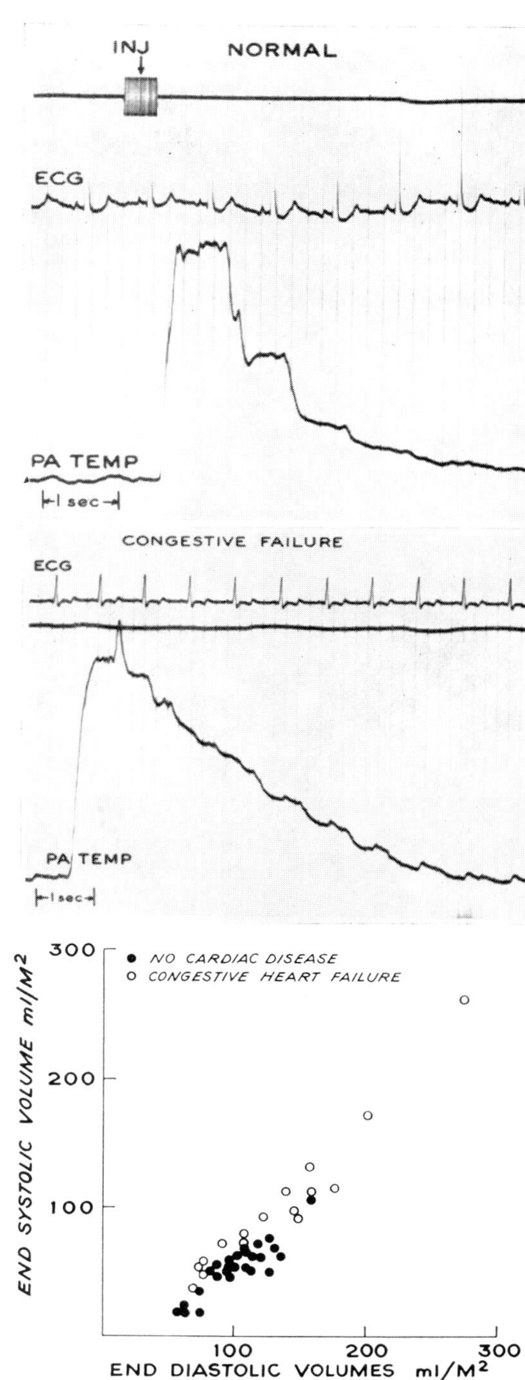

FIGURE 1-9. Thermodilution curves recorded from the pulmonary artery following the injection of cold saline into the right ventricle in a normal subject (*above*) and a patient with congestive heart failure (*below*). In the former, there are clear cut step functions corresponding to successive stroke outputs. The ESV/EDV ratio is obtained by dividing the distance from the baseline of a step at end-diastole by the distance of the comparable point of the preceding step. In the latter, the washout curve is more gradual, the steps are less clearly defined; the ESV/EDV ratio is clearly greater, reflecting less effective emptying of the ventricle. (From Rapaport, Wong, Ferguson, Bernstein and Wiegand, Circulation, *31*: 531, 1965.)

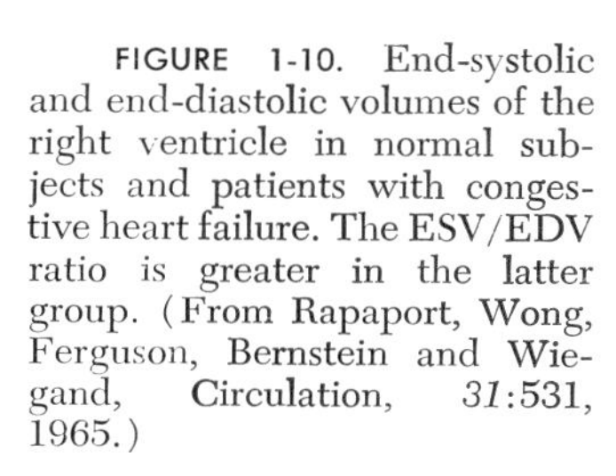

FIGURE 1-10. End-systolic and end-diastolic volumes of the right ventricle in normal subjects and patients with congestive heart failure. The ESV/EDV ratio is greater in the latter group. (From Rapaport, Wong, Ferguson, Bernstein and Wiegand, Circulation, *31*:531, 1965.)

the ratio increased to 66 per cent. In contrast, tilting had no significant effect on the volumes or on the ESV/EDV ratio in patients with congestive heart failure (Rapaport et al., 1966). In another study, the average values for right ventricular EDV, SV and ESV in normal subjects were 102, 45 and 57 ml. per $M.^2$ during supine rest, and 101, 51 and 50 ml. per $M.^2$ during supine exercise (Rapaport et al., 1965). Thus, exercise was associated with no change in EDV, an increase of 12 per cent in SV and a decrease of 12 per cent in ESV. In patients with congestive heart failure, both EDV and ESV increased during exercise.

Using a similar technique, Kreuzer et al. (1964) obtained average values in normal subjects of 110, 57 and 53 ml. per $M.^2$ for EDV, SV and ESV, respectively. Thus, the ESV/EDV ratio was 47 per cent. During inspiration, equivalent increases occurred in all three volumes so that the ESV/EDV ratio did not change.

Weigand and Jacob (1965) used both dye dilution and thermodilution techniques to estimate ESV and EDV of the left ventricle in dogs. There was close agreement between the results. With heart rates less than 100 per minute, the ESV/EDV ratio was 47 per cent, and at rates exceeding 120 per minute, it was 49 per cent. With more extreme alterations in rate, induced by electrical pacemaking and by stimulation of the vagus nerve, Bristow et al. (1963) demonstrated considerable alterations in the ratio. At the fastest rates, stroke volume was disproportionately decreased, and at the slowest rates, it was disproportionately increased.

THE ACCURACY OF DILUTION TECHNIQUES. Estimates of volume in the studies referred to above were of the same order of magnitude as those obtained by angiocardiographic methods. Other investigators have been less convinced concerning the accuracy of either dye dilution or thermodilution techniques. Thus, Hallerman et al. (1963) compared determinations of left ventricular EDV, SV and ESV in each of 12 dogs by the indicator dilution method, using Cardio-green dye, and cinéangiocardiography. While values for SV were comparable, EDV was 1.5 to 3.3 times greater, and ESV, up to 9.3 times greater with the dilution method. The results were not influenced by the heart rate. The data suggested that an error was present in estimates of volume based on the rate of washout of an indicator.

Sanmarco and Bartle (1964) reached similar conclusions in relation to the thermodilution technique. While measurements of left ventricular volume by biplane angiocardiography in dogs and humans were within 10 per cent of the actual volumes of the ventricular cavities, measurements of ESV and EDV by thermodilution were excessive. For example, in humans without myocardial disease, the EDV was 80 ± 10 ml. per $M.^2$ and the ESV/EDV ratio was 30 to 40 per cent by angiocardiography, whereas the EDV was 130 to 210 ml. per $M.^2$ and the ESV/EDV ratio was 65 to 80 per cent by thermodilution.

In the studies of Gorlin et al. (1964) and Wilcken (1965), who used thermodilution and dye dilution techniques, respectively, the estimates of EDV were approximately twice the estimates by angiocardiography in similar subjects (Arvidsson, 1961; Dodge et al., 1962).

The main problem relating to the use of dilution methods for measurement of ventricular volumes is that mixing of the injected indicator with blood is generally far from complete (Irisawa et al., 1960; Swan and Beck, 1960; Hallerman et al., 1963; Carleton et al., 1966). Yet complete mixing is a theoretical sine qua non for the derivation of ESV/EDV ratios from the washout step functions of dilution curves.

Aside from the problem of incomplete mixing, Rolett et al. (1964) found that the presence of valvular regurgitation, the transfer of heat or cold between the ventricular cavity and its wall, and the duration of the time constant of the sensing instrument could lead to inaccuracies in the measurement of the true rate of washout by thermodilution.

In an attempt to minimize difficulties due to inadequate mixing of indicator, Folse and Braunwald (1962) injected radioiodinated diodrast into the left ventricle, and used a scintillation counter placed on the chest wall over the ventricle to determine the fraction of isotope discharged per beat. In patients with no apparent abnormality of left ventricular function who were resting in the supine position, 37 ± 8 per cent was discharged per beat, and the end-diastolic volume of the ventricle was 89 ± 26 ml. per $M.^2$.

INTRACARDIAC AND INTRAVASCULAR PRESSURES

Ideally, the right atrium would be the most suitable zero level, with reference to atmospheric pressure, for the measurement of intracardiac and intravascular pressures. However, the depth of the right atrium in the anteroposterior plane of the thorax varies considerably from person to person. Therefore, it is customary to take an arbitrary level in subjects lying supine, such as halfway between the sternum and the back (Barratt-Boyes and Wood, 1958), or 5 cm. below the sternal angle (Braunwald et al., 1961), as a baseline for pressure measurements.

Barratt-Boyes and Wood (1958) measured the pressures in the great vessels and chambers of the right side of the heart in 26 normal subjects resting supine. Because of variations in the pressure during the two phases of the respiratory cycle, values during expiration and inspiration were averaged. Mean values (mm. Hg) for the right atrium, right ventricle, pulmonary artery and pulmonary artery wedge (indirect left atrium) were 9/4, 24/4–10, 22/17 and 15/9 mm. Hg, respectively; the pressure in the radial artery was 135/71 mm. Hg. The initial value for the diastolic pressure in the right ventricle (4 mm. Hg) corresponded with the sharp downswing of the pressure pulse early in diastole, following the opening of the tricuspid valve, while the second value (10 mm. Hg) was obtained at end-diastole

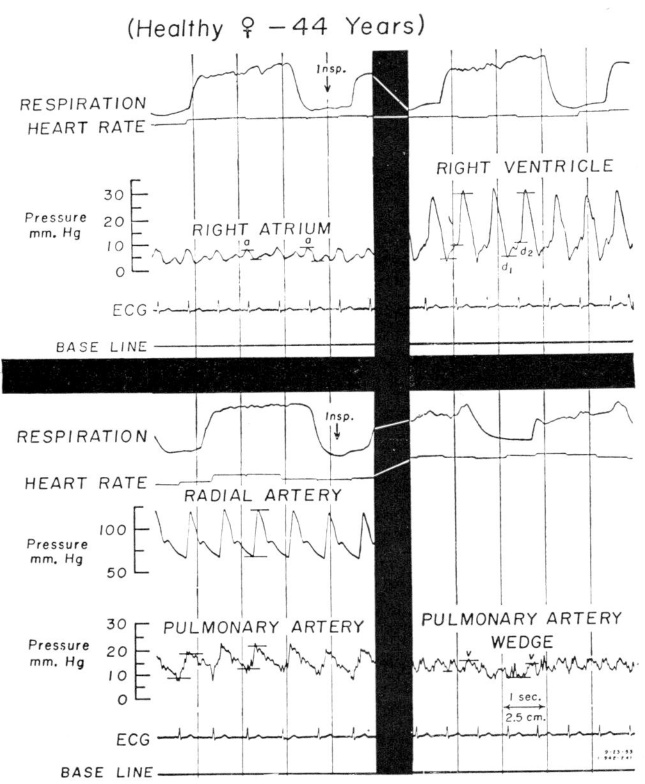

FIGURE 1-11. Pressure pulses from various sites in a normal subject. Short horizontal lines indicate the points at which maximal and minimal values are measured at each site. In the right ventricle, lines d_1 and d_2 indicate early diastolic and end-diastolic pressures. (From Barratt-Boyes and Wood, J. Lab. Clin. Med., *51*:72, 1958.)

(Fig. 1-11). There was no significant difference between the right atrial and the right ventricular diastolic pressures. There was a statistically significant, though small, systolic pressure gradient of 0 to 7 (mean 2) mm. Hg between the right ventricle and the pulmonary artery. The maximal pressure in the pulmonary artery wedge tracing usually occurred at the time of the *v* wave. There was a mean difference in pressure of 6 mm. Hg between the wedge and the right atrium. In these subjects, variations in pressure with the respiratory cycle were relatively slight. During expiration, the pressures in the right atrium, right ventricle, pulmonary artery, pulmonary artery wedge and radial artery were on the average 1, 2, 3, 3 and 4 mm. Hg higher than during inspiration.

It should be recalled that these pressures represent only the pressures within the heart chambers and vessels. Without a knowledge of the extracardiac intrathoracic pressure, the transmural or true distending pressures of the chambers and vessels remain unknown. Therefore, caution must be exercised in relating the intracardiac or intravascular pressures to other parameters of cardiac function, such as fiber length and heart or chamber volume. It should also be appreciated that the pulmonary artery wedge pressure represents, at best, a damped left atrial pressure pulse (Linden, 1963; Linden and Allison, 1963).

More detailed analysis shows that the right atrial pressure pulse has usually three positive waves *a*, *c* and *v*, and two negative waves or descents *x* and *y*. The *a* wave begins just before and reaches its peak during atrial systole; its initial part is due to passive filling and its latter part, to active contraction of the atrium. The decline in pressure following atrial systole, the *x* descent, is caused by relaxation of the atrium and by a drawing down of the valve ring as the ventricle contracts. The nadir of the *x* descent occurs at the time of maximal ejection of blood from the ventricle. The earlier portion of the *x* descent is interrupted by the *c* wave, which is attributed to bulging of the tricuspid valve into the right atrium during the period of isometric contraction of the ventricle (Fig. 1-12). During the latter part of ventricular systole, pressure rises again in the atrium, and the peak of the *v* wave occurs early in ventricular diastole, during the period of isometric relaxation that immediately precedes the opening of the tricuspid valve. The *y* descent commences at the opening of the tricuspid valve.

With the onset of ventricular systole, the intraventricular pressure increases rapidly. However, no blood can leave the ventricle until its pressure exceeds that in the pulmonary artery, thereby opening the pulmonary valve. During the remainder of systole, the pressure contours in the right ventricle

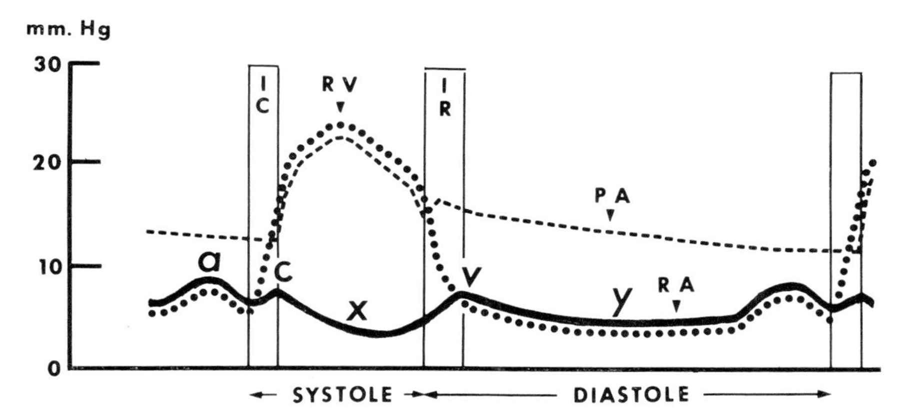

FIGURE 1-12. Diagram of pressure pulses from right atrium, right ventricle and pulmonary artery in a normal subject. Note the *a*, *c* and *v* waves and the *x* and *y* descents in the atrial pressure. The vertical bars labeled IC and IR represent the periods of isometric contraction and isometric relaxation of the right ventricle, respectively.

and pulmonary artery are similar (Fig. 1-12). An incisura is present in the pressure pulse of the pulmonary artery at the time of closure of the pulmonary valve.

Braunwald et al. (1961) measured the pressures in the left atrium and left ventricle using the technique of transseptal catheterization in 18 subjects with innocent cardiac murmurs. The mean left atrial pressure varied from 2 to 12 mm. Hg, with an average value of 8 mm. Hg. In all 18 subjects, the left atrial pressure exceeded that in the right atrium; the difference was 1 to 7 mm. Hg, with an average value of 4 mm. Hg. The average peak of the left atrial *v* wave exceeded that of the *a* wave by 2.4 mm. Hg. The left ventricular end-diastolic pressure of 5 to 12 mm. Hg (average 9 mm. Hg) was similar to the mean left atrial pressure.

The contour of the left atrial pressure pulse resembled that in the right atrium (Fig. 1-13).

As the systemic arterial pulse wave is transmitted from the proximal aorta to peripheral arteries, it undergoes a gradual transformation of contour. The systolic pressure increases, while there are smaller decreases in diastolic and mean pressures. Kroeker and Wood (1955) found pressures of 113 to 146 (mean 126) mm. Hg systolic, and 71 to 90 (mean 81) mm. Hg diastolic in the aorta of healthy young adults. The systolic pressure was nine per cent greater in the brachial artery, 10 per cent greater in the femoral artery and 12 per cent greater in the radial artery. The pulse pressure was 46 per cent greater in the radial artery than in the aorta, while the mean pressure was six per cent less. It was felt that a summation of the incident pulse wave with reflected waves from the periphery and resonance effects in the peripheral arteries could be responsible for the changes in pressure and contour.

The velocity of the pulse wave increases and the buildup time is shortened, as the arterial site moves distally (Fig. 1-14). There are differences in contour in the brachial and radial arteries as opposed to the femoral and

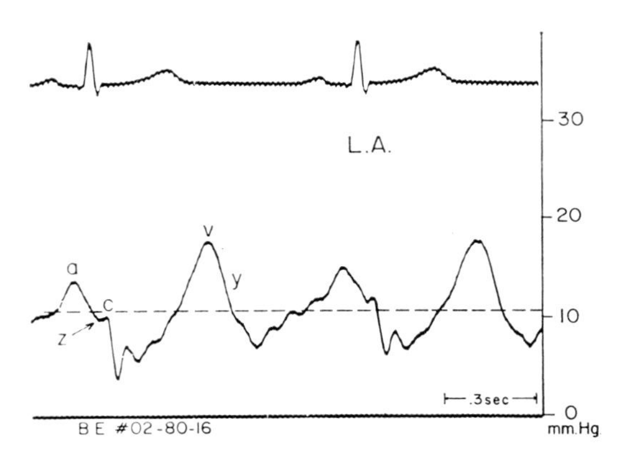

FIGURE 1-13. Pressure pulse in the left atrium of a normal subject. (From Braunwald, Brockenbrough, Frahm and Ross, Circulation, *24*:267, 1961.)

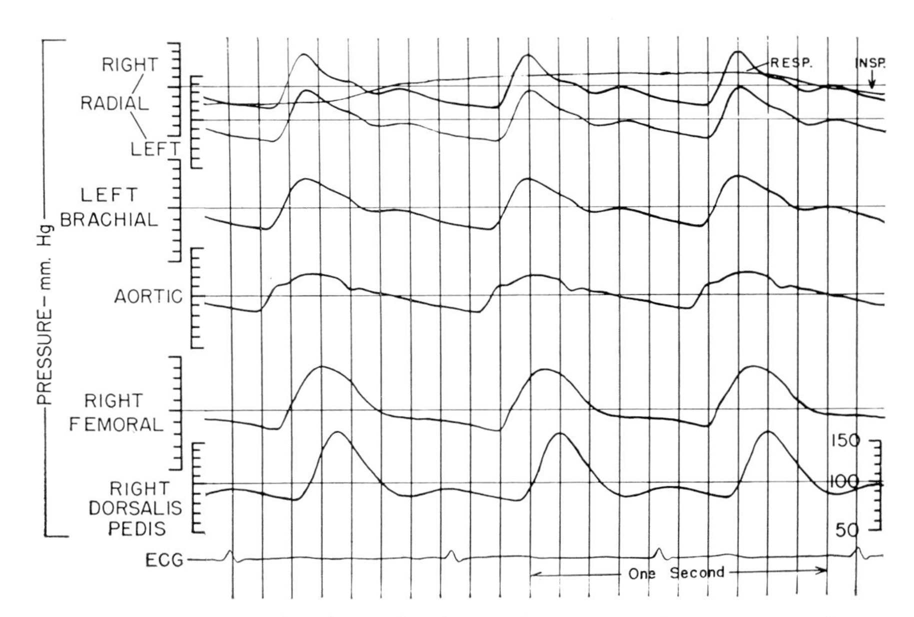

FIGURE 1-14. Central and peripheral arterial pressure pulses in a normal man. (From Kroeker and Wood, Circ. Research, 3:623, 1955.)

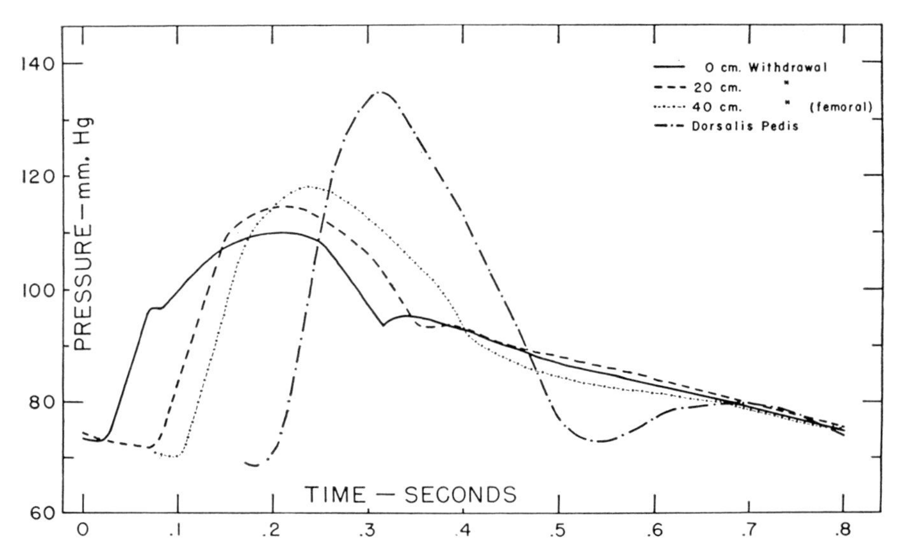

FIGURE 1-15. Pressure pulses in a normal subject recorded from thoracic aorta (0 cm. withdrawal), abdominal aorta (20 cm.) and femoral artery (40 cm.) through a catheter and from the dorsalis pedis artery through a needle. (From Remington and Wood, J. Appl. Physiol., 9:433, 1956.)

dorsalis pedis arteries. A double systolic wave occurs in the former, and the dicrotic notch becomes more conspicuous during transmission down the arm and forearm. In the femoral and dorsalis pedis arteries, there is a single systolic wave, and the dicrotic notch is poorly defined or absent (Remington and Wood 1956; Fig. 1-15).

Spencer et al. (1958) established the contour of the flow pulse along the normal unopened aorta of human subjects by recording with a square wave electromagnetic flowmeter. The contour at a given vessel segment was found to be the result of the transforming action of the arterial system on the ventricular ejection pulse. The resonant frequency, apparent from midsystole through diastole, was independent of heart rate, damped to extinction during diastole and renewed with each systole.

REFERENCES

Arvidsson, H.: Angiocardiographic determination of left ventricular volume. Acta Radiol., *56*:321, 1961.

Barratt-Boyes, B. G., and Wood, E. H.: The oxygen saturation of blood in the venae cavae, right heart chambers, and pulmonary vessels of healthy subjects. J. Lab. Clin. Med., *50*:93, 1957.

Barratt-Boyes, B. G., and Wood, E. H.: Cardiac output and related measurements and pressure values in the right heart and associated vessels, together with an analysis of the hemodynamic response to the inhalation of high oxygen mixtures in healthy subjects. J. Lab. Clin. Med., *51*:72, 1958.

Bevegård, B. S., Holmgren, A., and Jonsson, B.: Circulatory studies in well trained athletes at rest and during heavy exercise with special reference to stroke volume and the influence of body position. Acta Physiol. Scand., *57*:26, 1963.

Bing, R. J., Heimbecker, R., and Falholt, W.: Estimation of the residual volume of blood in the right ventricle of normal and diseased human hearts in vivo. Am. Heart J., *42*:483, 1951.

Braunwald, E., Brockenbrough, E. C., Frahm, C. J., and Ross, J., Jr.: Left atrial and left ventricular pressures in subjects without cardiovascular disease: observations in eighteen patients studied by transseptal left heart catheterization. Circulation, *24*:267, 1961.

Braunwald, E., and Frahm, C. J.: Studies on Starling's law of the heart. IV. Observations on the hemodynamic functions of the left atrium in man. Circulation, *24*:633, 1961.

Braunwald, E., Frahm, C. J., and Ross, J., Jr.: Studies on Starling's law of the heart. V. Left ventricular function in man. J. Clin. Invest., *40*:1882, 1961.

Braunwald, E., Frye, R. L., Aygen, M. M., and Gilbert, J. W., Jr.: Studies on Starling's law of the heart. III. Observations in patients with mitral stenosis and atrial fibrillation on the relationships between left ventricular end-diastolic segment length, filling pressure, and the characteristics of ventricular contraction. J. Clin. Invest., *39*:1874, 1960.

Brigden, W., Howarth, S., and Sharpey-Schafer, E. P.: Postural changes in the peripheral blood flow of normal subjects with observations of vasovagal fainting reactions, as a result of tilting, the lordotic posture, pregnancy and spinal anaesthesia. Clin. Sci., *9*:79, 1950.

Bristow, J. D., Crislip, R. L., Farrehi, C., Harris, W. E., Lewis, R. P., Sutherland, D. W., and Griswold, H. E.: Left ventricular volume measurements in man by thermodilution. J. Clin. Invest., *43*:1015, 1964.

Bristow, J. D., Ferguson, D. E., Mintz, F., and Rapaport, E.: The influence of heart rate on left ventricular volume in dogs. J. Clin. Invest., *42*:649, 1963.

Britman, N. A., and Levine, H. J.: Contractile element work: a major determinant of myocardial oxygen consumption. J. Clin. Invest., *43*:1397, 1964.

Brown, E., Goei, J. S., Greenfield, A. D. M., and Plassaras, G.: Circulatory responses to simulated gravitational shifts of blood in man induced by exposure of the body below the iliac crests to subatmospheric pressures. J. Physiol., *183*:607, 1966.

Carleton, R. A., Bowyer, A. F., and Graettinger, J. S.: Overestimation of left ventricular volume by the indicator dilution technique. Circ. Research, *18*:248, 1966.

Chapman, C. B., Baker, O., Reynolds, J., and Bonte, F. J.: Use of biplane cinéfluorography for measurement of ventricular volume. Circulation, *18*:1105, *1958*.

Chapman, C. B., Fisher, J. N., and Sproule, B. J.: Behavior of stroke volume at rest and during exercise in human beings. J. Clin. Invest., *39*:1208, 1960.

Chidsey, C. A., Weinback, E. C., Pool, P. E., and Morrow, A. G.: Biochemical studies of energy production in the failing human heart. J. Clin. Invest., *45*:40, 1966.

Cournand, A., Baldwin, J. S., and Himmelstein, A.: Cardiac Catheterization in Congenital Heart Disease. New York, Commonwealth Fund, 1949.

Culbertson, J. W., Wilkins, R. W., Inglefinger, F. J., and Bradley, S. E.: The effect of upright posture upon hepatic blood flow in normotensive and hypertensive subjects. J. Clin. Invest., *30*:305, 1951.

Dexter, L., Haynes, F. W., Burwell, C. S., Eppinger, E. C., Sagerson, R. P., and Evans, J. M.: Studies of congenital heart disease. II. Pressure and oxygen content of blood in right auricle, right ventricle and pulmonary artery in control patients, with observations on oxygen saturation and source of pulmonary "capillary" blood. J. Clin. Invest., *26*:554, 1947.

Dodge, H. T., Hay, R. E., and Sandler, H.: An angiographic method for directly determining left ventricular stroke volume in man. Circ. Research, *11*:739, 1962.

Dodge, H. T., Sandler, H., Ballew, D. W., and Lord, J. D., Jr.: The use of biplane angiocardiography for the measurement of left ventricular volume in man. Am. Heart J., *60*:762, 1960.

DuBois, D., and DuBois, E. F.: A height-weight formula to estimate the surface area of man. Proc. Soc. Exp. Biol. Med., *13*:77, 1916.

Evans, D. W., and Carpenter, P. B.: Errors involved in radiological heart volume determination by the ellipsoid-approximation technique. Brit. Heart J., *27*:429, 1965.

Folse, R., and Braunwald, E.: Determination of fraction of left ventricular volume ejected per beat and of ventricular end-diastolic and residual volumes: (experimental and clinical observations with a precordial dilution technic). Circulation, *25*:674, 1962.

Frank, G. B.: Calcium and the initiation of contraction. Circ. Research, *15*(Suppl. II):54, 1964.

Friedman, C. E.: Heart volume, myocardial volume and total capacity of the heart cavities in certain chronic heart disease: clinical, roentgenologic and pathoanatomic investigation of the problem of cardiac hypertrophy and dilatation and amount of residual blood of the heart. Acta Med. Scand., *140* (Suppl. 257):3, 1951.

Friesinger, G. C., Schaefer, J., Gaertner, R. A., and Criley, J. M.: Observations on the effects of left-sided injections of radio-opaque material. Clin. Research, *10*:172, 1962 (Abstract).

Fry, D. L., Grigg, D. M., Jr., and Greenfield, J. G., Jr.: Myocardial mechanics: tension-velocity-length relationships of heart muscle. Circ. Research, *14*:73, 1964.

Frye, R. L., and Braunwald, E.: Studies on Starling's law of the heart. I. The circulatory response to acute hypervolemia and its modification by ganglionic blockade. J. Clin. Invest., *39*:1043, 1960.

Gauer, O. H., and Thron, H. L.: Postural changes in the circulation. In: Handbook of Physiology. Section 2: Circulation. Volume 3. Washington, D.C., American Physiological Society, 1965.

Gleason, W. L., and Braunwald, E.: Studies on the first derivative of the ventricular pressure pulse in man. J. Clin. Invest., *41*:80, 1962.

Glick, G., Sonnenblick, E. H., and Braunwald, E.: Myocardial force-velocity relations studied in intact, unanesthetized man. J. Clin. Invest., *44*:978, 1965.

Goldblatt, A., Harrison, D. C., Glick, G., and Braunwald, E.: Studies on cardiac dimensions in intact, unanesthetized man. II. Effects of respiration. Circ. Research, *13*:455, 1963.

Gorlin, R., Rollett, E. L., Yurchak, P. M., and Elliott, W. C.: Left ventricular volume in man measured by thermodilution. J. Clin. Invest., *43*:1203, 1964.

Hallerman, F. J., Rastelli, G. C., and Swan, H. J. C.: Comparison of left ventricular volumes by dye dilution and angiographic methods in the dog. Am. J. Physiol., *204*:446, 1963.

Hill, A. V.: The heat of shortening and the dynamic constants of muscle. Proc. Roy. Soc. Lond., Ser. B, *126*:136, 1938.

Hill, A. V.: Abrupt transition from rest to activity in muscle. Proc. Roy. Soc. Lond., Ser. B, *136*:399, 1949.

Holmgren, A., and Ovenfors, C. O.: Heart volume at rest and during muscular work in the supine and in the sitting position. Acta Med. Scand., *167*:267, 1960.

Hugenholtz, P. G., Gamble, W. J., Monroe, R. G., and Polanyi, M.: The use of fiber-optics in clinical cardiac catheterization. II. In vivo dye dilution curves. Circulation, *31*:344, 1965.

Huxley, A. F.: Muscle structure and theories of contraction. Prog. Biophys. and Biophys. Chem., *7*:257, 1957.

Huxley, H. E.: The contractile structure of cardiac and skeletal muscle. Circulation, *24*:328, 1961.

Huxley, H. E., and Hanson, J.: Changes in the cross-striations of muscle during contraction and stretch and their structural interpretation. Nature, *173*:973, 1954.

Irisawa, H., Wilson, M. F., and Rushmer, R. F.: Left ventricle as a mixing chamber. Circ. Research, *8*:183, 1960.

Kaplan, S.: Pressure curve analysis. In: Intravascular Catheterization. Ed. Zimmerman. Second edition. Springfield, Thomas, 1966.

Kattus, A. A., Sinclair-Smith, B. C., Genest, J., and Newman, E. V.: The effect of exercise on the renal mechanism of electrolyte excretion in normal subjects. Bull. Johns Hopkins Hosp., *84*:344, 1949.

Kavaler, F., and Morad, M.: Paradoxical effects of epinephrine on excitation contraction coupling in cardiac muscle. Circ. Research, *18*:492, 1966.

Kjellberg, S. R., Lönroth, H., and Rudhe, U.: The effect of various factors on the roentgenological determination of the cardiac volume. Acta Radiol., *35*:413, 1951.

Kleiber, M.: Body size and metabolic rate. Physiol. Rev., *27*:511, 1947.

König, K., Reindell, H., and Roskamm, H.: The cardiac volume and the physical fitness of healthy men between the ages of 60 and 75 years: A contribution to the question of physiological insufficiency of old age. Arch. Kreislaufforsch., *39*:143, 1962.

Kreuzer, H., Bostroem, B., and Loogen, F. I.: Das enddiastolische und endsystolische Volumen des rechten Ventrikels beim Menschen in Ruhe. Z. Kreislaufforsch., *53*:790, 1964.

Kroeker, E. J., and Wood, E. H.: Comparison of simultaneously recorded central and peripheral arterial pressure pulses during rest, exercise and tilted position in man. Circ. Research, *3*:623, 1955.

Linden, R. J.: A comparison of gradients in the left atrial and pulmonary artery "wedge" pressure pulses. Clin. Sci., *25*:471, 1963.

Linden, R. J., and Allison, P. R.: The relationship between left atrial pressure and pulmonary artery "wedge" pressure in man. Clin. Sci., *25*:459, 1963.

Lurie, P. R., Gray, F. D., Jr., and Whittemore, R.: Cardiac catheterization and other physiological studies in fifty cases of congenital heart disease. Angiology, *3*:98, 1952.

Miller, G. A. H., Goodrich, R. G., and Swan, H. J. C.: Simplified method for calculating left ventricular volume from angiocardiograms. Radiology, *83*:1008, 1964.

Musshoff, K.: Die Methoden der röntgenologischen Herzvolumenbestimmung und ihre Fehlerbreite. Fortschr. Röntgenstr., *100*:165, 1964.
Nowy, H., Kikodse, K., and Zollner, N.: Vergleichende Messungen des Zentrale Blutvolumens und Herzminutenvolumens im Liegen und im Stehen. Z. Kreislaufforsch., *46*:393, 1957.
Patterson, S. W., Piper, H., and Starling, E. H.: The regulation of the heart beat. J. Physiol., *48*:465, 1914.
Pentecost, B. L., Irving, D. W., and Shillingford, J. P.: The effects of posture on the blood flow in the inferior vena cava. Clin. Sci., *24*:149, 1963.
Rahimtoola, S. H., Duffy, J. P., and Swan, H. J. C. Hemodynamic changes associated with injection of angiocardiographic contrast medium in assessment of valvular lesions. Circulation, *33*:52, 1966.
Rapaport, E., Wong, M., Escobar, E. E., and Martinez, G.: The effect of upright posture on right ventricular volumes in patients with and without heart failure. Am. Heart J., *71*:146, 1966.
Rapaport, E., Wong, M., Ferguson, R. E., Bernstein, P., and Wiegand, B. D.: Right ventricular volumes in patients with and without heart failure. Circulation, *31*:531, 1965.
Reeves, J. T., Grover, R. F., Blount, S. G., Jr., and Filley, G. F.: Cardiac output response to standing and treadmill walking. J. Appl. Physiol., *16*:283, 1961.
Remington, J. W., and Wood, E. H.: Formation of peripheral pulse contour in man. J. Appl. Physiol., *9*:433, 1956.
Roddie, I. C., and Shepherd, J. T.: Nervous control of the circulation in skeletal muscle. Brit. Med. Bull., *19*:115, 1963.
Rohrer, F.: Volumbestimmung von Körperhöhlen und Organen auf orthodiagraphischen Wege. Fortschr. Röntgenstr., *24*:285, 1916.
Rolett, E. L., Sherman, H., and Gorlin, R.: Measurement of left ventricular volume by thermodilution: an appraisal of technical errors. J. Appl. Physiol., *19*:1164, 1964.
Samueloff, S. L., Browse, N. L., and Shepherd, J. T.: Response of capacity vessels in human limbs to head-up tilt and suction on lower body. J. Appl. Physiol., *21*:47, 1966.
Sanmarco, M. E., and Bartle, S. H.: Left ventricular volume determinations: comparison of angiocardiographic and thermal washout techniques. Circulation, *30* (Suppl. III):151, 1964 (Abstract).
Sarnoff, S. J.: Myocardial contractility as described by ventricular function curves: observations on Starling's law of the heart. Physiol. Rev., *35*:107, 1955.
Sarnoff, S. J., Brockman, S. K., Gilmore, J. P., Linden, R. J., and Mitchell, J. H.: Regulation of ventricular contraction: influence of cardiac sympathetic and vagal nerve stimulation on atrial and ventricular dynamics. Circ. Research, *8*:1108, 1960A.
Sarnoff, S. J., Gilmore, P. J., Brockman, S. K., Mitchell, J. H., and Linden, R. J.: Regulation of ventricular contraction by the carotid sinus: its effect on atrial and ventricular dynamics. Circ. Research, *8*:1123, 1960B.
Sendroy, J., Jr., and Cecchini, L. P.: Determination of human body surface area from height and weight. J. Appl. Physiol., *7*:1, 1954.
Silver, A. W., Kirklin, J. W., and Wood, E. H.: Demonstration of preferential flow of blood from inferior vena cava and from right pulmonary veins through experimental atrial septal defects in dogs. Circ. Research, *4*:413, 1956.
Sjöstrand, T.: The regulation of the blood distribution in man. Acta Physiol. Scand., *26*:312, 1952.
Sonnenblick, E. H.: Force-velocity relations in mammalian heart muscle. Am. J. Physiol., *202*:931, 1962.
Sonnenblick, E. H.: Determinants of active state in heart muscle: force, velocity, instantaneous muscle length, time. Fed. Proc., *24*:1396, 1965.
Sonnenblick, E. H., Braunwald, E., and Morrow, A. G.: The contractile properties of human heart muscle: studies on myocardial mechanics of surgically excised papillary muscles. J. Clin. Invest., *44*:966, 1965.
Sonnenblick, E. H., Spiro, D., and Spotnitz, H. M.: The ultrastructural basis of

Starling's law of the heart: the role of the sarcomere in determining ventricular size and stroke volume. Am. Heart J., *68*:336, 1964.
Sonnenblick, E. H., Spotnitz, H. M., and Spiro, D.: Role of the sarcomere in ventricular function and the mechanism of heart failure. Circ. Research, *15* (Suppl. II):70, 1964.
Spencer, M. P., Johnston, F. R., and Denison, A. B., Jr.: Dynamics of the normal aorta. Circ. Research, *6*:491, 1958.
Spiro, D., and Sonnenblick, E. H.: Comparison of the ultrastructural basis of the contractile process in heart and skeletal muscle. Circ. Research, *15* (Suppl. II): 14, 1964.
Stam, A. C., Jr., and Honig, C. R.: A biochemical mechanism by which adrenergic mediators modify cardiac contraction. Am. J. Physiol., *209*:8, 1965.
Starling, E. H.: On the circulatory changes associated with exercise. J. Roy. Army Med. Corps, *34*:258, 1920.
Storstein, O., Humerfelt, S., Müller, O., and Rasmussen, H.: Studies in catheterization of the heart in cases of patent ductus arteriosus Botalli. Acta Med. Scand., *141*:419, 1952.
Sutherland, E. W., and Rall, T. W.: The relation of adenosine-3′,5′-phosphate and phosphorylase to the actions of catecholamines and other hormones. Pharm. Rev., *12*:265, 1960.
Swan, H. J. C., and Beck, W.: Ventricular nonmixing as a source of error in the estimation of ventricular volume by the indicator dilution technic. Circ. Research, *8*:989, 1960.
Taylor, H. L., and Tiede, K.: A comparison of the estimation of the basal cardiac output from a linear formula and the "cardiac index." J. Clin. Invest., *31*:209, 1952.
Tuckman, J., and Shillingford, J.: Effect of different degrees of tilt on cardiac output, heart rate and blood pressure in normal man. Brit. Heart J., *28*:32, 1966.
Wade, O. L., and Bishop, J. M.: Cardiac Output and Regional Blood Flow. Oxford, Blackwell, 1962.
Wang, Y., Blomquist, G., Rowell, L. B., and Taylor, H. L.: Central blood volume during upright exercise in normal subjects. Fed. Proc., *21*:124, 1962 (Abstract).
Wang, Y., Marshall, R. J., Taylor, H. L., and Shepherd, J. T.: Cardiovascular response to exercise in sedentary men and athletes. Physiologist, *3*:173, 1960 (Abstract).
Weigand, K. H., and Jacob, R.: Zur Frage der Restvolumenbestimmung des linken Ventrikels im natürlichen Kreislauf. Arch. Kreislaufforsch., *46*:97, 1965.
Wilcken, D. E. L.: The measurement of end-diastolic and end-systolic or residual volumes of the left ventricle in man, using a dye-dilution method. Clin. Sci., *28*:131, 1965.

Chapter 2

CARDIAC DYNAMICS DURING EXERCISE

SUPINE EXERCISE

The increase in cardiac output during exercise is related to the degree of dilatation of the blood vessels in skeletal muscle, and hence to the changes in metabolism. Warner (1965) demonstrated this relationship in dogs. When, at the onset of exercise, a balloon around the aorta was inflated sufficiently to maintain the resistance to outflow from the left ventricle about the same as that at rest, cardiac output did not increase. In addition to this basic relationship that is linked to metabolism, there is a reflex activation of sympathetic nerves to the heart and to resistance and capacitance blood vessels of the systemic circulation. This results in reflex adjustment of the peripheral vascular resistance so that the increased output from the left ventricle is directed to the active muscles, and the systemic arterial blood pressure is maintained within reasonable limits, despite the large increases in cardiac output.

From this viewpoint, the heart acts as an efficient force feed pump, designed to eject whatever volume it receives and capable of meeting the body's increased demands for oxygen by increases in heart rate or stroke volume. On the transition from rest to work, the heart rate increases immediately, at first rapidly and then more slowly, until a relatively steady state is achieved. With light or moderate work, this requires about two minutes, with heavy work, up to eight or ten minutes, and with very severe work, the pulse rate may not attain equilibrium (Åstrand et al., 1960).

The pulse rate increases in an approximately linear manner with increasing oxygen consumption. The cardiac output also increases as a linear function of oxygen consumption, at least up to submaximal work loads. Bevegård (1963A) found the following relationship in 27 healthy unconditioned subjects performing leg exercise in the supine position: cardiac output (liters per minute) = 6.13 × oxygen consumption (liters per minute STPD) + 6.24. Since cardiac output and heart rate increase during graded supine exercise as linear functions of oxygen consumption, and since the increase in stroke volume is slight, the arteriovenous difference in oxygen content (between aorta and pulmonary artery) is a rectangular hyperbolic function of both oxygen consumption and heart rate. The arteriovenous difference in the active limbs exceeds that for the body as a whole; this is most marked during milder grades of exercise (Reeves et al., 1961).

The increase in cardiac output during exercise performed in the supine position is due mainly to acceleration of the heart rate. The stroke volume increases by only 10 to 20 per cent of the resting value. This is true for both men and women and for both athletes and non-athletes. Ten healthy men studied by Bevegård et al. (1960) at rest and at two grades of exercise had mean values for oxygen consumption of 289, 1161 and 1690 ml. per minute, for cardiac output of 7.9, 13.4 and 17.9 liters per minute and for stroke volume of 116, 121 and 119 ml., respectively. With even heavier work, there was a slight further increase in stroke volume. Eight well trained athletes had a mean stroke volume of 150 ml. when resting supine; it increased by nine per cent during moderate work in the supine position (oxygen consumption about 1.8 liters per minute) and did not increase further during heavy exercise (oxygen consumption about 3.4 liters per minute).

X-ray films of the chest, exposed at constant times in the cardiac cycle and during full inspiration, showed that the heart size either remained unchanged or decreased slightly during exercise in the supine position that resulted in pulse rates of up to 160 per minute (Holmgren and Ovenfors, 1960).

Ross et al. (1965) exercised patients with no evidence of impaired cardiac reserve, in the supine position. Outputs of up to 10 liters per $M.^2$ per minute were attained. The heart rate increased considerably in all, while the stroke volume was virtually unchanged in four, increased in two and decreased in one. The mean systolic ejection periods decreased from 283 m.sec. at rest to 229 m.sec. during exercise, while the mean systolic ejection rates increased from 185 to 253 ml. per $M.^2$ per second. Subsequently, during rest, the hearts were stimulated electrically at rates comparable with those attained during the previous exercise. The subjects then exercised, and the normal increase in output was achieved entirely through an increase of stroke volume. The mean systolic ejection period decreased only slightly, from 228 m.sec. during electrical stimulation at rest to 222 m.sec. during exercise, while the mean ejection rates increased from 150 to 226 ml. per $M.^2$ per second.

Parasympathetic blockade increases the resting heart rate. The heart rate during moderate exercise is also greater after blockade than before. As the work load increases, the difference lessens. The maximal rate achieved during heavy exercise is identical with and without blockade; thus, in this circumstance, there is normally no parasympathetic influence on the heart (Robinson et al., 1953). Mechanical systole is more prolonged, the stroke volume is less, and, therefore, the mean rate of systolic ejection is less in a resting subject with cardioacceleration from parasympathetic blockade than in the same person performing exercise at an identical heart rate in the absence of blockade. In other words, myocardial contractility is greater during work than during rest at an identical heart rate (Levine et al., 1962). After blockade, the increase in output with exercise is accompanied by increasing stroke volume and end-diastolic pressure in the right ventricle (Bevegård, 1963B).

UPRIGHT EXERCISE

During exercise performed in the sitting position, the cardiac output also increases linearly with increasing oxygen consumption. The regression line, fitting the data for oxygen consumptions up to about 2 liters per minute [Cardiac output (liters per minute) = 5.9 × oxygen consumption (liters per minute STPD) + 4.36], parallels that derived for exercise in the supine position (Bevegård et al., 1960). Thus, the cardiac output is about 2 liters per minute less in the sitting position than it is for identical exercise in the supine position. Since the total oxygen consumpton is identical (McGregor et al., 1961), mixed venous blood is more desaturated when exercise is performed in the sitting position. With more severe exercise, the difference in output resulting from the different postures disappears.

Åstrand et al. (1964) found that subjects sitting on a bicycle ergometer attained maximal values for stroke volume during relatively light exercise, with a heart rate of about 110 per minute and an oxygen consumption of about 40 per cent of the aerobic work capacity (Fig. 2-1). Some subjects attained a cardiac output exceeding 25 liters per minute (Fig. 2-2), an oxygen consumption exceeding 4 liters per minute and an arteriovenous difference in oxygen content exceeding 16 ml. per 100 ml. (Fig. 2-3). In these healthy, fairly well trained men and women, maximal work could be maintained in the sitting position for at least six minutes without any decrease in stroke volume as compared with values during less severe exercise. Thus, at heart rates of up to 200 per minute, the diastolic filling period of the ventricles is sufficient to permit the heart to maintain a maximal stroke volume.

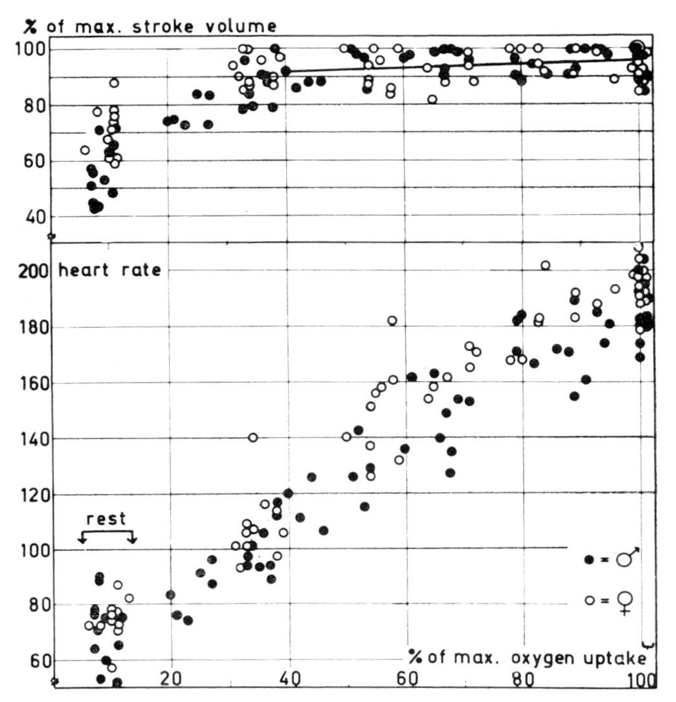

FIGURE 2-1. Stroke volume (as a percentage of the individual's maximal stroke volume) and heart rate at rest and during graded exercise in the sitting position up to maximal levels of exercise. For women, the average stroke volume at rest was 68 ml. and the maximal value during exercise was 100 ml. For men, the values were 88 and 134 ml., respectively. There was virtually no increase in stroke volume from work corresponding to one third of the maximal oxygen uptake (heart rates about 100 per minute) up to maximal levels of work (heart rates 170 to 210 per minute). (From Åstrand, Cuddy, Saltin and Stenberg, J. Appl. Physiol., *19*:268, 1964.)

The cardiac output during quiet standing is about 2 liters per minute less than it is in the supine position, the heart rate is faster, and the stroke volume averages only about 60 per cent of that during supine rest. On transition from quiet standing to exercise in the upright position, contraction of the muscles in the legs augments venous return and pulmonary blood volume (Daly et al., 1965). Even minor exercise, such as alternate static contraction and relaxation of the calf muscles, insufficient to increase oxygen consumption by more than 50 per cent, restores the stroke volume to a value approaching that during supine rest (Wang et al., 1960). Indeed, this mild exercise may be accompanied by no change or even a slight decrease in heart rate. As the severity of the exercise increases, the stroke volume continues to increase slowly so that as maximal exercise is approached, it slightly exceeds values obtained in the supine position at rest.

These results have been confirmed by most (Bevegård et al., 1960; Chapman et al., 1960; Damato et al., 1966) but not all (Tabakin et al.,

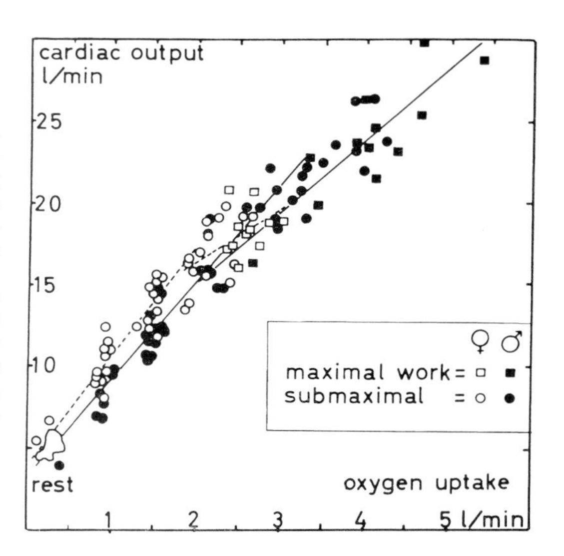

FIGURE 2-2. Individual values for cardiac output in relation to oxygen uptake at rest and during submaximal exercise in 23 subjects sitting on a bicycle ergometer. Regression lines (interrupted lines for women) were calculated for experiments where the oxygen uptake was (1) below 70% of the individual's maximum and (2) above this value. (From Åstrand, Cuddy, Saltin and Stenberg, J. Appl. Physiol., *19*:268, 1964.)

1964) investigators who have studied the effects of exercise on the inclined treadmill. Mean values for cardiac output, stroke volume and heart rate during supine rest, quiet standing and graded exercise are shown for a large series of 24 normal subjects (Damato et al., 1966; Fig. 2-4). The highest grade of exercise undertaken was well short of maximal; therefore, no statement could be made by these authors in relation to the suggestions by

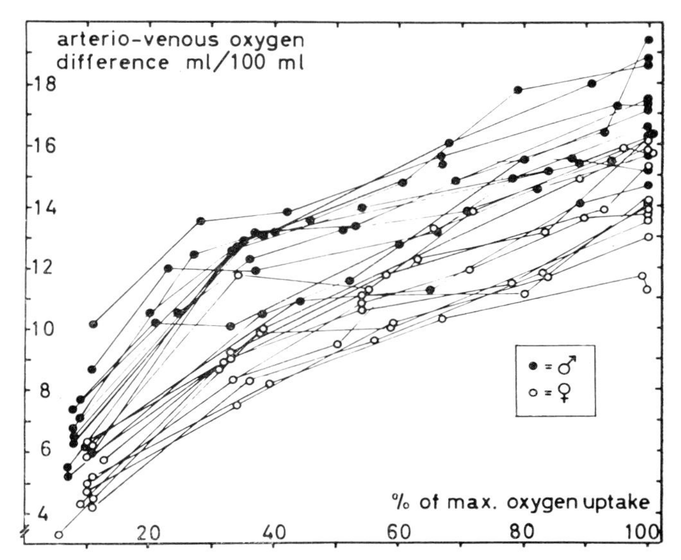

FIGURE 2-3. Increase in arteriovenous difference in oxygen content in 23 subjects from rest to maximal exercise in the sitting position. (From Åstrand, Cuddy, Saltin and Stenberg, J. Appl. Physiol., *19*:268, 1964.)

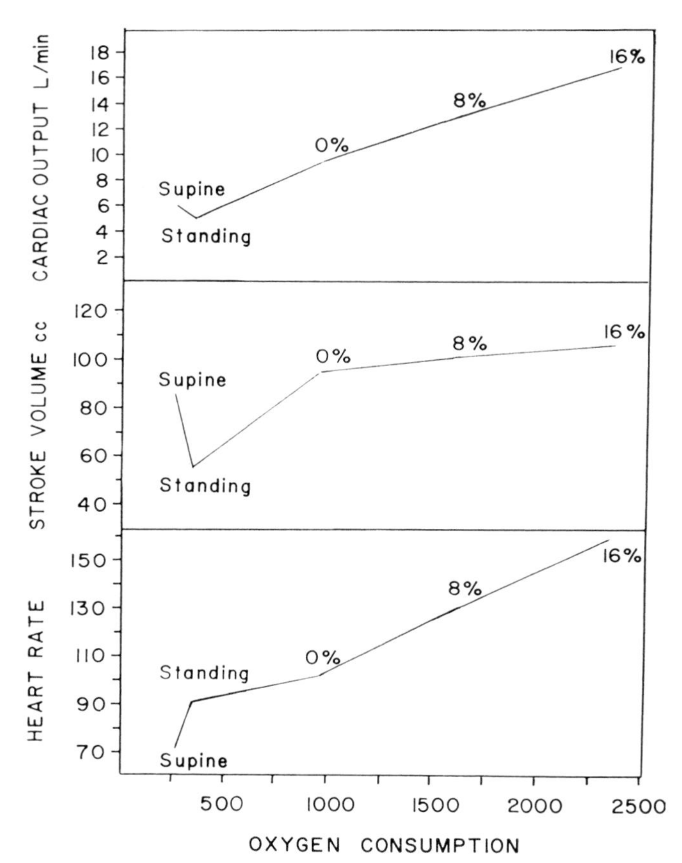

FIGURE 2-4. Relationship of mean values for cardiac output, stroke volume and heart rate to total oxygen consumption during supine rest, standing and walking on 0%, 8% and 16% inclines at 3 m.p.h. in 24 normal subjects. (From Damato, Galante and Smith, J. Appl. Physiol., *21*:959, 1966.)

Chapman et al. (1960) and by Rushmer (1959) that at maximal levels of exercise, stroke volume might become predominant in increasing cardiac output. However, as already noted (Fig. 2-1), there was no suggestion of such a role for stroke volume during maximal exercise in the sitting position (Åstrand et al., 1964).

Thus, in any discussion of the role of changes in stroke volume during muscular exercise, the position of the subject has to be taken into account. For example, in four healthy untrained men in whom the stroke volume during severe treadmill exercise was compared with that during rest in the supine position, there was little change (−9 to +23 per cent) compared with the increase in heart rate (+156 to +190 per cent). When, however, the comparison was made with values obtained during standing at rest, the increase in stroke volume (+61 to +110 per cent) was comparable to that of the heart rate (+77 to +122 per cent) (Wang et al., 1960).

Because of variations in response from subject to subject, it may be more valuable to compare results obtained during exercise corresponding with given percentages of each subject's maximal oxygen consumption, than to compare results obtained at standard grades of exercise (Figs. 2-1 and 2-3).

With the exception of maximal effort in well trained athletes, when there is a decrease in arterial oxygen saturation, probably due to relative hypoventilation (Rowell et al., 1964B), severe exercise is not accompanied by much change in arterial oxygen saturation (Holmgren and Linderholm, 1958). The breathing of oxygen has no measurable effect on cardiac output. Lowering the arterial oxygen saturation to 65 to 70 per cent during light and heavy work resulted in increases of cardiac output of only about 10 to 20 per cent more than the values when the saturation was normal. Thus, chemoreceptor activity secondary to arterial hypoxemia does not appear to be an important factor in the regulation of the circulation during exercise (Asmussen and Nielsen, 1955).

It is of interest that breathing 66 per cent oxygen greatly prolongs the breaking point of maximal exercise as compared with breathing air or 100 per cent oxygen. The oxygen reduces the pulmonary ventilation and the blood lactate response and allows the pCO_2 to attain higher levels (Bannister and Cunningham, 1954).

The hemoglobin concentration of the arterial blood increases during muscular work. This is due mainly to a decrease in plasma volume resulting from transfer of fluid from the vessels to the tissues. The increase in oxygen capacity of arterial blood in 10 healthy adult men from rest to exercise (oxygen consumption about 2 liters per minute) averaged 1.3 ml. per 100 ml. (Bevegård et al., 1960).

INTRACARDIAC AND INTRAVASCULAR PRESSURES

The mean pressure in the pulmonary artery in 10 healthy men increased from 12 mm. Hg at rest to 16 and 18 mm. Hg during exercise in the recumbent position that corresponded with oxygen consumptions of about 1 and 2 liters per minute, respectively (Bevegård et al., 1960). The systolic pressure in the pulmonary artery increased from 19 to 36 mm. Hg at the higher work load, while that in the right ventricle increased from 24 to 44 mm. Hg (Fig. 2-5). With high rates of flow (20 liters per minute or more), systolic pressure gradients of up to 20 mm. Hg were commonly recorded across the pulmonary valve. A comparable change occurred during exercise performed in the sitting position.

With increasing work loads, the systolic and mean pressures in the brachial artery also gradually increase. Occasionally, a transient decrease

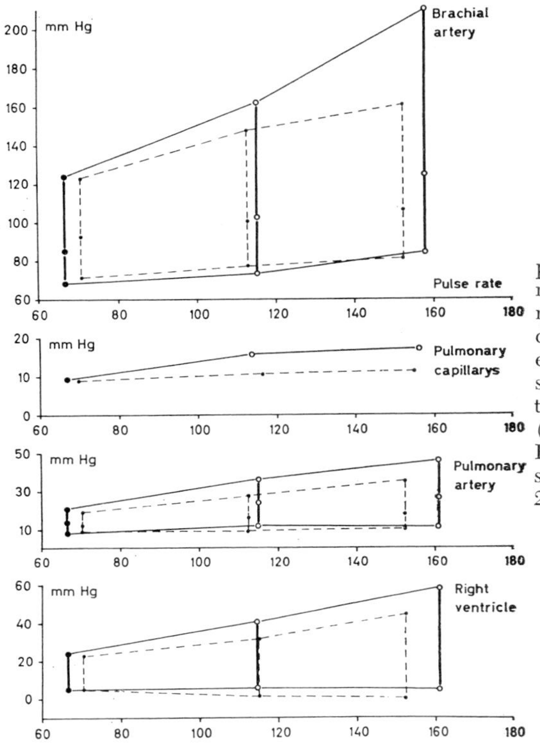

FIGURE 2-5. Mean values for pressures in brachial artery, pulmonary artery wedge, pulmonary artery and right ventricle during rest (filled circles) and exercise (empty circles) in the supine position in athletes (continuous lines) and non-athletes (interrupted lines). (From Bevegård, Holmgren and Jonsson, Acta Physiol. Scand., 57: 26, 1963.)

in systemic arterial pressure is noted at the onset of exercise. When severe exercise is continued for 30 minutes, the arterial pressure may decrease after the initial increase (Holmgren, 1956). Unlike peripheral arterial blood pressure, proximal aortic pressure remains almost constant during upright exercise which requires from 45 to 87 per cent of maximal oxygen consumption, despite large increases in cardiac output (Marx et al., 1967).

VENTRICULAR FUNCTION

Gorlin et al. (1965) employed a thermodilution method to estimate left ventricular end-systolic and end-diastolic volumes during exercise in the supine position in 20 subjects with normal or nearly normal left ventricles. The factors that appeared to determine the pattern of the response to exercise were increases in heart rate, in inotropic activity and in the diastolic length of heart muscle fibers. In 15 subjects, exercise was accompanied by a reduction of end-diastolic volume and by increases in the fraction of the volume ejected and in the velocity of ejection. In the other five subjects, the end-diastolic volume was increased, and a much greater stroke volume was ejected.

Further evidence of enhanced myocardial contractility was provided by studies of changes in cardiac dimensions. Braunwald et al. (1963) obtained biplane cinéradiograms in patients with silver-tantalum clips sutured to the surface of the heart. Pressures in the right and left ventricles were simultaneously measured by catheter tip micromanometers. End-systolic and end-diastolic dimensions of both ventricles decreased with the onset of exercise and remained at five to six per cent less than resting levels for the duration of exercise (Fig. 2-6). The consequent decrease in ventricular volume was considered to approximate one half of the resting stroke volume. At the same time, the peak rate of increase in ventricular pressure was augmented. The changes simulated those following injection of sympathomimetic amines. Although the increase in heart rate alone could have contributed to the aug-

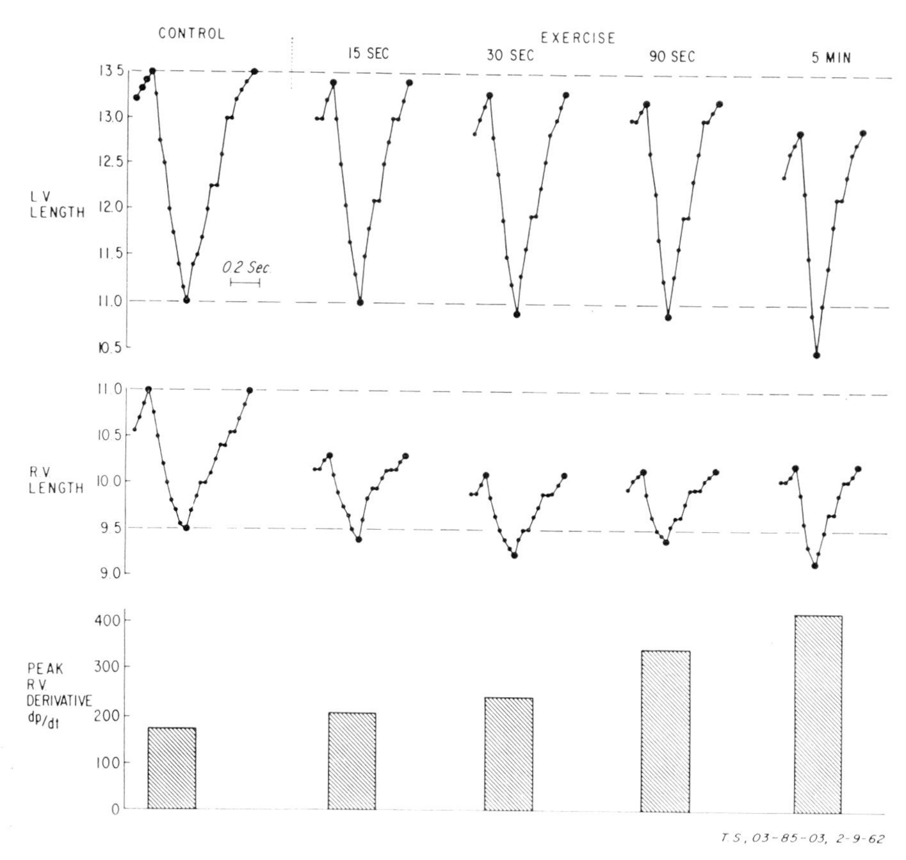

FIGURE 2-6. Distances between two clips on the left ventricle (LV) and two clips on the right ventricle (RV) during the control period and at various time intervals after the onset of exercise. The bars at the bottom show the peak derivative of the right ventricular pressure pulse (mm. Hg/sec.). (From Harrison, Goldblatt, Braunwald, Glick and Mason, Circ. Research, *13*:448, 1963.)

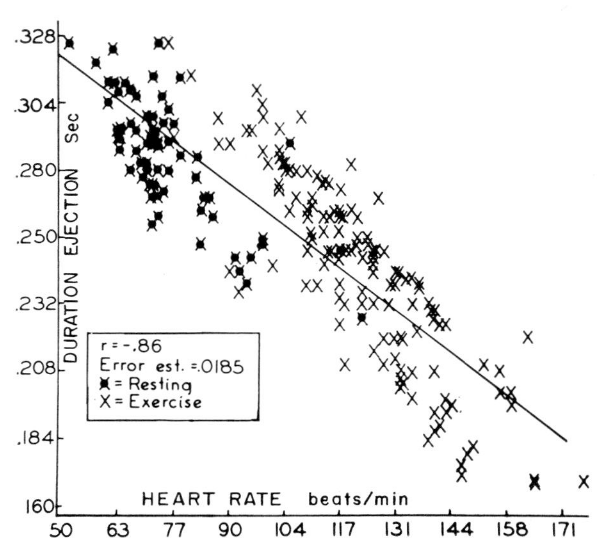

FIGURE 2-7. Relation of duration of left ventricular ejection to heart rate in normal subjects at rest and during exercise in the supine position. (From Jones and Foster, J. Appl. Physiol., *19*:279, 1964.)

mentation of the peak rate of increase in ventricular pressure, tachycardia induced by atropinization led to much smaller increases than did an identically fast heart rate induced by exercise (Gleason and Braunwald, 1962). Therefore, it seemed reasonable to conclude that the enhanced myocardial contractility resulted from increased activity of the sympathetic nervous system. Of necessity, the experiments were performed on patients following cardiac surgery, none of whom had normal hearts; the exercise was mild and brief, and was undertaken in the supine position. Whether comparable findings would be obtained in normal subjects, during severe exercise, or under different postural conditions is, therefore, not known.

Jones and Foster (1964) studied the duration of left ventricular ejection at rest and during leg exercise performed in the supine position. While it had some relationship with stroke volume and with arterial pressure, the duration of ejection was determined mainly by the heart rate (Fig. 2-7).

SEX AND AGE

The maximal working capacity and the maximal oxygen consumption are less in women than in men. The reduced working capacity is related to the smaller heart volume and blood volume which limit the increase in cardiac output (Holmgren et al., 1957). Åstrand (1952) found that the maximal oxygen consumption in 44 women averaged 2.9 liters per minute, or 29 per cent less than the value of 4.1 liters per minute in 42 men. After making the correction for differences in body size, the aerobic working capacity per Kg. body weight was 17 per cent less in women than in men (Åstrand 1956).

The average stroke volume during exercise in the supine position was 99 ml. in women and 120 ml. in non-athletic men (Bevegård 1963A). Changes in intracardiac and intravascular pressures were similar in men and women.

Åstrand et al. (1964) obtained values of 24.1 and 18.5 liters per minute for cardiac output during maximal exercise in the sitting position, in men and women, aged 20 to 31 years. In both sexes, stroke volume increased only slightly. Because of a lower concentration of hemoglobin in the blood, women had a greater cardiac output per liter of oxygen consumption during both submaximal and maximal exercise.

The resting cardiac output is less at rest in older subjects (Brandfonbrener et al., 1955; Lammerant, 1957). Above the age of 30, both heart rate and oxygen consumption during maximal work decrease progressively as age increases (Robinson, 1938; Valentin et al., 1955; Åstrand et al., 1959).

Granath et al. (1964) and Granath and Strandell (1964) measured cardiac output and intravascular pressures during rest and graded exercise in the supine and sitting positions, in apparently healthy men, aged 61 to 83 years. Values for cardiac output and stroke volume during rest in the supine position were less than in the young men studied by Bevegård et al. (1960) and Holmgren et al. (1960), but in the sitting position they were similar. The mean heart rate at a given level of oxygen consumption was similar during exercise in both the old and the young men. However, the cardiac output was less in the old men in relation to oxygen consumption. Therefore, the arteriovenous difference in oxygen content was greater and the stroke volume was less in the old men.

More recently, Becklake et al. (1965) arrived at opposite conclusions. In their studies, at any given level of oxygen consumption, the cardiac output tended to be higher and the arteriovenous difference, lower, in older than in younger subjects. Reasons for these different results are not certain. However, Becklake et al. employed an indirect Fick method to measure cardiac output; the possibility of methodological error cannot be ruled out.

Systemic arterial systolic pressure tends to be higher at rest in old men. Also, it increases to a greater extent with exercise than in young men (König et al., 1962). This presumably reflects impaired arterial elasticity due to increasing age. Resting levels of pulmonary artery and pulmonary artery wedge pressures are comparable in the old and the young. On changing from rest to exercise, the increase in pulmonary artery wedge and right ventricular end-diastolic pressure in the older subjects may reflect increased rigidity of the heart (Strandell, 1964). Calculated values for resistance in both pulmonary and systemic circuits are higher in older subjects.

ATHLETES

The aerobic work capacity of normal subjects is determined by the capacity of the cardiovascular system to transport oxygen. The maximal oxygen uptake is determined by the maximal heart rate, the size of the stroke volume and the amount of reduced hemoglobin in the blood returning to the lungs. The extent of the utilization of oxygen during exercise and, hence, the degree of desaturation of mixed venous blood depends on the distribution of the cardiac output between exercising muscles and other organs and tissues.

The total amount of hemoglobin, the heart volume and the blood volume are greater in relation to body weight in athletes than in non-athletes (Holmgren, 1956; Kjellberg et al., 1949; Sjöstrand, 1955). The capacity of the body to transport oxygen, expressed either as the maximal oxygen uptake (Åstrand 1952) or the amount of oxygen delivered per heart beat, is greater in athletes than in non-athletes.

Bock et al. (1928) showed that the pattern of response of the cardiac output in a marathon runner (de Mar) was qualitatively similar to that of untrained men; values for stroke volume were considerably greater, however, both at rest and during exercise. Wang et al. (1961) confirmed that athletes have larger stroke volumes, and that the pattern of response both to change of posture and to graded exercise is identical with that of non-athletes (Fig. 2-8). Five university swimmers and five young sedentary men were studied when resting supine, standing and walking on an inclined treadmill at increasing grades up to maximal exercise. During supine rest, average values for heart rate were 67 and 58 beats per minute, for cardiac index, 3.5 and 3.8 liters per $M.^2$ per minute, and for stroke volume index, 52 and 65 ml. per $M.^2$ for the non-athletes and athletes, respectively. On transition from the supine to the erect posture, the stroke volume index decreased by 35 per cent in the non-athletes and by 46 per cent in the athletes. With severe exercise (average oxygen consumption 3.2 liters per minute), the untrained subjects attained an average cardiac index of 10.5 liters per $M.^2$ per minute at a heart rate of 187 beats per minute; the stroke volume index was then 57 ml. per $M.^2$. The athletes, at an average oxygen uptake of 4.7 liters per minute, attained an average cardiac index of 13.7 liters per $M.^2$ per minute at a heart rate of 189 beats per minute; the corresponding stroke volume index was 73 ml. per $M.^2$. Thus, while athletes have a greater stroke volume index than non-athletes, in neither group are there large changes in stroke volume with increasing severity of exercise. The average increase of stroke volume in both groups compared with the control value during supine rest is no more than 10 or 12 per cent.

Bevegård (1963A) studied eight trained cyclists at rest and during exercise. The data were compared with those from 10 healthy but non-athletic men of similar age and size (Fig. 2-9). The resting arteriovenous

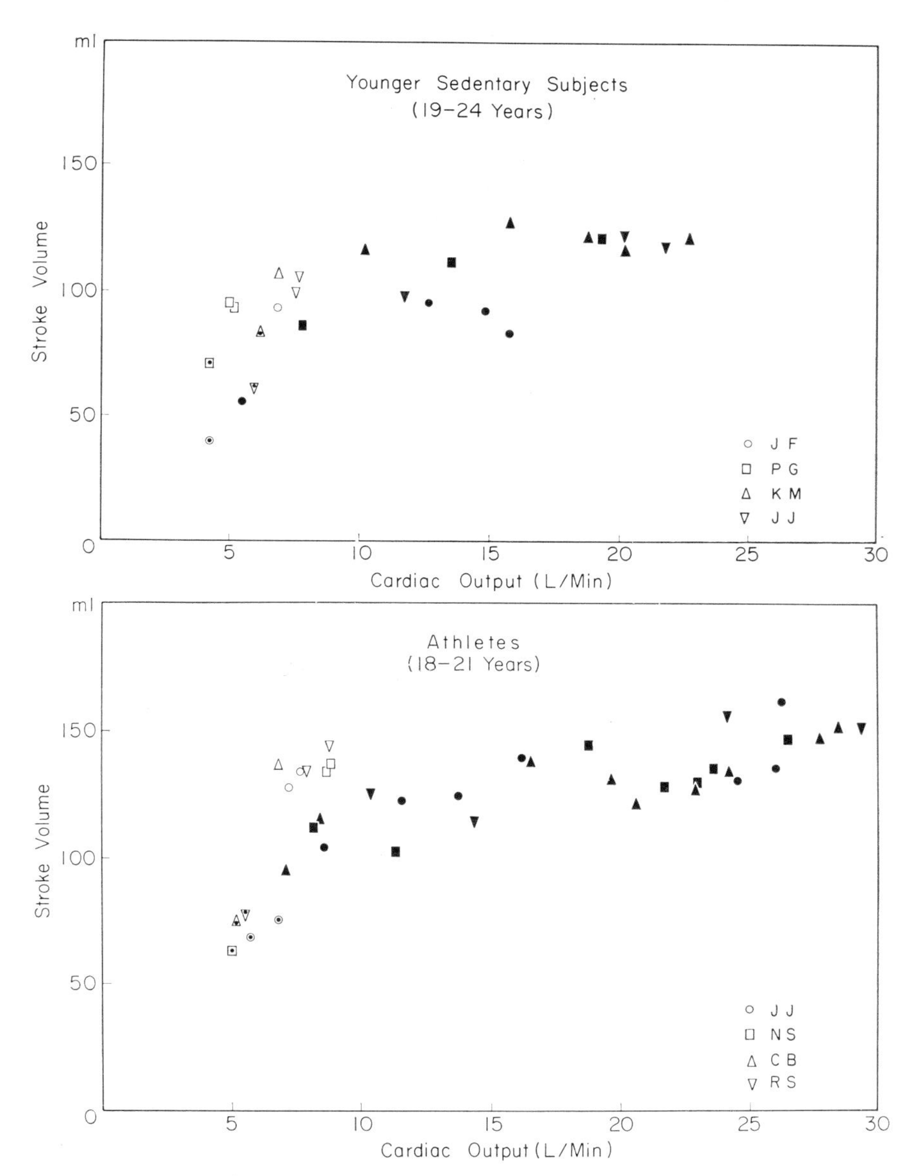

FIGURE 2-8. Stroke volume and cardiac output while at rest supine (empty symbols), at rest standing (empty symbols with black dots), and during graded exercise on a treadmill (filled symbols) in non-athletes (*top*) and athletes (*bottom*). (Wang, Shepherd, Marshall, Rowell and Taylor, unpublished data.)

difference in oxygen content was similar in the two groups during recumbency; the average was 39 and 37 ml. per liter, respectively. At a work load of 800 Kg.-M. per minute, the cardiac output was somewhat greater in rela-

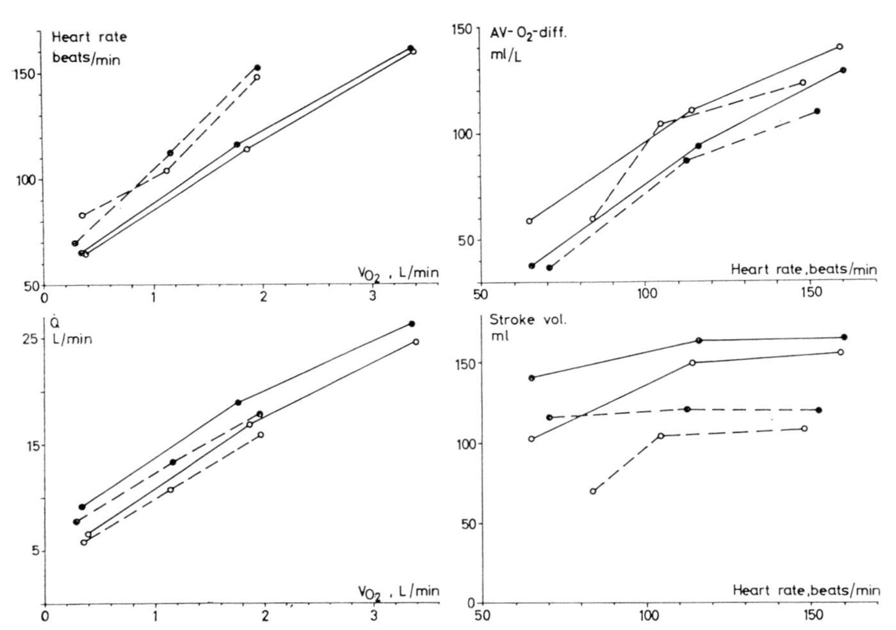

FIGURE 2-9. Effects of body position at rest and during exercise in athletes (continuous lines) and non-athletes (interrupted lines). Filled symbols = supine; empty symbols = sitting. (From Bevegård, Holmgren and Jonsson, Acta Physiol. Scand., 57:26, 1963.)

tion to oxygen consumption, and the arteriovenous difference was, therefore, somewhat less in athletes than in non-athletes. At 1600 Kg.-M. per minute (oxygen consumption about 3.4 liters per minute), the cardiac output of the athletes reached average values of 26.3 liters per minute in the supine position and 24.5 liters per minute in the sitting position. Both of these values coincided with the extrapolated regression lines for the data from non-athletes. The cardiac output at rest and at both work loads was about 2 liters per minute less in the sitting position, due to a smaller stroke volume in this position. This finding applied equally to athletes and non-athletes.

Training has variously been reported to result in higher (Asmussen and Nielsen, 1955B), lower (Tabakin et al., 1965) or unchanged (Freedman et al., 1955) levels of cardiac output in relation to a given work load or oxygen consumption. Andrew et al. (1966) made serial studies in both athletes and non-athletes before and after periods of athletic training, with each subject acting as his own control. In both groups, the cardiac output at any given work load was less after training. Since the oxygen consumption was unaffected, there was an increase in the arteriovenous difference in oxygen content. Grande and Taylor (1965) found an unchanged relationship between cardiac output and oxygen consumption before and after intensive conditioning in seven college men; after training they could achieve higher levels of both output and oxygen consumption.

Values for cardiac output, heart rate, stroke volume and arterial blood pressure in a group of athletes aged 45 to 55 years were similar, during both submaximal and maximal exercise, to those in young athletes (Grimby et al., 1966).

The relative slowing of the heart that occurs with training and that is characteristically found during rest in athletes results from increased vagal tone. There is, however, no evidence as to the precise mechanism whereby this occurs.

DIFFERENT TYPES OF EXERCISE

Pulmonary ventilation increased to a greater extent during arm exercise than during leg exercise when the levels of oxygen consumption were similar (Bevegård et al., 1966). The difference in ventilation was greater when the exercise was performed in the sitting position (12.5 liters per minute BTPS) than when it was performed during recumbency (8.3 liters per minute BTPS). It was due, in part, to an increased rate of breathing and, in part, to an increased tidal volume. The augmentation of ventilation during arm exercise could be of importance for maintaining the filling pressure of the ventricles and the stroke volume in the absence of the mechanical effect of the leg muscle pump. Granath and Strandell (1964) showed that in healthy old men there is a positive relationship between increases in ventilation and in ventricular filling pressure.

The heart rate also increases to a greater extent in relation to oxygen consumption during arm exercise than during leg exercise, particularly when the subject is upright (Collett and Liljestrand, 1924; Asmussen and Hemmingsen, 1958; Bevegård et al., 1966). The reason for this is unknown, but it is possible that during exercise of small muscle groups, such as the muscles of the arm, there is augmented sympathetic stimulation of the heart and peripheral blood vessels.

There was also a greater increase in aortic diastolic and mean pressures with arm exercise than with leg exercise when these were performed during recumbency; comparable changes were observed when the two types of exercise were performed with the subjects sitting (Bevegård et al., 1966). Åstrand et al. (1965) obtained similar results.

In 10 healthy trained subjects, the oxygen uptake and cardiac output during maximal arm exercise were 66 and 80 per cent, respectively, of the values obtained during maximal leg work in the sitting position. The uptake and output were the same during simultaneous maximal exercise of arms and legs as they were for maximal leg exercise alone (Stenberg et al., 1966).

Lind et al. (1964) studied the effects of sustained voluntary contraction of the hand. At a tension corresponding to 10 per cent of maximal voluntary contraction, the mean aortic pressure after one minute was increased by 10 mm. Hg; at 20 per cent tension, the increase was 32 mm. Hg and at 50 per cent tension, it was 40 mm. Hg. These confirmed the prior observations of Alam and Smirk (1938) who attributed the pressor response to sustained ischemic contraction of the forearm muscles to a proprioceptive reflex originating in the muscles.

At lower levels of static work, the increases in heart rate and cardiac output are disproportionate to the increase in oxygen consumption. The increase in output is in excess of the metabolic requirements of the contracted muscles. Blood flow to the forearm increases with contractions of the hand at tensions from 30 to 60 per cent of maximal voluntary contraction, reaching levels of 10 to 40 ml. per 100 ml. per minute in excess of the resting level (Humphreys and Lind, 1963). These results suggest that the blood supply to contracting forearm muscles is not occluded by the increased intramuscular pressure until the tension exerted exceeds 70 per cent of maximal voluntary contraction. In contrast, blood flow in the calf muscles is occluded with less than 20 per cent maximal tension (Barcroft and Millen, 1939), probably because the more striking shortening of the gastrocnemius and soleus muscles results in nipping of the arterial supply.

The increased aortic blood pressure during strong isometric contraction helps to oppose the impedance to blood flow imposed by the active muscles.

The trained men, aged 22 to 48 years, studied by Åstrand and Saltin (1961) performed maximal work of several types. Maximal values for oxygen consumption were similar during treadmill exercise, combined arm and leg exercise, cycling while in the sitting position and skiing; and for each of these types of exercise, the maximal heart rate was between 180 and 200 beats per minute. Maximal oxygen consumption during cycling in the supine position and swimming was about 15 per cent less, and during arm exercise alone, about 30 per cent less.

POSTPRANDIAL EXERCISE

Most earlier investigators, using the nitrous oxide or acetylene techniques, found that the resting cardiac output was increased for one to five hours after ingestion of meals of mixed composition (Grollman, 1929; Gladstone, 1935). More recently, Jones et al. (1965) found that the resting cardiac output was no greater shortly after a mixed meal than it was in the fasting state. Further, the output during exercise undertaken shortly after the meal was no different from that during identical exercise while fasting. However, the postprandial heart rate was faster, both at rest and during exercise, and the duration of systolic ejection was decreased even after correcting for the augmented rate. Arterial pO_2 and arterial pH were un-

TABLE 2-1. Effects of Recent Meal on Cardiac Index, Heart Rate, Oxygen Consumption, Systolic Ejection Period and Lactate/Pyruvate Ratio Both at Rest and During Exercise*

	REST		EXERCISE	
	BEFORE MEAL	AFTER MEAL	BEFORE MEAL	AFTER MEAL
Cardiac index (L./M.^{2}/min.)	3.67	3.57	7.36	7.50
Heart rate (beats/min.)	68	77	129	139
O_2 consumption (ml./M.^{2}/min.)	142	161	772	820
Systolic ejection period (m.sec.)	304	276	230	209
Lactate/pyruvate ratio	7.4	11.0	28.1	49.6

* From Jones, Thomas and Reeves, Am. Heart J., 69:668–676, 1965, The C. V. Mosby Company, St. Louis, Missouri.

changed, but the lactate/pyruvate ratio was increased (Jones et al., 1965; Table 2-1).

LeQuesne et al. (1960) attributed the relative tachycardia to a five per cent decrease in effective blood volume, and Castenfors (1961) also reported a correlation between the increase in pulse rate and the decrease in effective blood volume. It is possible that fluid is temporarily lost into either the lumen of the intestine or into the mesenteric tissues. Whatever the explanation, the effects (maintenance of normal levels of cardiac output and arterial blood pressure with an increased heart rate) resemble those that accompany removal of a small quantity of blood by phlebotomy.

Dagenais et al. (1966), however, showed that the resting cardiac output is considerably increased between 45 minutes and four and one half hours after both carbohydrate and protein meals. Protein meals, for example, resulted in increases of 14 beats per minute in heart rate, 2.4 liters per minute in cardiac output and 79 ml. per minute in oxygen consumption. The changes were maximal after three hours. During moderate exercise, these parameters were increased by about the same amount over values obtained with identical exercise in the fasting state. It is not known whether these increments persist during more severe grades of exercise. If they do, it follows that peak physical performance would be impaired following meals.

The increased lactate/pyruvate ratio (Jones et al., 1965) indicates some change in oxygen transport. Regan et al. (1961) evaluated the effects of alimentary lipidemia on myocardial performance during exercise. Prior to a meal, the consumption of oxygen by the left ventricle increased by 4.1 ml. per 100 g. during the exercise. Three and one half hours after a meal, the increase in subjects who developed lipidemia was only 1.53 ml. per 100 g. This more limited increase was accounted for, in large part, by a smaller increase in coronary blood flow. The lipidemia may have been associated with impaired diffusion of oxygen through the capillaries of the myocardium.

PROLONGED EXERCISE

Saltin and Stenberg (1964) studied subjects during a three hour spell of constant exercise at oxygen consumptions of about 75 per cent of their maximal levels. The body weight decreased by three to five per cent. Changes in blood volume were negligible. The major changes in the response of the heart during the prolonged exercise were a decrease in stroke volume and an increase in heart rate. The oxygen consumption and cardiac output both continued to increase very slightly in the later stages of the exercise. As Holmgren (1956) had previously shown, the systemic arterial pressure decreased slightly. Ekelund and Holmgren (1964), whose subjects cycled for one hour in the sitting position, reported steady levels for cardiac output, but a gradual increase in heart rate and oxygen consumption, thereby indicating that there was a gradual decrease in the stroke volume and an increase in the arteriovenous difference in oxygen content. The systemic arterial pressure decreased and the blood volume remained unchanged (Fig. 2-10).

Similar changes have been observed with prolonged exercise in the supine position. In both positions there was a slight increase in total ventilation, unchanged alveolar ventilation and a slight increase in dead space ventilation. The mean pressure in the pulmonary artery increased at the start of exercise; as exercise continued, the pressure returned half way to its original level. Ekelund (1967) attributed these changes during prolonged exercise to decreased tone in the capacity vessels with a consequential redistribution of the blood volume.

Michael et al. (1961) found that healthy men, aged 20 years, could exercise continuously for up to eight hours on a bicycle ergometer or treadmill without excessive fatigue provided that the heart rate, oxygen consumption and rectal temperature did not exceed 120 per minute, 1.4 liters

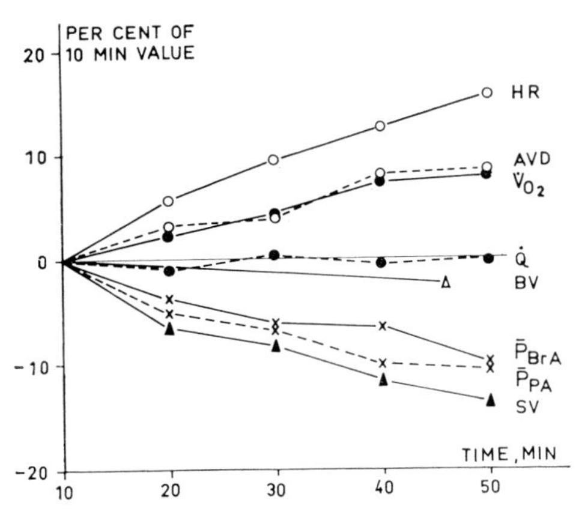

FIGURE 2-10. Responses to prolonged, non-steady state exercise. Mean values in six subjects (*from above down*) for heart rate, arteriovenous difference in oxygen content, oxygen consumption, cardiac output, blood volume, mean pressures in brachial and pulmonary arteries and stroke volume. (From Ekelund and Holmgren, Acta Physiol. Scand., 62: 240, 1964.)

per minute and 38°C., respectively. A heart rate of 140 per minute could not be maintained for longer than four hours, or a rate of 160 per minute for longer than two hours without extreme fatigue.

PULMONARY CIRCULATION

Indicator dilution methods have been used in an attempt to assess the changes in pulmonary blood volume during exercise. In earlier studies, indicator was injected into the right side of the heart and sampled from a peripheral artery. A volume (the central or intrathoracic blood volume) was derived from the curves. The assumption was made that changes in this volume reflected changes in the volume of blood in the lungs. Unfortunately, however, its limits do not conform to any fixed anatomical boundaries, but are determined by equivalence in a fourth dimension, namely time. The central blood volume consists of two components: the volume in the heart and lungs, and a systemic volume extending proximally from the aortic valve and distally to boundaries in all vessels equidistant in time with the sampling site. In an exercising subject, curves recorded simultaneously from both radial arteries, after reactive hyperemia had been induced in one arm, gave markedly different values for central blood volume (Marshall and Shepherd, 1961). This difference was obviously due to changes in the systemic rather than the cardiopulmonary component of the volume; its basis was the difference in the rates of flow of blood in the two brachial arteries. Thus, although exercise, or any other condition that alters patterns of flow in the arteries, may result in large changes in the calculated volume, the assumption cannot be made that these changes necessarily reflect changes in the volume of blood in the lungs (Marshall and Shepherd, 1961; McIntosh et al., 1961).

The advent of improved methods for catheterization of the chambers of the left side of the heart has permitted more accurate estimation of pulmonary blood volume. There are three possible approaches. In the first, indicator is injected into both the pulmonary artery and the left atrium and is sampled from a systemic artery. The difference in the calculated volumes gives the pulmonary blood volume (Milnor et al., 1960; Dock et al., 1961). In the second, indicator is injected into the pulmonary artery and is sampled from the left atrium (Levinson et al., 1964). In the third, indicator is injected into the right atrium and is sampled from the pulmonary artery and the left atrium; the difference between the two volumes is again regarded as the pulmonary blood volume (DeFreitas et al., 1964). Samet et al. (1966) compared the three methods, and found a close correlation between results derived by the first (mean pulmonary blood volume 262 ml. per $M.^2$) and third (mean volume 272 ml. per $M.^2$) methods in patients lying at rest in the supine position. The mean value derived by the second method was apparently overestimated (427 ml. per

M.^{2}), possibly because of the lack of a mixing chamber between the injection and sampling sites.

Although there may be a 10 to 15 per cent variation in reproducibility using these methods (Fishman, 1963), they provide a standard of reference for less direct methods: for example, external counting after injection of a radioactive tracer (Lammerant, 1957; Giuntini et al., 1963). It appears that, in normal subjects resting in the supine position, the pulmonary blood volume is about 10 per cent of the total blood volume.

The cardiopulmonary blood volume (between right atrium and aortic valve) can also be measured by the indicator dilution method. Levinson et al. (1966) found a mean value of 422 ml. per M.^{2}, representing 15 per cent of the total blood volume, in 15 normal subjects resting supine. There was a correlation between this volume and the stroke volume. However, these parameters are dependent variables, since cardiac output is the basis for calculating both of them. Therefore, it seems unwise to regard this correlation as evidence that the cardiopulmonary volume plays a role in the regulation of stroke volume. With mild leg exercise performed in the supine position, there was no significant change in cardiopulmonary blood volume (436 ml. per M.^{2}).

Wang et al. (1962) made similar observations in young men while at rest supine, standing and exercising on a treadmill. The volume during standing was 20 per cent less than that during supine rest. With exercise that resulted in cardiac outputs up to 20 liters per minute, the cardiopulmonary volume was similar to that recorded during supine rest.

While the total cardiopulmonary blood volume is scarcely altered by muscular exercise, this does not mean that changes in the distribution of the volume do not occur. Thus, there is evidence from radiographic studies (Ruosteenoja et al., 1958; Chapman et al., 1959; Harrison et al., 1963) that the cardiac volume diminishes during exercise. If the total cardiopulmonary volume is unchanged, then the pulmonary component must increase.

Roughton (1945) estimated that the blood volume of the pulmonary capillaries increased from about 60 ml. at rest to about 95 ml. during strenuous exercise. Johnson et al. (1960) found an increase in the diffusion capacity of carbon monoxide that was accounted for, in part, by an increase in the effective capillary blood volume and, in part, by an increased diffusion capacity of the alveolar capillary membrane. The calculated diffusion capacity for oxygen also increases with exercise; it does not limit the performance of exercise in normal man (Linderholm, 1959; Turino et al., 1963).

Lee and DuBois (1955) studied the pattern of blood flow in the pulmonary capillaries using a nitrous oxide method, with the subject enclosed in a body plethysmograph. When corrections are made for rhythmic variations in the gas volume of the lungs related to the cardiac cycle (Rigatto and Fishman, 1960), it is clear that pulmonary capillary flow is pulsatile. The rate of flow at any instant is proportional to the pressure gradient between pulmonary artery and left atrium (Bosman et al., 1964). Johnson et al. (1960) estimated that the transit time through average pulmonary capillaries was about one second at rest and 0.5 second during exercise that increased the pulmonary blood flow up to 14 to 17 liters per minute. Feisal et al. (1962) proposed a further method of partitioning the pulmonary blood volume: a combination of indicator dilution and plethysmographic techniques permitted quantitation of the arterial component of the volume. In resting subjects, the arterial component was 20 to 25 per cent of the total volume.

The distribution of total pulmonary blood flow has been assessed by using radioactive gases. The clearance rate of an inhaled gas, measured by counting over the chest during breath holding, is proportional to the rate of perfusion. In normal subjects standing upright, the clearance rate of radioactive carbon dioxide varied from about 20 per cent per second at the base of the lung to almost nil at the apex (West and Dollery, 1960; Fig. 2-11). This difference was reduced during moderate exercise. Similar results were obtained with radioactive carbon monoxide (Dollery et al., 1960). The findings suggested that during rest, most or all of the capillaries at the lung base were patent, but, because of the decreased perfusion pressure in the upright position, few at the apex were patent; with exercise, the increased pressure in the pulmonary artery changed the dis-

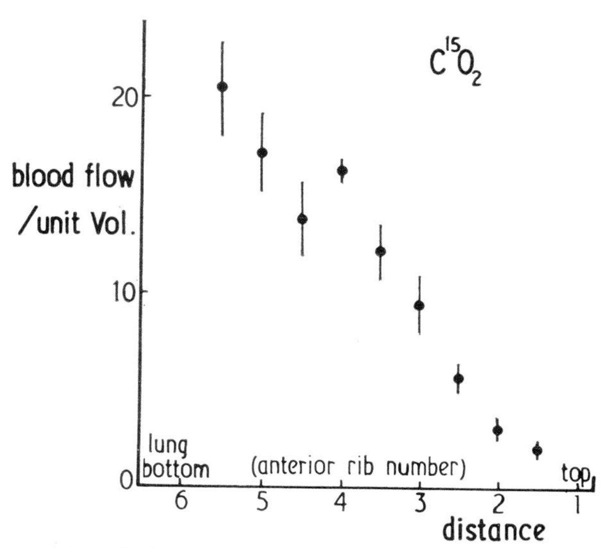

FIGURE 2-11. Normal distribution of blood flow in the upright human lung as measured with radioactive carbon dioxide in 16 normal subjects. Means and standard errors. Note the steady decrease from the bottom to the top of the lung; flow is almost nil at the apex. (From West, Jap. Heart J., 7:350, 1966.)

tribution of blood flow so that perfusion of the pulmonary vascular bed was more even.

INTEGRATION OF CARDIOVASCULAR CONTROL

With the onset of muscular contraction, there is immediate dilatation of the resistance vessels in the active muscles with an almost instantaneous reduction in local vascular resistance. The degree of vasodilatation is proportional to the metabolic rate of the active muscles. Since the speed of onset and magnitude of this dilatation is similar before and after sympathectomy of the limbs, it must be mediated through a local mechanism (Grant, 1938). It could result from the direct action of a chemical factor on the walls of the resistance vessels in the muscles or from an axon reflex initiated by a chemical stimulus (Hilton, 1953).

Breathing 100 per cent oxygen, which results in the addition of 1.5 to 1.8 volumes per cent of oxygen in physical solution in the blood, fails to reduce the dilatation for a given strength of contraction (Corcondilas et al., 1964). Thus, the magnitude of the increase in flow does not appear to be directly related to the oxygen tension of arterial blood. Holling and Verel (1957) recorded forearm blood flow in subjects lying supine before, during and after vertical elevation of the limb being studied. When the limb was held vertical, the blood flow was reduced by about one half, owing to a decrease in the perfusion pressure. The oxygen tension in the muscles decreased. There was no reactive hyperemia when the limb was subsequently lowered. Thus, as Barcroft (1964) concluded, there is no direct relation between the blood flow and the oxygen tension in muscle.

It has been postulated that cholinergic vasodilator fibers to the blood vessels in muscle may be activated during the early stage of exercise (Uvnäs, 1954). Even if this occurs in man, it is doubtful whether it makes a significant contribution to the hemodynamic response to exercise. While such a mechanism could certainly aid the local metabolites in causing dilatation at the onset of exercise, the almost instantaneous occurrence of locally mediated vasodilatation adjusted to the severity of the exercise would appear to make its postulation unnecessary (Corcondilas et al., 1964).

Since a decrease in blood pressure at the onset of exercise either does not occur, or is slight and transient, and since no decrease occurs with the transition from light to heavier exercise, rapidly adaptive changes must occur when further dilatation takes place in exercising muscles. Experiments in animals with electromagnetic flow meters in situ on the aorta or pulmonary artery have shown that there is an immediate increase in cardiac output (Rushmer et al., 1960; Donald and Shepherd, 1964). Both in man exercising in the supine position and in the dog, the immediate increase in cardiac output is accounted for by an increase in heart rate, and the stroke volume remains constant. Presumably, the blood volume in the lungs and great veins can provide a sufficient reservoir for increased cardiac demands during the first few seconds.

THE MUSCLE PUMP. With the first contraction of the active muscles, their veins are compressed; this immediately increases the venous return to the right ventricle (the muscle pump). This is especially important during upright exercise. The increased venous return from the leg muscles facilitates rapid filling of the heart and also, by reducing the pressure in the veins of the leg and foot, increases the perfusion pressure in the lower limbs. The activation of the muscle pump is accompanied by changes in the postcapillary vessels (mainly veins) of the systemic circulation. Statements are frequently made that 65 to 75 per cent of the total blood volume is contained in the systemic veins, but such figures are no more than inspired guesses, since no method has been devised for accurate determination of this volume in life. The postcapillary vessels of the various components of the systemic vascular bed probably act in uniformity as part of the total reservoir system (Shepherd, 1966). This system, by virtue of its viscoelastic properties, may passively undergo extensive changes in volume, with small changes in transmural pressure. Also, by virtue of the smooth muscle in its walls, this system can actively change its volume and concomitantly alter the intraluminal pressure. Although in the past, certain parts of this capacitance system such as the spleen, liver and skin have been regarded as specific blood depots, these are the components of the total system, and, therefore, they do not function independently. Little would be gained by releasing blood from one portion of the venous system merely to sequester it in another. Thus, the smooth muscle of the walls of capacitance vessels, in contrast with that of resistance vessels, is little affected by local regulatory mechanisms. Active changes in mural tension are mediated through a centrally integrated neurogenic mechanism which has an efferent pathway consisting of sympathetic adrenergic nerves.

REFLEX CONSTRICTION OF VESSELS. Muscular exercise causes a reflex increase in tension of the venous walls in both exercising and nonexercising limbs, which persists throughout the exercise and is proportional to the severity of the work (Fig. 2-12). It is interesting that this occurs in the exercising limbs in the face of the powerful local mechanism that causes dilatation of the resistance vessels in the active muscles (Bevegård and Shepherd, 1965A and B). This stiffening of the venous system, in combination with the muscle pump in the lower limbs and the abdominothoracic pump, aids venous return, and thereby maintains or increases the filling pressure of the right ventricle, augments the pulmonary blood volume, and contributes to the filling pressure of the left ventricle.

The systemic resistance vessels are influenced by local factors, but their overall activity is regulated by the autonomic nervous system. They constitute a system of tubes arranged in parallel; alterations in their caliber,

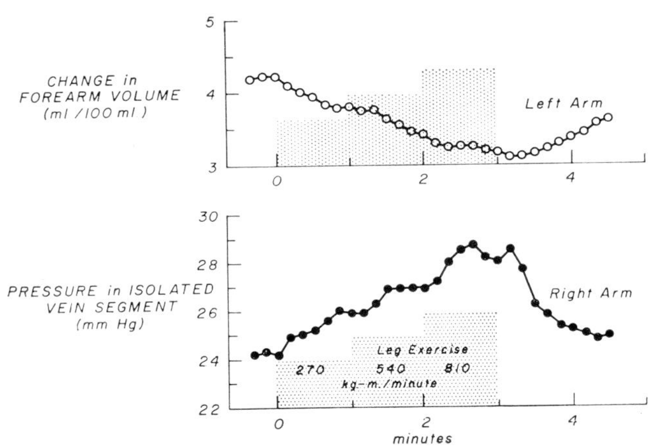

FIGURE 2-12. Effect of graded leg exercise on capacity of forearm vessels (*above*) and on pressure in an isolated venous segment (*below*). Simultaneous measurements in both upper limbs. (From Bevegård and Shepherd, J. Appl. Physiol., *20*:1, 1965.)

individually or in groups, regulate the distribution of the output of the left ventricle. During exercise, there is increased activity of the adrenergic fibers to the resistance vessels; like that to the vessels of the capacitance system, it is graded to the severity of the exercise. At the onset of leg exercise, although a transient dilatation of muscle vessels in the resting forearm may precede their constriction, the resistance vessels in the skin constrict immediately. With continued exercise, blood flow through the skin eventually increases, since reflex dilatation caused by the rise in body temperature opposes the reflex constriction caused by the exercise. As a result, during leg exercise corresponding with an oxygen consumption of up to 2 liters per minute, blood flow is partially redistributed from the muscle to the skin of the forearm, while the total blood flow to the forearm is little changed. With more severe exercise, the reflex vasoconstriction in the resting muscle is such that the total forearm flow decreases (Fig. 2-13).

In the hand, there is a balance between a reflex increase in sympathetic constrictor tone resulting from the exercise and a reflex decrease in constrictor tone resulting from the increase in body temperature. At the onset of exercise, the increase in constrictor tone predominates so that blood flow decreases. As exercise continues, the blood flow increases. It is clear that the blood flow is still opposed by the reflex constriction induced by the exercise, since it undergoes a further rapid and marked increase at the end of exercise, despite the fact that the arterial pressure is then decreasing. A similar compromise between the needs for increased blood flow in active muscles and for temperature regulation is present when exercise is undertaken in hot environments (Bishop et al., 1957A; Muth et al., 1958; Mitchell et al., 1958; Blair et al., 1961; Bevergård and Shepherd, 1966B).

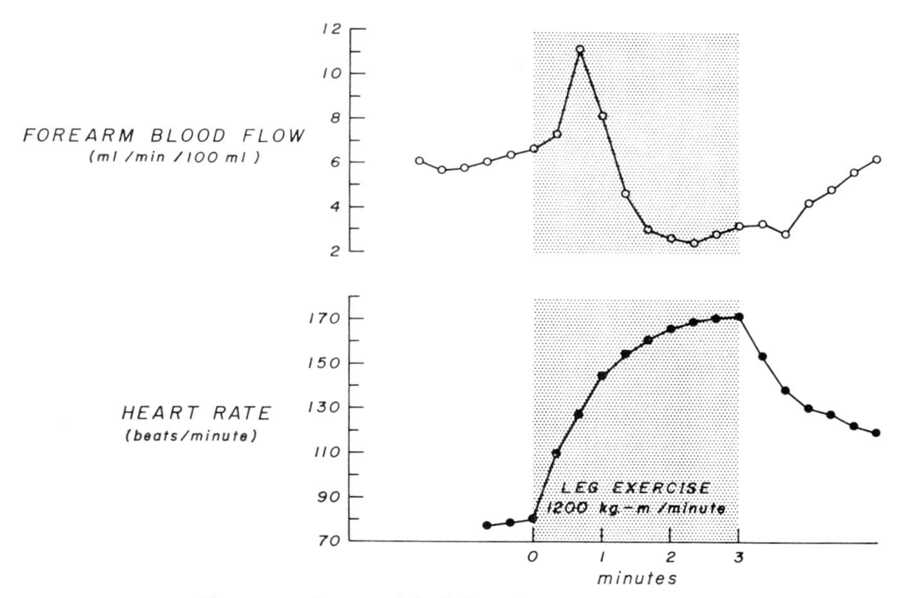

FIGURE 2-13. Changes in forearm blood flow during moderately severe leg exercise (1200 Kg.-M. per minute): average values for eight studies in three normal subjects. (From Bevegård and Shepherd, J. Appl. Physiol., *21*:123, 1966.)

Measurement of changes in vascular resistance in internal organs is difficult. The hepatic and splanchnic blood flow probably decreases reciprocally with the intensity of the exercise. Bishop et al. (1957B) measured the oxygen saturation of systemic arterial and hepatic venous blood in eight normal subjects before, during and after exercise. The arterio-venous difference in oxygen saturation in the liver increased during exercise in each subject; the largest increase occurred in the subject exercising hardest. The results suggested an average decrease of 400 ml. per minute in splanchnic blood flow. Rowell et al. (1964A), who measured the rate of clearance of indocyanine green dye by the liver, concluded that large decreases, in excess of 80 per cent, in estimated hepatic blood flow occurred during severe upright exercise. The renal blood flow also decreases with exercise. White and Rolf (1948), Chapman et al. (1948), Radigan and Robinson (1949) and Castenfors (1967) found a progressive decrease in renal plasma flow. With mild exercise (oxygen consumption about 900 ml. per minute), there is little or no change in cerebral blood flow or metabolism (Zobl et al., 1965).

The increased adrenergic nervous activity caused by exercise not only increases resistance to flow in vascular beds outside the active muscles, but also acts to adjust the metabolic vasodilatation throughout the total active musculature so that oxygen extraction from the blood is optimal (Strandell and Shepherd, 1967). As a result of this increased activity, there is a less marked decrease in systemic vascular resistance so that systemic arterial blood pressure is maintained, and the increased output of the left ventricle is directed to the active muscles.

As was discussed earlier, the cardiac output is less and the arteriovenous difference in oxygen content is greater when exercise is performed in the upright as opposed to the supine position, at least up to moderately severe work loads. It may be that the reflex increase in sympathetic adrenergic activity resulting from the upright position reinforces that caused by the exercise, to provide even more effective redistribution of flow to the active muscles.

It is also possible that, with conditioning, a more efficient distribution of blood may contribute to the increased exercise tolerance. The importance of such distribution of the cardiac output to the active muscles is illustrated by subjects with vasoregulatory asthenia (Holmgren et al., 1957; Graf, 1966). They have a normal stroke volume, but their working capacity is markedly reduced because of faulty regulation of the distribution of their peripheral blood flow. This results in an abnormally low arteriovenous difference in oxygen content (Holmgren et al., 1957).

The importance of the reflex constriction of resistance vessels in non-exercising parts in the maintenance of systemic arterial blood pressure during exercise can be demonstrated in a number of ways. Normal subjects, for example, have a decrease rather than an increase in systemic arterial pressure (Taylor and Donald, 1960), or a lesser increase (Kahler et al., 1962) during exercise after receiving the adrenergic neuronal blocking drug guanethidine. Again, patients with postural hypotension sustain a marked decrease in systemic arterial blood pressure during mild exercise in the supine position even in the presence of a normal increase in cardiac output. This is due to absent or impaired reflex vasoconstriction as a consequence of the autonomic denervation (Marshall et al., 1961; Bevegård et al., 1962). Patients with severe mitral stenosis may have little or no increase in cardiac output during exercise, yet the blood pressure is maintained because of an exaggerated vasoconstrictor response in non-exercising tissues (Muth et al., 1958).

RECEPTORS CONCERNED WITH REFLEX VASOCONSTRICTION. The receptors and afferent pathways concerned in this reflex increase in the tension of vascular smooth muscle of the capacitance and resistance systems are unknown. The increased tension does not result from the changes in respiration or blood chemistry associated with exercise (Bevegård and Shepherd, 1966B); the reflex possibly originates in the working muscles.

Rhythmic exercise or isometric contraction of small muscle groups results in a greater increase in aortic pressure in relation to oxygen consumption than when larger muscle groups are used. If the reflex originates in the active muscles, it may be that powerful contraction of small muscle groups may cause an even greater activation of the reflex than occurs when larger muscle groups contract less powerfully.

Again, if the receptors for the reflex are in the muscles, the stimulus to the heart and blood vessels will continue, whether or not the circulation

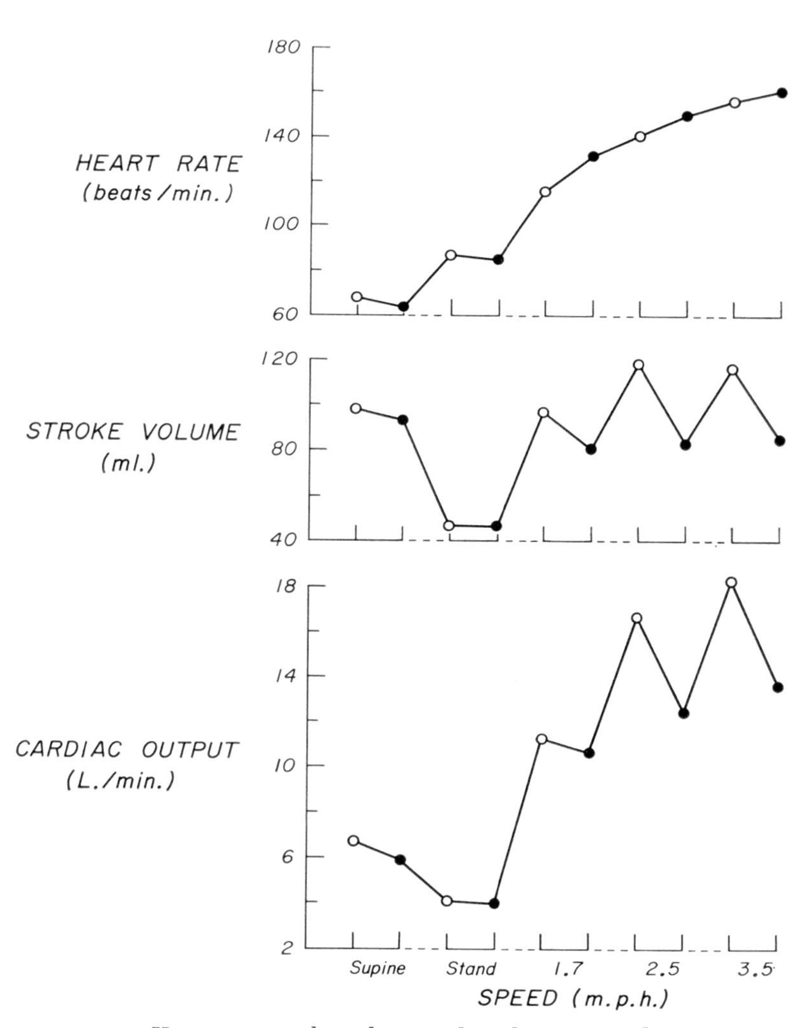

FIGURE 2-14. Heart rate, stroke volume and cardiac output during supine rest, standing and graded exercise on an inclined treadmill. Empty symbols: data with circulation to lower limbs unobstructed. Filled symbols: data obtained during inflation of pneumatic cuffs around the thighs to pressures exceeding systolic arterial pressure. (Shepherd and Marshall, unpublished data.)

to the active muscles is maintained. Thus, the intermittent inflation of pneumatic cuffs around the thighs to pressures exceeding systolic pressure during continuous exercise causes a decrease in stroke volume and cardiac output, without a change in heart rate (Fig. 2-14).

The increase in blood pressure and heart rate during exercise is modified by the arterial baroreceptors. They continue to oppose the increase, but they cannot prevent it. In the upright position, the arterial blood pressure may be relatively little changed. Since the baroreceptors have little influence on capacitance vessels in man, the venoconstriction caused by exercise is not opposed by reflex dilatation of veins from increased stimulation of the high pressure baroreceptors (Bevegård and Shephard, 1966A).

ROLE OF THE SYMPATHETIC NERVOUS SYSTEM. The rate of mobilization of free fatty acids into the blood increases during exercise (Basu et al., 1960; Friedberg et al., 1963; Havel et al., 1964). The concentration of glycerol in blood plasma also increases; this suggests that the mobilization of free fatty acids results from more rapid hydrolysis of triglycerides in adipose tissue (Carlson et al., 1963A). The mobilization probably results from increased activity of the sympathetic nervous system (Vendsalu, 1960), and, in particular, from the liberation of norepinephrine at sympathetic nerve endings in adipose tissue, since the concentration of free fatty acids increases with exercise even after adrenalectomy (Basu et al., 1960). Thus, activation of the sympathetic nervous system, in addition to its hemodynamic effects, may play a role in supplying fuel to working skeletal muscles.

Sympathetic nerve stimulation does not alter the compliance of the ventricles. Since time is required to dissipate the inertial and viscous forces of systole, and since the increased sympathetic activity during work shortens this phase of the cardiac cycle by increasing myocardial contractility, the ventricles are able to regain their full passive compliance during diastole (Sonnenblick et al., 1966). During systole, the force generated by the contraction of the ventricular myocardium ejects blood against the opposing pressure in the arterial system. In addition to the increased contractility, a greater force of cardiac contraction can be generated by the Frank-Starling mechanism. Starling (1920) was well aware that in most normal circumstances, the influence of the mechanism is modified by the activity of the autonomic nervous system. It is the only mechanism by which the heart can modify its stroke volume independently in the two ventricles on a beat to beat basis.

During exercise, the normal heart uses a combination of mechanisms to increase its output, which include an increase in heart rate, the Frank-Starling mechanism and an increase in contractility. There is a balance between the regulatory mechanisms that increase heart rate and stroke volume, so that the increase in output is accomplished mainly by increases in rate. In certain circumstances, changes in stroke volume make the major contribution, such as on transition from rest to work in the erect position. Dogs with complete cardiac denervation, which greatly reduces the initial acceleration of rate at the onset of exercise, achieve the same rapid increase in cardiac output as do intact dogs, through a major increase of stroke volume (Donald and Shepherd, 1964; Donald et al., 1964).

Since atropine has no effect on the maximal heart rate achieved during exercise in normal subjects, there is no parasympathetic influence on the heart during maximal work (Robinson et al., 1953). The maximal cardiac output could be limited by ventricular filling. Since an acute increase in blood volume and central venous pressure does not result in any additional increase in cardiac output during maximal exercise, it seems that the maximal cardiac output is not restricted by extracardiac factors limiting ventricular filling, but that the upper limit must be determined by the heart itself (Robinson et al., 1966).

REFERENCES

Alam, M., and Smirk, F. H.: Blood pressure raising reflexes in health, essential hypertension, and renal hypertension. Clin. Sci., *3*:259, 1938.

Andrew, G. M., Guzman, C. A., and Becklake, M. R.: Effect of athletic training on exercise cardiac output. J. Appl. Physiol., *21*:603, 1966.

Asmussen, E., and Hemmingsen, I.: Determination of maximum working capacity at different ages in work with the legs or with the arms. Scand. J. Clin. Lab. Invest., *10*:67, 1958.

Asmussen, E., and Nielsen, M.: Cardiac output during muscular work and its regulation. Physiol. Rev., *35*:778, 1955.

Åstrand, I., Åstrand, P.-O., Christensen, E. H., and Hedman, R.: Circulatory and respiratory adaptation to severe muscular work. Acta Physiol. Scand., *50*:254, 1960.

Åstrand, I., Åstrand, P.-O., and Rodahl, K.: Maximal heart rate during work in older men. J. Appl. Physiol., *14*:562, 1959.

Åstrand, P.-O.: Experimental Studies of Physical Working Capacity in Relation to Sex and Age. Copenhagen, Ejnar Munksgaard, 1952.

Åstrand, P.-O.: Human physical fitness with special reference to sex and age. Physiol. Rev., *36*:307, 1956.

Åstrand, P.-O., Cuddy, T. E., Saltin, B., and Stenberg, J.: Cardiac output during submaximal and maximal work. J. Appl. Physiol., *19*:268, 1964.

Åstrand, P.-O., Ekblom, B., Messin, R., Saltin, B., and Stenberg, J.: Intraarterial blood pressure during exercise with different muscle groups. J. Appl. Physiol., *20*:253, 1965.

Åstrand, P.-O., and Saltin, B.: Maximal oxygen uptake and heart rate in various types of muscular activity. J. Appl. Physiol., *16*:977, 1961.

Bannister, R. G., and Cunningham, D. J. C.: Effects on respiration and performance during exercise of adding oxygen to the inspired air. J. Physiol., *125*:118, 1954.

Barcroft, H.: Circulatory changes accompanying the contraction of voluntary muscle. Aust. J. Exp. Biol. Med. Sci., *42*:1, 1964.

Barcroft, H., and Millen, J. L. E.: The blood flow through muscle during sustained contraction. J. Physiol., *97*:17, 1939.

Basu, A., Passmore, R., and Strong, J. A.: The effect of exercise on the level of non-esterified fatty acids in the blood. Quart. J. Exp. Physiol., *45*:312, 1960.

Becklake, M. R., Frank, H., Dagenais, G. R., Ostiguy, G. L., and Guzman, C. A.: Influence of age and sex on exercise cardiac output. J. Appl. Physiol., *20*:938, 1965.

Bevegård, S.: The effect of cardioacceleration by methylscopolamine nitrate on the circulation at rest and during exercise in supine position, with special reference to the stroke volume. Acta Physiol. Scand., *57*:61, 1963B.

Bevegård, S.: Studies on the regulation of the circulation in man: With special reference to the stroke volume and the effects of muscular work, body position and artificially induced variations of the heart rate. Acta Physiol. Scand., *57* (Suppl. 200):1, 1963A.

Bevegård, B. S., Freyschuss, U., and Strandell, T.: Circulatory adaptation to arm and leg exercise in supine and sitting position. J. Appl. Physiol., *21*:37, 1966.

Bevegård, B. S., Holmgren, A., and Jonsson, B.: The effect of body position on the circulation at rest and during exercise, with special reference to the influence on the stroke volume. Acta Physiol. Scand., *49*:279, 1960.

Bevegård, S., Holmgren, A., and Jonsson, B.: Circulatory studies in well trained athletes at rest and during heavy exercise, with special reference to stroke volume and the influence of body position. Acta Physiol. Scand., *57*:26, 1963.

Bevegård, B. S., Jonsson, B., and Karlöf, I.: Circulatory response to recumbent exercise and head-up tilting in patients with disturbed sympathetic cardiovascular control (postural hypotension): Observations on the effect of norepinephrine infusion and antigravity suit inflation in the head-up tilted position. Acta Med. Scand., *172*:623, 1962.

Bevegård, B. S., and Shepherd, J. T.: Changes in tone of limb veins during supine exercise. J. Appl. Physiol., *20*:1, 1965A.

Bevegård, B. S., and Shepherd, J. T.: Effect of local exercise of forearm muscles on forearm capacitance vessels. J. Appl. Physiol., *20*:968, 1965B.

Bevegård, B. S., and Shepherd, J. T.: Circulatory effects of stimulating the carotid arterial stretch receptors in man at rest and during exercise. J. Clin. Invest., *45*:132, 1966A.

Bevegård, B. S., and Shepherd, J. T.: Reaction in man of resistance and capacity vessels in forearm and hand to leg exercise. J. Appl. Physiol., *21*:123, 1966B.

Bishop, J. M., Donald, K. W., Taylor, S. H., and Wormald, P. N.: The blood flow in the human arm during supine leg exercise. J. Physiol., *137*:294, 1957A.

Bishop, J. M., Donald, K. W., Taylor, S. H., and Wormald, P. N.: Changes in arterial-hepatic venous oxygen content differences during and after supine leg exercise. J. Physiol., *137*:309, 1957B.

Blair, D. A., Glover, W. E., and Roddie, I. C.: Vasomotor responses in the human arm during leg exercise. Circ. Research, *9*:264, 1961.

Bock, A. V., Vancaulaert, C., Dill, D. B., Fölling, A., and Hurxthal, L. M.: Studies in muscular activity. III. Dynamic changes occurring in man at work. J. Physiol., *66*:136, 1928.

Bosman, A. R., Honour, A. J., Lee, G. de J., Marshall, R. M., and Stott, F. D.: A method for measuring instantaneous pulmonary capillary blood flow and right ventricular stroke volume in man. Clin. Sci., *26*:247, 1964.

Brandfonbrener, M., Landowne, M., and Shock, N. W.: Changes in cardiac output with age. Circulation, *12*:557, 1955.

Braunwald, E., Goldblatt, A., Harrison, D. C., and Mason, D. T.: Studies on cardiac dimensions in intact, unanesthetized man. III. Effects of muscular exercise. Circ. Research, *13*:448, 1963.

Carlson, L. A., Ekelund, L.-G., and Orö, L.: Studies on blood lipids during exercise. IV. Arterial concentration of plasma free fatty acids and glycerol during and after prolonged exercise in normal men. J. Lab. Clin. Med., *61*:724, 1963A.

Castenfors, H.: Circulatory dynamics during experimentally induced dumping reactions, with special reference to the splanchnic circulation and the dye method employed for splanchnic flow measurements. Scand. J. Clin. Lab. Invest., *13* (Suppl. 62):1, 1961.

Castenfors, J.: Renal function during exercise. Acta Physiol. Scand., *70* (Suppl. 293):1, 1967.

Chapman, C. B., Baker, O., and Mitchell, J. H.: Left ventricular function at rest and during exercise. J. Clin. Invest., *38*:1202, 1959.

Chapman, C. B., Fisher, J. N., and Sproule, B. J.: Behavior of stroke volume at rest and during exercise in human beings. J. Clin. Invest., *39*:1208, 1960.

Chapman, C. B., Henschel, A., Minckler, J., Forsgren, A., and Keys, A.: The effect of exercise on renal plasma flow in normal male subjects. J. Clin. Invest., *27*:639, 1948.

Collett, M. E., and Liljestrand, G.: The minute volume of the heart in man during some different types of exercise. Skand. Arch. f. Physiol., *45*:29, 1924.

Corcondilas, A., Koroxenidis, G. T., and Shepherd, J. T.: Effect of a brief contraction of forearm muscles on forearm blood flow. J. Appl. Physiol., *19*:142, 1964.

Dagenais, G. R., Oriol, A., and McGregor, M.: Hemodynamic effects of carbohydrate and protein meals in man: rest and exercise. J. Appl. Physiol., *21*:1157, 1966.

Daly, W. J., Krumholz, R. A., and Ross, J. C.: The venous pump in the legs as a determinant of pulmonary capillary filling. J. Clin. Invest., *44*:271, 1965.

Damato, A. N., Galante, J. G., and Smith, W. H.: Hemodynamic response to treadmill exercise in normal subjects. J. Appl. Physiol., *21*:959, 1966.

DeFreitas, F. M., Faraco, E. Z., Nedel, N., DeAzevedo, D. F., and Zaduchliver, J.: Determination of pulmonary blood volume by single intravenous injection of one indicator in patients with normal and high pulmonary vascular pressures. Circulation, *30*:370, 1964.

Dock, D. S., Kraus, W. L., McGuire, L. B., Hyland, J. W., Haynes, F. W., and Dexter, L.: Pulmonary blood volume in man. J. Clin. Invest., *40*:317, 1961.

Dollery, C. T., Dyson, N. A., and Sinclair, J. D.: Regional variations in uptake of radioactive CO in the normal lung. J. Appl. Physiol., *15*:411, 1960.

Donald, D. E., Milburn, S. E., and Shepherd, J. T.: Effect of cardiac denervation on the maximal capacity for exercise in the racing greyhound. J. Appl. Physiol., *19*:849, 1964.

Donald, D. E., and Shepherd, J. T.: Initial cardiovascular adjustment to exercise in dogs with chronic cardiac denervation. Am. J. Physiol., *207*:1325, 1964.

Ekelund, L.-G.: Circulatory and respiratory adaptation during prolonged exercise of moderate intensity in the sitting position. Acta Physiol. Scand., *69*:327, 1967.

Ekelund, L.-G., and Holmgren, A.: Circulatory and respiratory adaptation, during long-term, non-steady state exercise, in the sitting position. Acta Physiol. Scand., *62*:240, 1964.

Feisal, K. A., Soni, J., and DuBois, A. B.: Pulmonary arterial circulation time, pulmonary arterial blood volume, and the ratio of gas to tissue volume in the lungs of dogs. J. Clin. Invest., *41*:390, 1962.

Fishman, A. P.: Dynamics of the pulmonary circulation. In: Handbook of Physiology. Section 2: Circulation, Volume 2, Washington, D.C., American Physiological Society, 1963.

Freedman, M. E., Snider, G. L., Brostoff, P., Kimelblot, S., and Katz, L. N.: Effects of training on response of cardiac output to muscular exercise in athletes. J. Appl. Physiol., *8*:37, 1955.

Friedberg, S. J., Sher, P. B., Bogdonoff, M. D., and Estes, E. H.: The dynamics of plasma free fatty acid metabolism during exercise. J. Lipid Research, *4*:34, 1963.

Giuntini, C., Lewis, M. L., Luis, A. S., Sales, L. A., and Harvey, R. M.: A study of the pulmonary blood volume in man by quantitative radiocardiography. J. Clin. Invest., *42*:1589, 1963.

Gladstone, S. A.: Cardiac output and related functions under basal and post-prandial conditions: A clinical study. A.M.A. Arch. Int. Med., *55*:533, 1935.

Gleason, W. L., and Braunwald, E.: Studies on the first derivative of the ventricular pressure pulse in man. J. Clin. Invest., *41*:80, 1962.

Gorlin, R., Cohen, L. S., Elliott, W. C., Klein, M. D., and Lane, F. J.: Effect of supine exercise on left ventricular volume and oxygen consumption in man. Circulation, *32*:361, 1965.

Graf, K.: Grösse und Reagibilität der Extremitätendurchblutung bei Vasoregulatorischer Asthenie. Acta Universitatis Upsaliensis, Uppsala, Almqvist and Wiksells, 1966.

Granath, A., Jonsson, B., and Strandell, T.: Circulation in healthy, old men studied by right heart catheterization at rest and during exercise in supine and sitting position. Acta Med. Scand., *176*:425, 1964.

Granath, A., and Strandell, T.: Relationships between cardiac output, stroke volume and intracardiac pressures at rest and during exercise in supine position and some anthropometric data in healthy old men. Acta Med. Scand., *176*:447, 1964.

Grande, F., and Taylor, H. L.: Adaptive changes in the heart, vessels and patterns of control under chronically high loads. In: Handbook of Physiology. Section 2: Circulation, Volume 3, Washington, D.C., American Physiological Society, 1965.

Grant, R. T.: Observations on the blood circulation in voluntary muscle in man. Clin. Sci., *3*:157, 1938.

Grimby, G., Nilsson, N. J., and Saltin, B.: Cardiac output during submaximal and maximal exercise in active middle-aged athletes. J. Appl. Physiol., *21*:1150, 1966.

Grollman, A.: Physiological variations in the cardiac output of man. III. The effect of the ingestion of food on the cardiac output, pulse rate, blood pressure, and oxygen consumption of man. Am. J. Physiol., *89*:366, 1929.

Harrison, D. C., Goldblatt, A., Braunwald, E., Glick, G., and Mason, D. T.: Studies on cardiac dimensions in intact, unanesthetized man: I. Description of techniques and their validation; II. Effects of respiration; III. Effects of muscular exercise. Circ. Research, *13*:448, 1963.

Havel, R. J., Carlson, L. A., Ekelund, L.-G., and Holmgren, A.: Turnover rate and oxidation of different free fatty acids in man during exercise. J. Appl. Physiol., *19*:613, 1964.

Hilton, S. M.: Experiments on the post-contraction hyperaemia of skeletal muscle. J. Physiol., *120*:230, 1953.

Holling, H. E., and Verel, D.: Circulation in the elevated forearm. Clin. Sci., *16*:197, 1957.

Holmgren, A.: Circulatory changes during muscular work in man: With special reference to arterial and central venous pressures in the systemic circulation. Scand. J. Clin. Lab. Invest., *8* (Suppl. 24):1, 1956.

Holmgren, A., Jonsson, B., Levander, M., Linderholm, H., Sjöstrand, T., and Ström, G.: Low physical working capacity in suspected heart cases due to inadequate adjustment of peripheral blood flow (vasoregulatory asthenia). Acta Med. Scand., *158*:413, 1957.

Holmgren, A., Jonsson, B., and Sjöstrand, T.: Circulatory data in normal subjects at rest and during exercise in recumbent position, with special reference to the stroke volume at different work intensities. Acta Physiol. Scand., *49*:343, 1960.

Holmgren, A., and Linderholm, H.: Oxygen and carbon dioxide tensions of arterial blood during heavy and exhaustive exercise. Acta Physiol. Scand., *44*:203, 1958.

Holmgren, A., and Ovenfors, C. O.: Heart volume at rest and during muscular work in the supine and in the sitting position. Acta Med. Scand., *167*:267, 1960.

Humphreys, P. W., and Lind, A. R.: The blood flow through active and inactive muscles of the forearm during sustained handgrip contractions. J. Physiol., *166*:120, 1963.

Johnson, R. L., Jr., Spicer, W. S., Bishop, J. M., and Forster, R. E.: Pulmonary capillary blood volume, flow and diffusing capacity during exercise. J. Appl. Physiol., *15*:893, 1960.

Jones, W. B., and Foster, G. L.: Determinants of duration of left ventricular ejection in normal young men. J. Appl. Physiol., *19*:279, 1964.

Jones, W. B., Thomas, H. D., and Reeves, T. J.: Circulatory and ventilatory responses to postprandial exercise. Am. Heart J., *69*:668, 1965.

Kahler, R. L., Gaffney, T. E., and Braunwald, E.: The effects of autonomic nervous system inhibition on the circulatory response to muscular exercise. J. Clin. Invest., *41*:198, 1962.

Kjellberg, S. R., Rudhe, U., and Sjöstrand, T.: The amount of hemoglobin and the blood volume in relation to the pulse rate and cardiac volume during rest. Acta Physiol. Scand., *19*:136, 1949.

König, K., Reindell, H., and Roskamm, H.: Das Herzvolumen und die Leistungsfähigkeit bei 60-75 jährigen gesunden Männern. Arch. Kreislaufforsch., *39*:143, 1962.

Lammerant, J.: Le Volume Sanguin des Poumons chez l'homme. Bruxelles, Éditions Arscia, 1957.

Lee, G. de J., and DuBois, A. B.: Pulmonary capillary blood flow in man. J. Clin. Invest., *34*:1380, 1955.

LeQuesne, L. P., Hobsley, M., and Hand, B. H.: The dumping syndrome. I. Factors responsible for the symptoms. Brit. Med. J., *i*:141, 1960.

Levine, H. J., Neill, W. A., Wagman, R. J., Krasnow, N., and Gorlin, R.: The effect of exercise on mean left ventricular ejection rate in man. J. Clin. Invest., *41*:1050, 1962.

Levinson, G. E., Frank, M. J., and Hellems, H. K.: The pulmonary vascular volume in man: measurement from atrial dilution curves. Am. Heart J., *67*:734, 1964.

Levinson, G. E., Pacifico, A. D., and Frank, M. J.: Studies of cardiopulmonary blood volume: Measurement of total cardiopulmonary blood volume in normal human subjects at rest and during exercise. Circulation, *33*:347, 1966.

Lind, A. R., Taylor, S. H., Humphreys, P. W., Kennelly, B. M., and Donald, K. W.: The circulatory effects of sustained voluntary muscle contraction. Clin. Sci., *27*:229, 1964.

Linderholm, H.: Diffusing capacity of the lungs as a limiting factor for physical working capacity. Acta Med. Scand., *163*:61, 1959.

Marshall, R. J., Schirger, A., and Shepherd, J. T.: Blood pressure during supine exercise in idiopathic orthostatic hypotension. Circulation, *24*:76, 1961.

Marshall, R. J., and Shepherd, J. T.: Interpretation of changes in "central" blood volume and slope volume during exercise in man. J. Clin. Invest., *40*:375, 1961.

Marx, H. J., Rowell, L. B., Conn, R. D., Bruce, R. A., and Kusumi, F.: Maintenance of aortic pressure and total peripheral resistance during exercise in heat. J. Appl. Physiol., *22*:519, 1967.

McGregor, M., Adam, W., and Sekelj, P.: Influence of posture on cardiac output and minute ventilation during exercise. Circ. Research, *9*:1089, 1961.

McIntosh, H. D., Gleason, W. L., Miller, D. E., and Bacos, J. M.: A major pitfall in the interpretation of "central blood volume." Circ. Research, *9*:1223, 1961.

Michael, E. D., Jr., Hutton, K. E., and Horvath, S. M.: Cardiorespiratory responses during prolonged exercise. J. Appl. Physiol., *16*:997, 1961.

Milnor, W. R., Jose, A. D., and McGaff, C. J.: Pulmonary vascular volume, resistance, and compliance in man. Circulation, *22*:130, 1960.

Mitchell, J. H., Sproule, B. J., and Chapman, C. B.: Factors influencing respiration during heavy exercise. J. Clin. Invest., *37*:1693, 1958.

Muth, H. A. V., Wormald, P. N., Bishop, J. M., and Donald, K. W.: Further studies of blood flow in the resting arm during supine leg exercise. Clin. Sci., *17*:603, 1958.

Radigan, L. R., and Robinson, S.: Effects of environmental heat stress and exercise on renal blood flow and filtration rate. J. Appl. Physiol., *2*:185, 1949.

Reeves, J. T., Grover, R. F., Filley, G. F., and Blount, S. G., Jr.: Circulatory changes in man during mild supine exercise. J. Appl. Physiol., *16*:279, 1961.

Regan, T. J., Timmis, G., Gray, M., Binak, K., and Hellems, H. K.: Myocardial oxygen consumption during exercise in fasting and lipemic subjects. J. Clin. Invest., *40*:624, 1961.

Rigatto, M., and Fishman, A. P.: The pulsatile nature of the pulmonary capillary blood flow. J. Clin. Invest., *39*:1626, 1960.

Robinson, B. F., Epstein, S. E., Kahler, R. L., and Braunwald, E.: Circulatory effects of acute expansion of blood volume: Studies during maximal exercise and at rest. Circ. Research, *19*:26, 1966.

Robinson, S.: Experimental studies of physical fitness in relation to age. Arbeitsphysiol., *10*:251, 1938.

Robinson, S., Pearcy, M., Brueckman, F. R., Nicholas, J. R., and Miller, D. I.: Effects of atropine on heart rate and oxygen intake in working man. J. Appl. Physiol., *5*:508, 1953.

Ross, J., Jr., Linhart, J. W., and Braunwald, E.: Effects of changing heart rate in man by electrical stimulation of the right atrium: Studies at rest, during exercise, and with isoproterenol. Circulation, *32*:549, 1965.

Roughton, F. J. W.: Average time spent by blood in the human lung capillary and its relation to the rates of CO uptake and elimination in man. Am. J. Physiol., *143*:621, 1945.

Rowell, L. B., Blackmon, J. R., and Bruce, R. A.: Indocyanine green clearance and estimated hepatic blood flow during mild to maximal exercise in upright man. J. Clin. Invest., *43*:1677, 1964A.

Rowell, L. B., Taylor, H. L., Wang, Y., and Carlson, W. S.: Saturation of arterial blood with oxygen during maximal exercise. J. Appl. Physiol., *19*:284, 1964B.

Ruosteenoja, R., Linko, E., Lind, J., and Sollberger, A.: Heart volume changes at rest and during exercise. Acta Med. Scand., *162*:263, 1958.

Rushmer, R. F.: Postural effects on the baselines of ventricular performance. Circulation, *20*:897, 1959.

Rushmer, R. F., Smith, O. A., Jr., and Lasher, E. P.: Neural mechanisms of cardiac control during exertion. Physiol. Rev., *40* (Suppl. 4):27, 1960.

Saltin, B., and Stenberg, J.: Circulatory response to prolonged severe exercise. J. Appl. Physiol., *19*:833, 1964.

Samet, P., Bernstein, W. H., Lopez, A., and Levine, S.: Methodology of true pulmonary blood volume determination. Circulation, *33*:847, 1966.

Shepherd, J. T.: Role of the veins in the circulation. Circulation, *33*:484, 1966.

Sjöstrand, T.: Das Sportherz. Deutsche Med. Wchnschr., *80*:963, 1955.

Sonnenblick, E. H., Ross, J., Covell, J. W., and Braunwald, E.: Alterations in resting length-tension relations of cardiac muscle induced by changes in contractile force. Circ. Research, *19*:980, 1966.

Starling, E. H.: On the circulatory changes associated with exercise. J. Roy. Army Med. Corps, *34*:258, 1920.

Stenberg, J., Åstrand, P.-O., Ekblom, B., Royce, J., and Saltin, B.: Hemodynamic response to work with different muscle groups, sitting and supine. J. Appl. Physiol., *22*:61, 1967.

Strandell, T.: Circulatory studies on healthy old men: With special reference to the limitation of the maximal physical working capacity. Acta Med. Scand., *175* (Suppl. 414):1, 1964.

Strandell, T., and Shepherd, J. T.: The effect in humans of increased sympathetic activity on the blood flow to active muscles. Acta Med. Scand. *182* (Suppl. 472):146, 1967.

Tabakin, B. S., Hanson, J. S., and Levy, A. M.: Effects of physical training on the cardiovascular and respiratory response to graded upright exercise in distance runners. Brit. Heart J., *27*:205, 1965.

Tabakin, B. S., Hanson, J. S., Merriam, T. W., Jr., and Caldwell, E. J.: Hemodynamic response of normal men to graded treadmill exercise. J. Appl. Physiol., *19*:457, 1964.

Taylor, S. H., and Donald, K. W.: The circulatory effects of bretylium tosylate and guanethidine. Lancet, *ii*:389, 1960.

Turino, G. M., Bergofsky, E. H., Goldring, R. M., and Fishman, A. P.: Effect of exercise on pulmonary diffusing capacity. J. Appl. Physiol., *18*:447, 1963.

Uvnäs, B.: Sympathetic vasodilator outflow. Physiol. Rev., *34*:608, 1954.

Valentin, H., Venrath, H., Von Mallinckrodt, H., and Gurakar, M. Die maximale Sauerstoffaufnahme in den verschiedenen Altersklassen: Eine praktisch wichtige Herz-Kreislauf-Funktionsprüfung im Vita-maxima-Bereich. Ztschr. Alterforsch., 9:291, 1955.

Vendsalu, A.: Studies on adrenaline and noradrenaline in human plasma. Acta Physiol. Scand., *49*(Suppl. 173):1, 1960.

Wang, Y., Blomqvist, G., Rowell, L. B., and Taylor, H. L.: Central blood volume during upright exercise in normal subjects. Fed. Proc., *21*:124, 1962 (Abstract).

Wang, Y., Marshall, R. J., and Shepherd, J. T.: The effect of changes in posture and of graded exercise on stroke volume in man. J. Clin. Invest., *39*:1051, 1960.

Wang, Y., Shepherd, J. T., Marshall, R. J., Rowell, L., and Taylor, H. L.: Cardiac response to exercise in unconditioned young men and in athletes. Circulation, *24*:1064, 1961 (Abstract).

Warner, H. R.: Control of the circulation as studied with analog computer technics. In: Handbook of Physiology. Section 2: Circulation, Volume 3, Washington, D.C., American Physiological Society, 1965.

West, J. B.: Influence of hydrostatic pressure on the pulmonary circulation. Jap. Heart J., *7*:350, 1966.

West, J. B., and Dollery, C. T.: Distribution of blood flow and ventilation-perfusion ratio in the lung, measured with radioactive carbon dioxide. J. Appl. Physiol., *15*:405, 1960.

White, H. L., and Rolf, D.: Effects of exercise and of some other influences on the renal circulation in man. Am. J. Physiol., *152*:505, 1948.

Zobl, E. G., Talmers, F. N., Christensen, R. C., and Baer, L. J.: Effect of exercise on the cerebral circulation and metabolism. J. Appl. Physiol., *20*:1289, 1965.

Chapter 3

ALTERATION OF EXTERNAL ENVIRONMENT

- Temperature
- Low and High Oxygen Pressures
- Blood Hydrogen-Ion Concentration and Carbon Dioxide Tension
- Acclimatization to Altitude
- Negative and Positive Pressure Breathing
- Effects of Gravity
- Diving

TEMPERATURE

Bazett et al. (1948) and Eichna et al. (1951) measured the temperature at various sites in arteries, veins and the right side of the heart in afebrile subjects. The temperature in the larger veins increased as they approached the heart. The temperatures within the inferior vena cava, the right ventricle, the pulmonary artery and the proximal portion of the femoral artery were equal and averaged 0.3 degrees C. less than rectal temperature. In the hepatic and internal jugular veins, the temperature equaled that in the rectum. Afonso et al. (1962) passed a thermistor tipped catheter into the left atrium and pulmonary veins in subjects with atrial septal defect or patent foramen ovale and found that the temperatures were identical with those in the pulmonary artery and pulmonary capillaries. Thus, there is no significant change in the temperature of blood as it traverses the lungs. A different technique, the helium-argon method, was used to measure the temperature of alveolar capillaries in man (Edwards et al., 1963) and dog (Edwards, 1964); there was no significant difference between it and the temperatures in right and left sided cardiac chambers.

The temperature of the body core (Bazett, 1949) is determined by the balance between heat production and heat loss. Heat is continually produced in such organs as muscle, liver and heart. During rest, sufficient heat is generated to raise the core temperature at the rate of 1 degree C. per hour, and during moderate work, with an energy expenditure of 300 kcal. per hour, it would increase at the rate of 5 degrees C. per hour, if no means were available for its dissipation. The efficiency of thermal regulation is evident from the ease with which these quantities of heat are dissipated, even in climates in which additional heat is gained by convection or radiation (Leithead and Lind, 1964). Shivering, the involuntary contraction of skeletal muscles that comes into play in order to maintain or increase body temperature, is a rapidly adjustable component of heat production.

Heat is lost mainly from the respiratory tract, by warming inspired air and by evaporation; and from the skin, by radiation, conduction and convection, and by insensible water loss and eccrine sweating. Sweating and alterations in blood flow through the skin can be rapidly and finely adjusted by the body's thermoregulatory mechanisms. Thus, they are the most important modalities of heat loss for the maintenance of an optimal body temperature (Pickering, 1958).

THERMOREGULATORY MECHANISMS. Blood flow through the skin is regulated partly by reflex action from receptors in the skin, different from those serving sensation, and partly by activation of central receptors, that respond to changes in blood temperature of as little as 0.2 degree C. (Pickering, 1958). Folkow et al. (1949) produced cutaneous vasodilatation in cats by heating a localized part of the hypothalamus, but in man, the precise site of the central temperature receptors is unknown. The changes in the caliber of blood vessels are affected by changes in the activity of their sympathetic nerves. The work of Appenzeller and Schnieden (1963) supported the view of Kerslake and Cooper (1950) that the vasodilatation in the skin during body heating is partly dependent on afferent nervous pathways. Thus, anesthesia of the area of skin to which heat is applied abolishes the reflex. The reflex appears to depend on the presence of intact nerve fibers to and from structures higher than the brain stem, since it is abolished in some patients with lesions in the latter site. Division of the sympathetic nerve supply to the legs abolishes the reflex vasodilator response in the hands to heating the legs, although it does not abolish the sensation of heat in the legs (Cooper and Kerslake, 1953). Hence, the receptors responsible for the perception of warmth play no part in reflex vasodilatation.

As body heating continues, the rising blood temperature activates the central receptors in the brain. This results in increased activity of the cholinergic sympathetic fibers to the sweat glands and in a reduction of the number of constrictor impulses to the skin vessels. Sweating and cutaneous vasodilatation follow. During sweating, a proteolytic enzyme passes through the walls of the cells in the glands into the surrounding tissue fluids where it breaks down proteins to form the polypeptide bradykinin. This causes a pronounced vasodilatation in the skin around the sweat glands.

Koroxenidis et al. (1961) measured cardiac output and blood flow through the hand and forearm in eight normal subjects in an attempt to estimate the increase in the total blood flow through skin during body heating. After 50 minutes of heating by immersing the feet and legs in water at 44 degrees C. and wrapping the body with blankets (Gibbon and Landis, 1932), the oral temperature had risen to between 99.5 and 100.8 degrees F. The cardiac output had increased by 1.9 to 4.5 (mean 3.3) liters per minute, mainly through an increase in heart rate. On the assumption that blood flow through the internal organs and tissues did not change, this would indicate an increase of 1.0 to 2.5 (mean 1.8) liters per $M.^2$ per minute in blood flow to the skin.

The increased blood flow through the skin of the hands, ears and glabrous portion of the lips is due mainly to release of sympathetic vasoconstrictor tone which occurs soon after heating commences. In other areas of the skin, including the forearm and forehead, the formation of bradykinin as a consequence of sweating is responsible for the continued vasodilatation (Roddie et al., 1956, Gaskell, 1956; Fox and Hilton, 1958; Fox et al., 1960A and B; Blair et al., 1961). The increase in flow to the skin of the forearm, and presumably other regions where bradykinin is liberated, parallels the increase in cardiac output (Fig. 3-1).

Indirect heating does not change the blood flow to resting muscles. The increase of flow to the limbs is due solely to an increase in flow to the skin (Barcroft et al., 1955; Roddie et al., 1956; Edholm et al., 1956). Complete information is not available about changes in flow in the internal organs.

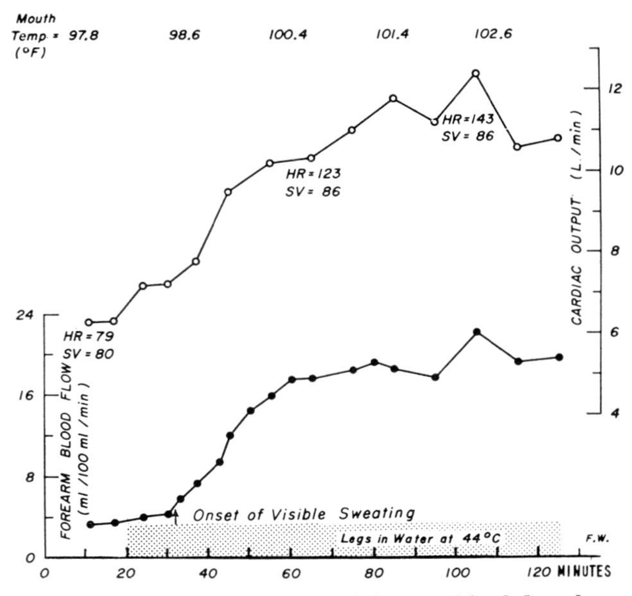

FIGURE 3-1. Changes in cardiac output and forearm blood flow during body heating. (From Koroxenidis, Shepherd and Marshall, J. Appl. Physiol., *16*:869, 1961.)

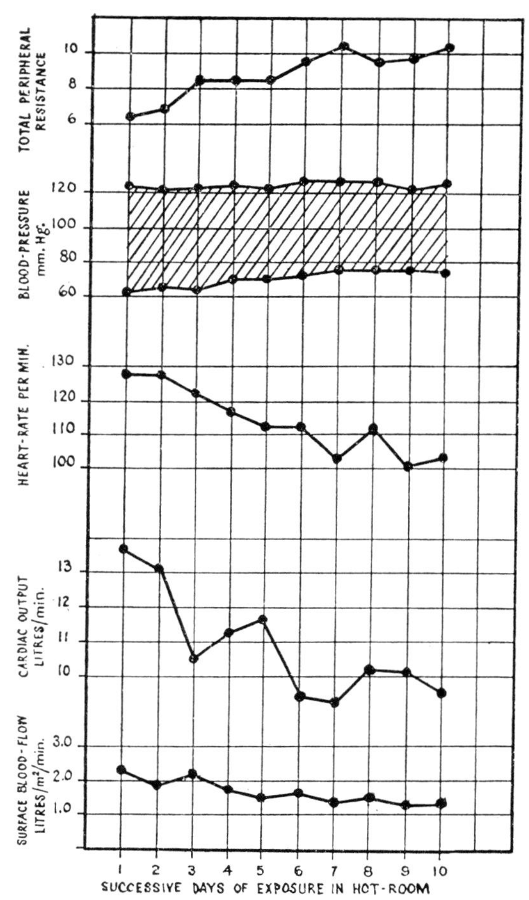

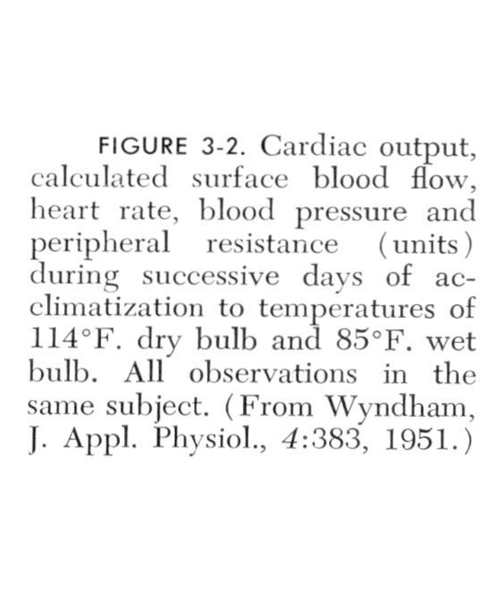
FIGURE 3-2. Cardiac output, calculated surface blood flow, heart rate, blood pressure and peripheral resistance (units) during successive days of acclimatization to temperatures of 114°F. dry bulb and 85°F. wet bulb. All observations in the same subject. (From Wyndham, J. Appl. Physiol., *4*:383, 1951.)

Crossley et al. (1966) studied the interrelation of the thermoregulatory and baroreceptor reflexes in the control of blood flow through the skin. When blood was transferred from the body to the legs during indirect heating, vasoconstriction took precedence over thermoregulatory dilatation.

ENVIRONMENTAL ACCLIMATIZATION. The circulatory adjustments of acclimatization to a hot and humid environment (114 degrees F. dry bulb and 85 degrees F. wet bulb) include reduction in cardiac output, heart rate and pulse pressure and an increase in systemic vascular resistance (Wyndham, 1951). The blood vessels in the skin participate in the decrease in vasodilatation (Fig. 3-2). Heart rate and rectal temperature decrease rapidly during the first few days of exposure to heat, whereas sweat rates increase more gradually during acclimatization (Eichna et al., 1945; Robinson et al., 1943; Bass et al., 1955; Wyndham et al., 1954).

Whitney (1954) reported that, after repeated exposure to heat, the forearm volume during exposure is decreased; he attributed this to a decrease in the size of the venous reservoir. Wood and Bass (1960) had seven young men walk on a treadmill four times a day for six to nine days at a temperature of 120 degrees F. dry bulb and 80 degrees F. wet bulb. Forearm blood flow was measured and curves were obtained relating venous pressure and forearm volume. Disappearance of the symptoms of heat exhaustion (dizziness, weakness and nausea) during exercise coincided with the development of maximal venoconstriction and minimal levels of arteriolar dilatation on the third day of acclimatization. These vasomotor adaptations decreased after the fourth day, even though subjective and objective evidence of heat acclimatization persisted.

In studies of adaptation to heat, subjects usually perform an accurately controlled daily work routine in a known hot environment. The degree of adaptation is assessed from the differences in the physiological responses between the beginning and the end of the series of exposures. The changes during acclimatization include increased sweat production, a lower pulse rate while working in the heat, lower temperatures in skin and body core and less discomfort during the exposure. This type of approach in the laboratory closely simulates the natural situation, when man goes from a cool to a hot climate. The degree of acclimatization to heat exposure may be based on measurements both of the adaptive changes such as increases in sweat loss, and of the benefits they confer such as reduction in body temperature. Decreases in pulse rate and in subjective discomfort could be due, in part at least, to specific adaptations by the cardiovascular and central nervous systems, respectively; alternatively, they could simply be further evidence of the benefits that accrue from the improved capacity to eliminate heat.

In their studies, Fox et al. (1963) assumed that the degree of adaptation is in some way determined by the intensity and duration of activation of the thermoregulatory system, and that the increase of body core temperature is the most direct method of activating the thermoregulatory system (Benzinger, 1961). The body temperature of 18 men was increased to 37.3, 37.9 and 38.5 degrees C. and maintained at these levels for one half, one or two hours daily. Although the rate of sweating increased progressively during the 12 days of the study, the heart rate either did not change or actually increased, and the sensation of discomfort increased rather than decreased. The progressive increase in the rate of sweating was probably due to increased secretory capacity of the sweat glands rather than to a change in the activity of the central nervous system (Fox et al., 1962).

CIRCULATORY AND METABOLIC RESPONSE. Circulatory and metabolic responses to work in heat were examined by Williams et al. (1962). There were no significant differences in cardiac output or arteriovenous difference in oxygen content during identical grades of work performed in hot (97 degrees F. dry bulb and 93 degrees F. wet bulb) and in comfortable (70 degrees F.) conditions. The heart rate was much greater at all grades up to nearly maximal work in the heat; at maximal work, the difference in rate was no longer present. Reciprocal differences occurred in stroke volume. Since the cardiac output was similar in the hot and the comfortable environments, and since it seems reasonable to assume that the blood flow through skin must have been greater during exercise in the heat, then either less blood was going to the active muscles, or there was a greater decrease in blood flow to other organs and tissues not involved in the exercise.

In resting men, the skin blood flow during severe heating has been estimated at 1.8 liters per $M.^2$ per minute. However, the reflex vasodilatation responsible for this may be opposed during exercise by reflex constriction caused by the exercise, resulting in a less pronounced increase in flow. Thus, at maximal or near maximal rates of work in the heat, blood may be shunted from the skin and probably the viscera to the working muscles. It may be concluded that, during brief periods of severe work in hot conditions, muscle metabolism takes precedence over heat regulation. This is reflected in the higher rectal temperatures of men working in heat.

Rowell et al. (1966) measured cardiac output and central blood volume in normal men during exercise on separate occasions at 78 degrees F. and 110 degrees F. Indicator was injected into the low superior vena cava and sampled from the descending thoracic aorta. The exercise required from 43 to 86 per cent of the maximal oxygen consumption at both temperatures. Cardiac output was less at the higher than at the lower temperature; the difference increased as exercise became more severe. Since the oxygen consumption was the same, the arteriovenous difference in oxygen content was greater with work in the heat. The central blood volume and stroke volume were both 16 per cent less at the higher temperature. Greater reduction of hepatic and renal blood flow at the higher temperature made available more blood for skin and active muscles (Rowell et al., 1965).

Saltin (1964) studied his subjects at rest and during severe exercise under normal conditions, and after dehydration in a sauna bath that reduced the body weight by up to 5.2 per cent. At maximal loads in the sitting position, stroke volume was less and heart rate greater following dehydration; cardiac output was almost identical with that before dehydration. The changes in stroke volume and heart rate correlated with the reduction in body weight and plasma volume. When submaximal work was performed in the supine position, no increase in heart rate was noted after, as compared with before, dehydration. During maximal exercise in the sitting position, oxygen consumption, cardiac output and stroke volume were identical before and after dehydration. To explain these findings, Saltin suggested that the level of vasomotor activity, particularly in capacitance vessels, may be higher following dehydration. Redistribution of the blood volume might then enable normal values for stroke volume and cardiac output to be attained, despite the reduction in the total blood volume.

Oxygen consumption is a measure of energy expenditure. In a comfortable environment, the heart rate for a given individual during the steady state of exercise has a relatively linear relationship to oxygen consumption (Asmussen and Nielsen, 1955A). This, however, does not hold when dissipation of body heat is impaired by excessive clothing or by a thermally stressful environment. In such conditions, although oxygen consumption is comparable with that during identical work performed in comfortable surroundings, the heart rate is greater and may increase progressively throughout the exposure, in spite of intermittent rest periods (Brouha et al., 1963). Thus, heart rate is a more reliable indicator than is oxygen consumption of the stress during work in a hot environment. Nevertheless, attempts to assess energy expenditure from changes in pulse rates or body temperature during or just after work in the heat may be misleading, since the magnitude of such changes is affected by the degree of acclimatization.

Dill and Consolazio (1962) studied the effects of aging on the ability to work in extreme heat. There was little change in the response of the pulse rate to graded exercise; however, the ability to perform very heavy work was impaired because of a reduction by about one fourth in the maximal level of oxygen consumption.

LOW AND HIGH OXYGEN PRESSURES

Inhalation of 12 per cent oxygen in nitrogen reduces the saturation of arterial blood to 65 to 70 per cent (Asmussen and Nielsen, 1955B). It is accompanied by an increase in cardiac output of 10 to 20 per cent during both rest and exercise, as compared with values obtained while breathing air (Fig. 3-3). The heart rate is 15 to 30 per cent greater with the low oxygen mixture. Since oxygen consumption is unchanged, the arteriovenous difference in oxygen saturation narrows.

In 17 healthy men, blockade of beta adrenergic receptors reduced by about half the elevation in cardiac output and heart rate associated with inhalation of 7.5 per cent oxygen for seven to 10 minutes. The hypoxia did not increase plasma concentrations of epinephrine or norepinephrine. Thus, the cardiac sympathetic nerves are activated during acute hypoxia. Blockade of alpha and beta receptors in the forearm did not modify the vasodilatation in the forearm induced by hypoxia. The mechanism of the vasodilatation in the forearm is unknown; it is not due to the accompanying hypocapnia (Richardson et al., 1967).

Asmussen and Nielsen (1955B) found that the cardiac output while breathing 100 per cent oxygen at one atmosphere was identical with that

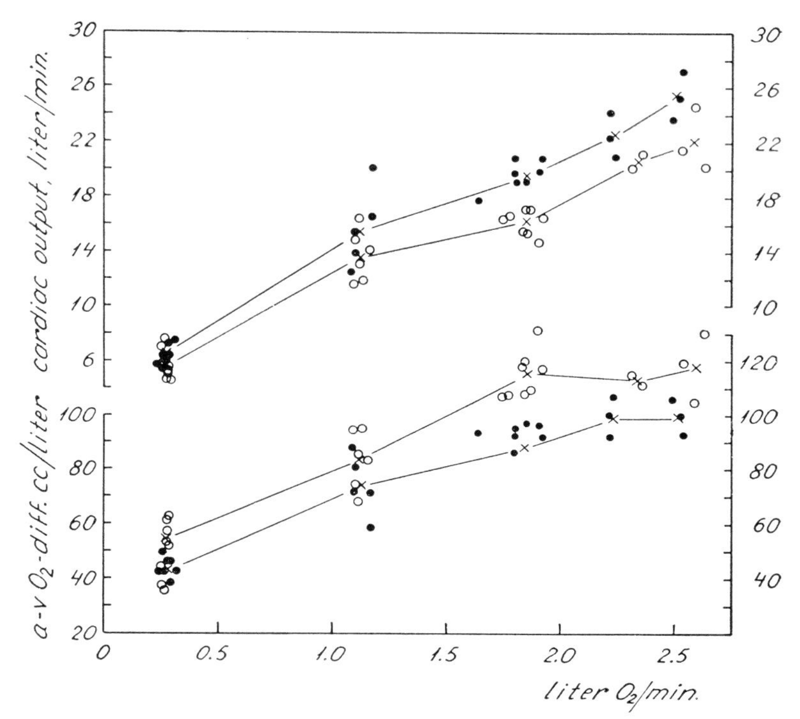

FIGURE 3-3. Cardiac output and arteriovenous difference in oxygen content (both on ordinate) related to oxygen consumption (abscissa) at rest and during work. Empty symbols: experiments with air; filled symbols: experiments with low concentration of oxygen. The lines connect average values (x) for different grades of work. (From Asmussen and Nielsen, Acta Physiol. Scand., 35:73, 1955.)

while breathing air, and the heart rate was four to eight per cent slower. Eggers et al. (1962) and Daly and Bondurant (1962) reported small but statistically significant decreases in cardiac output and heart rate. The mean arterial pressure, and therefore the peripheral vascular resistance, increased; these increases persisted for at least 40 minutes after the inhalation of 100 per cent oxygen ceased. Since the decreases in cardiac output and heart rate were no longer noted following administration of atropine, they were mediated through vagal activity. In the studies of Whalen et al. (1965), however, changes in cardiac output and heart rate during the breathing of 100 per cent oxygen failed to reach statistical significance.

The solubility of a slightly soluble gas such as oxygen is proportionate to its partial pressure. In man, plasma contains about 0.1 ml. oxygen in physical solution for every 30 mm. Hg of pO_2. Thus, when breathing air, the arterial pO_2 averages 90 mm. Hg, and 0.3 ml. oxygen is present in solution; when breathing 100 per cent oxygen at one atmosphere, the pO_2 averages 500 mm. Hg, and 1.5 ml. oxygen is in solution; when breathing

TABLE 3-1. Changes in Blood Gases and Hemodynamics During Inhalation of Air and 100 Per Cent O_2 at One and Three Atmospheres*

CONDITION	ARTERIAL PO_2 (MM. HG)	VENOUS PO_2 (MM. HG)	CARDIAC OUTPUT (L./MIN.)	HEART RATE (/ MIN.)	STROKE VOLUME (ML.)	MEAN B.P. (MM. HG)	SYSTEMIC RESIST-ANCE (UNITS)
Air, 1 atm.	89	41	6.1	75	81	89	15
Air, 3 atm.	402	68	5.7	68	85	88	16
O_2, 1 atm.	507	57	5.8	71	82	90	16
O_2, 3 atm.	1721	424	5.3	63	86	92	18

* Adapted from data of Whalen et al., Am. J. Cardiol., *15*:638, 1965.

100 per cent oxygen at three atmospheres, the pO_2 averages 1720 mm. Hg, and almost 6 ml. oxygen is in solution (Whalen et al., 1965). In the last situation, the physically dissolved oxygen is sufficient to meet tissue demands during rest. No oxygen need dissociate from the fully saturated hemoglobin; thus, it is theoretically possible to survive for limited periods of time with hyperbaric oxygenation in the absence of hemoglobin (Boerema et al., 1960). Eight of the ten resting subjects studied by Whalen et al. (1965) had an average pO_2 of 420 mm. Hg in mixed venous blood, when breathing 100 per cent oxygen at three atmospheres. Despite loss of the buffering power of reduced hemoglobin (Peters and Van Slyke, 1931), the venous pCO_2 increased by only 4 mm. Hg, and the venous pH decreased only from 7.42 to 7.40.

During hyperbaric oxygen breathing, there was a significant decrease in cardiac output and heart rate, compared with values obtained during the breathing of either air or 100 per cent oxygen at one atmosphere. The mean arterial blood pressure was unchanged, and therefore, the peripheral vascular resistance was increased (Table 3-1). Lambertsen et al. (1953) also reported bradycardia and little change in blood pressure during inhalation of oxygen at three atmospheres.

BLOOD HYDROGEN-ION CONCENTRATION AND CARBON DIOXIDE TENSION

HYPERVENTILATION. Hyperventilation reduces arterial pCO_2 and increases its pH. Vigorous voluntary hyperventilation that reduced arterial pCO_2 by 50 per cent increased cardiac output from 7.5 to 10.5 liters per minute, decreased mean arterial blood pressure by 23 mm. Hg, and decreased the systemic vascular resistance by 45 per cent (Burnum et al., 1954). McGregor et al. (1962) reported an increase in cardiac output of 38 ml. per minute for each liter of hyperventilation per minute. For hyperventilation exceeding 100 liters per minute, there was little additional increase in output (Donevan et al., 1962). Tachycardia accounted for most or all of the increased output in these various studies. When 4.5 per cent carbon dioxide was breathed, the resultant hyperventilation was accompanied by a smaller increase in cardiac output (average, 15 ml. per liter of hyperventilation) than during voluntary hyperventilation with air (McGregor et al., 1962).

Richardson et al. (1961) designed experiments to dissociate the effects of vigorous respiratory movements from those resulting from the reduced arterial pCO_2. The carbon dioxide concentration of expired air was continually monitored during hyperventilation, and sufficient carbon dioxide was added to the inspired air to maintain the arterial pCO_2 at a normal level. Hyperventilation was no longer accompanied by increases in cardiac output and heart rate or by decreases in arterial blood pressure and peripheral resistance.

Observations of the peripheral circulation have supported the conclusion that the circulatory effects of voluntary hyperventilation result from the hypocapnia. There is usually an increase in blood flow through the normal forearm and invariably an increase in flow through the nerve blocked or sympathectomized forearm; thus, a nervous reflex is not responsible (Burnum et al., 1954; Roddie et al., 1957). Hyperventilation of similar degree, induced by inhaling five per cent carbon dioxide in oxygen, is accompanied by little or no increase in flow through either the normal or nerve blocked forearm (Roddie et al., 1957).

Do the accentuated changes in intrathoracic pressure or the increased work of breathing during voluntary hyperventilation contribute to the increased cardiac output? Donevan et al. (1962) were unable to show that the increased output was related to the mechanical effect of increased intrathoracic pressure transients on venous return. However, as Asmussen (1943) also stated, the possibility could not be excluded that thoraco-abdominal pressure gradients contributed to the increased output. When the intrathoracic pressure changes of hyperventilation were simulated by increasing airway resistance without changing ventilation, there was no consistent increase in cardiac output (Donevan et al., 1962). Therefore, the increased work of breathing is not an important factor. A further potential factor is the reflex constriction of limb veins, mediated by sympathetic adrenergic fibers, that is induced by voluntary hyperventilation. The afferent arc of this reflex is unknown (Eckstein et al., 1958; Samueloff et al., 1966). If such venoconstriction were widespread, it could contribute to the filling pressure of the heart, thereby increasing the output.

ALKALEMIA AND ACIDEMIA. The effects of chemically induced variations in pH and pCO_2 of blood on cardiac output and blood flow through skeletal muscle were investigated by Richardson et al. (1961). Infusions of 500 to 600 ml. 0.5 M sodium bicarbonate increased the pH on the average from 7.39 to 7.52 and also increased arterial pCO_2 and carbon dioxide content. The resting cardiac output increased by 32 per cent, and the peripheral resistance decreased by 22 per cent (average values). There was little change in arterial pressure or respiration and no increase in forearm blood flow. Acidemia was induced by infusions of 500 to 800 ml. 0.2 M lactic acid or 0.17 M ammonium chloride. The pH was reduced on the average from 7.42 to 7.34; there was a moderate reduction of carbon dioxide content and no change in pCO_2. No change occurred in cardiac output, arterial pressure or peripheral resistance. The depth of respiration was increased, but the rate was unchanged. Forearm blood flow was also unchanged. However, when sympathetic vasoconstrictor impulses to the forearms were blocked with intra-arterial infusions of phenoxybenzamine, both alkalemia and acidemia caused increases in flow.

It is probable that both alkalemia and acidemia have a direct dilator effect on the systemic vascular bed, but that in acidemia this is opposed by constriction due to stimulation of the medullary vasomotor center. Bernthal (1938) showed that the addition of sodium bicarbonate to blood perfusing the carotid chemoreceptor has little effect on the vasomotor center. Thus, the unopposed vasodilatation during alkalemia leads to a reduction in peripheral resistance and an increase in cardiac output, whereas during acidemia, the opposing dilator and constrictor effects result in no change.

Alkalemia decreases cerebrovascular resistance and increases cerebral blood flow (Schieve and Wilson, 1953) and, as noted before, does not affect blood flow through the intact forearm. Data are not available for other organs and tissues. Therefore, the precise distribution of the increased blood flow during alkalemia is unknown.

HYPERCAPNIA. Inhalation of 7.5 per cent carbon dioxide resulted in an increase in cardiac output of 139 ml. per minute per liter increase in ventilation (Rankin et al., 1960). Subjects breathing seven per cent carbon dioxide had average increases in minute ventilation from 9 to 44 liters, in arterial pCO_2 from 42 to 52 mm. Hg, in mean arterial blood pressure from 89 to 105 mm. Hg, in heart rate from 70 to 87 beats per minute and in cardiac output from 5.7 to 8.2 liters per minute (Richardson et al., 1961). All these changes were significant at the $p < 0.01$ level, in contrast to the absence of any significant change when comparable hyperventilation was performed in the presence of normal arterial pCO_2 (Table 3-2).

Hypercapnia does not affect blood flow in the intact forearm or calf, but it increases flow following blockade of alpha adrenergic receptors. Thus, the direct dilator action on the vessels of skeletal muscle is normally opposed by increased vasoconstrictor activity. Renal blood flow is reduced and renal vascular resistance increased during the inhalation of 10 per cent carbon dioxide (Little et al., 1949). Cerebral blood flow increases by about 0.8 liter per minute during the breathing of seven per cent carbon dioxide (Schieve and Wilson, 1953); this accounts for about one third of the increase in cardiac output. Presumably increased splanchnic blood flow accounts for the remainder.

TABLE 3-2. Effect on the Circulation of *A* Hyperventilation with Arterial pCO_2 Maintained Constant and of *B* Hyperventilation Accompanied by Hypercapnia*

MEASUREMENT	UNITS	CONTROL	*A* HYPERVEN-TILATION	CONTROL	*B* HYPERVEN-TILATION AND HYPER-CAPNIA
Arterial pCO_2	mm. Hg	38	36	42	59
Arterial pH	units	7.37	7.38	7.38	7.25
Ventilation	L./min.	12	40	9	44
Heart rate	beats/min.	70	75	71	88
Cardiac output	L./M.^{2}/min.	3.6	3.6	2.9	4.2
Peripheral resistance	units	14	15	17	13

* Adapted from data of Richardson, Wasserman and Patterson, J. Clin. Invest., *40*:31, 1961.

The increased pCO_2, rather than the decreased pH, appears to be the important factor, since it has already been pointed out that acidemia of comparable degree, induced by infusion of ammonium chloride or lactic acid, does not affect cardiac output (Richardson et al., 1961). McGregor et al. (1962) have shown that, although pCO_2 and ventilation both increase during the first two minutes of inhalation of 8.4 per cent carbon dioxide, the cardiac output does not increase until four minutes have elapsed. Thus, as is also true for hypocapnia, the precise means by which hypercapnia increases cardiac output is not clear. Perhaps it is related to increased concentrations of catecholamines in plasma (Sechzer et al., 1960).

ACCLIMATIZATION TO ALTITUDE

Although changes in temperature and humidity do occur with increasing altitude, diminished oxygen tension is the main factor that influences bodily function. There is no evidence for any specific effect of reduced barometric pressure per se.

Since inspired air is saturated with water vapor before reaching the lungs, the sum of the partial pressures of all the gases in alveolar air is 47 mm. Hg less than atmospheric. The partial pressure of oxygen is diluted by that of carbon dioxide. Increased alveolar ventilation, which leads to more rapid removal of carbon dioxide and hence to an increased partial pressure of oxygen in the alveoli, is the most important mechanism compensating for the low atmospheric oxygen tension at high altitudes.

A second decrease in partial pressure occurs as oxygen moves from alveoli to pulmonary capillaries. At sea level, there is an alveolar-capillary or alveolar-arterial loss of about 10 mm. Hg, accounted for by the resistance of the membrane to diffusion, by venoarterial shunting and by pseudoshunting resulting from alteration of the ventilation/perfusion ratio in different parts of the lung (Tenney, 1962). Finally, as blood passes from systemic arteries to veins, the decrease in pO_2 is determined by the relationship between metabolic activity and blood flow (or cardiac output) and by that portion of the oxygen dissociation curve for hemoglobin over which the changes occur.

Table 3-3 shows the relation, at different altitudes, of air density, alveolar pO_2 and pCO_2, arterial pO_2 and the oxygen saturation of arterial blood. At 2000 M., the 20 per cent reduction in atmospheric pressure has practically no measurable effect on cardiovascular function. However, dyspnea is felt earlier during strenuous exercise than at sea level. At 4300 M., the 40 per cent reduction in atmospheric pressure causes temporary effects due to hypoxia, but after a few days, there is adaptation to a nearly normal pattern. Only during physical labor is there an obvious reduction in performance. However, only well acclimatized persons can tolerate the 60 per cent reduction at 7000 M. The absolute ceiling for survival of persons previously acclimatized to high altitude is about 9000 M., where the atmospheric pressure is 225 mm. Hg.

During the first few days of exposure to high altitudes, alveolar ventilation is increased, and alveolar pCO_2 is decreased approximately in proportion to the reduction in barometric pressure (Rahn and Otis, 1949). The hyperventilation exceeds that occurring during shorter periods (minutes to hours) of exposure to a similarly low pO_2. Also, ventilation is not immediately restored to normal when a gas mixture with a high pO_2 is then given. Increased ventilation persists for several days on return to sea level. The chemical sensitivity of the respiratory center is altered, as is shown by increased ventilation in response to breathing gas mixtures containing carbon dioxide.

Although renal excretion of bicarbonate eventually restores blood pH to normal in chronically acclimatized men (Hurtado and Aste-Salazar,

TABLE 3-3. Alveolar and Arterial Gas Tensions and Oxygen Saturation of Arterial Blood at Various Altitudes (All Pressures in mm. Hg)*

		ALTITUDE (METERS)					
		100	2000	4300	7000	9000	11,500
Barometric pressure		750	600	450	300	225	150
Alveolar pressures	water vapor	47	47	47	47	47	47
	nitrogen	562	442	322	202	140	81
	CO_2	38	35	27	23	13	–
	oxygen	103	76	54	30	25	–
Arterial pO_2		95	70	50	28	24	–
Arterial HbO_2 (%)		97	94	87	60	50	–

* Adapted from data of Balke, Am. J. Cardiol., *14*:796, 1964.

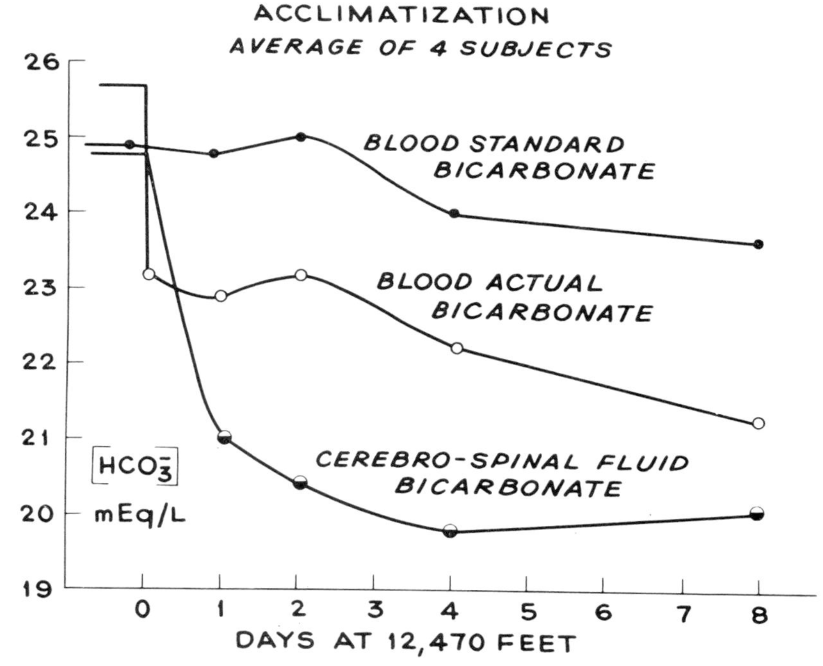

FIGURE 3-4. Bicarbonate (HCO_3^-) changes in blood and cerebrospinal fluid (CSF) during acclimatization. Standard HCO_3^- of blood is the plasma HCO_3^- concentration in blood equilibrated at 37°C with a pCO_2 of 40 mm. Hg and pO_2 exceeding 100 mm. Hg; it was calculated from the nomogram of Astrup and Anderson. Plasma HCO_3^- is the actual concentration in the plasma of arterial blood. (Courtesy of Dr. J. W. Severinghaus.)

1948), the kidney does not play the major role in initial acclimatization to high altitude. Therefore, Severinghaus et al. (1963) further analyzed the altered responsiveness of the respiratory center in four men during acclimatization from sea level to 3800 M. for eight days. They found that the medullary respiratory chemoreceptor drive, initially reduced at altitude because of alkalosis resulting from hyperventilation, was restored to normal during acclimatization through reduction in the bicarbonate content of cerebrospinal fluid.

The incremental ventilatory drive was supplied by peripheral chemoreceptors. The barrier between blood and cerebrospinal fluid appeared to respond to the initial alkalosis of hyperventilation by actively reducing the fluid's content of bicarbonate (Fig. 3-4). Their data suggested that the pH of cerebrospinal fluid was thus regulated by active transport by the blood-fluid barrier.

Most of the body's adaptations to high altitude are respiratory in nature. Compensatory changes in the circulation are required, however,

TABLE 3-4. Changes in the Blood at Various Altitudes*

	ALTITUDE (METERS)					
	0	3100	3600	4600	4600	6500
Blood volume (ml./Kg.)	79.6	83	96	100.5	104	—
Hemoglobin (g./100 ml.)	15.3	16.8	18.8	20.1	20.7	24.8
O_2 capacity (ml./100 ml.)	20.6	22.5	25.2	27.0	27.8	33.3
O_2 saturation (per cent)	97	91	87	80.5	80.5	± 65
O_2 content (ml./100 ml.)	20.0	20.5	21.9	21.7	22.4	± 21.7
Source	1	3	3	1	3	2

* From Balke, B.: Cardiac performance in relation to altitude. Am. J. Cardiol., *14*:796, 1964 (Reuben H. Donnelley Corp., publisher). Data collected from Hurtado (1956), Luft (1941), and Rotta (1961).

until deficiencies in the provision of gas transport have been corrected, mainly through an increase in hemoglobin level.

BLOOD VOLUME. Douglas et al. (1913), during the Anglo-American Pike's Peak expedition, found an initial decrease in blood volume at 4200 M., with a subsequent return to normal. Asmussen and Consolazio (1941) reported similar results. Hurtado et al. (1945), however, found an increased blood volume during early acclimatization in a number of subjects. During the later stages of acclimatization, the total blood volume is undoubtedly increased (Table 3-4). The pulmonary blood volume shares in this increase (Roy et al., 1967). The increased oxygen capacity of blood results from an increase in the erythrocyte count. Keys (1938) found mean values (millions per cubic millimeter) in residents at various altitudes of 5.3 at sea level, 5.8 at 2500 M., 6.2 at 3500 M., 6.6 at 4500 M., 7.3 at 5500 M. and 8.2 at 6500. The increase in the capacity of arterial blood balances the decrease in percentage saturation, so that the oxygen content in long acclimatized subjects at different altitudes is similar.

CARDIAC AND RESPIRATORY FUNCTION AT REST. There is no significant difference between the resting cardiac indices of residents at sea level and of residents at high altitudes (Rotta et al., 1956; Peñaloza et al., 1963; Banchero et al., 1966; Table 3-5). Since there is a transient increase in cardiac output immediately after going from sea level to high altitude (Christensen and Forbes, 1937; Klausen, 1966), absence of such an increase in residents at high altitudes is one of the features of chronic acclimatization (Rotta et al., 1956).

Rotta et al. (1956) found a slight increase in the arteriovenous difference in oxygen content in residents at high altitudes, but Peñaloza et al. (1963) and Banchero et al. (1966) reported almost identical values. In residents of Lima, Peru, which is near sea level (150 M.), the oxygen capacity and content of arterial blood were 19.85 and 19.04 ml. per 100 ml., respectively, but at Morococha (4540 M.), they were 29.90 and 20.24 ml. per 100 ml. The arterial pO_2 at 4540 M. was 42 mm. Hg, and the pH was 7.42. The minute ventilation was higher at 4540 M. (8.1 liters per minute) than at sea level (6.5 liters per minute), but there was no significant difference in oxygen consumption; the values were 161 and 153 ml. per $M.^2$ per minute, respectively.

CARDIAC AND RESPIRATORY FUNCTION DURING WORK. Pugh et al. (1964), during a Himalayan expedition that lasted eight months, measured oxygen consumption, minute ventilation and heart rate during exercise in six subjects at various altitudes between sea level and 7440 M. Oxygen consumption for a given work load was constant and independent of altitude, up to the maximal load that could be maintained for five minutes. Maximal oxygen consumption decreased with increasing altitude and reached a mean value of 1.42 liters per minute at the highest altitude. Minute ventilation was independent of altitude for light and moderate loads but increased with increasing altitudes, as maximal oxygen consumption was approached; thus, at altitudes above 4650 M., minute volumes of 140 to 200 liters (BTPS) were recorded. Heart rates were higher for given work loads at greater altitudes.

Cardiac output was estimated by the acetylene method in the same subjects at sea level and after two to three months residence at 5800 M. (Pugh, 1964). Measurements were made during graded exercise. At 5800 M., the output for given work loads was similar to that at sea level, but the higher work loads could not be completed (Fig. 3-5). With loads of 300 and 600 Kg.-M. per minute, the arteriovenous differences in oxygen content were also similar, but with higher loads at 5800 M., there was no further increase in the difference because of the reduced oxygen content of arterial blood. Since heart rates were higher at altitudes during performance of the lowest two loads, stroke volumes were less. The maximal heart rates that could be sustained during exercise averaged only 136 per minute at altitude, possibly due to a direct effect of hypoxia on the A-V node (Åstrand and Åstrand, 1958), as compared with 182 per minute at sea level; however, there was considerable individual variation.

When oxygen was breathed at sea level pressure, work capacity at 5800 M. was restored almost to normal. A load of 1500 Kg.-M. per minute could be sustained for four minutes (as compared with six minutes at sea level), heart rates at the lowest work loads were lower, and in most subjects, the maximal heart rate was increased.

TABLE 3-5. Cardiac Indices During Rest in Permanent Residents at or Near Sea Level and at High Altitudes

		CARDIAC INDEX LITERS PER $M.^2$ PER MINUTE	
AUTHOR	YEAR	SEA LEVEL	HIGH ALTITUDE
Rotta et al.	1956	3.5	3.3
Peñaloza et al.	1963	4.0	3.7
Banchero et al.	1966	4.0	4.0

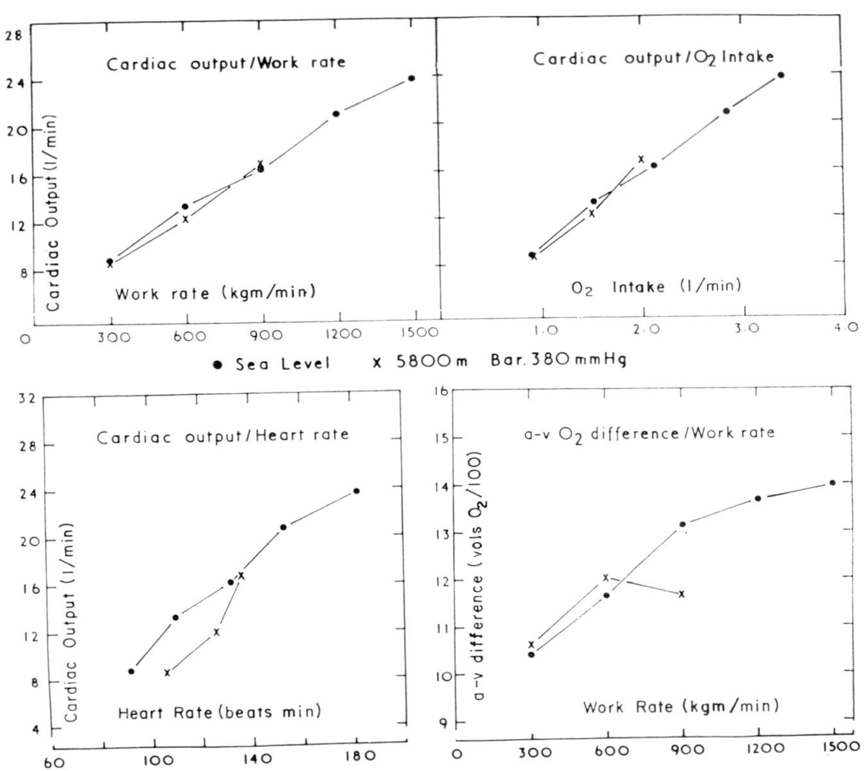

FIGURE 3-5. Relations of cardiac output to work rate, to oxygen consumption and to heart rate, and relation of arteriovenous difference in oxygen content to work rate at sea level (● — ●) and at 5800 M. (x — x): mean values for four subjects. (From Pugh, J. Appl. Physiol., *19*:441, 1964.)

The response to exercise during acute hypoxia differs from that described by Pugh for the acclimatized mountaineers. The cardiac output during acute hypoxia is greater, the arteriovenous difference in content of oxygen is less, and relative bradycardia does not occur at high work loads (Asmussen and Nielsen, 1955A). Some of the differences can be accounted for by differences in hemoglobin concentration and blood viscosity. Figure 3-6 shows HbO_2 dissociation curves for normal blood at sea level and for the blood of the subjects studied at 5800 M. Had the HbO_2 capacity of the latter subjects been no greater than that of the former, the content of arterial blood at the ambient pO_2 of approximately 30 mm. Hg would have been only 10 to 12 ml. per 100 ml., and it would have been impossible for them to achieve their observed arteriovenous differences in oxygen content of 10 to 11 ml. per 100 ml. They could have achieved an adequate supply of oxygen to their active muscles only at the expense of a further considerable increase in cardiac output. This is what occurs in acute hypoxia, and it illustrates the sparing effect of additional hemoglobin on cardiac output. As Dill (1938) pointed out, compensatory polycythemia has the disadvantage that blood viscosity is increased; however, this appears to be adequately compensated, since the arterial blood pressure is no greater during exercise at high altitudes than at sea level.

Cardiac and respiratory adjustments to exercise have also been studied in subjects who were born and had spent their entire lives at high altitudes. Thus, Sherpa porters, accustomed to life at 5800 M., could sustain greater work loads than the Caucasian mountaineers, with their two to three months of acclimatization (Pugh et al., 1964). One Sherpa achieved a maximal oxygen consumption of 2.7 liters per minute and a maximal heart rate of 186 beats per minute, while working at 1200 and 1400 Kg.-M. per minute, respectively. Natives living at 4500 M. in the Andes achieved heart rates of 180 beats per minute during severe treadmill exercise. There was only a slight increase in stroke volume (Theilen et al., 1955).

Banchero et al. (1966) compared the response to a standard exercise test (pedaling for seven minutes at 300 Kg.-M. per $M.^2$ per minute) of healthy natives of high altitudes and of healthy natives of towns near sea level. All subjects were tested at the altitudes to which they were accustomed. Among the group at sea level, the exercise increased the minute ventilation from 6.5 to 28.1 liters per minute, the oxygen consumption from 153 to 719 ml. per $M.^2$ per minute, the arteriovenous difference in oxygen content from 4.0 to 10.6 ml. per 100 ml. and the cardiac output from 4.0 to 6.8 liters per $M.^2$ per minute. The mean increase in heart rate was 89 per

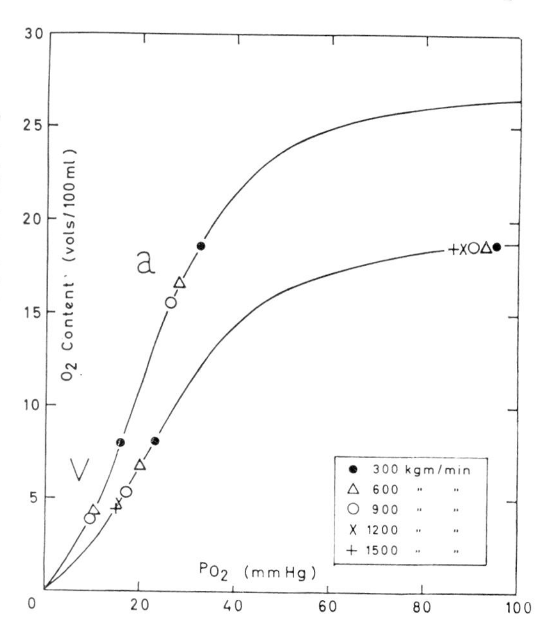

FIGURE 3-6. HbO_2 dissociation curves for blood at sea level (*below*) and at 5800 M. (*above*), showing the effect of increased hemoglobin concentration on the transport of oxygen. Curves were calculated from standard HbO_2 dissociation curves using the following average values for pH and for Hb (g./100 ml.): at sea level, pH 7.4 and Hb 13.8; at 5800 M., pH 7.5 (Henderson-Hasselbalch) and Hb 20.3. Arterial (a) and mixed venous (v) points are shown for various rates of work. (From Pugh, J. Appl. Physiol., *19*:441, 1964.)

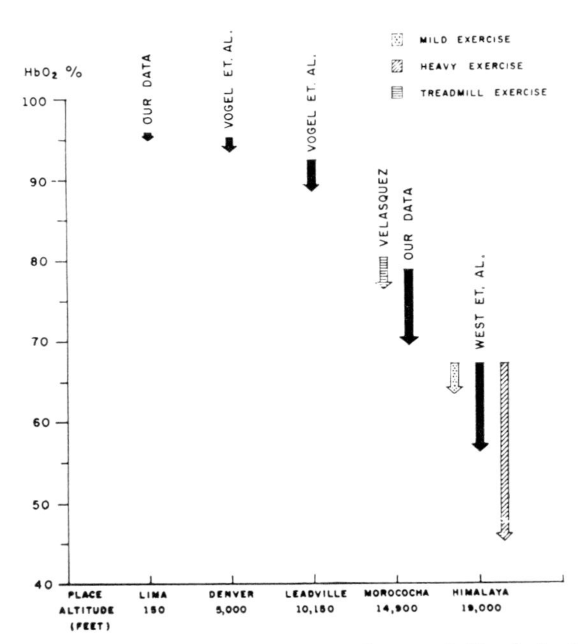

FIGURE 3-7. Changes in oxygen saturation of arterial blood during exercise at different altitudes. At high altitudes, the desaturation becomes more marked with exercise. The magnitude of the change increases with increases in the altitude or in the work intensity. (From Banchero, Sime, Peñaloza, Cruz, Gamboa and Marticorena, Circulation, *33*:249, 1966.)

cent, and there was no consistent change in stroke volume. The arterial oxygen saturation was unchanged. Among those at high altitude, the exercise increased the minute ventilation from 8.1 to 37.4 liters per minute, the oxygen consumption from 161 to 779 ml. per M.^{2} per minute, the arteriovenous difference in oxygen content from 4.1 to 10.3 ml. per 100 ml. and the cardiac output from 4.0 to 7.7 liters per M.^{2} per minute. The mean increase in heart rate was 84 per cent, and there was no consistent change in stroke volume. The arterial oxygen saturation decreased from 78 to 69 per cent.

The identical behavior of cardiac output, oxygen consumption and arteriovenous difference in oxygen content in these groups of natives at sea level and at high altitude indicates that the quantitative response of the circulation to work is determined by the intensity of the work and is independent of the level of altitude. By contrast, Alexander et al. (1966) found that normal healthy men living in Leadville, Colorado, at 3000 M. had cardiac outputs that were less than values at sea level during both rest and submaximal exercise. Since the subnormal responses of cardiac output could not be accounted for by changes in pulmonary vascular resistance, acid-base balance, sympathetic nervous activity, blood volume or ventricular filling pressure, they suggested that chronic hypoxia may depress the myocardium, and lead to decreases in myocardial contractile force and stroke volume.

The decrease in the oxygen saturation of arterial blood during exercise at altitude has been noted by other workers. Figure 3-7, which includes data from a number of studies, shows that as altitude increases, the fall in arterial oxygen saturation during exercise becomes more marked. The data of West et al. (1962), which are included, also show that at the same altitude, the arterial saturation decreases further as the severity of exercise increases. Since at high altitudes, the resting value for arterial pO_2 is on the steep part of the HbO_2 dissociation curve (Hurtado et al., 1945), a slight decrease in pO_2 during exercise is sufficient to account for a large decrease in arterial oxygen saturation.

PULMONARY HYPERTENSION. An additional feature of the circulation at high altitudes is the presence of pulmonary hypertension. Vogel et al. (1962) reported mean pressures in the pulmonary artery of normal subjects of 13 mm. Hg at sea level, 16 mm. Hg in Denver (1600 M.), 15 mm. Hg in Mexico City (2200 M.), 25 mm. Hg in Leadville, Colorado (3000 M.) and 28 mm. Hg in Morococha, Peru (4500 M.). Exercise caused a modest increase in pressure in men living below 3000 M. but doubled the pressure in men living at 3000 M. or higher. Banchero et al. (1966) also found that, at 4500 M., exercise that approximately doubled the cardiac output increased the mean pulmonary artery pressure from 29 to 60 mm. Hg (Fig. 3-8). There were no significant changes in pulmonary artery wedge (indirect left atrial) pressures with exercise. The mean value for pulmonary

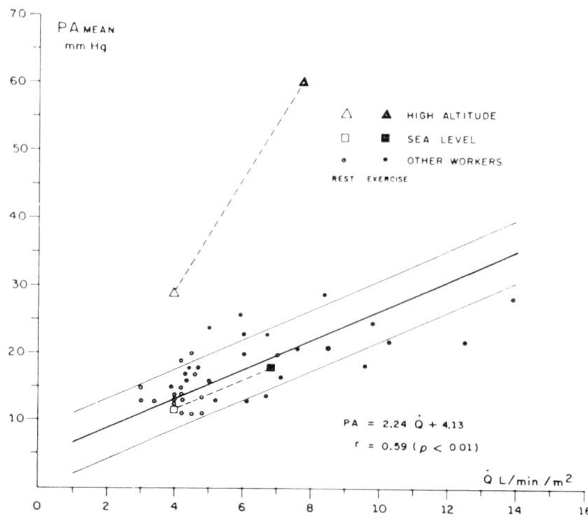

FIGURE 3-8. Relation of mean pulmonary artery pressure to cardiac output during work of varying intensity at sea level. The regression line is shown with lines at ±1 standard error. Note the different relationship at high altitude. (From Banchero, Sime, Peñaloza, Cruz, Gamboa and Marticorena, Circulation, 33:249. 1966.)

vascular resistance was 332 dyne sec. cm.$^{-5}$ during rest at the high altitude, and it did not change significantly with exercise. The comparable value in subjects resting at sea level was 73 dyne sec. cm.$^{-5}$.

The genesis of the pulmonary hypertension of high altitude is not settled. From his review of the literature, Fishman (1961) concluded that in man, pulmonary hypertension results mainly from the flow of polycythemic blood through vessels lined by hypertrophied muscle cells. He felt that there was still no proof that the pulmonary hypertension of high altitudes results from vasoconstriction. Arias-Stella and Saldaña (1962, 1963) found an increased content of smooth muscle in the pulmonary arteries and arterioles of natives of high altitudes, from one month of age upwards. They concluded that hypoxia delays the involution of the fetal and neonatal structure of the pulmonary arteries, an involution which, at sea level, occurs during the first six months of life. Peñaloza et al. (1962) measured the pulmonary artery pressure in a group of children native to high altitudes; the average mean pressure was 45 mm. Hg between one and five years of age and 28 mm. Hg between six and 14 years. They felt that the structure of the arteries was a more important factor than increased blood viscosity since, when dwellers at high altitudes are taken to sea level, the polycythemia disappears before the pulmonary artery pressure decreases. The chronic pulmonary hypertension results in enlargement of the right ventricle (Rotta, 1961).

An increased content of muscle in the arteries and arterioles would also account for the failure of pulmonary vascular resistance to decrease during exercise. As pointed out earlier, an increase in cardiac output during exercise is accompanied by an equivalent increase in the pressure gradient between the main pulmonary artery and the pulmonary capillaries (Fig. 3-8). The studies of Banchero et al. (1966), however, suggested that vasoconstriction may play at least a contributory role in the abnormal vascular response to exercise. Thus, there was a lesser increment in the pulmonary artery pressure during exercise at high altitudes when oxygen or acetylcholine were simultaneously given. Vasoconstriction could conceivably be triggered by the abnormal degree of arterial oxygen desaturation.

Pulmonary edema has been reported to result from sudden exposure to high altitudes. Most commonly, it occurs in residents at high altitudes on their return from spending time at sea level. The pulmonary artery wedge pressure is normal, but the pulmonary artery pressure is very high, up to 144 mm. Hg (Hultgren et al., 1964). No improvement follows the use of digitalis or antibiotic drugs; therefore, heart failure or infection of the respiratory tract cannot be incriminated. There is prompt improvement with best rest and inhalation of oxygen, or with return to lower altitudes. Marticorena et al. (1964) felt that pulmonary edema results from an exaggeration of the usual hemodynamic changes resulting from anoxia, together with increased capillary permeability.

An analogous condition, brisket disease, occurs in cattle exposed to high altitudes; it has been the object of extensive physiological studies in recent years (Hecht et al., 1962).

NEGATIVE AND POSITIVE PRESSURE BREATHING

Continuous negative pressure breathing, with average pressures of −16 and of −9 mm. Hg during inspiration and expiration, respectively, decreased the central venous pressure by an average of 10.5 mm. Hg in healthy young men. After 20 to 30 minutes, the cardiac index had increased from 2.6 to 3.4 liters per $M.^2$ per minute and the pulse rate, from 66 to 80 beats per minute (average values). The plasma volume did not change. Since the arterial pCO_2 did not change, the hemodynamic effects could not be related to alterations in carbon dioxide tension in the body (Kilburn and Sieker, 1960).

Continuous positive pressure breathing increased the rate of breathing and produced average airway pressures of +20 mm. Hg and +14 mm. Hg during expiration and inspiration, respectively. The central venous pressure increased by an average of 11 mm. Hg. In six subjects who did not hyper-

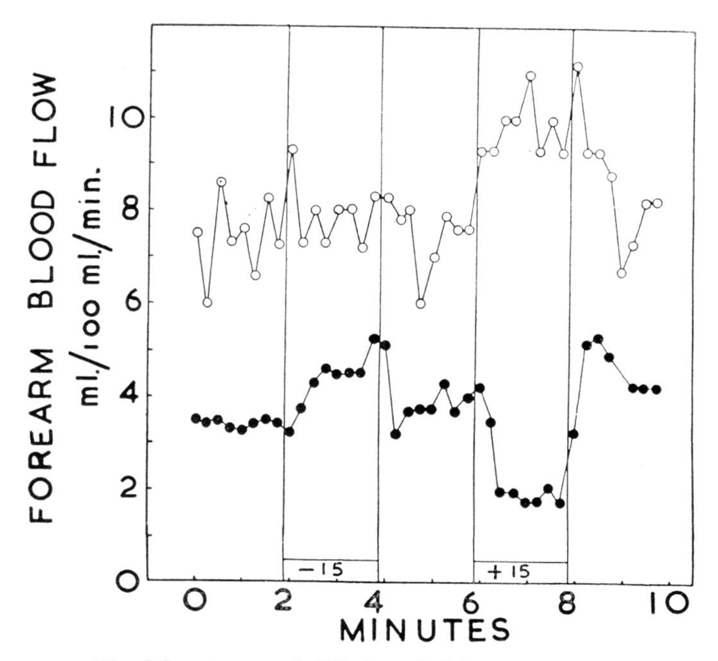

FIGURE 3-9. Blood flow in normal (filled symbols) and nerve blocked (empty symbols) forearms during pressure breathing. From two to four and from six to eight minutes air was breathed at pressures 15 mm. Hg below and 15 mm. Hg above atmospheric, respectively. (From Blair, Glover and Kidd, Clin. Sci., *18*:9, 1959.)

ventilate, the cardiac output decreased, on the average, from 3.7 to 2.5 liters per $M.^2$ per minute, and the heart rate increased from 75 to 92 beats per minute. In others who hyperventilated, the output was unchanged or decreased slightly. The plasma volume was unchanged (Kilburn and Sieker, 1960).

The experiments summarized above provided evidence that decreased intrathoracic pressure per se aids in aspirating blood into the central venous reservoir.

With intermittent positive pressure breathing, Werkö (1947) noted increases in mean systemic and pulmonary arterial pressures and decreases in cardiac output. The systemic vascular resistance increased, and the pulmonary vascular resistance increased in three of five subjects.

Although negative pressure breathing and voluntary hyperventilation both cause modest increases in cardiac output, there are differences in the response of the peripheral blood vessels. Negative pressure breathing increases, and positive pressure breathing decreases, forearm blood flow (Fig. 3-9). The changes in flow are mediated by the sympathetic nervous system and are not related to changes in perfusion pressure, hyperventilation or humoral substances (Blair et al., 1959). The increased blood flow with hyperventilation is, by contrast, related to hypocapnia.

EFFECTS OF GRAVITY

Acceleration occurs when a moving object increases speed, changes direction or both. An increase in velocity without a change in direction is referred to as *linear acceleration.* The equation expressing this is $g = \frac{(V_1 - V_0)^2}{64.4\,S}$, where V_0 is the original and V_1 the final velocity (feet per second), S is the distance (feet) over which the change in velocity occurs, and g is the unit of acceleration equal to the acceleration of gravity (32.2 feet per second per second). An object moving at a constant speed but continually changing direction is accelerating in a radial fashion. This is the form of acceleration experienced by the aviator as he maneuvers his plane into spins and turns and pulls out of dives. It is also the form produced in human centrifuges for experimental purposes. The equation expressing *radial acceleration* in g units is $g = \frac{V^2}{32.2\,r}$, where V is the velocity (feet per second) and r is the radius (feet) of change in direction. *Angular acceleration* relates to the situation in which an object simultaneously increases speed and changes direction.

In response to all three types of acceleration, there is a reactive force resulting from the inertia of the body. This force is proportional to the mass of the body and to the magnitude of the acceleration, and it acts in a direction opposite to that of the acceleration. It becomes apparent as weight. The force of gravity gives man the weight to which he is accustomed. When man's force environment is suddenly increased two fold by acceleration, his body weight is doubled. The effects of acceleration in man, however, depend not only on its magnitude, but also on its rate, its direction of application, the duration of its application, and the type of support and restraint with which he is provided. They are most pronounced when the direction of acceleration is parallel to the long axis of the body in either the foot to head direction (*headward acceleration*) or the head to foot direction (*footward acceleration*) and are much less pronounced when it is perpendicular to the long axis of the body (*forward, backward* or *lateral acceleration*).

HEADWARD ACCELERATION. The effects of headward acceleration are shown in Fig. 3-10. This shows the hydrostatic distances separating vari-

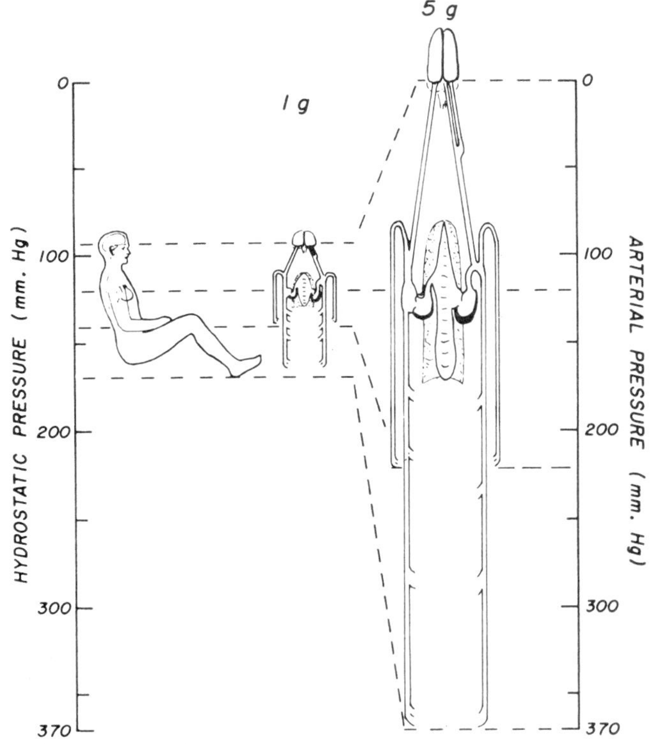

FIGURE 3-10. Diagrams of hydrostatic pressures in the circulation of a man sitting at 1 g and during headward acceleration at 5 g. The *center* diagram shows that, at 1 g, the range of arterial systolic pressures (mm. Hg) is from 96 at the head through 120 at the heart to 170 at the heels. The *right* diagram shows how this range of pressures is magnified five fold at 5 g, varying from 0 at the head through 120 at the heart to 370 at the heels. At 5 g, in the absence of muscular contraction, a venous pressure of 250 mm. Hg would be required to return blood from the heels to the heart. (From Lindberg and Wood. In: Physiology of Man in Space. (J. H. U. Brown, Ed.) New York, Academic Press, 1963.)

ous sites in the circulation in a seated man subjected to 1 g and 5 g. It can be predicted on the basis of the weight of blood and of the vertical distance between various parts of the body that, at 1 g, if arterial systolic pressure is 120 mm. Hg at the level of the heart, it would be about 96 mm. Hg at head level and 170 mm. Hg at the heels. At 5 g, the weight of blood is five times as great; therefore, there would be fivefold differences in hydrostatic pressure in the vascular system. If one again assumes an arterial systolic pressure of 120 mm. Hg at the heart, pressure at the base of the brain would be 0 mm. Hg, while that at the heels would be 370 mm. Hg. In a fully erect man, the differences in pressure would, of course, be even greater.

From these considerations, it is evident that the ability of man to withstand headward acceleration is determined mainly by the cardiovascular system (Lindberg and Wood, 1963).

During headward acceleration of rapid onset (1 to 2 g per second), there is an immediate decrease in arterial pressure at the level of the head; loss of peripheral vision occurs in some subjects at an acceleration of 3.5 to 4.5 g, and vision is completely lost between 4 and 5 g. Impaired hearing and unconsciousness usually occur at an acceleration 0.5 to 1 g. or more above that causing complete loss of vision. In contrast to the decrease in arterial pressure at the level of the head, little or no decrease occurs at the level of the heart.

Several seconds after the onset of the acceleration, the arterial pressure at the level of the head increases. The heart rate starts to increase almost at the instant of the onset of acceleration; it increases progressively until the arterial pressure increases, at which time it slows. The recovery of arterial pressure at the level of the head and the increase in heart rate are considered to result from reflexes initiated by a decrease in arterial pressure in the carotid sinus. Although the pressure in the carotid sinus falls at the instant of onset of acceleration, the pressor reflex does not become fully effective for six to 10 seconds. The importance of the autonomic nervous system as a mediator of compensatory reflexes is clear from the pronounced reduction in tolerance to headward acceleration after autonomic blockade with tetraethylammonium chloride (Lindberg and Wood, 1963).

During headward acceleration at 4 g, the right atrial pressure decreases to average values of −10 to −15 mm. Hg (Lindberg et al., 1961). The esophageal pressure, which reflects changes in intrathoracic pressure, is even more negative. This probably results from downward displacement of the diaphragm. Inflation of an antiblackout suit, by compressing the abdomen, prevents the descent of the diaphragm and thereby prevents an excessively negative pressure from occurring in both the right atrium and the extracardiac intrathoracic space.

Vision is lost more readily than consciousness because the effective arterial pressure in the eye is less than that of the brain. The retinal circulation is normally opposed by an intraocular pressure of about 18 mm. Hg.

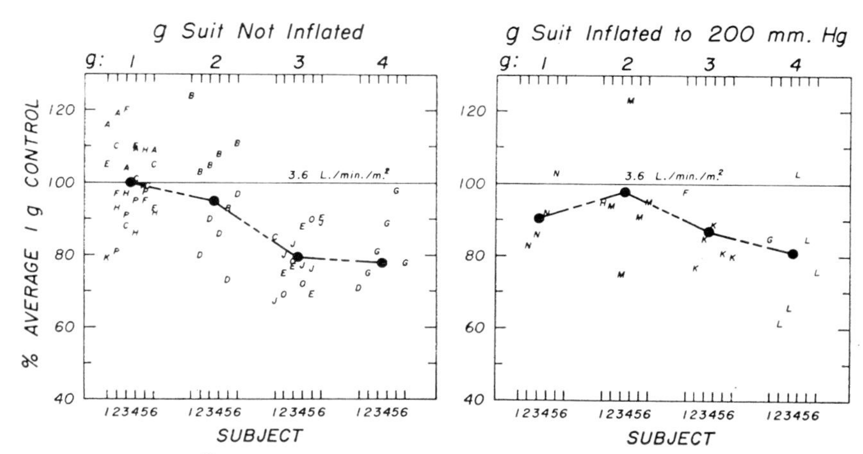

FIGURE 3-11. Effect of headward acceleration on cardiac output. Values were obtained from indicator dilution curves recorded with the subject stationary in a centrifuge cockpit (1 g) (control measurements) and 20 to 40 seconds after attaining plateaux of acceleration at 2, 3, and 4 g. Values for individual subjects were then plotted vertically over the identifying numerals (1 to 6) on the abscissa for each of the four levels of acceleration. The temporal sequence of observations on each subject was randomized. Control (1 g) measurements alternated with measurements at 2, 3 or 4 g. For each subject, the precise sequence was indicated by plotting them alphabetically (A,B,C . . . P). The letter I was omitted to avoid confusion with the numeral 1.

Each value for each subject was plotted as a percentage of his average cardiac output obtained from the three to five measurements at 1 g. Note that the first two measurements for each subject (A and B) tended to give the highest values, doubtless due to apprehension. Despite the ±20 per cent variation in control values, the systematic decrease in output shortly after the achievement of plateaux of acceleration is apparent (thick interrupted line). (From Lindberg, Sutterer, Marshall, Headley and Wood, Aerospace Med., *31*:817, 1960.)

The cerebral circulation is protected by the hydrostatic effect of the column of cerebrospinal fluid extending from the brain to the sacrum; in addition, the negative pressure in the internal jugular vein helps to maintain an effective arteriovenous pressure gradient, even when arterial pressure is low.

Howard (1959) used the direct Fick method to measure changes in cardiac output during headward acceleration in two subjects lying supine in a fully extended position. The output decreased by 32 per cent at 2 g and by 40 per cent at 2.4 g. Because of concomitant tachycardia, there were even greater changes in stroke volume. The oxygen consumption increased by about one third during the period of acceleration.

Lindberg et al. (1960) found wide individual variations during acceleration up to 4 g; there was, however, a mean decrease of 22 per cent in cardiac output 20 to 40 seconds after an acceleration of 4 g was attained (Fig. 3-11). The heart rate increased by 56 per cent, the stroke volume was almost halved, and the mean arterial pressure at heart level was increased by 27 per cent (average values from six subjects). The ratio of arterial pressure at heart level to cardiac output was greatly increased, as compared with its value at 1 g. Repeated measurements of cardiac output during accelerations of up to 3.5 g for periods of 10 minutes showed no further systematic decrease (Lindberg et al., 1961).

Rushmer (1947) showed that the abdominal contents act as a hydrostatic system, so that during headward acceleration, pooling of blood in the splanchnic bed is prevented in large part by the increased pressure in the dependent parts of the abdominal cavity. Thus, the vein walls would have to support only a fraction of the venous pressure at any level of the abdomen, and serious venous distention would not occur unless venous pressures were increased independently of the increase in intra-abdominal pressure.

The increased weight of the blood and tissues resulting from acceleration affects respiration both mechanically and physiologically. With increasing headward acceleration, the abdominal contents, and particularly the liver, are displaced footward, thus pulling down the diaphragm. This results in increases of total lung volume and of functional residual volume. The tidal volume and the rate of breathing increase, but the vital capacity is decreased, probably because of limitation of diaphragmatic movement. The compliance of the lung is decreased, necessitating an increase in the work of breathing (Bondurant, 1958). Alterations in the ventilation/perfusion ratio may account for the decrease of 14 per cent in the oxygen saturation of arterial blood in some subjects during the 30 seconds immediately after attaining an acceleration of 4 g (Lindberg et al., 1961). This change is then reversed, and no further desaturation occurs during the remainder of the 10 minute exposure to acceleration.

FOOTWARD ACCELERATION. Again, the important alterations in the body's function relate predominantly to changes in hydrostatic pressure throughout the cardiovascular system. It is true that the lung volume decreases as the abdominal contents are displaced headward, but this is not sufficiently pronounced at the low levels of acceleration that are tolerable to cause any serious disturbance in respiratory function.

Acceleration at 3 g leads to increases of pressure by 70 to 90 mm. Hg in the carotid artery and jugular vein. The increase in arterial pressure exceeds that in venous pressure, so that the pressure gradient is more than adequate to maintain cerebral blood flow. Tolerance to footward acceleration is limited by symptoms related to cranial and cerebral congestion; for example, facial suffusion, throbbing head pain, confusion and occasionally, unconsciousness (Lindberg and Wood, 1963). The increased pressure in the carotid sinus reflexly increases vagal activity; this is evident from sinus bradycardia, A-V nodal rhythm and some periods of sinus or nodal arrest (Gamble et al., 1949). Profound bradycardia, by decreasing cardiac output, decreases mean arterial pressure at the level of the brain but does not affect the pressure in the jugular veins. Therefore, the arteriovenous pressure gradient in the brain suddenly decreases, with resultant impaired perfusion. This probably explains the onset of unconsciousness in some subjects during footward acceleration.

When footward acceleration is maintained in excess of 3 g for more than 15 seconds, petechiae are noted in the face and neck. They result from rupture of small veins that have been subjected to overdistention. The brain is protected, since its increased venous pressure is opposed by an equal increase in pressure in the cerebrospinal fluid and in its extension, the subarachnoid space. This holds at all levels of the cerebrospinal cavity (Rushmer et al., 1947).

TRANSVERSE ACCELERATION. Forward acceleration implies acceleration in the ventral direction, so that the reactive force is from the front towards the back; it is often referred to as "eyeballs in" acceleration. Backward acceleration is the reverse of this. Up to the present time, lateral acceleration has not been a practical problem in aviation or space flight. However, the principle of the vector of acceleration pointing in one direction and that of inertial force in the opposite direction still applies through the coronal plane of the body.

These forms of acceleration, directed through the anteroposterior and lateral axes of the body, are conveniently referred to collectively as *transverse acceleration*. They excite little reflex activity in the cardiovascular system, since their vectors are at right angles to the columns of blood in the long axis of the body, and consequently, the baroreceptors are not stimulated. Tolerance to forward and backward acceleration is more than three times that to headward acceleration; therefore, spacecraft are being designed so that their pilots are exposed to these forms rather than to headward acceleration. Thus, with purely transverse acceleration, visual and cerebral symptoms usually do not occur at less than 20 g. The predominant hydrostatic effect is rupture of small vessels in the skin in areas where external counterpressure is lacking.

Forward acceleration up to 5 g was accompanied by no change or, at most, a slight increase in cardiac output and usually some increase in heart rate. An increase averaging 12 mm. Hg in right atrial pressure at the onset of 5 g acceleration presumably was caused by compression of the thoracic and abdominal contents (Lindberg et al., 1961).

Figure 3-12 shows the predicted effects of forward acceleration in the lungs. At 0 g or weightlessness (left diagram), the mean pressures in all pulmonary arteries, irrespective of their positions in the thorax, would be equal (for example, 20 cm. H_2O); the same would apply to all pulmonary veins (for example, 10 cm. H_2O). The center diagram shows the pressures in the vessels at the front and back of the lungs at 1 g; an anteroposterior dimension of 20 cm. is assumed. At 5 g (right diagram), the arterial and venous pressures at the back of the lung would be 70 and 60 cm. H_2O, respectively, and at the front, they would be −30 and −40 H_2O, respec-

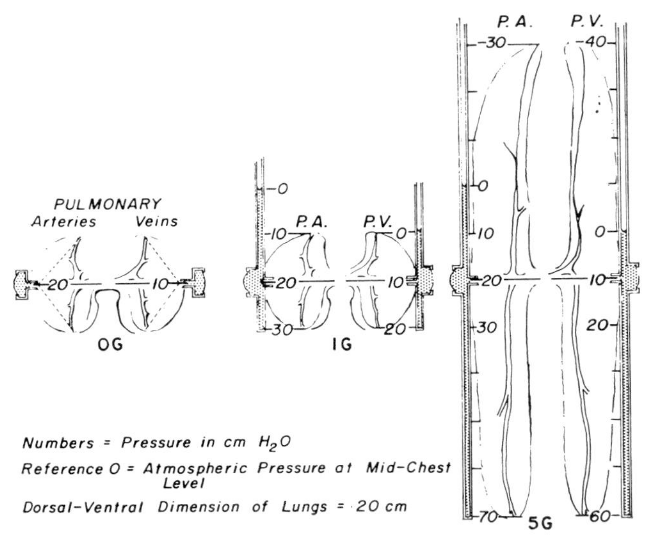

FIGURE 3-12. Effects of exposure to 0, 1 and 5 g on pulmonary vascular pressures. Mean arterial and venous pressures at mid-chest level are assumed to remain constant at 20 and 10 mm. Hg, respectively. Note the predicted arterial and venous pressures of 70 and 60 mm. Hg in the dorsa of the lungs at 5 g. (From Wood, Nolan, Donald and Cronin, Fed. Proc., *22*:1024, 1963.)

tively, if they did not collapse. The pressure in the pulmonary capillaries in the dorsal regions of the lungs would greatly exceed the oncotic pressure of the blood, so that an early onset of pulmonary edema would be expected (Wood et al., 1963).

In dogs, pressures in the right and left atria and the pulmonary artery are increased at the mid-chest level during forward acceleration in the horizontal position (Lindberg et al., 1962). If this is also true for man, then the pressures in the dorsal regions of the lungs would be even greater than those predicted in Fig. 3-12.

The heart and trachea move dorsally during forward acceleration, and the increased radiolucency of the ventral portions of the lungs suggests that most of the blood flow is through the dorsal portions. The compliance of the lungs is decreased, and there are increases in tidal volume and in the rate of breathing (Cherniack et al., 1959). The vital capacity and the maximal breathing capacity are decreased to 30 and 58 per cent of their control values, respectively; these changes indicate a restrictive defect rather than an obstruction to ventilation. During more extreme forward acceleration (above 10 g), the tidal volume, due to immobility of thoracic and abdominal contents, may be less than the volume of the anatomical dead space.

In eight normal subjects, arterial oxygen saturation progressively decreased with increasing forward acceleration (Nolan et al., 1963). At 5.6 g, it began to decrease from the normal value of 97 per cent after 10 to 20 seconds and reached an average of 86 per cent after 130 seconds. Desaturation also occurred when 99.6 per cent oxygen was breathed; values as low as 93 per cent were recorded; subsequent x-ray films of the chest showed appearances suggestive of areas of atelectasis. The desaturation, therefore, was probably due to blood flow through inadequately ventilated or atelectatic zones in the dorsa of the lungs (functional venoarterial shunting). The atelectasis in turn probably resulted from the increased weight of blood and lung parenchyma, from increased intra- and extravascular pressures and from associated increases in intra-pleural pressures in the dorsal zones.

In theory, total immersion of the body in water would protect against the effects of sustained spells of high acceleration, were it not for the gas containing cavities and particularly the lungs. There is no known method for applying hydrostatically controlled counterpressure to the tracheobronchial system in order to compensate for differences in pressure between dorsal and ventral zones. It can be calculated that, at 30 g transverse acceleration, the difference in hydrostatic pressure from the front to the back of the lung would exceed 400 mm. Hg for a person of average size. Despite this, man has successfully withstood sustained backward acceleration in excess of 30 g when totally immersed in water (Gray and Webb, 1960).

DIVING

Certain mammals, birds and reptiles have the ability to slow down and redistribute their circulation during diving. Blood flow to the limbs, skeletal muscles elsewhere and certain viscera is markedly reduced. There is bradycardia without a decrease in systemic arterial blood pressure. Lactic acid, formed and stored in the muscles during a prolonged dive, floods into the circulation when breathing is resumed.

Scholander et al. (1962) studied 31 Australian aboriginal skin divers. The dives rarely exceeded 60 seconds. The blood pressure was maintained, although the heart rate was halved; blood lactate levels remained normal until after surfacing, when they suddenly increased. Thus, the adjustment resembled that of other diving species. This asphyxial defense mechanism dates from birth, since fetal bradycardia is common during delivery, and an acute rise in blood levels of lactic acid after delivery has been documented. Cardiac arrhythmias sometimes occur during diving.

Since bradycardia and arrhythmias may occur during simple breath holding (Lamb et al., 1958), Olsen et al. (1962) compared the cardiovascular response to breath holding under water with that to simple breath holding. Bradycardia was more marked, and arrhythmias, which were mainly of the cardioinhibitory type (sinus bradycardia, sinus arrhythmia, sinus arrest with A-V nodal or ventricular escape, A-V nodal rhythm and partial or complete heart block) were more frequent with submersion. Sinus rhythm was restored with the first beat after resurfacing; the rate often was faster than that prior to breath holding. *T* waves frequently became tall and peaked in both situations. Irving (1963) confirmed that the heart slows during voluntary breath holding in air, but that the effect is more striking with submersion. The onset and degree of bradycardia were not affected by vigorous underwater swimming. Indeed, bradycardia was more consistent and more marked in practiced and capable swimmers.

Bradycardia during simple breath holding occurs prior to the demonstration of any major change in arterial pO_2 or pCO_2 (Powell and Sunahara, 1958), and it is abolished by pretreatment with atropine. Therefore, it is probably mediated by the vagus nerve. It is of interest that immersion of the body in water at 25 degrees C. usually slows the heart, even when the head is out of water and air is breathed normally (Keatinge and Evans 1961). It is unsettled whether this is a baroreceptor mediated response to cutaneous vasoconstriction.

REFERENCES

Afonso, S., Rowe, G. G., Castillo, C. A., and Crumpton, C. W.: Intravascular and intracardiac blood temperatures in man. J. App. Physiol., *17*:706, 1962.

Alexander, J. K., Grover, R. F., and Hartley, L. H.: Reduction of cardiac output in man at high altitude. Clin. Research, *14*:121, 1966. (Abstract).

Appenzeller, O., and Schnieden, H.: Neurogenic pathways concerned in reflex vasodilation in the hand with especial reference to stimuli affecting the afferent pathway. Clin. Sci., *25*:413, 1963.

Arias-Stella, J., and Saldaña, M.: The muscular pulmonary arteries in people native to high altitudes. Medicina Thorac., *19*:484, 1962.

Arias-Stella, J., and Saldaña, M.: Terminal portion of the pulmonary arterial tree in people native to high altitudes. Circulation, *28*:915, 1963.

Asmussen, E.: CO_2-breathing and output of the heart. Acta Physiol. Scand., *6*:176, 1943.

Asmussen, E., and Consolazio, F. C.: The circulation at rest and work on Mount Evans (4,300 m.). Am. J. Physiol., *132*:555, 1941.

Asmussen, E., and Nielsen, M.: Cardiac output during muscular work and its regulation. Physiol. Rev., *35*:778, 1955A.

Asmussen, E., and Nielsen, M.: The cardiac output in rest and work at low and high oxygen pressures. Acta Physiol. Scand., *35*:73, 1955B.

Åstrand, P.-O., and Åstrand, I.: Heart rate during muscular work in man exposed to prolonged hypoxia. J. Appl. Physiol., *13*:75, 1958.

Balke, B.: Cardiac performance in relation to altitude. Am. J. Cardiol., *14*:796, 1964.

Banchero, N., Sime, F., Peñaloza, D., Cruz, J., Gamboa, R., and Marticorena, E.: Pulmonary pressure, cardiac output, and arterial oxygen saturation during exercise at high altitude and at sea level. Circulation, *33*:249, 1966.

Barcroft, H., Bock, K. D., Hensel, H., and Kitchin, A. H.: Die Muskeldurchblutung des Menschen bei indirekter Erwärmung und Abkühlung. Pflüg. Arch. Ges. Physiol., *261*:199, 1955.

Bass, D. E., Kleeman, C. R., Quinn, N. M., Henschel, A., and Hegnauer, A. H.: Mechanisms of acclimatization to heat in man. Medicine, *34*:323, 1955.

Bazett, H. C.: The regulation of body temperatures. In: Physiology of Heat Regulation and the Science of Clothing. Ed. Newburg. Philadelphia and London, Saunders, 1949.

Bazett, H. C., Lowe, L., Newton, M., Eisenberg, L., Day, R., and Forster, R., II.:

Temperature changes in blood flowing in arteries and veins in man. J. Appl. Physiol., *1*:3, 1948.

Benzinger, T. H.: The quantitative mechanism and the sensory receptor organ of human temperature control in warm environment. Ann. Int. Med., *54*:685, 1961.

Bernthal, T.: Chemo-reflex control of vascular reactions through carotid body. Am. J. Physiol., *121*:1, 1938.

Blair, D. A., Glover, W. E., and Kidd, B. S. L.: The effect of continuous positive and negative pressure breathing upon the resistance and capacity blood vessels of the human forearm and hand. Clin. Cci., *18*:9, 1959.

Blair, D. A., Glover, W. E., and Roddie, I. C.: Cutaneous vasomotor nerves to the head and trunk. J. Appl. Physiol., *16*:119, 1961.

Boerema, I., Meyne, N. G., Brummelkamp, W. K., Bouma, S., Mensch, M. H., Kamermans, F., Stern Hanf, M., and Van Aalderen, W.: Life without blood. A study of the influence of high atmospheric pressure and hypothermia on dilution of blood. J. Cardiovasc. Surg., *1*:133, 1960.

Bondurant, S.: Effect of acceleration on pulmonary compliance. Fed. Proc., *17*:18, 1958.

Brouha, L., Maxfield, M. E., Smith, P. E., Jr., and Stopps, G. J.: Discrepancy between heart rate and oxygen consumption during work in the warmth. J. Appl. Physiol., *18*:1095, 1963.

Burnum, J. F., Hickam, J. B., and McIntosh, H. D.: Effect of hypocapnia on arterial blood pressure. Circulation, *9*:89, 1954.

Cherniack, N. S., Hyde, A. S., and Zechman, F. W., Jr.: Effect of transverse acceleration on pulmonary function. J. Appl. Physiol., *14*:914, 1959.

Christensen, E. H., and Forbes, W. H.: Der Kreislauf in grossen Höhen. Skand. Arch. f. Physiol., *76*:75, 1937.

Cooper, K. E., and Kerslake, D. McK.: Abolition of nervous reflex vasodilatation by sympathectomy of the heated area. J. Physiol., *119*:18, 1953.

Crossley, R. J., Greenfield, A. D. M., Plassaras, G. C., and Stephens, D.: The interrelation of thermoregulatory and baroreceptor reflexes in the control of the blood vessels in the human forearm. J. Physiol., *183*:628, 1966.

Daly, W. J., and Bondurant, S.: Effects of oxygen breathing on the heart rate, blood pressure, and cardiac index of normal men—resting, with reactive hyperemia, and after atropine. J. Clin. Invest., *41*:126, 1962.

Dill, D. B.: Life, Heat and Altitude. Cambridge, Mass., Harvard Univ. Press, 1938, p. 132.

Dill, D. B., and Consolazio, F. C.: Responses to exercise as related to age and environmental temperature. J. Appl. Physiol., *17*:645, 1962.

Donevan, R. E., Anderson, N. M., Sekelj, P., Papp, O., and McGregor, M.: Influence of voluntary hyperventilation on cardiac output. J. Appl. Physiol., *17*:487, 1962.

Douglas, C. G., Haldane, J. S., Henderson, Y., and Schneider, E. C.: Physiological observations made on Pike's Peak, Colorado, with special reference to low barometric pressures. Phil. Trans. Roy. Soc. Lond., *203*:185, 1913.

Eckstein, J. W., Hamilton, W. K., and McCammond, J. M.: Pressure-volume changes in the forearm veins of man during hyperventilation. J. Clin. Invest., *37*:956, 1958.

Edholm, O. G., Fox, R. H., and MacPherson, R. K.: The effect of body heating on the circulation in skin and muscle. J. Physiol., *134*:612, 1956.

Edwards, A. W. T.: Alveolar capillary temperature compared with aortic and bronchial wedge temperatures. J. Appl. Physiol., *19*:760, 1964.

Edwards, A. W. T., Velasquez, T., and Farhi, L. E.: Determination of alveolar capillary temperature. J. Appl. Physiol., *18*:107, 1963.

Eggers, G. W. N., Jr., Paley, H. W., Leonard, J. J., and Warren, J. V.: Hemodynamic responses to oxygen breathing in man. J. Appl. Physiol., *17*:75, 1962.

Eichna, L. W., Bean, W. B., Ashe, W. F., and Nelson, N.: Performance in relation to environmental temperature. Reactions of normal young men to hot humid (simulated jungle) environment. Bull. Johns Hopkins Hosp., *76*:25, 1945.

Eichna, L. W., Berger, A. R., Rader, B., and Becker, W. H.: Comparison of intracardiac and intravascular temperatures with rectal temperature in man. J. Clin. Invest., *30*:353, 1951.
Fishman, A. P.: Respiratory gases in the regulation of the pulmonary circulation. Physiol. Rev., *41*:214, 1961.
Folkow, B., Ström, G., and Uvnäs, B.: Cutaneous vasodilatation elicited by local heating of the anterior hypothalamus in cats and dogs. Acta Physiol. Scand., *17*: 317, 1949.
Fox, R. H., Goldsmith, R., Hampton, I., and Lewis, H. E.: The mechanism of the increase in sweating capacity by heat acclimatization. J. Physiol., *162*:59P, 1962 (Abstract).
Fox, R. H., Goldsmith, R., and Kidd, D. J.: Cutaneous vasomotor nerves in the human ear and forehead. J. Physiol., *150*:12P, 1960A (Abstract).
Fox, R. H., Goldsmith, R., and Kidd, D. J.: The cutaneous vasomotor control in the human nose, lip and chin. J. Physiol., *150*:22P, 1960B (Abstract).
Fox, R. H., Goldsmith, R., Kidd, D. J., and Lewis, H. E.: Acclimatization to heat in man by controlled elevation of body temperature. J. Physiol., *166*:530, 1963.
Fox, R. H., and Hilton, S. M.: Bradykinin formation in human skin as a factor in heat vasodilatation. J. Physiol., *142*:219, 1958.
Gamble, J. L., Jr., Shaw, R. S., Henry, J. P., and Gauer, O. H.: Cerebral dysfunction during negative acceleration. J. Appl. Physiol., *2*:133, 1949.
Gaskell, P.: Are there sympathetic vasodilator nerves to the vessels of the hands? J. Physiol., *131*:647, 1956.
Gibbon, J. H., Jr., and Landis, E. M.: Vasodilatation in the lower extremities in response to immersing the forearms in warm water. J. Clin. Invest., *11*:1019, 1932.
Gray, R. F., and Webb, M. G.: High G Protection. U.S. Naval Air Development Center, NADC-MA-5910: 1-18, 1960.
Hecht, H. H., Kuida, H., Lange, R. L., Thorne, J. L., and Brown, A. M.: Brisket disease. III. Clinical features and hemodynamic observations in altitude-dependent right heart failure of cattle. Am. J. Med., *32*:171, 1962.
Howard, P.: Changes in the cardiac output during positive radial acceleration. J. Physiol., *147*:49P, 1959 (Abstract).
Hultgren, H. N., Lopez, C. E., Lundberg, E., and Miller, H.: Physiological studies of pulmonary edema at high altitude. Circulation, *29*:393, 1964.
Hurtado, A., and Aste-Salazar, H.: Arterial blood gases and acid-base balance at sea level and at high altitudes. J. Appl. Physiol., *1*:304, 1948.
Hurtado, A., Merino, C., and Delgado, E. Influence of anoxemia on hemopoietic activity. A.M.A. Arch. Int. Med., *75*:284, 1945.
Irving, L.: Bradycardia in human divers. J. Appl. Physiol., *18*:489, 1963.
Keatinge, W. R., and Evans, M.: The respiratory and cardiovascular response to immersion in cold and warm water. Quart. J. Exp. Physiol., *46*:83, 1961.
Kerslake, D. McK., and Cooper, K. E.: Vasodilatation in the hand in response to heating the skin elsewhere. Clin. Sci., *9*:31, 1950.
Keys, A.: Die Wirkung des Höhenklimas und die Akklimatisierungsprozesse in grosser Höhe. Ergebn. inn. Med. u. Kinderh., *54*:585, 1938.
Kilburn, K. H., and Sieker, H. O.: Hemodynamic effects of continuous positive and negative pressure breathing in normal man. Circ. Research, *8*:660, 1960.
Klausen, K.: Cardiac output in man in rest and work during and after acclimatization to 3,800 m. J. Appl. Physiol., *21*:609, 1966.
Koroxenidis, G. T., Shepherd, J. T., and Marshall, R. J.: Cardiovascular responses to acute heat stress. J. Appl. Physiol., *16*:869, 1961.
Lamb, L. E., Dermksian, G., and Sarnoff, C. A.: Significant cardiac arrhythmias induced by common respiratory maneuvers. Am. J. Cardiol., *2*:563, 1958.
Lambertsen, C. J., Kough, R. H., Cooper, D. Y., Emmel, G. L., Loeschcke, H. H., and Schmidt, C. F.: Comparison of relationship of respiratory minute volume to pCO_2 and pH of arterial and internal jugular blood in normal man during

hyperventilation produced by low concentrations of CO_2 at 1 atmosphere and by O_2 at 3.0 atmospheres. J. Appl. Physiol., *5*:803, 1953.

Leithead, C. S., and Lind, A. R.: Heat Stress and Heat Disorders. Philadelphia, Davis, 1964.

Lindberg, E. F., Marshall, H. W., Sutterer, W. F., McGuire, T. F., and Wood, E. H.: Studies of cardiac output and circulatory pressures in human beings during forward acceleration. Aerospace Med., *33*:81, 1962.

Lindberg, E. F., Sutterer, W. F., Marshall, H. W., Headley, R. N., and Wood, E. H.: Measurement of cardiac output during headward acceleration using the dye-dilution technique. Aerospace Med., *31*:817, 1960.

Lindberg, E. F., and Wood, E. H.: Acceleration. In: Physiology of Man in Space. New York, Academic Press, 1963, p. 61.

Lindberg, E. F., Wood, E. H., Sutterer, W. F., Marshall, H. W., and Headley, R. N.: Effect of headward and forward accelerations on the cardiovascular system. USAF Wright Air Develop. Division, Tech. Rep. No. 60-634, 1961.

Little, W. J., Vera, J. W. A., and Hoobler, S. W.: The effects of breathing CO_2 on blood pressure and renal circulation in normotensive and hypertensive subjects. Fed. Proc., *8*:98, 1949.

Marticorena, E., Tapia, F. A., Dyer, J., Severino, J., Banchero, N., Gamboa, R., Kruger, H., and Peñaloza, D.: Pulmonary edema by ascending to high altitudes. Dis. Chest., *45*:273, 1964.

McGregor, M., Donevan, R. E., and Anderson, N. M.: Influence of carbon dioxide and hyperventilation on cardiac output in man. J. Appl. Physiol., *17*:933, 1962.

Nolan, A. C., Marshall, H. W., Cronin, L., Sutterer, W. F., and Wood, E. H.: Decreases in arterial oxygen saturation and associated changes in pressures and roentgenographic appearance of the thorax during forward ($+G_x$) acceleration. Aerospace Med., *34*:797, 1963.

Olsen, C. R., Fanestil, D. D., and Scholander, P. F.: Some effects of breath holding and apneic underwater diving on cardiac rhythm in man. J. Appl. Physiol., *17*:461, 1962.

Peñaloza, D., Sime, F., Banchero, N., and Gamboa, R.: Pulmonary hypertension in healthy man born and living at high altitudes. Medicina Thorac., *19*:449, 1962.

Peñaloza, D., Sime, F., Banchero, N., Gamboa, R., Cruz, J., and Marticorena, E.: Pulmonary hypertension in healthy men born and living at high altitudes. Am. J. Cardiol., *11*:150, 1963.

Peters, J. P., and Van Slyke, D. D.: Quantitative Clinical Chemistry. Volume 1, Baltimore, Williams and Wilkins, 1931, p. 539.

Pickering, G. W.: Regulation of body temperature in health and disease. Lancet, *i*:1 and 59, 1958.

Powell, T. J., and Sunahara, F. A.: A physiological evaluation of the Flack Test. J. Aviation Med., *29*:444, 1958.

Pugh, L. G. C. E.: Cardiac output in muscular exercise at 5,800 m. (19,000 ft.). J. Appl. Physiol., *19*:441, 1964.

Pugh, L. G. C. E., Gill, M. B., Lahiri, S., Milledge, J. S., Ward, M. P., and West, J. B.: Muscular exercise at great altitudes. J. Appl. Physiol., *19*:431, 1964.

Rahn, H., and Otis, A. B.: Survival differences breathing air and oxygen at equivalent altitudes. Proc. Soc. Exp. Biol. Med., *70*:185, 1959.

Rankin, J., McNeill, R. S., and Forster, R. E.: Influence of increased alveolar CO_2 tension on pulmonary diffusing capacity for CO in man. J. Appl. Physiol., *15*:543, 1960.

Richardson, D. W., Kontos, H. A., Raper, A. J., and Patterson, J. L., Jr.: Modification by beta-adrenergic blockade of the circulatory response to acute hypoxia in man. J. Clin. Invest., *46*:77, 1967.

Richardson, D. W., Wasserman, A. J., and Patterson, J. L., Jr.: General and regional circulatory responses to change in blood pH and carbon dioxide tension. J. Clin. Invest., *40*:31, 1961.

Robinson, S., Turrell, E. S., Belding, H. S., and Horvath, S. M.: Rapid acclimatization to work in hot climates. Am. J. Physiol., *140*:168, 1943.

Roddie, I. C., Shepherd, J. T., and Whelan, R. F.: Evidence from venous oxygen saturation measurements that the increase in forearm blood flow during body heating is confined to the skin. J. Physiol., *134*:444, 1956.

Roddie, I. C., Shepherd, J. T., and Whelan, R. F.: Humoral vasodilatation in forearm during voluntary hyperventilation. J. Physiol., *137*:80, 1957.

Rotta, A.: The cardiovascular system at altitude. In: Cardiology. An Encyclopedia of the Cardiovascular System. Ed. Luisada. Volume 5, part 25. New York, McGraw-Hill, 1961, p. 3.

Rotta, A., Canepa, A., Hurtado, A., Velasquez, T., and Chavez, R.: Pulmonary circulation at sea level and at high altitudes. J. Appl. Physiol., *9*:328, 1956.

Rowell, L. B., Blackmon, J. R., Martin, R. H., Mazzarella, J. A., and Bruce, R. A.: Hepatic clearance of indocyanine green in man under thermal and exercise stresses. J. Appl. Physiol., *20*:384, 1965.

Rowell, L. B., Marx, H. J., Bruce, R. A., Conn, R. D., and Kusumi, F.: Reductions in cardiac output, central blood volume, and stroke volume with thermal stress in normal men during exercise. J. Clin. Invest., *45*:1801, 1966.

Roy, S. B., Bhatia, M. L., and Gadhoke, S.: Response of pulmonary blood volume to 64 to 114 weeks of intermittent stay at high altitudes. Am. Heart J., *74*:192, 1967.

Rushmer, R. F.: A roentgenographic study of the effect of a pneumatic antiblackout suit on the hydrostatic columns in man exposed to positive radial acceleration. Am. J. Physiol., *151*:459, 1947.

Rushmer, R. F., Beckman, E. L., and Lee, D.: Protection of the cerebral circulation by the cerebrospinal fluid under the influence of radial acceleration. Am. J. Physiol., *151*:355, 1947.

Saltin, B.: Circulatory response to submaximal and maximal exercise after thermal dehydration. J. Appl. Physiol., *19*:1125, 1964.

Samueloff, S. L., Bevegård, B. S., and Shepherd, J. T.: Temporary arrest of the circulation to a limb for the study of venomotor reactions in man. J. Appl. Physiol., *21*:341, 1966.

Schieve, J. F., and Wilson, W. P.: The changes in cerebral vascular resistance of man in experimental alkalosis and acidosis. J. Clin. Invest., *32*:33, 1953.

Scholander, P. F., Hammel, H. T., LeMessurier, H., Hemmingsen, E., and Garey, W.: Circulatory adjustment in pearl divers. J. Appl. Physiol., *17*:184, 1962.

Sechzer, P. H., Egbert, L. D., Linde, H. W., Cooper, D. Y., Dripps, R. D., and Price, H. L.: Effect of CO_2 inhalation on arterial pressure, ECG and plasma catecholamines and 17-OH corticosteroids in normal man. J. Appl. Physiol., *15*:454, 1960.

Severinghaus, J. W., Mitchell, R. A., Richardson, B. W., and Singer, M. M.: Respiratory control at high altitude suggesting active transport regulation of CSF pH. J. Appl. Physiol., *18*:1155, 1963.

Tenney, S. M.: Physiological adaptations to life at high altitude. Mod. Concepts Cardiovasc. Dis., *31*:713, 1962.

Theilen, E. O., Gregg, D. E., and Rotta, A.: Exercise and cardiac work response at high altitude. Circulation, *12*:383, 1955.

Vogel, J. H., Weaver, W. F., Rose, R. L., Blount, S. G., and Grover, R. F.: Pulmonary hypertension on exertion in normal man living at 10,150 feet (Leadville, Colorado). Medicina Thorac., *19*:461, 1962.

Werkö, L.: The influence of positive pressure breathing on the circulation in man. Acta Med. Scand., Suppl. *193*:1, 1947.

West, J. B., Lahiri, S., Gill, M. B., Milledge, J. S., Pugh, L. G. C. E., and Ward, M. P.: Arterial oxygen saturation during exercise at high altitude. J. Appl. Physiol., *17*:617, 1962.

Whalen, R. E., Saltzman, H. A., Holloway, D. H., Jr., McIntosh, H. D., Sieker, H. O., and Brown, I. W., Jr.: Cardiovascular and blood gas responses to hyperbaric oxygenation. Am. J. Cardiol., *15*:638, 1965.

Whitney, R. J.: Circulatory changes in the forearm and hand of man with repeated exposure to heat. J. Physiol., *125*:1, 1954.

Williams, C. G., Bredell, G. A. C., Wyndham, C. H., Strydom, N. B., Morrison, J. F., Peter, J., Fleming, P. W., and Ward, J. S.: Circulatory and metabolic reactions to work in heat. J. Appl. Physiol., *17*:625, 1962.

Wood, E. H., Nolan, A. C., Donald, D. E., and Cronin, L.: Influence of acceleration on pulmonary physiology. Fed. Proc., *22*:1024, 1963.

Wood, J. E., and Bass, D. E.: Responses of the veins and arterioles of the forearm to walking during acclimatization to heat in man. J. Clin. Invest., *39*:825, 1960.

Wyndham, C. H.: Effect of acclimatization on circulatory responses to high environmental temperatures. J. Appl. Physiol., *4*:383, 1951.

Wyndham, C. H., Strydom, N. B., Morrison, J. F., Du Toit, F. D., and Kraan, J. G.: Responses of unacclimatized men under stress of heat and work. J. Appl. Physiol., *6*:681, 1954.

Chapter 4

EMOTIONAL AND METABOLIC CHANGES

- Emotion
- Fainting
- Pregnancy
- Anemia
- Obesity
- Inactivity

EMOTION

Studies of the cardiovascular responses to acute emotional stress have sometimes had conflicting results, in part because the responses may be transient and difficult to quantitate, and in part because the same subject may at different times have different responses to the same stress. There is some evidence that the character of the response may be related to the specific nature of the emotional stimulus. Most commonly, however, there is an increase in systolic and diastolic arterial pressure, heart rate and cardiac output.

Brod et al. (1959) subjected eight normal reclining subjects to stressful mental arithmetic so that they became tense, nervous and embarrassed (Table 4-1). The mean arterial blood pressure increased from 100 to 122 mm. Hg, and the cardiac output increased from 5.3 to 7.4 liters per minute (average values). The forearm blood flow invariably increased, from 2.0 to 5.5 ml. per 100 ml. per minute (average values), while forearm vascular resistance decreased. Changes in renal blood flow were difficult to interpret, since the duration of the stimulus was too brief to permit the collection of urine samples adequate for determination of PAH clearance, but it is probable that the flow was decreased. Values calculated for total systemic resistance were sometimes increased and sometimes decreased, but there was thought to be no basic difference between these two types of response. The change in total resistance depends on the balance between vasodilatation in muscle and vasoconstriction in the kidney and splanchnic circulation; when the former was dominant, the value for total systemic resistance was reduced and vice versa (Brod, 1965). Cerebral vascular resistance was un-

TABLE 4-1. Hemodynamic Effects of Emotional Stress (Mental Arithmetic) in Normotensive Subjects*

		BRACHIAL ARTERY BLOOD PRESSURE MM. HG		CARDIAC OUTPUT L./MIN.		FOREARM BLOOD FLOW ML./100 ML./MIN.	
AGE (YR.)	SEX	BEFORE STRESS	DURING STRESS	BEFORE STRESS	DURING STRESS	BEFORE STRESS	DURING STRESS
51	F	114/77	132/85	4.33	6.65	2.5	3.2
27	F	114/72	156/100	4.15	5.10	0.7	2.1
34	F	128/72	146/79	6.41	9.99	4.5	11.6
43	F	116/71	146/100	5.45	5.96	3.5	5.8
45	F	137/75	168/91	4.20	4.81	1.1	3.0
47	F	118/74	138/92	5.50	5.05	1.2	3.0
21	M	147/85	162/102	6.55	12.92	0.9	1.9
26	M	154/86	187/108	5.94	8.75	2.0	13.3
Mean Values		129/77	154/95	5.32	7.40	2.0	5.5

* Adapted from Brod, Fencl, Hejl and Jirka, Clin. Sci., *18*:269, 1959.

changed during the performance of mental arithmetic but decreased during anxiety (Sokoloff et al., 1955). If constriction of capacitance vessels, which has been demonstrated in the limbs (Fig. 4-1), is widespread, this may contribute to the increase in cardiac output.

Although changes in muscle blood flow have been measured only in the

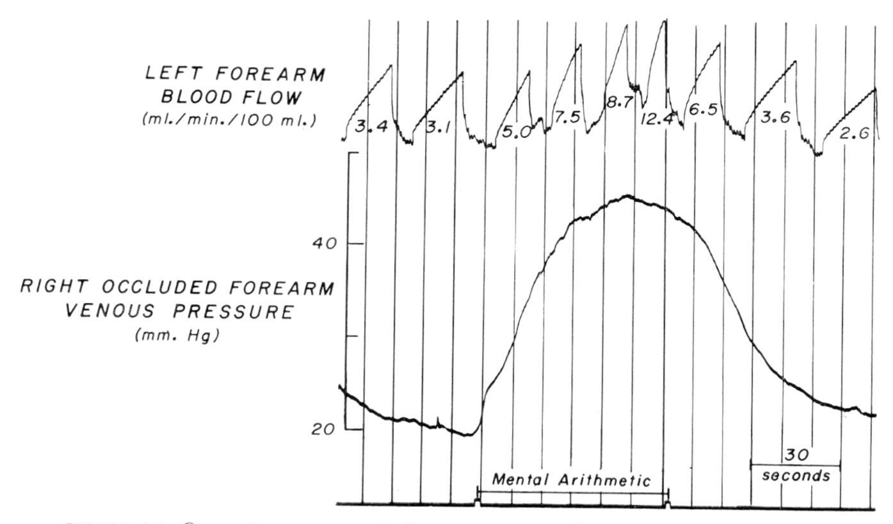

FIGURE 4-1. Opposite responses in forearm veins and resistance vessels to stress of mental arithmetic. Changes in venous pressure in the right forearm, to which the circulation was arrested, were proportional to the change in tension of the smooth muscle of the vein wall. The changes in tension are reflexly mediated by sympathetic adrenergic fibers. (Shepherd, unpublished data.)

forearm and the calf, it is likely that vasodilatation occurs in all skeletal muscle. The vasodilatation differs from that accompanying exercise. During exercise, the metabolic rate and the rate of consumption of glucose are greatly increased, and the arteriovenous difference in oxygen content in muscle is widened. During emotional stress, the metabolic rate is only slightly increased, glucose consumption is unchanged, and the arteriovenous difference is narrowed. Capillary filtration is increased with the augmented blood flow during exercise, but it is not increased during emotional stress (Brod et al., 1959; Brod, 1965). It has been inferred from this that the increased flow during emotion may bypass the usual capillary bed of the muscles.

Emotionally induced hyperemia of muscle is thought to result from the combined effects of two factors: (1) increased levels of epinephrine in the blood, and (2) activation of cholinergic vasodilator fibers. These fibers, which have been described in the cat and dog (Uvnäs, 1954), run with sympathetic adrenergic fibers to blood vessels of skeletal muscle; their activity is reduced or abolished by atropinization. The relative importance of these two factors is controversial (Greenfield, 1966). Evidence for the role of the cholinergic vasodilator fibers is clear from the demonstration that the magnitude of the hyperemia is diminished by stellate ganglion block and by infusion of atropine into the artery of the limb being studied (Blair et al., 1959; Barcroft et al., 1960).

Mental stress is not the only stimulus that causes reflex cholinergic vasodilatation (Abboud and Eckstein, 1966). The application of ice to the forehead and the Valsalva maneuver stimulate adrenergic vasoconstrictor pathways and cholinergic vasodilator pathways simultaneously. Since the former predominates, the vasodilator effect is unmasked only after adrenergic blockade.

Harris et al. (1964) used hypnosis to induce 20 episodes of intense fear and anger in nine subjects. Fear resulted in mean changes from control levels of +37 beats per minute (heart rate), +1.05 liters per $M.^2$ per minute (cardiac index) and −13 ml. (stroke volume). The mean arterial pressure increased by 10 mm. Hg, the right atrial pressure decreased, and peripheral resistance was also decreased. Beta-adrenergic blockade diminished the cardioaccelerator response but did not alter the responses of cardiac output or arterial pressure.

Anger had almost identical effects. The respiratory rate more than doubled, and two-thirds of the subjects developed respiratory alkalosis (arterial pH, 7.66 to 7.71). Plasma levels of hydrocortisone doubled, to a mean peak value of 25 μg./100 ml., and in two of three subjects, plasma levels of non-esterified fatty acids also doubled.

The possibility of a relationship between prolonged or recurrent emotional stress and the development of persistent hypertension has often been discussed (Wolf, 1955). Although hypertension can be induced in animals subjected to repeated unpleasant stimuli, and it may occur acutely in man from exposure to unusual stresses, such as those of the battlefield (Graham, 1945), there is, at present, little evidence that emotional stress is a major factor in the genesis of prolonged hypertension in man.

The subject under stress often becomes aware of his sinus tachycardia. Abnormal cardiac rhythms have only occasionally been reported (Harvey and Levine, 1952), but more recent experience with equipment for constant monitoring and tape recording of the electrocardiogram in unrestrained subjects has shown that they may occur more often than has generally been thought. For example, Semler (1965) recorded episodes of paroxysmal ventricular tachycardia in an apparently healthy 16 year old boy studying for a test, and of repetitive atrial flutter in a 57 year old man just after scolding his daughter. Alterations in the *ST* segments and *T* waves of the electrocardiogram are sometimes observed (Stevenson et al., 1951; Semler, 1965). While the significance of these changes is not certain, they could be related to endogenous release of epinephrine (Hartwell et al., 1942).

Emotional stress is also capable of altering the levels of cholesterol and triglycerides in the blood (Wolf et al., 1962). Hypercholesterolemia occurs during the stress of university examinations (Thomas and Murphy, 1958; Grundy and Griffin, 1959; Dreyfuss and Czaczkes, 1959). The clotting time of blood was also increased in 36 medical students on the morning of a final examination in medicine (Dreyfuss and Czaczkes, 1959).

The stimulus of cold results in hemodynamic changes resembling those caused by psychological factors. Keatinge et al. (1964) studied the response of normal subjects, sitting and supine, to a shower of ice cold water (0 – 2.5 degrees C.) run over the chest and abdomen for two minutes at 6 liters per minute. The respiratory rate increased from about 15 to 30 per minute and the tidal volume, from 770 to 1700 ml., while the arterial pCO_2 decreased from 40 to 28 mm. Hg. The average systemic arterial pressure with the subjects seated increased from 146/73 to 158/85 mm. Hg and the heart rate, from 114 to 147 beats per minute. With the subjects supine, the values changed from 134/69 to 166/90 mm. Hg and from 77 to 102 beats per minute, respectively. There was no significant change in plasma epinephrine levels during the showers, and the concentration of norepinephrine increased by an average of only 0.32 μg. per liter of plasma.

The cardiac output was measured in two subjects in the sitting position. In the first, it increased from 7.9 to 12.4 liters per minute, while the arterial blood pressure increased from 142/83 to 185/97 mm. Hg. In the second, it increased from 6.5 to 13.0 liters per minute, with an arterial blood pressure rise of 136/85 to 170/114 mm. Hg. In both subjects, the transmural atrial pressure increased.

The intense hyperventilation which accompanied the cold showers appeared to play no part in causing the hypertension, although it may have contributed to the tachycardia.

These changes can be explained by activation of the sympathetic adrenergic nerves to the heart and blood vessels with an increase in the force and frequency of cardiac contraction, rather than to release of catecholamines from the adrenal medulla. The reflex could be mediated through the tegmentum of the midbrain and the hypothalamus, since stimulation of these areas in cats caused similar changes (Abrahams et al., 1960). Application of cold also causes reflex venoconstriction in the limbs; if this were widespread, it could help to increase the filling pressure of the heart and thus contribute to the increase in cardiac output.

FAINTING

The commonest cause of loss of consciousness is the simple faint (vasodepressor syncope), which often occurs in response to pain or to an unpleasant emotional experience such as the sight of blood. Other precipitating causes include an uncomfortable environment such as a hot and crowded room, prolonged bed rest, fatigue, hypoxia, hunger and recent loss of blood. Fainting generally occurs when the subject is upright or sitting, but it can also occur during recumbency. The clinical features include pallor, sweating, nausea, hyperventilation, yawning, bradycardia, dilatation of the pupils and loss of consciousness. Many of these findings persist after consciousness is regained, and if the subject stands up too soon, he may again lose consciousness.

Foster (1888) believed that the decrease in blood pressure during fainting resulted from vagal inhibition of the heart. Lewis (1932) found that, although atropine abolished the bradycardia, it had little effect upon the hypotension or the level of consciousness. Therefore, he regarded vasodilatation as the primary cause of the decrease of arterial pressure, and introduced the term *vasovagal syndrome* to emphasize the combined etiological role of alterations in the behavior of peripheral vessels and in vagal activity.

Fainting associated with loss of blood has been extensively studied. After removal of a large volume of blood from a normal subject by venesection, the cardiac output and right atrial pressure are decreased. The systemic arterial pressure is at first maintained through constriction of resistance vessels. With the onset of fainting, the cardiac output does not usually decrease further, but there is a marked reduction in systemic vascular resistance (Fig. 4-2). The blood flow through skeletal muscle such as that of the forearm increases (Barcroft et al., 1944). Since there is simultaneously a decrease in arterial blood pressure, it is clear that there is marked vasodilatation in skeletal muscle. Vasodilatation does not occur in the forearm of patients following cervicodorsal sympathectomy. Therefore, it is mediated by sympathetic nerves rather than by humoral factors such as endogenous epinephrine. The vasodilatation may be mediated by release of sympathetic vaso-

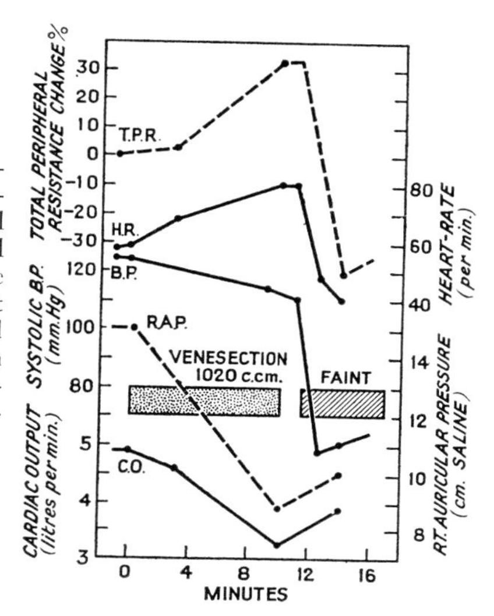

FIGURE 4-2. Faint induced by venesection. Up to the end of the venesection, arterial pressure was maintained by peripheral vasoconstriction (increased total peripheral resistance) in spite of a decreasing cardiac output. During the faint, the cardiac output increased slightly, and the fall in blood pressure was, therefore, due to decrease in peripheral resistance. (From Barcroft, Edholm, McMichael and Sharpey-Schafer, Lancet, *i*:489, 1944.)

constrictor tone (Löfving, 1961) or alternatively, as Barcroft and Edholm (1945) suggested, by increased activity of sympathetic vasodilator fibers.

Bradycardia, vasodilatation in skeletal muscle and decreased arterial blood pressure also occur during spontaneous or emotional fainting (Brigden et al., 1950; Greenfield, 1951). Anderson et al. (1946) studied the effects of prolonged inhalation of gas mixtures containing seven to eight per cent oxygen by normal subjects. At the onset of unconsciousness, 80 per cent had tachycardia and increased arterial blood pressure, but the remaining 20 per cent had typical vasovagal or vasodepressor reactions with increased forearm blood flow. It is likely, therefore, that the physiological alterations responsible for hemorrhagic fainting, emotional fainting and some instances of hypoxic fainting are similar.

Some of the effects resulting from acute hemorrhage during light general anesthesia differ from those in conscious subjects (de Wardener et al., 1953). Loss of up to 1460 ml. blood led to decreases in cardiac output and forearm blood flow. In 12 cases, changes in blood pressure and pulse rate were small or moderate; in only two was there severe hypotension accompanied by bradycardia. Hemorrhage of this order causes vagovagal fainting, with vasodilatation in skeletal muscle in about 80 per cent of conscious subjects lying supine. In the anesthetized patients, the vessels in muscle were constricted, even in the two subjects with severe hypotension and bradycardia. This suggested that posthemorrhagic hypotension during anesthesia was due mainly to the decrease in cardiac output and not, as in conscious subjects, to dilatation of vessels in muscle.

In contrast with the increased blood flow to the skeletal muscle of unanesthetized subjects during fainting, flow to the splanchnic bed (Bearn et al., 1951) and kidneys (de Wardener and McSwiney, 1951) is reduced.

Cutaneous vasodilatation may occur (Snell et al., 1955). As consciousness is lost, the electroencephalogram shows slow waves of large amplitude (Gastaut and Fischer-Williams, 1957). At this stage, cerebral blood flow is reduced by about one third (Finnerty et al., 1954). The cerebral hypoxia is mainly responsible for the hyperventilation. Hyperventilation leads to hypocapnia, and this, in turn, may further reduce arterial pressure and cerebral blood flow (Kety and Schmidt, 1946), contribute to the increased blood flow in skeletal muscle (Burnum et al., 1954) and therefore further aggravate the circulatory disturbance.

Postsyncopal oliguria is common. It may be related to excessive release of antidiuretic hormone (Brun et al., 1946).

FAINTING DUE TO CHANGE IN POSTURE. Brigden et al. (1950) pointed out that normal subjects who have had a venesection in the supine position (insufficient to cause syncope) have changes similar to those associated with tipping from the horizontal to the vertical position. In both situations, right atrial pressure and cardiac output decrease, the heart rate increases, and arterial blood pressure is unchanged. Thus, tipping into the erect posture is equivalent to a functional hemorrhage.

However, the response differed in some subjects who gave a history of fainting easily. Immediately after being tipped, they developed vasoconstriction, but several minutes later forearm blood flow (mainly muscle) increased, the blood pressure decreased, and the heart rate slowed. At this stage, the subjects could reverse the changes by voluntary or involuntary muscular contractions. The sighing respirations, by causing reflex venoconstriction, could have aided the muscle pump in augmenting venous return and thus maintaining the filling pressure of the heart (Samueloff et al., 1966). If they failed to contract their muscles, the blood pressure fell to very low levels, and the other phenomena of vasovagal or vasodepressor syncope occurred, including extreme bradycardia, sweating, pallor, unconsciousness and, occasionally, epileptiform fits.

A more detailed study of the effects of tilting normal young men to 60 degrees was carried out by Weissler et al. (1957A). Twenty per cent fainted spontaneously; the remainder could be induced to faint by taking sodium nitrate by mouth 10 to 15 minutes before being tilted. The cardiac index tended to fall slightly, from 2.9 to 2.5 liters per $M.^2$ per minute (mean values), with the onset of syncope (Table 4-2); decreases in arterial blood pressure and peripheral resistance were more striking. Prior treatment with atropine prevented the relative bradycardia but did not prevent the change in cardiac output. Rapid inflation of an antigravity suit reversed the syncopal reaction.

Thus, it seems that the major factor responsible for fainting is the sudden decrease in peripheral vascular resistance in such vascular beds as those of skeletal muscle (Barcroft and Edholm, 1945), and liver (Bearn et al., 1951). This is not compensated for by the increase in cardiac output that

TABLE 4-2. Hemodynamic Changes in Vasodepressor Syncope*

SUBJECT	CARDIAC INDEX (L./M.²/MIN.)			MEAN ARTERIAL PRESSURE (MM. HG)			PERIPHERAL RESISTANCE (DYNE SEC. CM.⁻⁵)		
	CON-TROL	SYN-COPE	CHANGE	CON-TROL	SYN-COPE	CHANGE	CON-TROL	SYN-COPE	CHANGE
1	3.5	2.2	−1.3	100	38	−62	1128	689	−439
2	2.5	1.6	−0.9	74	30	−44	1302	812	−490
3	3.2	2.5	−0.7	85	26	−59	1125	426	−699
4	2.9	2.3	−0.6	80			1108		
5	2.4	1.9	−0.5	82	55	−27	1407	1226	−181
6	2.7	2.5	−0.2	87	57	−30	1358	956	−402
7	2.2	2.5	+0.3	67	27	−40	1132	392	−740
8	3.8	4.3	+0.5	95	32	−63	1064	320	−744
Mean . . .	2.9	2.5	−0.4	84	38	−46	1217	689	−528

All data obtained while the subjects were in the 60° head up tilt position.

* From Weissler, A. M., Warren, J. V., Estes, E. H., Jr., McIntosh, H. D., and Leonard, J. J.: Vasodepressor syncope. Factors influencing cardiac output. Circulation, *15*:875, 1957. By permission of the American Heart Association, Inc.

occurs in normal persons in other situations in which there is extensive peripheral vasodilatation. Lack of a compensatory increase in output could be explained by either vagal inhibition of the heart or by inadequate venous return. Since atropinization does not affect the magnitude of the cardiac output during fainting (Weissler et al., 1957B), the former is probably unimportant. The fact that inflation of an antigravity suit abolished the hypotension suggests that reduced venous return is of paramount importance. In the forearm, there is no evidence of either venoconstriction or venodilatation during fainting (Stampfer et al., 1967). Negative pressure breathing also reverses the syncopal reaction, possibly because the increased venous return from activity of the abdominothoracic pump is augmented by increased return from reflex constriction of the systemic capacitance venous system. Although the hypocapnia resulting from hyperventilation may contribute to the circulatory changes, it is probably not an essential component of the reaction (Weissler et al., 1957A).

Prolonged standing with exaggerated lumbar lordosis can cause fainting. In this posture, pressure in the inferior vena cava rises, while there are decreases in right atrial pressure and in cardiac output. The basis for these changes appears to be partial compression of the vena cava, with consequent pooling of blood in the lower half of the body. The propensity of some women to faint in the latter stages of pregnancy is probably explained by the exaggerated lumbar lordosis.

Orthostatic fainting readily occurs in the presence of conditions that interfere with the development of compensatory vasoconstriction in arteriolar beds. After spinal anesthesia, there is persistent arterial dilatation in the anesthetized portion of the body; relatively slight tipping of the body from the horizontal position may lead to an acute fall of blood pressure accompanied by vasodilatation in the forearm (Brigden et al., 1950). The exaggerated decrease in cardiac output with tipping during spinal anesthesia is contributory (Pugh and Wyndham, 1950).

Fainting also occurs readily on standing in a relaxed manner following strenuous exercise (Eichna et al., 1947). It is the result of pooling of blood in the lower extremities, in addition to the dilatation of the resistance blood vessels in the muscles resulting from the exercise.

The nature of the receptors concerned in fainting are unknown. The possibility that lowering of the right atrial pressure may stimulate sensory receptors in that chamber has been suggested. Noble and Taylor (1953) recovered a posterior pituitary-like antidiuretic substance from the urine of subjects recovering from faints. These and other factors were discussed by Barcroft and Swan (1953).

FAINTING DUE TO RESPIRATORY MANEUVERS. During the Valsalva maneuver, in which the intrathoracic pressure is maintained at +40 mm. Hg or more, there is a progressive decrease in arterial blood pressure and in left ventricular stroke output for the first six or seven seconds due to obstruction of systemic venous return. When the blood supply to the brain is sufficiently depleted, syncope may result (Klein et al., 1964). This is most likely to happen when the subject performs the maneuver in the upright position. Occasional attacks of dizziness are common among trumpet players, who can achieve intrathoracic pressures up to +160 mm. Hg for a few seconds and +80 mm. Hg for prolonged notes (Sharpey-Schafer, 1965).

That fainting is not more common in normal subjects performing the maneuver is due to the fact that reflex peripheral vasoconstriction becomes established after about seven seconds. In patients with autonomic neuropathy from such causes as diabetes and tabes dorsalis, reflex vasoconstriction does not occur, and the arterial pressure continues to decline throughout the maneuver and eventually reaches very low levels. This absence of reflex vasoconstriction also explains the lack of overshoot of arterial pressure that consistently occurs in normal persons a few seconds after cessation of the maneuver (Fig. 4-3).

The combination of hyperventilation, which, by inducing hypocapnia, causes cerebral vasoconstriction, and a Valsalva maneuver (or its equivalent) is particularly prone to cause syncope. This is illustrated by certain well known display performances in young men or boys (Howard et al., 1951). In the "mess trick," the victim is persuaded to hyperventilate; the operator stands behind him and suddenly and violently compresses his chest. The victim automatically closes his glottis, strains against the pressure and thereby unconsciously performs a Valsalva maneuver. He promptly loses consciousness. In the "fainting lark," popular among school boys, the subject first squats, which causes reflex vasodilatation, and hyperventilates; he then suddenly stands and performs a Valsalva maneuver.

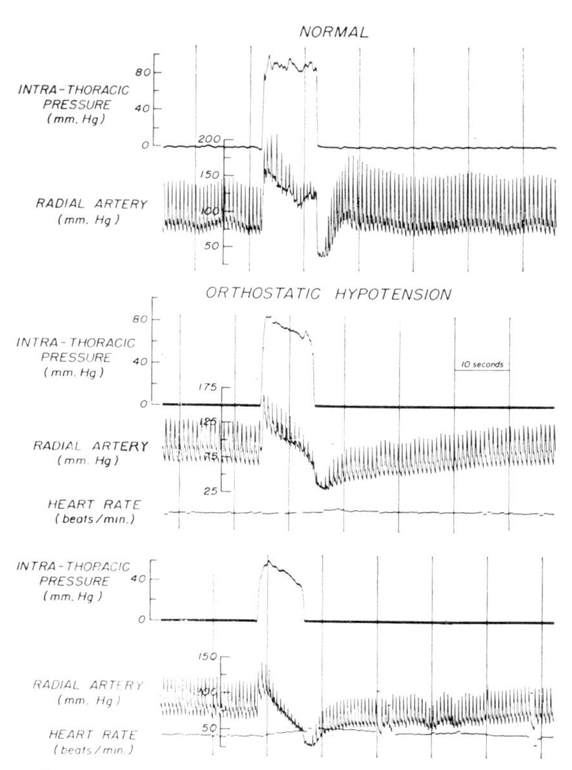

FIGURE 4-3. Effects of Valsalva maneuver in a normal subject (*upper*) and in two patients (*middle and lower*) with idiopathic orthostatic hypotension (autonomic neuropathy). (From Marshall, Schirger and Shepherd, Circulation, *24*:76, 1961.)

Paroxysmal coughing may also lead to syncope. The intrathoracic pressure is commonly raised to 200 mm. Hg, and pressures as high as 450 mm. Hg have been recorded (Sharpey-Schafer, 1953A). There is reflex dilatation of peripheral arterioles (Sharpey-Schafer, 1953B); this, together with a marked reduction of left ventricular stroke volume, may reduce the arterial blood pressure sufficiently to cause transient syncope (Fig. 4-4). Other factors predisposing to syncope during and after coughing include compression of intracranial capillaries and veins (McIntosh et al., 1956) due to the great increase in cerebrospinal fluid pressure (Hamilton et al., 1944), and a concussive effect caused by the sudden increase in intracranial pressure (Kerr and Eich, 1961). Evidence for the latter is that the loss of consciousness may precede the decrease in blood pressure.

Syncope has also been described in association with micturition. In older males with nocturnal frequency, the performance of a Valsalva maneuver at the start of micturition may be responsible. An additional mechanism may be the loss of arterial and venous tone following the release

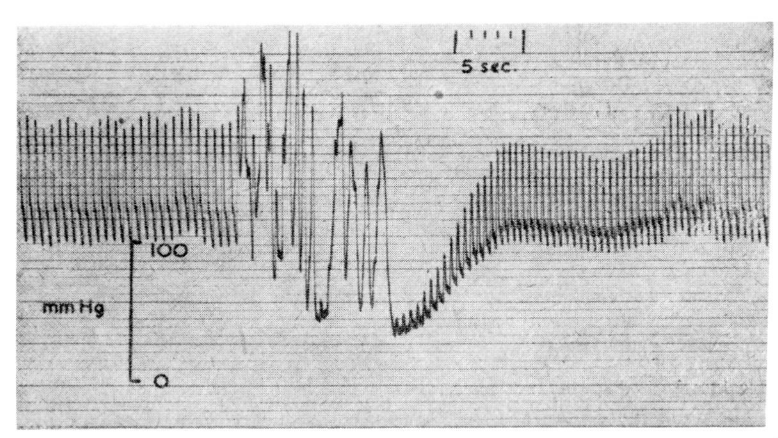

FIGURE 4-4. Effect of severe spell of coughing on arterial blood pressure. The large cough transients are followed by hypotension. (From Sharpey-Schafer, Brit. Med. J., *ii*:860, 1953.)

of tension in the wall of the bladder. Syncope may also occur in younger men when they stand to void immediately after rising from bed (Lyle et al., 1961). This syncope may be related more to motionless standing than to the act of voiding itself. In one case, transient heart block with a ventricular rate of 20 per minute was documented and was attributed to vagal overactivity (Coggins et al., 1964).

PREGNANCY

The resting heart rate increases gradually up to about the thirtieth week of pregnancy, and then it declines towards term. However, the maximal increase in the rate is only about 10 beats per minute. In the absence of complications, there is little change in systolic arterial blood pressure, while diastolic pressure decreases slightly, particularly around the thirtieth week. Systolic pressures in the right ventricle and pulmonary artery, and the pulmonary artery wedge pressure do not differ from those in the non-pregnant state.

A gradual increase in blood volume up to the thirtieth week has been well documented (Thomson et al., 1938; White, 1949; Hytten and Paintin, 1963); the peak values are 25 to 50 per cent above normal (Fig. 4-5). Although the red cell mass increases, the increase in plasma volume is proportionately greater, so that the hematocrit and hemoglobin level are reduced (physiological hydremia of pregnancy). Whereas the red cell mass continues to increase until term, the plasma volume decreases during the last month; at this time, therefore, the hematocrit and hemoglobin level return towards normal (Caton et al., 1951). The total body content of water, on the other hand, rises continuously until term (Haley and Woodbury, 1956). The body hematocrit:venous hematocrit ratio was found to be 0.924 in pregnant women as compared with 0.902 in non-pregnant normal subjects (Muldowney and Flanagan, 1964).

The precise distribution of the increased blood volume is uncertain, although obviously some of it is accommodated in the blood vessels of the uterus and placenta. There is some suggestion (Werkö, 1954) that the volume of blood in the lungs may decrease during the last month of pregnancy. For reasons to be discussed, the veins of the lower part of the body may contain increased quantities of blood.

The venous pressure in the arms is unaltered. When the venous pressure in the legs is measured with the patient lying supine, it is found to increase throughout pregnancy (Brigden et al., 1950); the increase ranges from 7 to 10 mm. Hg. Compression of the inferior vena cava by the enlarged uterus has beeen clearly demonstrated. In the supine position, changes in intrathoracic pressure are not transmitted to the caudal end of the vena cava, whereas they are readily transmitted in the lateral decubitus position (Scott and Kerr, 1963). Phlebograms reveal almost complete ob-

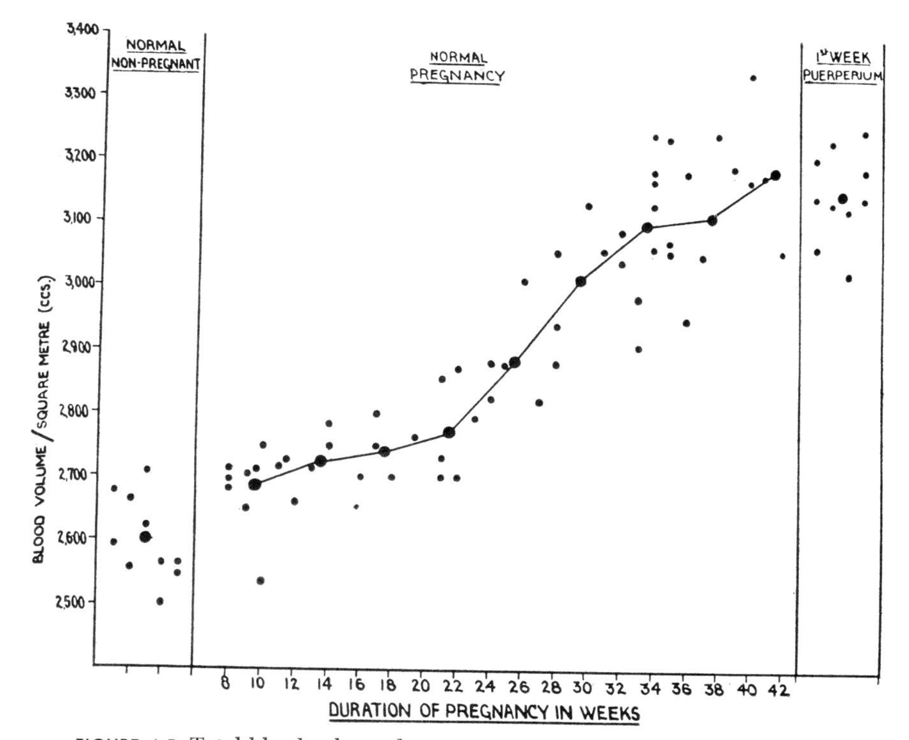

FIGURE 4-5. Total blood volume during pregnancy. Individual values are shown as small dots and mean values for four week periods, as larger dots. *Left:* values in non-pregnant control subjects; *right:* values obtained during the puerperium. (From White, Trans. Edinb. Obst. Soc., Session 102, 14, 1949.)

struction to the passage of contrast medium at the level of the bifurcation of the vena cava; venous return from the legs and pelvis is diverted via lumbar and paravertebral veins (Kerr et al., 1964). In some women, impaired venous return and the consequent decrease in cardiac output result in syncope (Howard et al., 1953) which is quickly reversed by rolling over from the supine to the lateral decubitus position. While bradycardia and decreased systemic vascular resistance may accompany the syncope, more commonly an increase in systemic vascular resistance compensates for the decrease in output so that the arterial blood pressure is unaffected (Lees et al., 1967).

The supine posture may also interfere with renal function. Chesley and Sloan (1964) performed renal function tests in ten women during the last two months of pregnancy. The patients lay on their backs on one day and on their sides on the previous or subsequent day. Urine output and rates of excretion of sodium and chloride were more than twice as great in the lateral position and, in nine of the 10 women, effective renal plasma flow and glomerular filtration rates were also greater in the lateral position. These alterations were attributed to local disturbances in venous flow resulting from compression by the gravid uterus. Thus, when tests are performed with the patient lying supine (as they usually are), the results may convey a misleading impression that renal function is impaired.

It has long been realized that the cardiac output is increased during pregnancy. From his clinical observations, MacDonald (1878) felt that "the amount of blood circulating through the mother's vessels during the latter months of pregnancy is increased beyond question." In 1949, Hamilton used the direct Fick method to measure cardiac output in 24 control women and 68 women at various stages of pregnancy. Mean values (liters per minute, uncorrected for differences in body build) were 4.5 (control), 4.3 at six to nine weeks, 5.1 at ten to 13 weeks and 5.7 at 21 weeks. The last value was maintained until about the thirty-sixth week, and then the output decreased towards normal at term (Fig. 4-6). Bader et al. (1955), who attempted to adjust their data for differences in body build by using the DuBois formula, also found a considerable increase in output midway through pregnancy and a decline towards normal values in the last month (Table 4-3). They also studied the effects of mild leg exercise on the circulation and concluded that the response was quantitatively similar to that in non-pregnant women.

In order to make serial studies in the same patients, Walters et al. (1966) used an earpiece densitometer to record indicator dilution curves for cardiac output. Initial values, at the eighth and eleventh weeks, were unexpectedly high, possibly due to apprehension. When these were excluded, the maximal value for output was 6.7 liters per minute at 28 to 31 weeks; it declined to 5.6 liters per minute during the last month and to 5.3 liters per minute a few weeks to months after delivery. Adams (1954), who

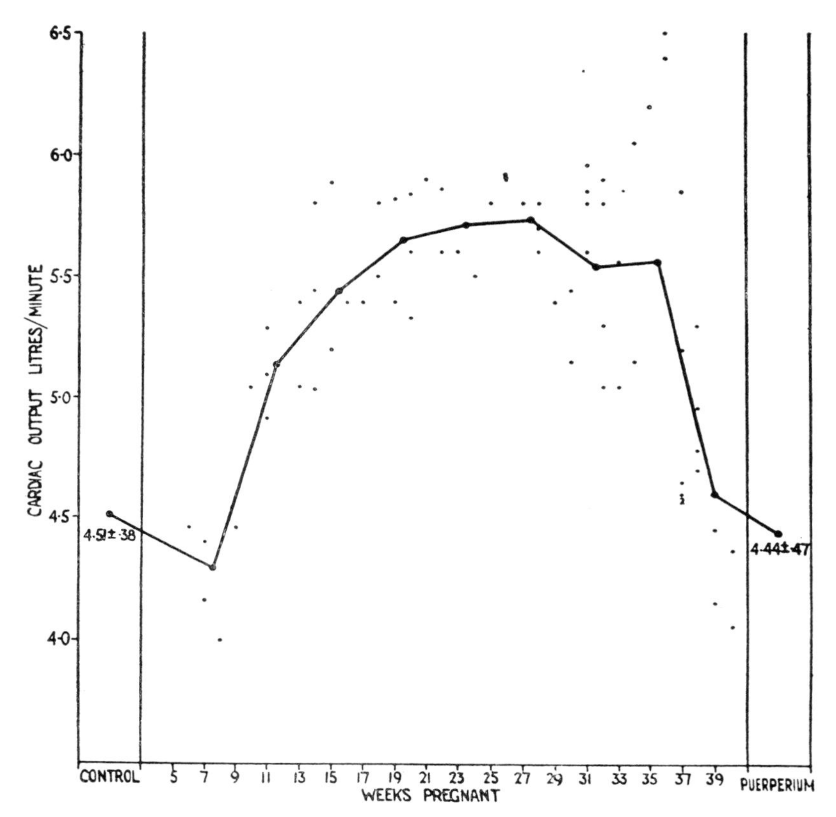

FIGURE 4-6. Cardiac output during normal pregnancy. Mean values for cardiac output in non-pregnant control subjects and in the puerperium are also shown. (From Hamilton, Trans. Edinb. Obst. Soc., Session 102, 1, 1949.)

also used the indicator dilution method, found a peak increase of 32 per cent at about the twenty-eighth week and a decline to normal at term.

The results of the studies quoted above are similar and indicate that the peak value for resting cardiac output is increased by about 25 to 30 per cent over that in the non-pregnant state. The precise cause of this increase is not settled. Although the metabolic rate is increased because of the demands of the fetus and of increased activity of the thyroid gland, the increase is relatively slight and does not fully account for the increase in output. Thus, Bader et al. (1955) found less than 10 per cent increase in oxygen consumption. As a corollary, the arteriovenous difference in oxygen content was reduced to 3.4 ml. per 100 ml. at 28 weeks and returned to normal values (4.4 ml. per 100 ml.) in the terminal weeks of pregnancy. The hypervolemia also cannot satisfactorily account for the increased cardiac output, since the latter declines in the third trimester while the blood volume continues to increase until the thirty-sixth week. However,

TABLE 4-3. Cardiac Output and Oxygen Consumption During Pregnancy*

NUMBER OF SUBJECTS	WEEKS OF PREGNANCY	MEAN CARDIAC INDEX		MEAN O_2 UPTAKE	
		L./M.^{2}/MIN.	S.D.	ML./M.^{2}/MIN.	S.D.
8	14-24	4.09	0.39	138	12
8	25-27	4.26	0.74	143	15
10	28-30	3.93	0.65	137	21
9	31-35	3.60	0.55	142	13
11	36-40	3.44	0.44	150	10

* Adapted from Bader, Bader, Rose and Braunwald, J. Clin. Invest., *34*:1524, 1955.

if the blood volume was redistributed during the last three months, with relatively more outside the thorax (Werkö, 1954) and therefore less available for cardiac filling, no discrepancy would be present. The consistent absence of any increase in end-diastolic pressure in the right ventricle during the last month, compared with its slight elevation in some patients previously (Bader et al., 1955), would also be compatible with a reduction in cardiothoracic blood volume.

Attempts have been made to measure blood flow in the uterus of normal women at or close to term. Using the nitrous oxide method during operation, Assali et al. (1960) found values of 6.6 to 12.0 ml. per 100 g. per minute, which were similar to those of Metcalfe et al. (1955). Lysgaard and Lefèvre (1965) injected Xenon^{133} through the abdominal wall into the myometrium during the last trimester and found a range of 2.0 to 32.0 ml. per 100 g. per minute. The total uterine flow thus could account for only a fraction of the increase in cardiac output.

The increases in heart rate, blood volume and cardiac output are well tolerated by normal women, but in the presence of heart disease, especially mitral stenosis, they impose a substantial additional burden on the heart. The increased rate of flow through a narrow mitral valve orifice, together with an increased pulmonary blood volume, may lead to severe congestion or pulmonary edema, particularly when there are precipitating factors such as anemia, strenuous exercise, emotion, paroxysmal rapid heart action or intercurrent infection of the respiratory tract. There is a close correlation between the time of onset of cardiac failure and the magnitude of the circulatory load.

ANEMIA

Roy et al. (1963) studied 51 patients, with an average age of 34 years, who had chronic anemia mainly caused by ankylostomiasis. The hemoglobin levels ranged from 1.5 to 6.5 (mean 3.7) g. per 100 ml. There was an inverse correlation between hemoglobin level and cardiac index (Fig. 4-7). The cardiac index exceeded 5 liters per M.^{2} per minute in all but one

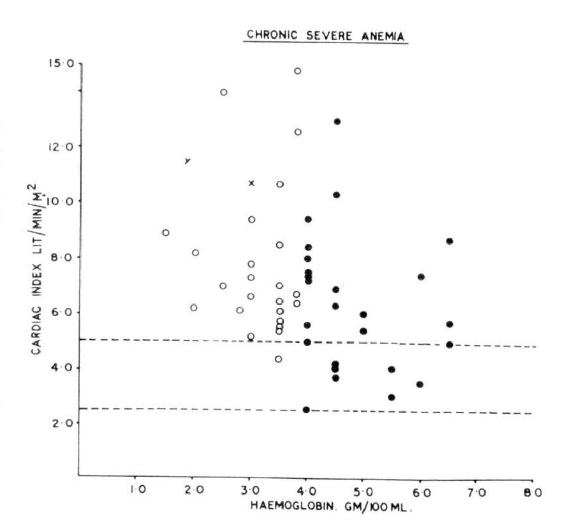

FIGURE 4-7. Cardiac index during rest in severe anemia showing hemoglobin levels of 4.0 to 6.5 g. per 100 ml. (filled circles) and hemoglobin levels less than 4.0 g. per 100 ml. (empty circles). All measurements by indicator dilution method except for three (crosses) by direct Fick method. Interrupted lines: the authors' range of normal values. (From Roy, Bhatia, Mathur and Virmani, Circulation, *28*:346, 1963.)

of the patients with levels less than 4.0 g. per 100 ml. and in 60 per cent of those with levels of 4.0 to 6.0 g. per 100 ml. The resting heart rate varied widely from 65 to 120 beats per minute; there was little correlation between heart rate and cardiac output. The increased output was achieved mainly by an increase in stroke volume; mean values (ml. per $M.^2$) were 88 in the more severe and 68 in the less severe group. Since the oxygen consumption was in the normal range (115 to 160 ml. per $M.^2$ per minute), the arteriovenous difference in oxygen content was decreased. It averaged 2.25 ml. per 100 ml. in the more severe and 3.0 ml. per 100 ml. in the less severe group, as compared with a value of 4.1 ml. per 100 ml. in 65 normal control subjects.

Wade and Bishop (1962), from a review of the literature, were unable to show any close relationship between hemoglobin levels and resting values for cardiac output, although the cardiac output was always increased when the hemoglobin was less than 6 g. per 100 ml.

At rest, the pulmonary artery and pulmonary artery wedge pressures are normal. The systemic arterial systolic pressure is also normal, whereas the diastolic pressure is reduced, especially in severe anemia. Therefore, the resistance in the pulmonary and systemic circulations is decreased, and the work load of the ventricle is only slightly increased. The right atrial pressure usually remains normal.

In mild and moderate anemia, the needs of the tissues are met mainly by an increased percentage of oxygen extraction from the blood, but in severe anemia, there is also an increase in blood flow. Verel and Duff (1959) showed that, with hemoglobin levels above 4 g. per 100 ml., the forearm blood flow did not exceed the upper limit of normal (6 ml. per 100 ml. per minute), but with lower levels, flow was invariably increased.

The increase occurred when the oxygen saturation of forearm venous blood had fallen to less than 15 per cent (normal range 56 to 75 per cent); in other words, it occurred only when further extraction of oxygen was virtually impossible. The means by which the resistance vessels dilate in response to tisssue hypoxia is unknown.

The means by which the increase in cardiac output is achieved is also uncertain, but it seems reasonable to suppose that it may be a consequence of systemic vasodilatation and of reduced viscosity of blood; both of these changes contribute to the decrease in systemic vascular resistance. When the right atrial and pulmonary capillary pressure are normal, there is no obvious correlation between output and filling pressure. However, because of the shape of the pressure-volume curve of the ventricles, small changes in filling pressure in an individual, easily hidden in the wide scatter of values in a group of subjects, might be of significance in increasing the fiber length and thus in altering the force of myocardial contraction. Of 25 subjects studied before and after treatment of severe anemia, 17 showed a decreased output when their hemoglobin levels were restored to 10 to 12.5 g. per 100 ml., and this was accompanied by a decrease in filling pressure in the right side of the heart (Roy et al., 1963).

If there is a significant change in filling pressure in anemia, it could, in theory, result from constriction of systemic veins, from increased blood volume or from a combination of both. Sharpey-Schafer (1963) claimed that tone in the veins of the forearm is increased. While the plasma volume may be increased by 30 per cent in chronic severe anemia, the total blood volume is reduced (Backman, 1961). Others have found that the plasma volume is within normal limits or even reduced (Sharpey-Schafer, 1944). Therefore, the increased cardiac output cannot be attributed to hypervolemia. Justus et al. (1957), from animal experiments, suggested that a humoral factor may be involved.

An increase in peripheral blood flow was referred to earlier. Cerebral (Heyman et al., 1952), coronary (Bing and Daley, 1951) and splanchnic (Myers, 1951) blood flows are all increased. In contrast, Bradley and Bradley (1947) found decreases of 44 and 28 per cent in renal blood flow in men and women, respectively. Since the kidneys normally receive blood flow in excess of that required for their nutrition, this reduction in flow may be regarded as a useful adaptation making available additional blood for other organs.

When anemia is acutely induced in anesthetized dogs, and the total blood volume is maintained constant, cardiac output increases reciprocally with the decrease in hematocrit (Fowler et al., 1958; Richardson and Guyton, 1959; Murray et al., 1962). As in man, however, the circulatory adjustments are insufficient to maintain a normal delivery of oxygen to the body tissues. The amount of oxygen reaching the tissue is maximal only when the hematocrit is normal; it is reduced both in polycythemia and anemia (Richardson and Guyton, 1959; Murray et al., 1962). However, when the total blood volume is increased at the same time as the hematocrit is decreased, the filling pressure of the ventricles is increased. This leads to an increase in cardiac output, to which an increase in stroke volume makes the major contribution, sufficient to deliver the normal quantity of red cells to the body (Corcondilas et al., 1964).

HEMODYNAMIC RESPONSE TO EXERCISE. Most of the anemic patients studied by Bishop et al. (1955) had greater increases than normal subjects in cardiac output during exercise. One had a cardiac output of 13 liters per $M.^2$ per minute at an oxygen uptake of about 530 ml. per $M.^2$ per minute. Normal subjects attain comparable outputs only during much more strenuous exercise, with an oxygen uptake two to three times as great. Despite the abnormally great cardiac output in relation to the grade of exercise undertaken, the hemoglobin content of the blood was so low that the coefficient of oxygen utilization (the percentage of arterial oxygen content extracted by the tissues) was increased well above the normal. As with normal persons performing moderate exercise in the supine position, the increase in cardiac output was almost entirely accounted for by an increase in heart rate.

Sproule et al. (1960) found cardiac outputs of 23.4 ± 5.5 liters per minute in 15 normal subjects during exercise at their maximal oxygen uptake of 3.22 ± 0.46 liters per minute. The cardiac output in nine patients with severe anemia was almost identical, 23.6 ± 4.2 liters per minute, but their corresponding maximal oxygen uptake was only 1.84 ± 0.62 liters per minute.

OBESITY

Alexander and his colleagues (1962-1964) made detailed observations of the effects of chronic obesity on the cardiovascular system. Their subjects, mainly women, were aged 22 to 59 years and weighed 40 to 120 Kg. in excess of ideal weights. The total blood volume was increased in proportion to the excess of body weight (Fig. 4-8*A*). Red cells and plasma contributed in the normal proportions, so that the hematocrit was unchanged. Cardiac output was also increased (Fig. 4-8*B*). When the excessive weight was approximately equal to predicted normal weight, blood volume and cardiac output were increased by about 20 and 30 per cent, respectively. Since the resting heart rate was within normal limits, the stroke volume was considerably greater than in non-obese persons of comparable body build and age. The arteriovenous difference in oxygen content was also normal (about 4.5 ml. per 100 ml.); thus, the increase in cardiac output was paralleled by an increase in oxygen consumption.

Cerebral blood flow averaged 58 ml. per 100 g. brain per minute, and oxygen uptake averaged 3.1 ml. per 100 g. brain per minute; both values

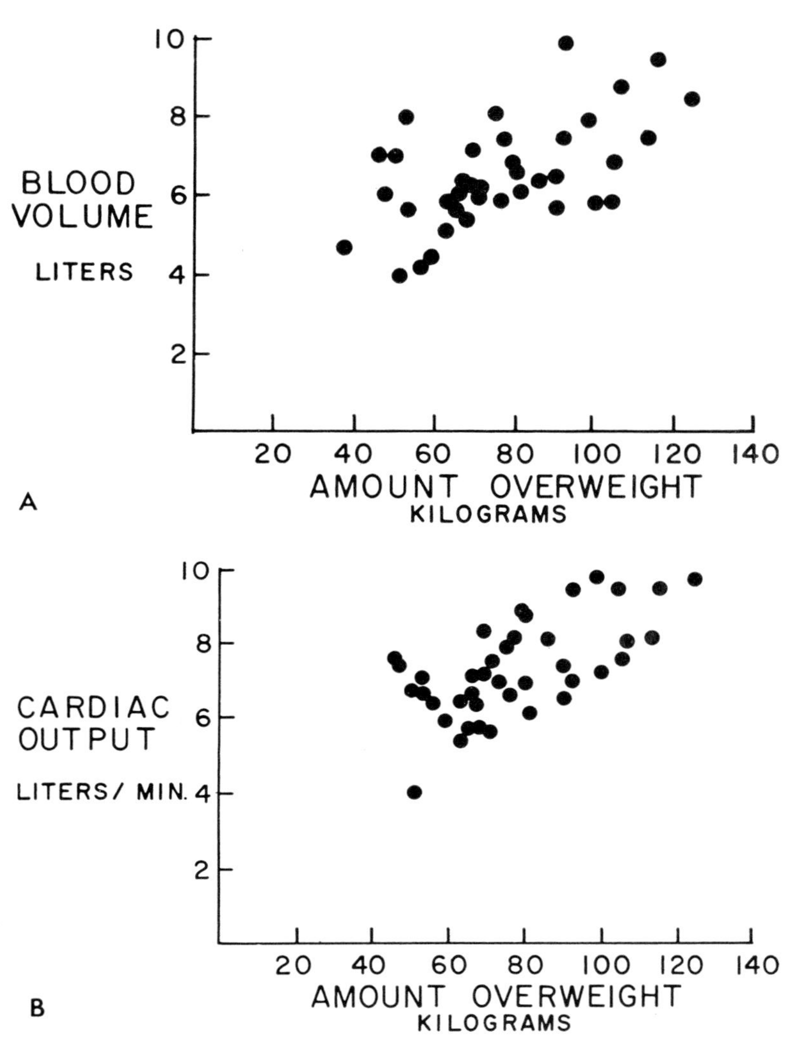

FIGURE 4-8. *A*. Relation between blood volume and excess body weight in 40 extremely obese subjects. *B*. Relation between cardiac output and excess body weight. (From Alexander, Dennis, Smith, Amad, Duncan and Austin, Cardiovasc. Res. Cent. Bull., Baylor Univ. Sch. Med., *1*:39, Winter, 1962-63.)

were normal (Smith and Alexander, 1960). Renal blood flow and glomerular filtration rate were normal. Hepatic blood flow, measured by the sulfobromophthalein extraction method, was increased from 1150 to 1450 ml. per minute; this accounted for only a small fraction of the increase in cardiac output. If it is assumed that muscle blood flow is approximately normal, then it would appear that most of the excessive blood flow is distributed to the fat depots. The fact that the increases in both blood flow and blood volume were relatively small per kilogram of excess weight is consistent with the fact that adipose tissue is much less vascular than most other tissues.

Although some obese persons are hypertensive, others are not, and there is no correlation between mean arterial pressure and body weight. The pulmonary artery pressure is usually normal. In those with increased pressures in the pulmonary artery, the wedge pressure which reflects increased diastolic pressures in the left ventricle is usually increased to a similar degree.

Although the total heart weight is increased, its relative weight is similar to that of non-obese subjects (Amad et al., 1965).

Alveolar hypoventilation is common in extreme obesity and may lead to a syndrome characterized by somnolence, cyanosis, polycythemia, right ventricular hypertrophy and right ventricular failure, sometimes referred to as the *Pickwickian syndrome* (Auchincloss et al., 1955; Sieker et al., 1955; Burwell et al., 1956). In the patients of Sieker et al. (1955), who had Cheyne-Stokes respiration, the arterial oxygen saturation cycled from 90 to 95 per cent at the onset of apnea to 68 to 74 per cent at the onset of breathing. Arterial pCO_2 levels were high. The pulmonary artery pressure was moderately increased, probably secondary to hypoxemia, and the wedge pressure and the cardiac output were normal. The hypoventilation results from the extreme obesity interfering with mechanics of respiration. However, other factors such as chronic lung disease may be contributory, for in many cases the evidence for hypoventilation is slim (Auchincloss and Gilbert, 1959). The syndrome is reversible following adequate loss of weight.

EFFECTS OF EXERCISE. Oxygen consumption and pulmonary ventilation were almost twice as great in extremely obese subjects as in normal

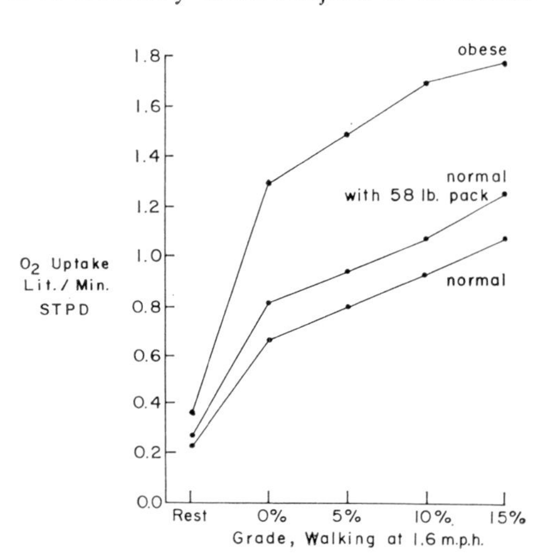

FIGURE 4-9. Oxygen uptake in normal and obese subjects at rest and during treadmill exercise at various grades. (From Turell, Austin and Alexander, J. Lab. Clin. Med., *64*:107, 1964.)

subjects performing identical exercise (Turell et al., 1964; Fig. 4-9). Mechanical efficiency and oxygen debt in relation to oxygen consumption during exercise were similar in the two groups. In 39 of 40 very obese subjects, the relation between changes in oxygen uptake and cardiac output with exercise was normal. The mean increase in cardiac output per 100 ml. increase in total oxygen consumption was 966 ml. per minute. For comparable increments in oxygen uptake, the obese subjects had higher rates of breathing and lower tidal volumes. Since excessively high respiratory rates for a given minute ventilation result in disproportionate augmentation of dead space ventilation, alveolar hypoventilation during exercise is at least a theoretical possibility in some obese subjects. It could cause slight reductions in alveolar oxygen tension in the first two minutes of exercise. During the steady state of exercise, however, obese subjects increase their ventilation sufficiently to maintain normal alveolar carbon dioxide tensions (Auchincloss et al., 1963).

INACTIVITY

Donald et al. (1953) studied the effects in 36 subjects of altering the posture in bed. In the supine position, the cardiac output averaged 5.9 liters per minute. When the subjects were propped up at a 70 degree angle, it averaged 5.6 liters per minute. This change, although statistically significant, was unlikely to be of clinical importance. Changes in stroke volume, from 69 to 62 ml., and in heart rate, from 87 to 90 beats per minute, were also small.

Interest in the effects of prolonged rest on the heart and circulation stems from problems of convalescence (Browse, 1965) and from the prospect of prolonged flight in space, free from gravitational stress. The major loss of performance in the six healthy subjects studied by Taylor et al. (1949) before, during and after three to four weeks of almost complete rest in bed was in relation to the cardiovascular system. The heart volume (measured by roentgenkymography) decreased by 17 per cent. The cardiac output at rest was unchanged. The resting pulse rate increased by an average of 0.5 beat per minute for each day of bed rest. The pulse rate after walking for half an hour at 3.5 m.p.h. on a 10 per cent grade was 40 beats per minute more after the bed rest than it was previously. Tolerance to 68 degree passive head up tilt, judged by changes in heart rate and systolic arterial pressure, was decreased, although fainting did not occur (Table 4-4). Miller et al. (1964) found that after four weeks of complete bed rest, there was an average decrease of 550 ml. in plasma volume and 180 ml. in red cell mass. In conformity with the findings of Taylor et al. (1949), there was a lack of correlation between the decreases of blood volume and of orthostatic tolerance.

Deitrich et al. (1948) obtained similar results in four healthy young

TABLE 4-4. Mean Values for Pulse Rate and Systolic Blood Pressure in Six Men When Supine and Tilted to 68° Before and After Bed Rest*

CONDITION	MEASUREMENT	CONTROL	DAYS AFTER BED REST					
			1	2	8	9	15	16
Supine		51	65	62	58	57	61	60
Tilted	Pulse Rate	64	102	89	90	86	84	81
Difference	(beats/min.)	13	37	27	32	29	23	21
Supine		113	120	113	115	110	114	110
Tilted	Systolic B.P.	113	106	109	109	109	107	108
Difference	(mm. Hg)	0	14	4	6	1	7	2

* Adapted from Taylor, Henschel, Brozek and Keys, J. Appl. Physiol., *2*:223, 1949.

men immobilized for prolonged periods. Birkhead et al. (1963) kept their subjects horizontal for 40 days, although arm and leg movements were permitted. Subsequently, exercise tolerance was impaired and, for any given exercise, the cardiac output was greater than previously. As the work load increased, the stroke volume became less, and the heart rate was excessively high.

Prolonged immersion in water, like bed rest, decreases tolerance for tilting, for headward acceleration and for exercise (Graybiel and Clark, 1961; Graveline, 1962; Benson et al., 1962).

REFERENCES

Abboud, F. M., and Eckstein, J. W.: Reflex vasoconstrictor and vasodilator responses in man. Circ. Research, *18* (Suppl. I):96, 1966.

Abrahams, V. C., Hilton, S. M., and Zbrosyna, A.: Active muscle vasodilatation produced by stimulation of the brain stem: its significance in the defense reaction. J. Physiol., *154*:491, 1960.

Adams, J. Q.: Cardiovascular physiology in normal pregnancy: Studies with dye dilution technique. Am. J. Obst. Gyn., *67*:741, 1954.

Alexander, J. K.: Obesity and cardiac performance. Am. J. Cardiol., *14*:860, 1964.

Alexander, J. K.: Obesity and the Circulation. Mod. Concepts Cardiovasc. Dis., *32*:799, 1963.

Alexander, J. K., Dennis, E. W., Smith, W. G., Amad, K. H., Duncan, W. C., and Austin, R. C.: Blood volume, cardiac output and distribution of systemic blood flow in extreme obesity. Cardiovasc. Res. Cent. Bull. Baylor Univ. Sch. Med., *1*:39, Winter, 1962-63.

Amad, K. H., Brennan, J. C., and Alexander, J. K.: The cardiac pathology of chronic exogenous obesity. Circulation, *32*:740, 1965.

Anderson, D. P., Allen, W. J., Barcroft, H., Edholm, O. G., and Manning, G. W.: Circulatory changes during fainting and coma caused by oxygen lack. J. Physiol., *104*:426, 1946.

Assali, N. S., Rauramo, L., and Peltonen, T.: Measurement of uterine blood flow and uterine metabolism. VIII. Uterine and fetal blood flow and oxygen consumption in early human pregnancy. Am. J. Obst. Gyn., *79*:86, 1960.

Auchincloss, J. H., Jr., Cook, E., and Renzetti, A. D.: Clinical and physiological aspects of a case of obesity, polycythemia and alveolar hypoventilation. J. Clin. Invest., *34*:1537, 1955.

Auchincloss, J. H., Jr., and Gilbert, R.: The cardio-respiratory syndrome related to obesity: Clinical manifestations and pathologic physiology. Prog. Cardiovasc. Dis., *1*:423, 1959.

Auchincloss, J. H., Jr., Sipple, J., and Gilbert, R.: Effect of obesity on ventilatory adjustment to exercise. J. Appl. Physiol., *18*:19, 1963.

Backman, H.: Circulatory studies in slowly developing anaemias. Scand. J. Clin. Lab. Invest., *13*:1, 1961.

Bader, R. A., Bader, M. E., Rose, D. J., and Braunwald, E.: Hemodynamics at rest and during exercise in normal pregnancy as studied by cardiac catheterization. J. Clin. Invest., *34*:1524, 1955.

Barcroft, H., Brod, J., Hejl, Z., Hirsjärvi, E. A., and Kitchin, A. H.: The mechanism of the vasodilatation in the forearm muscle during stress (mental arithmetic). Clin. Sci., *19*:577, 1960.

Barcroft, H., and Edholm, O. G.: On the vasodilatation in human skeletal muscle during posthaemorrhagic fainting. J. Physiol., *104*:161, 1945.

Barcroft, H., Edholm, O. G., McMichael, J., and Sharpey-Schafer, E. P.: Posthaemorrhagic fainting. Study by cardiac output and forearm flow. Lancet, *i*: 489, 1944.

Barcroft, H., and Swan, H. J. C.: Sympathetic Control of Human Blood Vessels. London, Arnold, 1953.

Bearn, A. G., Billing, B., Edholm, O. G., and Sherlock, S.: Hepatic blood flow and carbohydrate changes in man during fainting. J. Physiol., *115*:442, 1951.

Benson, V. G., Beckman, E. L., Coburn, K. R., and Chambers, R. M.: Effects of weightlessness as simulated by total body immersion upon human response to positive acceleration. Aerospace Med., *33*:198, 1962.

Bing, R. J., and Daley, R.: Behavior of the myocardium in health and disease as studied by coronary sinus catheterization. Am. J. Med., *10*:711, 1951.

Birkhead, N. C., Blizzard, J. J., Daly, J. W., Haupt, G. J., Issekutz, B., Jr., Myers, R. N., and Rodahl, K.: Cardiodynamic and metabolic effects of prolonged bed rest. Technical Documentary Report No. AMRL-TDR:63-37, May, 1963.

Bishop, J. M., Donald, K. W., and Wade, O. L.: Circulatory dynamics at rest and on exercise in the hyperkinetic states. Clin. Sci., *14*:329, 1955.

Blair, D. A., Glover, W. E., Greenfield, A. D. M., and Roddie, I. C.: Excitation of cholinergic vasodilator nerves to human skeletal muscles during emotional stress. J. Physiol., *148*:633, 1959.

Bradley, S. E., and Bradley, G. P.: Renal function during chronic anemia in man. Blood, *2*:192, 1947.

Brigden, W., Howarth, S., and Sharpey-Schafer, E. P.: Postural changes in the peripheral blood flow of normal subjects with observations on vasovagal fainting reactions as a result of tilting, the lordotic posture, pregnancy and spinal anaesthesia. Clin. Sci., *9*:79, 1950.

Brod. J.: Coordination of circulation during emotion. Proc. Internat. Union Physiol. Sci., XXIII Internat. Congress, *IV*:157, 1965.

Brod, J., Fencl, V., Hejl, Z., and Jirka, J.: Circulatory changes underlying blood pressure elevation during acute emotional stress (mental arithmetic) in normotensive and hypertensive subjects. Clin. Sci. *18*:269, 1959.

Browse, N. L.: Effect of bed rest on resting calf blood flow of healthy adult males. Brit. Med. J., *i*:1721, 1962.

Browse, N. L.: The Physiology and Pathology of Bed Rest. Springfield, Thomas, 1965.

Brun, C., Knudson, E. O. E., and Raaschou, F.: Kidney function and circulatory collapse, post-syncopal oliguria. J. Clin. Invest., *25*:568, 1946.

Burnum, J. F., Hickam, J. B., and McIntosh, H. D.: The effect of hypocapnia on arterial blood pressure. Circulation, *9*:89, 1954.

Burwell, C. S., Robin, E. D., Whaley, R. D., and Bickelmann, A. G.: Extreme obesity associated with alveolar hypoventilation—a Pickwickian syndrome. Am. J. Med., *21*:811, 1956.

Caton, W. L., Roby, C. C., Reid, D. E., Caswell, R., Maletskos, C. J., Fluharty, R. G., and Gibson, J. G., II: The circulating red cell volume and body hematocrit in

normal pregnancy and the puerperium: by direct measurement using radioactive red cells. Am. J. Obst. Gyn., *61*:1207, 1951.
Chesley, L. C., and Sloan, D. M.: Effect of posture on renal function in late pregnancy. Am. J. Obst. Gyn., *89*:754, 1964.
Coggins, C. H., Lillington, G. A., and Gray, C. P.: Micturition syncope. Arch. Int. Med., *113*:14, 1964.
Corcondilas, A., Donald, D. E., and Shepherd, J. T.: Influence of blood volume on cardiovascular response to anemia in the dog. Proc. Soc. Exp. Biol. Med., *117*: 661, 1964.
Deitrich, J. E., Whedon, G. D., and Shorr, E.: The effects of immobilization on various metabolic and physiologic functions of normal men. Am. J. Med., *4*:3, 1948.
de Wardener, H. E., and McSwiney, R. R.: Renal haemodynamics in vaso-vagal fainting due to haemorrhage. Clin. Sci., *10*:209, 1951.
de Wardener, H. E., Miles, B. E., Lee, G. de J., Churchill-Davidson, H., Wylie, D., and Sharpey-Schafer, E. P.: Circulatory effects of haemorrhage during prolonged light anaesthesia in man. Clin. Sci., *12*:175, 1953.
Donald, K. W., Bishop, J. M., Cumming, G., and Wade, O. L.: The effect of nursing positions on the cardiac output in man. Clin. Sci., *12*:199, 1953.
Dreyfuss, F., and Czaczkes, J. W.: Blood cholesterol and uric acid of healthy medical students under stress of an examination. A.M.A. Arch. Int. Med., *103*:708, 1959.
Eichna, L. W., Horvath, S. M., and Bean, W. B.: Post-exertional orthostatic hypotension. Am. J. Med. Sci., *213*:641, 1947.
Finnerty, F. A., Jr., Witkin, L., and Fazekas, J. F.: Cerebral hemodynamics during cerebral ischemia induced by acute hypotension. J. Clin. Invest., *33*:1227, 1954.
Foster, M.: A Textbook of Physiology. Fifth edition. London, Macmillan, 1888.
Fowler, N. O., Bloom, W. L., and Ward, J. A.: Hemodynamic effects of hypervolemia with and without anemia. Circ. Research., *6*:163, 1958.
Gastaut, H., and Fischer-Williams, M.: Electroencephalographic study of syncope. Lancet, *ii*:1018, 1957.
Graham, J. D. P.: High blood pressure after battle. Lancet, *i*:239, 1945.
Graveline, D. E.: Maintenance of cardiovascular adaptability during prolonged weightlessness. Aerospace Med., *33*:297, 1962.
Graybiel, A., and Clark, B.: Symptoms resulting from prolonged immersion in water. The problem of zero G asthenia. Aerospace Med., *32*:181, 1961.
Greenfield, A. D. M.: Emotional faint. Lancet, *i*:1302, 1951.
Greenfield, A. D. M.: Survey of the evidence for active neurogenic vasodilatation in man. Fed. Proc., *25*:1607, 1966.
Grundy, S. M., and Griffin, A. C.: Effects of periodic mental stress on serum cholesterol levels. Circulation, *19*:496, 1959.
Haley, H. B., and Woodbury, J. W.: Body composition and body water metabolism in normal pregnancy. Surg. Gyn. Obst., *103*:227, 1956.
Hamilton, H. F. H.: Symposium on haemodynamics in pregnancy. 1. Cardiac output in pregnancy. Trans. Edinb. Obst. Soc., Session 102, 1, 1949.
Hamilton, W. F., Woodbury, R. A., and Harper, H. T., Jr.: Arterial, cerebrospinal and venous pressures in man during cough and strain. Am. J. Physiol., *141*:42, 1944.
Harris, W. S., Schoenfeld, C. D., Gwynne, P. H., Weissler, A. M., and Warren, J. V.: Observations on the cardiovascular response to fear and anger. Circulation, *30* (Supplement III):92, 1964 (Abstract).
Hartwell, A. S., Burrett, J. B., Graybiel, A. B., and White, P. D.: The effect of exercise and four commonly used drugs on the normal human electrocardiogram, with particular reference to T wave changes. J. Clin. Invest., *21*:409, 1942.
Harvey, W. P., and Levine, S. A.: Paroxysmal ventricular tachycardia due to emotion. J.A.M.A., *150*:479, 1952.

Heyman, A., Patterson, J. L., and Duke, T. W.: Cerebral circulation and metabolism in sickle cell and other chronic anemias, with observations on effect of oxygen inhalation. J. Clin. Invest., *31*:824, 1952.

Howard, B. K., Goodson, J. H., and Mengert, W. F.: Supine hypotensive syndrome in late pregnancy. Obst. Gyn., *1*:371, 1953.

Howard, P., Leathart, G. L., Dornhorst, A. C., and Sharpey-Schafer, E. P.: The "mess trick" and the "fainting lark." Brit. Med. J., *ii*:382, 1951.

Hytten, F. E., and Paintin, D. B.: Increase in plasma volume during normal pregnancy. J. Obst. Gyn. Brit. Cwlth., *70*:402, 1963.

Justus, D. W., Cornett, R. W., and Hatcher, J. D.: A humoral influence on cardiovascular adjustment to acute and chronic post hemorrhagic anemia in dogs. Circ. Research., *5*:207, 1957.

Keatinge, W. R., McIlroy, M. B., and Goldfien, A.: Cardiovascular responses to ice-cold showers. J. Appl. Physiol., *19*:1145, 1964.

Kerr, A., Jr., and Eich, R. A.: Cerebral concussion as a cause of cough syncope. A.M.A. Arch. Int. Med., *108*:138, 1961.

Kerr, M. G., Scott, D. B., and Samuel, E.: Studies of the inferior vena cava in late pregnancy. Brit. Med. J., *i*:532, 1964.

Kety, S. S., and Schmidt, C. F.: The effects of active and passive hyperventilation on cerebral blood flow, cerebral oxygen consumption, cardiac output and blood pressure of normal young men. J. Clin. Invest., *25*:107, 1946.

Klein, L. J., Saltzman, H. A., Heyman, A., and Sieker, H. O.: Syncope induced by the Valsalva maneuver. A study of the effects of arterial blood gas tensions, glucose concentration and blood pressure. Am. J. Med., *37*:263, 1964.

Lees, M. M., Scott, D. B., Kerr, M. G., and Taylor, S. H.: The circulatory effects of recumbent postural change in late pregnancy. Clin. Sci., *32*:453, 1967.

Lewis, T.: A lecture on vaso-vagal syncope and the carotid sinus mechanism with comments on Gower's and Nothnagel's syndrome. Brit. Med. J., *i*:873, 1932.

Löfving, B.: Cardiovascular adjustments induced from the rostral cingulate gyrus with special reference to sympatho-inhibitory mechanisms. Acta Physiol. Scand., Suppl. 184:1, 1961.

Lyle, C. B., Jr., Monroe, J. T., Jr., Flinn, D. E., and Lamb, L. E.: Micturition syncope. Report of 24 cases. New Eng. J. Med., *265*:982, 1961.

Lysgaard, H., and Lefèvre, H.: Myometrial blood flow in pregnancy measured with $Xenon^{133}$. Acta Obst. Gynec. Scand., *44*:401, 1965.

MacDonald, A.: The Bearings of Chronic Disease of the Heart Upon Pregnancy, Parturition and Childbed. London, Churchill, 1878.

Marshall, R. J., Schirger, A., and Shepherd, J. T.: Blood pressure during supine exercise in idiopathic orthostatic hypotension. Circulation, *24*:76, 1961.

McIntosh, H. D., Estes, E. H., and Warren, J. V.: The mechanism of cough syncope. Am. Heart J., *52*:70, 1956.

Metcalfe, J., Romney, S. L., Ramsey, L. H., Reid, D. E., and Burwell, C. S.: Estimation of uterine blood flow in normal human pregnancy at term. J. Clin. Invest., *34*:1632, 1955.

Miller, P. B., Johnson, R. L., and Lamb, L. E.: Effects of four weeks of absolute bed rest on circulatory functions in man. Aerospace Med., *35*:1194, 1964.

Muldowney, F. P., and Flanagan, B.: The body-haematocrit:venous haematocrit ratio in normal human pregnancy. Clin. Sci., *27*:329, 1964.

Murray, J. F., Gold, P., and Johnson, B. L., Jr.: Systemic oxygen transport in induced normovolemic anemia and polycythemia. Am. J. Physiol., *203*:720, 1962.

Myers, J. D.: Effects of anemia on hepatic blood flow and splanchnic metabolism. Am. J. Med., *11*:248, 1951.

Noble, R. L., and Taylor, N. B. G.: Antidiuretic substances in human urine after haemorrhage, fainting, dehydration and acceleration. J. Physiol., *122*:220, 1953.

Pugh, L. G. C. E., and Wyndham, C. H.: The circulatory effects of high spinal anaesthesia in hypertensive and control subjects. Clin. Sci., *9*:189, 1950.

Richardson, T. Q., and Guyton, A. C.: Effect of polycythemia and anemia on cardiac output and other circulatory factors. Am. J. Physiol., *197*:1167, 1959.

Roy, S. B., Bhatia, M. L., Mathur, V. S., and Virmani, S.: Hemodynamic effects of chronic severe anemia. Circulation, *28*:346, 1963.

Samueloff, S. L., Bevegård, B. S., and Shepherd, J. T.: Temporary arrest of circulation to a limb for the study of venomotor reactions in man. J. Appl. Physiol., *21*:341, 1966.

Scott, D. B., and Kerr, M. G.: Inferior vena caval pressure in late pregnancy. J. Obst. Gyn. Brit. Cwlth., *70*:1044, 1963.

Semler, H. J.: Cardiac disorders during acute emotional stress. Circulation, *32* (Suppl. II):192, 1965 (Abstract).

Sharpey-Schafer, E. P.: Cardiac output in severe anemia. Clin. Sci., *5*:125, 1944.

Sharpey-Schafer, E. P.: Effect of respiratory acts on the circulation. In: Handbook of Physiology. Section 2: Circulation, Volume 3, Washington, D.C., American Physiological Society, 1965.

Sharpey-Schafer, E. P.: Effects of coughing on intra-thoracic pressure, arterial pressure and peripheral blood flow. J. Physiol., *122*:351, 1953B.

Sharpey-Schafer, E. P.: Mechanism of syncope after coughing. Brit. Med. J., *ii*:860, 1953A.

Sharpey-Schafer, E. P.: Venous tone: effects of reflex changes, humoral agents and exercise. Brit. Med. Bull., *19*:145, 1963.

Sieker, H. O., Estes, E. H., Jr., Kelser, G. A., and McIntosh, H. D.: A cardiopulmonary syndrome associated with extreme obesity. J. Clin. Invest., *34*:916, 1955.

Smith, W. G., and Alexander, J. K.: Cerebral haemodynamics and oxygen utilization in extreme obesity. Clin. Sci., *20*:33, 1960.

Snell, E. S., Cranston, W. I., and Gerbrandy, J.: Cutaneous vasodilatation during fainting. Lancet, *i*:693, 1955.

Sokoloff, L., Mangold, R., Weihsler, R. L., Kennedy, C. H., and Kety, S. S.: The effect of mental arithmetic on cerebral circulation and metabolism. J. Clin. Invest., *34*:1101, 1955.

Sproule, B. J., Mitchell, J. H., and Miller, W. F.: Cardiopulmonary physiological response to heavy exercise in patients with anemia. J. Clin. Invest., *39*:378, 1960.

Stampfer, M., Epstein, S. E., and Beiser, G. D.: Arterial and venous responses during vasovagal syncope. Physiologist *10*:313, 1967 (Abstract).

Stevenson, I. P., Duncan, C. H., and Ripley, H. S.: Variations in the electrocardiogram changes in emotional states. Geriatrics, *6*:164, 1951.

Taylor, H. L., Henschel, A., Brozek, J., and Keys, A.: Effects of bed rest on cardiovascular function and work performance. J. Appl. Physiol., *2*:223, 1949.

Thomas, C. B., and Murphy, E. A.: Further studies on cholesterol levels in the Johns Hopkins medical students: effect of stress at examinations. J. Chron. Dis., *8*:661, 1958.

Thomson, K. J., Hirsheimer, A., Gibson, J. G., II, and Evans, W. A., Jr.: Studies on the circulation in pregnancy. III. Blood volume changes in normal pregnant women. Am. J. Obst. Gyn., *36*:48, 1938.

Turell, D. J., Austin, R. C., and Alexander, J. K.: Cardiorespiratory response of very obese subjects to treadmill exercise. J. Lab. Clin. Med., *64*:107, 1964.

Uvnäs, B.: Sympathetic vasodilator outflow. Physiol. Rev., *34*:608, 1954.

Verel, D., and Duff, R. S.: Circulatory adjustments of voluntary muscle in anemia. J. Appl. Physiol., *14*:225, 1959.

Wade, O. L., and Bishop, J. M.: Cardiac Output and Regional Blood Flow. Oxford, Blackwell, 1962.

Walters, W. A. W., MacGregor, W. G., and Hills, M.: Cardiac output at rest during pregnancy and the puerperium. Clin. Sci., *30*:1, 1966.

Weissler, A. M., Leonard, J. J., and Warren, J. V.: Effect of posture and atropine on the cardiac output. J. Clin. Invest., *36*:1656, 1957B.

Weissler, A. M., Warren, J. V., Estes, E. H., Jr., McIntosh, H. D., and Leonard, J. J.: Vasodepressor syncope. Factors influencing cardiac output. Circulation, *15*:875, 1957A.

Werkö, L.: Pregnancy and heart disease. Acta Obst. Gyn. Scand., 33:162, 1954.

White, R.: Symposium on haemodynamics in pregnancy. III. Blood volume in pregnancy. Trans. Edinb. Obst. Soc., Session 102, 14, 1949.

Wolf, S., Cardon, P. V., Jr., Shepard, E. M., and Wolff, H. G.: Life Stress and Essential Hypertension: A Study of Circulatory Adjustments in Man. Baltimore, Williams and Wilkins, 1955.

Wolf, S., McCabe, W. R., Yamamoto, J., Adsett, C. A., and Schottstaedt, W. W.: Changes in serum lipids in relation to emotional stress during rigid control of diet and exercise. Circulation, 25:379, 1962.

Chapter 5

CARDIOVASCULAR REFLEXES

- Nervous Control of the Resting Heart Rate
- Carotid and Aortic Mechanoreceptors
- Systemic Arterial Chemoreceptors
- Cardiac Receptors
- Pulmonary Receptors

The baroreceptor function of the carotid sinus was described by Hering in 1923. Many studies have subsequently been conducted in animals on the site, structure, reflex connections and functions of receptors concerned in cardiovascular reflexes (Heymans and Neil, 1958). These receptors can be classified as the systemic arterial, cardiac and pulmonary mechano- and chemoreceptors.

Since complex surgical preparations are necessary to isolate one set of receptors and their reflex connections, opportunities for their study in man are rare. Therefore, reference will be made in this chapter to some related work in animals in order to illustrate the multiplicity and complexity of the cardiovascular reflexes which may contribute to the hemodynamic responses to a given stimulus.

NERVOUS CONTROL OF THE RESTING HEART RATE

Carlsten et al. (1957) studied the effect of direct stimulation of the vagus nerve in man at maximal strength and increasing frequencies, after the normal discharge of the fibers to the heart had been blocked by a local anesthetic solution. A plot of the frequency of stimulation against the heart rate or blood pressure gave a hyperbolic curve, typical of autonomic neuroeffectors with a nearly maximal effect at 10 impulses per second. This suggested that vagal tone under normal conditions is maintained by a relatively low frequency. Their observations also suggested that the vagal fibers do not exert a negative inotropic effect on the ventricles. Vagal stimulation does, however, increase the refractory period of the atrioventricular conduction system (Linhart et al., 1965).

Robinson et al. (1966) studied the control of heart rate by the autonomic nervous system in conscious man by observing the effects of beta-adrenergic blockade with propranolol and of parasympathetic blockade with atropine. In resting subjects, during either sympathetic or parasympathetic blockade alone, the heart rate increased when the systemic arterial pressure was decreased below control values and slowed when the pressure was increased. It appeared, therefore, that the relative roles of the sympathetic and parasympathetic systems in mediating a change in the heart rate of resting subjects are nearly equal.

CAROTID AND AORTIC MECHANORECEPTORS

The carotid sinus nerve was stimulated directly in man during operations in the neck (Carlsten et al., 1958). This caused reflex bradycardia and a decrease in the systemic arterial blood pressure. Maximal responses to stimulation were obtained with frequencies of 40 to 60 impulses per second.

Studies of the potential value of electrical stimulation of the mechanoreceptors in the carotid sinus in the treatment of hypertension have recently been undertaken in animals and man. Griffith and Schwartz (1964) found that prolonged stimulation of a carotid sinus nerve in hypertensive dogs with transection of the contralateral nerve resulted in a return of pressure to prehypertensive control levels; in normotensive animals, the reduction of pressure was slight and transient. During prolonged stimulation by an implanted radiofrequency stimulator, the cardiac output in dogs made hypertensive by encasing the kidneys in plastic bags was reduced by 38 per cent and the diastolic blood pressure, by 33 per cent (mean values) (Neistadt and Schwartz, 1966). Parsonnet et al. (1966) found that responsiveness was lost in the course of long term stimulation of the sinus nerve. Tuckman et al. (1966) implanted stimulators in three patients with accelerated hypertension. In the supine position, the mean arterial blood pressure was reduced from 156 to 125 mm. Hg and the heart rate, from 92 to 69 per minute, while the cardiac output decreased by 14 per cent and the peripheral resistance, by seven per cent. Renal function was not depressed. The long term effects of mechanoreceptor stimulation are unknown.

The carotid arterial mechanoreceptors can also be stimulated in man by decreasing the pressure in a box enclosing the neck (Ernsting and Parry, 1957; Bevegård and Shepherd, 1966). Since the arteries traversing the neck are in free communication with the aorta when blood is flowing, the intravascular pressures are unchanged immediately after the application of subatmospheric pressure; therefore, the pressure difference across the walls of the vessels is increased. When the pressure in the box surrounding the neck is lowered in steps, the heart rate and systemic arterial pressure decrease in an almost rectilinear manner (Fig. 5-1). These effects

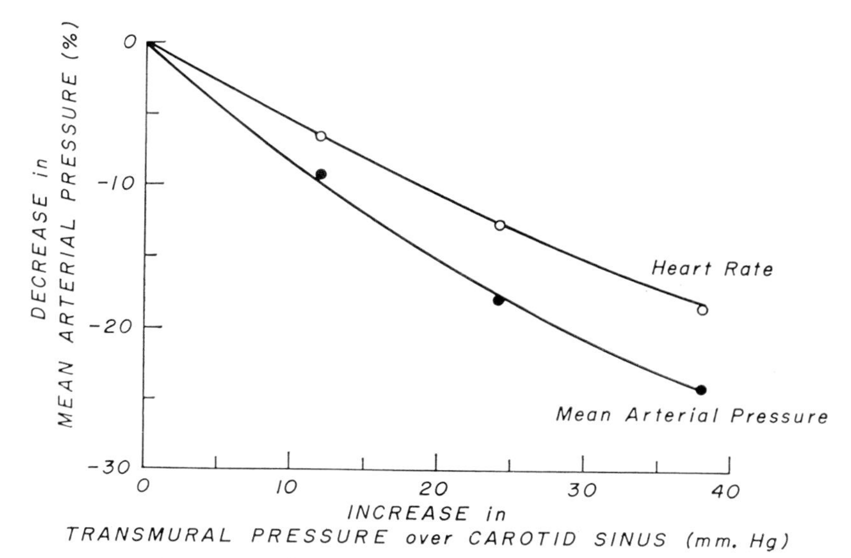

FIGURE 5-1. Percentage changes of heart rate and mean systemic arterial pressure as functions of increasing transmural pressure over the carotid sinus: mean values from six normal resting subjects. (From Bevegård and Shepherd, J. Clin. Invest., *45*:132, 1966.)

are sustained for the duration of the increase in transmural pressure; thus, there seems to be little buffering effect from other baroreceptor areas. The decreases in heart rate and blood pressure are accompanied by a proportionate decrease in cardiac output and by dilatation of the resistance vessels in the forearm (Table 5-1). After the injection of atropine, the response of the heart rate is abolished, but that of the blood pressure is unaffected. The former is therefore mediated by the vagus, while the latter is due mainly to reduction of sympathetic constrictor impulses to the systemic resistance vessels. As yet, there are no studies of changes in vascular beds other than the forearm in response to changes in carotid sinus pressure.

When the activity of the carotid sinus mechanoreceptors is decreased in man by compression of both common carotid arteries low in the neck, the systemic arterial blood pressure increases. Surprisingly, a decrease in the caliber of the resistance vessels in the hand or forearm does not contribute to the increase of pressure (Roddie and Shepherd, 1957). However, changes in the resistance of other vascular beds have not been studied, nor has the cardiac output been measured.

It is believed by some that in animals, a decrease of pressure in the carotid sinus, by causing a widespread constriction of systemic veins, results in an increase in cardiac output which contributes to the increase in systemic arterial blood pressure (Heymans and Neil, 1958). However, others showed that there was no significant change in cardiac output in

TABLE 5-1. Some Effects of Carotid Sinus Stimulation in Resting Subjects*

CONDITION	HEART RATE	ARTERIAL B.P. (MEAN)	CARDIAC OUTPUT	STROKE VOLUME
	/min.	mm. Hg	L./min.	ml.
Control	68	88	6.4	101
−20 mm. Hg suction	63	80	5.9	98
Control	69	89	5.8	94
−40 mm. Hg suction	60	73	5.2	94
Control	69	91	5.9	96
−60 mm. Hg suction	57	69	5.2	97

* Adapted from data of Bevegård and Shepherd, J. Clin. Invest., *45*:132, 1966.

dogs, cats or rabbits during bilateral carotid arterial occlusion, at a time when the systemic arterial pressure was markedly increased, and they concluded that the increased pressure was due solely to reflex constriction of the resistance vessels caused by increased activity of their efferent sympathetic adrenergic fibers (Corcondilas et al., 1964). Observations on the limb veins in animals (Browse et al., 1966) and man (Bevegård and Shepherd, 1966) have shown that if the veins respond at all to changes in carotid sinus pressure, they do so to a minor degree; the major changes occur in the sympathetic nerves to the resistance vessels and the heart. The inotropic effect of increased activity of the cardiac sympathetic nerves caused by a decrease in carotid sinus pressure helps to maintain cardiac output in the face of the increased systemic vascular resistance.

Bevegård and Shepherd (1966) stimulated the carotid sinus by applying subatmospheric pressure to the neck during supine leg exercise. As the heart rate and systemic arterial blood pressure increased with the exercise, the absolute decreases in these measurements resulting from the suction were the same as at rest; the percentage decreases were less. As in resting subjects, the decrease in systemic pressure was accounted for by a moderate decrease in cardiac output and by active dilatation of the resistance vessels, at least in the inactive limbs. Since leg exercise reflexly constricts resistance vessels in forearm muscle (see page 53), the reflex vasodilatation resulting from carotid sinus stimulation can be more convincingly demonstrated during exercise than at rest. While the carotid sinus mechanism, through negative feedback, continues to oppose the increases in heart rate and blood pressure during exercise, its effects are overcome by the stimulus of exercise; therefore, the net result is an increase in both heart rate and blood pressure. The carotid sinus mechanism is less effective in opposing the increase in heart rate than that in blood pressure. It thus appears that the sensitivity of the arterial mechanoreceptor system to induced changes in pressure does not undergo any substantial alteration in the transition from rest to exercise. At any given level of arterial blood pressure, the heart rate is higher than at rest, but when arterial pressure is changed, the magnitude of the alteration in heart rate is similar under both conditions.

Although activity of the carotid sinus mechanoreceptors does not initiate the changes in the circulation during exercise, it may be regarded as providing the feedback necessary for regulating cardiac performance so that the output of the heart is precisely adjusted to the decrease in systemic vascular resistance, and so to the metabolic demands (Robinson et al., 1966).

Reflex constriction of the capacity vessels, in combination with the muscle pump, is important for maintaining adequate filling of the heart during exercise (see page 53). Since increasing the pressure in the carotid sinus does not cause any opposing reflex dilatation of veins, to oppose the reflex constriction induced by muscular exercise, the beneficial effect of reflex venoconstriction persists during exercise, regardless of the increase in systemic arterial blood pressure.

SYSTEMIC ARTERIAL CHEMORECEPTORS

The first of the peripheral chemoreceptor reflexogenic zones was discovered by Heymans and Heymans (1927). However, measurements of the reflex effect of chemoreceptor stimulation on the cardiac output and systemic vascular resistance have been made only recently (Daly and Scott, 1962). Daly and Ungar (1966) isolated the carotid and aortic bodies in dogs and perfused them separately with blood, the composition of which could be controlled. Stimulation of the carotid bodies in spontaneously breathing animals by hypoxic hypercapnic blood caused small and variable changes in systemic vascular resistance, whereas stimulation of the aortic bodies invariably increased the vascular resistance. When pulmonary ventilation was maintained constant, stimulation of the carotid bodies consistently increased the systemic vascular resistance. These constrictor responses represent the primary vascular effects of chemoreceptor stimulation. In the spontaneously breathing animal, the vasoconstrictor response from the carotid bodies is opposed by a pneumogenic vasodilator reflex initiated by the concomitant hyperpnea. Since the respiratory effects of aortic body stimulation are relatively weak, the primary vasoconstrictor response predominates.

The effects of hypoxia and hypercapnia on the cardiovascular system of normal man have been studied (see Chapter 3), but the responses are so complex that the primary roles of the aortic and carotid chemoreceptors cannot be analyzed.

CARDIAC RECEPTORS

Receptors have been described in the walls of the superior and in-

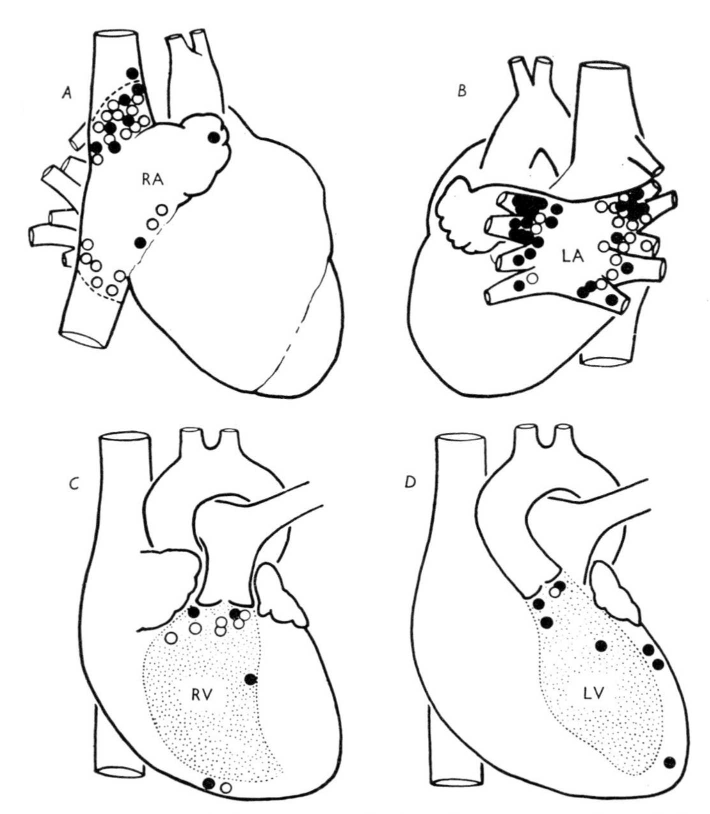

FIGURE 5-2. Diagrams of the position of 92 cardiac receptors located by electrophysiological means in dogs. Each receptor is indicated by a circle; open circle, afferent fiber in right vagus; filled circle, afferent fiber in left vagus. *A*, right lateral view of the heart; *B*, posterior view; *C*, *D*, anterior view. The receptors were distributed as follows: *A*, right atriovenous region, 28; *B*, left atriovenous region, 45; *C*, right ventricle, 11; *D*, left ventricle, 8. Only those ventricular receptors which had a cardiac rhythm are depicted in this diagram. In *A*, the interrupted line indicates the attachment of the pericardium. In *C* and *D*, the stippling represents the cavities of the right and left ventricles, respectively. (From Coleridge, Coleridge and Kidd, J. Physiol., *174*:323, 1964.)

ferior venae cavae at their junctions with the right atrium, at the tricuspid valve orifice, in the pulmonary veins or the adjacent parts of the posterior wall of the left atrium, in the ventricles and in the main coronary arteries (Fig. 5-2). All the afferent fibers coming from these receptors are contained in the cervical vagus (Coleridge et al., 1957, 1964A).

Type A atrial receptors increase their rate of discharge during atrial systole, and type B are said to discharge only during atrial filling (Paintal, 1953). It has been suggested that the former respond to changes in pressure and the latter to atrial distention; however, according to the state of venous filling of the heart, the type A discharge can be converted into a type B and vice versa (Neil and Joels, 1961).

Attempts have been made to relate changes in pressure and distention of the atria and large veins to changes in heart rate and arterial blood pressure. Intravenous infusions of blood or saline may cause an increase in the heart rate of both anesthetized and conscious dogs (Bainbridge, 1915; Coleridge and Linden, 1955; Jones, 1962). This was attributed by Bainbridge (1915) to a reflex effect from the increase in right atrial pressure. Evidence for this claim is lacking. Distention of the right atrium or venae cavae in some experiments had no effect on heart rate, and in others, an increase in right atrial pressure caused bradycardia; also, any increase in heart rate resulting from infusion may be due to activity of chemoreceptors (Aviado and Schmidt, 1959; Ledsome and Linden, 1964).

Distention of the junctional regions between pulmonary veins and left atrium increases the heart rate and usually the mean arterial blood pressure (Ledsome and Linden, 1964). The afferent path for this reflex lies in the vagus nerves and the efferent path, in the cardiac sympathetic nerves. The increased sympathetic activity may well be accompanied by increased contractility of atrial and ventricular muscle; the reflex might then provide the heart with another way, in addition to the Starling mechanism, for adjusting its output to its input.

Afferent impulses in the vagus nerves have been recorded from two types of receptors in the ventricles. One type appears to act as a mechanoreceptor since it has a pulsatile discharge, apparently related to rhythmical changes in ventricular pressure or volume or both. Twelve of the 19 ventricular endings with a cardiac rhythm were situated in the endocardium or myocardium at the base of the heart near the origins of the pulmonary artery and aorta (Fig. 5-2). None were found in the interventricular septum. The second type is characterized by an irregular and usually sparse discharge. These receptors are near the epicardial surface of the ventricles (Coleridge et al., 1964A). The physiological role of these receptors is unknown (Ross et al., 1961). Injection of veratrum alkaloids into the left coronary artery causes reflex bradycardia and hypotension (Bezold reflex) by activating fibers whose endings are situated in or near the ventricular epicardium (Sleight, 1964).

CORONARY MECHANORECEPTORS. Brown (1965) studied the response of afferent cardiac vagal fibers to changes in pressure within the coronary arteries and identified a new group of receptors, the coronary mechanoreceptors. These have phasic activity with each heart beat; bursts of impulse activity are limited to systole in some and diastole in others, and still others are active in both phases of the cardiac cycle. Most of the receptors are probably in or near the main coronary arteries. Bradycardia and hypotension occur when these receptors are exposed to small doses of veratrine injected into the coronary arteries or to an increase of pressure.

These coronary mechanoreceptors are therefore implicated in the Bezold reflex. They may also initiate the depressor reflex arising from the left coronary artery (Brown, 1966). In cats, the efferent fibers of the coronary depressor reflex are both sympathetic and vagal; the afferent fibers are in the vagus nerves. It is unlikely that the nerve fibers that transmit the impulses signaling pain in myocardial ischemia are involved in the coronary depressor reflex. These fibers run with the cardiac sympathetic nerves and enter the spinal cord with the upper dorsal posterior nerve roots (Brown and Brewin, 1965).

Thus, in dogs and cats, there are at least three receptor mechanisms in the ventricles; some, like the atrial receptors, may be activated by changes in pressure, volume or both and some, by chemical substances. No observations are available in man.

PULMONARY RECEPTORS

The presence of baroreceptors in the pulmonary artery has been demonstrated by electrophysiological techniques (Coleridge et al., 1961; Coleridge and Kidd, 1963). Inflation of the lung causes a reflex increase in heart rate which is abolished by denervation of both lungs; both afferent and efferent pathways of this lung inflation reflex are in the vagi. This response is distinct from the reflex increase in heart rate resulting from distention of the pulmonary veins; this latter reflex, whose efferent pathway lies in the sympathetic nerves, is unaffected by denervation of the lungs (Ledsome and Linden, 1964).

Reflexes have been induced by injecting chemical substances into the pulmonary artery. The pulmonary depressor chemoreflex (systemic hypotension and bradycardia) and pulmonary respiratory reflex (apnea followed by rapid shallow respiration) can be evoked in the dog by veratridine and mepyramine, respectively (Dawes and Comroe, 1954). Injection of capsaicin (a decylenic acid amide of vanillylamine) causes bradycardia, systemic hypotension and apnea (Coleridge et al., 1964B, 1965). Some of these reflex effects can be elicited mechanically; thus, pulmonary arterial mechanoreceptors may play a part in them. The fibers concerned are different from the pulmonary stretch fibers, described by Adrian (1933), that are involved in the conventional Hering-Breuer reflex. The role of any of these reflexes in the regulation of respiration or circulation remains uncertain.

In animals, lung inflation excites pulmonary stretch receptors which mediate the Hering-Breuer inflation reflex (Widdicombe, 1964); this inhibits respiratory activity. The fact that bilateral vagotomy in anesthetized animals slows and deepens breathing is usually cited as evidence for the tonic influence of the Hering-Breuer reflex in quiet breathing. In man, inflation of the lungs with large volumes of air produces considerable in-

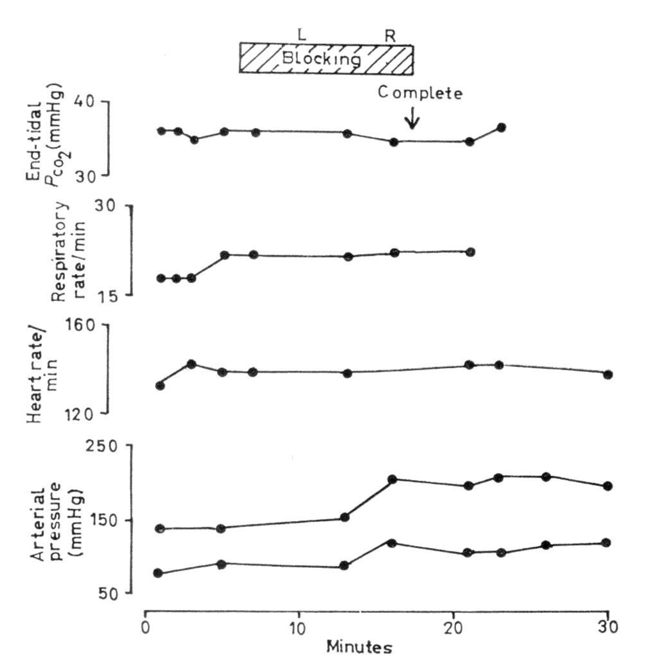

FIGURE 5-3. The effect on end-tidal pCO_2, respiratory rate, heart rate and systemic arterial pressure of blockade of the glossopharyngeal and vagus nerves in a normal man. (From Guz, Noble, Widdicombe, Trenchard, Mushin and Makey, Clin. Sci., *30*:161, 1966A.)

spiratory inhibition; this response is abolished by bilateral vagal nerve block in both anesthetized and conscious subjects. However, inflation volumes within the usual tidal range produce little or no inhibition. This suggests that vagal afferent fibers from the lungs do not modulate the pattern of normal breathing, and that the Hering-Breuer reflex is activated by distention of the lungs only if the inflation volumes are large.

In two anesthetized subjects, electrical stimulation cephalad to the site of vagal nerve block inhibited inspiration, especially when the frequencies were 50 to 100 per second (Guz et al., 1964). A decrease in systemic arterial pressure was not observed unless stimulation of the vagus nerve caused a series of coughs. The decrease in pressure with coughing resulted from a decrease in cardiac output due to impaired venous return. The lack of any increase in systemic arterial blood pressure with bilateral vagal nerve block suggests that tonic aortic mechanoreceptor activity is absent with arterial pressures up to 130/80 mm. Hg (the arterial pressure level in the conscious patient). The fact that electrical stimulation of vagal afferent fibers did not produce a decrease of arterial pressure unless coughing occurred provides additional evidence against the existence of cardiopulmonary depressor mechanisms in man.

Guz et al. (1966A) made further studies in two healthy men, aged 29 and 39 years, of the effect of bilateral block of the vagus and glossopharyngeal nerves with local anesthetic solution. Atropine was given to block vagal efferent activity. The nerve block had no effect on the pattern or sensation of normal breathing but resulted in a prolongation of maximal breath holding time at all lung volumes, with alleviation of the customarily associated distress, and in an increase in systemic arterial blood pressure (Fig. 5-3).

Possible mechanisms underlying these results are the block of lung volume receptors and the abolition of peripheral chemoreceptor activity. The interpretation was complicated by the blockade of the fibers in the glossopharyngeal nerves originating in the chemoreceptors of the carotid body which rendered the subjects insensitive to hypoxia (Guz et al., 1966B). From the available evidence, it was concluded that the drive to inspiration during breath holding arises from receptors in the lungs and is mediated by the vagus nerve. The increase in arterial pressure caused by blocking the ninth and tenth cranial nerves is of interest since it shows the baroreceptor tone is keeping the arterial pressure normal in conscious supine man. Since hypertension does not occur with vagal block alone (Guz et al., 1964), the aortic mechanoreceptors may play little part in the control of arterial pressure. However, study of the effects of blockade of the glossopharyngeal nerves will be required to establish the relative importance of carotid and aortic mechanoreceptors in the control of the circulation in man.

REFERENCES

Adrian, E. D.: Afferent impulses in the vagus and their effect on respiration. J. Physiol., *79*:332, 1933.

Aviado, D. M., Jr., and Schmidt, C. F.: Cardiovascular and respiratory reflexes from the left side of the heart. Am. J. Physiol., *196*:726, 1959.

Bainbridge, F. A.: The influence of venous filling upon the rate of the heart. J. Physiol., *50*:65, 1915.

Bevegård, S. B., and Shepherd, J. T.: Circulatory effects of stimulating the carotid arterial stretch receptors in man at rest and during exercise. J. Clin. Invest., *45*:132, 1966.

Brown, A. M.: Mechanoreceptors in or near the coronary arteries. J. Physiol., *177*: 203, 1965.

Brown, A. M.: The depressor reflex arising from the left coronary artery of the cat. J. Physiol., *184*:825, 1966.

Brown, A. M., and Brewin, E. G.: Cardiac afferent nerve fibers in sympathetic nerves. Clin. Res., *13*:89, 1965.

Browse, N. L., Donald, D. E., and Shepherd, J. T.: The role of the veins in the carotid sinus reflex. Am. J. Physiol., *210*:1424, 1966.

Carlsten, A., Folkow, B., Grimby, G., Hamberger, C-A., and Thulesius, O.: Cardiovascular effects of direct stimulation of the carotid sinus nerve in man. Acta Physiol. Scand., *44*:138, 1958.

Carlsten, A., Folkow, B., and Hamberger, C-A.: Cardiovascular effects of direct vagal stimulation in man. Acta Physiol. Scand., *41*:68, 1957.

Coleridge, H. M., Coleridge, J. C. G., and Kidd, C.: Cardiac receptors in the dog, with particular reference to two types of afferent endings in the ventricular wall. J. Physiol., *174*:323, 1964A.

Coleridge, H. M., Coleridge, J. C. G., and Kidd, C.: Role of the pulmonary arterial baroreceptors in the effects produced by capsaicin in the dog. J. Physiol., *170*:272, 1964B.

Coleridge, H. M., Coleridge, J. C. G., and Luck, J. C.: Pulmonary afferent fibers of small diameter stimulated by capsaicin and by hyperinflation of the lungs. J. Physiol., *179*:248, 1965.

Coleridge, J. C. G., Hemingway, A., Holmes, R. L., and Linden, R. J.: The location of atrial receptors in the dog: a physiological and histological study. J. Physiol., *136*:174, 1957.

Coleridge, J. C. G., and Kidd, C.: Reflex effects of stimulating baroreceptors in the pulmonary artery. J. Physiol., *166*:197, 1963.

Coleridge, J. C. G., Kidd, C., and Sharp, J. C.: The distribution, connections and histology of baroreceptors in the pulmonary artery, with some observations on the sensory innervations of the ductus arteriosus. J. Physiol., *156*:591, 1961.

Coleridge, J. C. G., and Linden, R. J.: The effect of intravenous infusion upon the heart rate of the anesthetized dog. J. Physiol., *128*:310, 1955.

Corcondilas, A., Donald, D. E., and Shepherd, J. T.: Assessment by two independent methods of the role of cardiac output in the pressor response to carotid occlusion. J. Physiol., *170*:250, 1964.

Daly, M. de B., and Scott, M. J.: An analysis of the primary cardiovascular reflex effects of stimulation of the carotid body chemoreceptors in the dog. J. Physiol., *162*:555, 1962.

Daly, M. de B., and Ungar, A.: Comparison of the reflex responses elicited by stimulation of the separately perfused carotid and aortic body chemoreceptors in the dog. J. Physiol., *182*:379, 1966.

Dawes, G. S., and Comroe, J. H., Jr.: Chemoreflexes from the heart and lungs. Physiol. Rev., *34*:167, 1954.

Ernsting, J., and Parry, D. J.: Some observations on the effects of stimulating the stretch receptors in the carotid artery of man. J. Physiol., *137*:45P, 1957 (Abstract).

Griffith, L. S. C., and Schwartz, S. I.: Reversal of renal hypertension by electrical stimulation of the carotid sinus nerve. Surgery, *56*:232, 1964.

Guz, A., Noble, M. I. M., Trenchard, D., Cochrane, H. L., and Makey, A. R.: Studies on the vagus nerves in man: their role in respiratory and circulatory control. Clin. Sci., 27:293, 1964.

Guz, A., Noble, M. I. M., Widdicombe, J. G., Trenchard, D., and Mushin, W. W.: Peripheral chemoreceptor block in man. Resp. Physiol., *1*:38, 1966B.

Guz, A., Noble, M. I. M., Widdicombe, J. G., Trenchard, D., Mushin, W. W., and Makey, A. R.: The role of vagal and glossopharyngeal afferent nerves in respiratory sensation, control of breathing and arterial pressure regulation in conscious man. Clin. Sci., *30*:161, 1966A.

Hering, H. E.: Der Karotisdruckversuch. Münch. Med. Wchnschr., *10*:1285, 1923.

Heymans, J. F., and Heymans, C.: Sur les modifications directes et sur la régulation reflexe de l'activité du centre respiratoire de la tête isolée du chien. Arch. Int. Pharmacodyn., *33*:273, 1927.

Heymans, C., and Neil, E.: Reflexogenic Areas of the Cardiovascular System. London, Churchill, 1958.

Jones, J. J.: The Bainbridge reflex. J. Physiol., *160*:298, 1962.

Ledsome, J. R., and Linden, R. J.: A reflex increase in heart rate from distension of the pulmonary vein-atrial junctions. J. Physiol., *170*:456, 1964.

Linhart, J. W., Braunwald, E., and Ross, J., Jr.: Determinants of the duration of the refractory period of the atrioventricular nodal system in man. J. Clin. Invest., *44*:883, 1965.

Neil, E., and Joels, N.: The impulse activity in cardiac afferent vagal fibers. Arch. exp. Path. Pharmak., *240*:453, 1961.

Neistadt, A., and Schwartz, S. I.: Implantable carotid sinus nerve stimulator for reversal of hypertension. Surg. Forum, *17*:123, 1966.

Paintal, A. S.: A study of right and left atrial receptors. J. Physiol., *120*:596, 1953.

Parsonnet, V., Myers, G. H., Holcomb, B. S., and Zucker, I. R.: Radio-frequency stimulation of the carotid baroreceptors in the treatment of hypertension. Surg. Forum, *17*:125, 1966.

Robinson, B. F., Epstein, S. E., Beiser, G. D., and Braunwald, E.: Control of heart rate by the autonomic nervous system. Circ. Research, *19*:400, 1966.

Roddie, I. C., and Shepherd, J. T.: The effects of carotid artery compression in man with special reference to changes in vascular resistance in the limbs. J. Physiol., *139*:377, 1957.

Ross, J., Jr., Frahm, C. J., and Braunwald, E.: The influence of intracardiac baroreceptors on venous return, systemic vascular volume, and peripheral resistance. J. Clin. Invest., *40*:563, 1961.

Sleight, P.: Cardiovascular depressor reflex from the epicardium of the left ventricle in the dog. J. Physiol., *173*:321, 1964.

Tuckman, J., Reich, T., Goodman, B., Freidman, E., and Jacobson, J. H., II: Effects of radio-frequency carotid sinus nerve stimulation in patients with severe hypertension. Circulation, *34* (Suppl. III):231, 1966 (Abstract).

Widdicombe, J. G.: Respiratory reflexes. Handbook of Physiology. Section 3: Respiration, Volume 1, Washington, D.C., American Physiological Society, 1964.

Chapter 6

CATECHOLAMINES

SYNTHESIS AND METABOLISM

Norepinephrine and epinephrine are the principal catecholamines formed in the body. Both are synthesized from their precursor, tyrosine, by a series of enzymatic reactions. The initial step in the reaction is hydroxylation of tyrosine to 3,4-dihydroxyphenylalanine (DOPA) by the enzyme tyrosine hydroxylase (Nagatsu et al., 1964). DOPA decarboxylase converts DOPA to 3,4-dihydroxyphenylethylamine (dopamine), and this, in turn, is converted to norepinephrine by dopamine-β-oxidase (Fig. 6-1). The enzyme phenylethanolamine-N-methyl transferase, which in mammals is virtually restricted to the adrenal medulla (Axelrod, 1962), converts norepinephrine to epinephrine.

Both norepinephrine and epinephrine are secreted by the adrenal medulla. This is essentially a large sympathetic ganglion, the cells of which have lost their axons and have become specialized for secretion of their products directly into the bloodstream. The polyhedral chromaffin cells secrete the catecholamines in response to stimulation by preganglionic cholinergic fibers, or by circulating secretagogue substances. Stimulation leads to the release of both norepinephrine and epinephrine. The fetal adrenal medulla contains only norepinephrine; epinephrine appears some time after birth. It is uncertain whether there are separate types of chromaffin cells in the adult gland responsible for the formation of the two catecholamines (Eränkö, 1962). It may be that the cells containing acid phosphatase secrete mostly epinephrine, whereas those showing fluorescence secrete norepinephrine. The average combined content of norepinephrine and epinephrine in the adrenal medulla is 2 to 4 mg. per g.

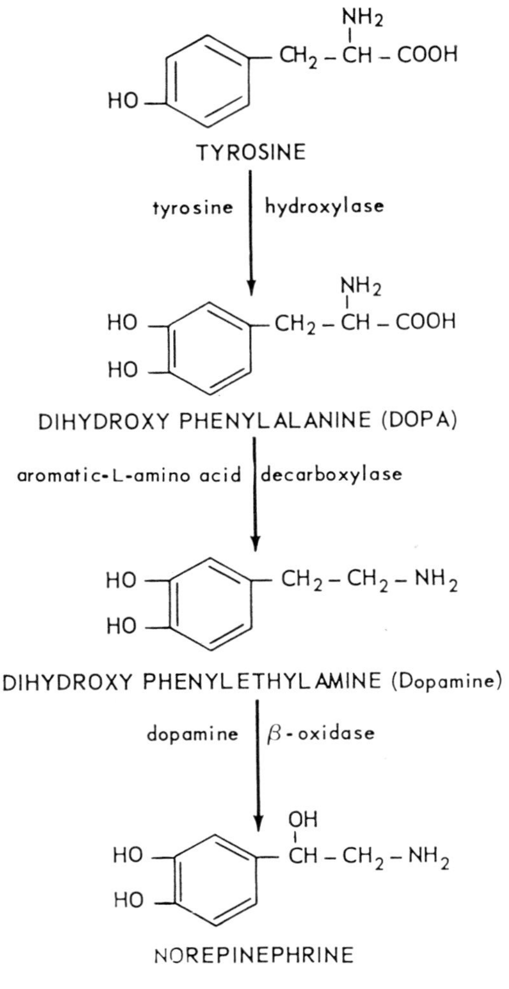

NH_2
$HO-C_6H_4-CH_2-CH-COOH$

TYROSINE

tyrosine hydroxylase

NH_2
$(HO)_2C_6H_3-CH_2-CH-COOH$

DIHYDROXY PHENYLALANINE (DOPA)

aromatic-L-amino acid decarboxylase

$(HO)_2C_6H_3-CH_2-CH_2-NH_2$

DIHYDROXY PHENYLETHYLAMINE (Dopamine)

dopamine β-oxidase

OH
$(HO)_2C_6H_3-CH-CH_2-NH_2$

NOREPINEPHRINE

FIGURE 6-1. Biosynthesis of norepinephrine. (From Engelman and Sjoerdsma, Circ. Research, *18* [Suppl. I]:104, 1966.)

That epinephrine is formed almost exclusively in the adrenal medulla is clear from the fact that, following bilateral adrenalectomy, it almost disappears from the urine, although the excretion of norepinephrine is little altered (von Euler et al., 1954). Norepinephrine is synthesized in the brain, extra-adrenal chromaffin tissue and at sympathetic nerve terminals (von Euler, 1946). However, little or no norepinephrine is released in an unchanged form from the brain into the circulation. Circulating norepinephrine is therefore derived partially from the adrenal medulla but mainly from postganglionic adrenergic sympathetic nerve terminals. These terminals, specialized extensions of the neurones, have the capacity to synthesize, store, release and metabolize norepinephrine.

The presence of all three enzymes concerned in the formation of norepinephrine from tyrosine in sympathetically innervated tissues is evidence that norepinephrine is synthesized locally by the sympathetic nerves (Udenfriend, 1964). Although the nerve endings can take up norepinephrine from circulating blood, the isolated perfused heart can form norepinephrine at a rate comparable to that estimated to occur in vivo (Spector et al., 1963). It is uncertain whether the rate of synthesis is limited under all circumstances in the same manner. The major rate limiting step appears to be the hydroxylation of tyrosine (Udenfriend, 1964). Thus, potent inhibitors of DOPA decarboxylation and of dopamine-β-oxidation do not readily lower tissue levels of norepinephrine, whereas α-methyl tyrosine, a potent inhibitor of tyrosine hydroxylase, blocks the conversion of tyrosine to norepinephrine (Spector et al., 1965).

Catecholamines in chromaffin cells and adrenergic nerve terminals exist in granules; this can be demonstrated by electron microscopy (Potter and Axelrod, 1963). Since they are bound and stored in the granules, they are protected from destruction by monoamine oxidase, and their diffusion out of the cells is retarded (Kopin, 1964). Other functions of the granules include taking up dopamine from the circulation, its oxidation to norepinephrine, release of stored catecholamine in response to an appropriate physiological or pharmacological stimulus, and inactivation of free catecholamine released locally from the sympathetic nerve ending or arriving via the circulation (Wurtman, 1966).

Small quantities of catecholamines are continually released into the circulation. Stimuli such as mental stress, muscular exercise and hypoglycemia lead to release of large quantities. Thus, the levels of catecholamines in the blood may fluctuate widely during normal daily activity. The fate of circulating catecholamine depends on the organ or tissue to which it is delivered. Organs with a rich sympathetic innervation, such as the heart, take it up and store it in the granules of sympathetic nerve terminals. The liver inactivates it enzymatically (Vendsalu, 1960); catechol-O-methyl transferase converts norepinephrine to normetanephrine and epinephrine to metanephrine. These compounds are then either returned to the circulation and excreted unchanged, conjugated, or converted by monoamine oxidase to 3-methoxy-4-hydroxy mandelic acid. Because of a blood-brain barrier, little or no circulating catecholamine is taken up by the brain.

The kidney inactivates most of the catecholamine that it receives, but a small portion is excreted unchanged. The normal 24-hour content in the urine is 20 to 60 μg norepinephrine, but under conditions of severe stress, up to 485 μg may be excreted (Goodall et al., 1957). Epinephrine and norepinephrine are excreted during severe muscular exercise (von Euler and Hellner, 1952). Goodall (1962) showed that the urinary output of norepinephrine was increased during and immediately after, but not before, centrifugation. Thus, it appeared to be related to the physical stresses of the procedure. On the other hand, epinephrine levels were increased before as

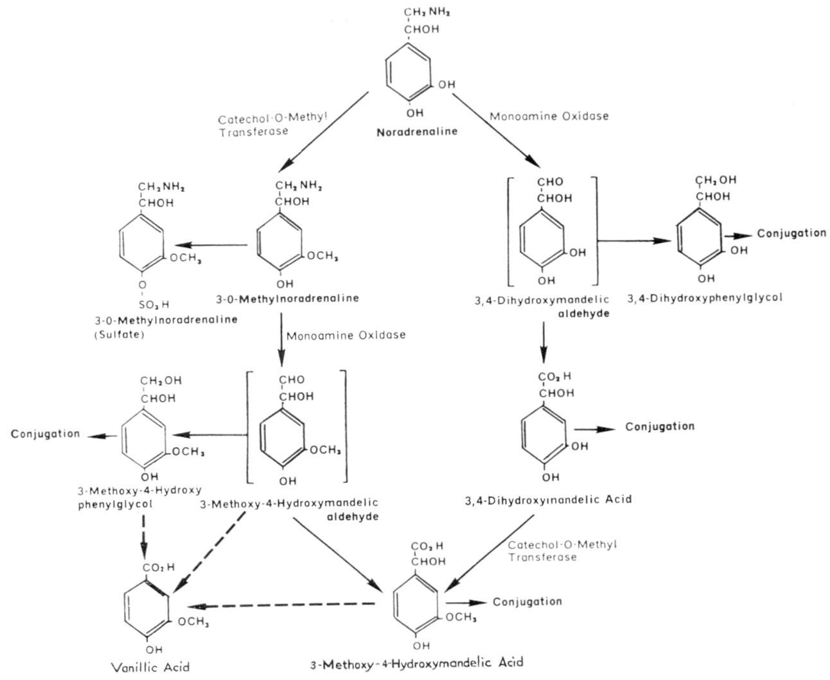

FIGURE 6-2. Alternative pathways for the metabolism of norepinephrine. (From Goodall and Rosen, J. Clin. Invest., *42*:1578, 1963.)

well as during and after centrifugation; therefore, this change was related to the emotional concomitants rather than to the physical stress.

When epinephrine or norepinephrine are infused into normal man, both oxidative deamination and O-methylation occur in the initial inactivation (Fig. 6-2). All but about four per cent of the infused dose is metabolized to O-methylated and deaminated compounds that appear in the urine. The percentage excreted as each metabolite is fairly constant between different individuals (La Brosse et al., 1958; Goodall et al., 1959).

The situation is different in patients with pheochromocytoma. Patients with similar values for the excretion of free catecholamines may have differences up to tenfold in their excretion rates of metabolites (Crout et al., 1961). Crout and Sjoerdsma (1964) measured the 24-hour urinary content of free norepinephrine and epinephrine, of total normetanephrine plus metanephrine and of 3-methoxy-4-hydroxy mandelic acid in 24 patients with pheochromocytoma. In addition, 23 tumors were assayed for norepinephrine and epinephrine and nine for normetanephrine plus metanephrine. They found marked individual variation in the rates of production and turnover of catecholamines. In some tumors (usually less than 50 g. weight), the catecholamine store was replaced rapidly, and relatively pure norepinephrine (sometimes epinephrine) was secreted into the host. In others (usually over 50 g. weight), the store turned over more slowly, and a considerable proportion of the catecholamines were evidently metabolized directly in the tumor. It was concluded that the intracellular binding of catecholamines, the regulation of catecholamine synthesis and the activity of catecholamine degrading enzymes may all be abnormal in the cells of pheochromocytomas.

The dynamics of norepinephrine metabolism may also be abnormal in essential hypertension. Gitlow et al. (1964) infused dl-β-H^3 norepinephrine into five normal persons and five patients with essential hypertension. Three hours later, the exponential rate of clearance of the H^3 norepinephrine from the plasma was greater in the hypertensive than in the normotensive subjects.

THE SYMPATHETIC NEUROEFFECTOR JUNCTION

This junction consists of the nonmyelinated termination of a postganglionic sympathetic neurone and its effector cell. The effector cell receives the catecholamine, which acts at a specific site or receptor. No specific cellular component has yet been identified as the adrenergic receptor, nor is the chemical composition of the receptor known. The concept of specific adrenergic receptors stems from observations on the effects of drugs rather than from anatomical studies. Thus, Dale (1906) found that preparations of ergot antagonized the excitatory effects of epinephrine but did not affect its inhibitory actions. Ahlquist (1948) extended these observations by showing that a series of sympathomimetic amines had varying capacities to provoke excitatory and inhibitory responses in blood vessels, uterus, intestine and other tissues. He postulated that two general types of adrenergic receptors, which he termed alpha and beta, existed, and that the effect of any sympathomimetic agent depended on its predilection for one or other of these receptors. In the cardiovascular system, stimulation of alpha adrenergic receptors results in constriction of resistance and capacity vessels, whereas stimulation of beta receptors dilates resistance vessels, constricts capacity vessels and augments both myocardial contractility and automaticity (that is, increases the rate of discharge of the sinuatrial and of subsidiary pacemakers).

The adrenergic receptor sites can be activated by norepinephrine released from adrenergic nerves or by circulating catecholamine. The two naturally occurring catecholamines, norepinephrine and epinephrine, as well as the majority of synthetic sympathomimetic amines, stimulate both alpha and beta adrenergic receptors to varying degrees. Isopropylnorepinephrine (isoproterenol) stimulates exclusively beta adrenergic receptors, whereas the actions of phenylephrine and methoxamine are almost exclusively on alpha adrenergic receptors. The beta adrenergic receptors in skeletal muscle have no neuroeffector.

From the work of Sutherland and Rall (1960), it appears that catecholamines, whether released at nerve terminals or arriving via the circulation, stimulate the membrane enzyme adenyl cyclase. This, in the presence of magnesium, catalyzes the intracellular formations of cyclic 3′5′ adenosine monophosphate (AMP) and inorganic phosphate from adenosine triphosphate. Cyclic 3′,5′ AMP appears to be responsible for altering cardiac contractility.

DRUGS THAT ACT ON ADRENERGIC STRUCTURES. Drugs can interfere with the functions of the adrenergic nervous system by acting at various sites. They may be classified as follows (Moran, 1966):

(1) Ganglion blocking drugs. These inhibit the synthesis or release of acetylcholine in the paravertebral sympathetic ganglia, or block neural transmission across the ganglia.

(2) Adrenergic nerve terminal blocking drugs. These reduce the amount of free norepinephrine released from the nerve terminals and hence reduce sympathetic nervous activity. Their modes of action vary. Reserpine depletes the nerve terminals of norepinephrine. Its primary site of action is on the binding mechanism in the granules, so that norepinephrine leaks into the cytoplasm and is modified by monoamine oxidase (Crout, 1966). Considerable depletion of adrenergic nerve norepinephrine stores is required before there is demonstrable functional impairment; thus, the positive chronotropic response to stimulation of the cardioaccelerator nerves is lost only after myocardial tissue stores of norepinephrine have been depleted by 90 per cent (from about 3.0 to 0.3 μg per g.). Bretylium prevents the release of norepinephrine (Boura and Green, 1959). Guanethidine and bethanidine induce an initial release of norepinephrine directly on to the receptor sites, but prolonged administration does not cause depletion comparable with that occurring during administration of reserpine. The net effects of continued administration of guanethidine are complex and result from decreased release of norepinephrine from the adrenergic nerve terminals, impaired storage mechanisms for exogenous catecholamines and both indirect (Harrison et al., 1963) and direct (Abboud and Eckstein, 1962) sympathomimetic actions. The effects of bethanidine are intermediate between those of bretylium and guanethidine (Fewings et al., 1964).

Compounds such as α-methyldopa and methyltyrosine, although they are inhibitors of DOPA decarboxylase, are also substrates of decarboxylase. When they enter the sympathetic terminals, they are decarboxylated and oxidized to the corresponding norepinephrine analogues, α-methylnorepinephrine and metaraminol (Udenfriend, 1964). They replace stoichiometric amounts of norepinephrine. Both compounds are capable of being released on nerve stimulation. Thus, adrenergic transmission is altered through replacement of norepinephrine by the substitute or false transmitters (Crout,

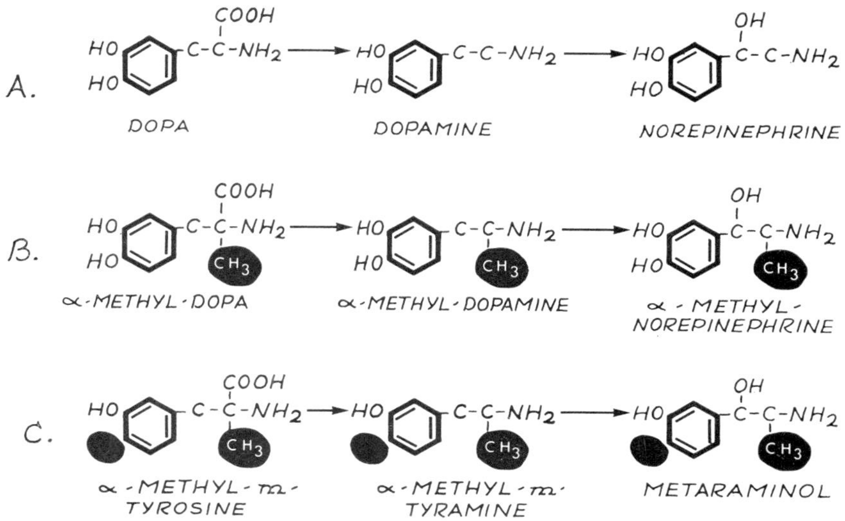

FIGURE 6-3. Biosynthetic pathways for: *A*, norepinephrine, *B*, α-methyl-norepinephrine, and *C*, metaraminol. The dark circles identify structural differences from corresponding compounds in the norepinephrine pathway. (From Crout, Circ. Research, *18* [Suppl. I]:120 1966.)

1966; Fig. 6-3). Since their potency is less than that of norepinephrine, the net result is inhibition of the transmission process. For example, metaraminol has only about one twentieth of the effect of norepinephrine on adrenergic receptors.

After administration of drugs that block transmission through ganglia or nerve terminals, the cardiovascular system remains responsive to sympathomimetic agents that act *directly* on adrenergic receptors.

(3) ADRENERGIC RECEPTOR BLOCKING DRUGS. These interfere with the action of the neurotransmitter or of injected sympathomimetic amines on the effector cells.

Alpha adrenergic receptors are blocked by ergot alkaloids, phenoxybenzamine (Dibenzyline) and related haloalkylamines, and substituted imidazolines such as tolazoline (Priscoline) and phentolamine (Regitine).

The first drug to be developed that specifically blocked beta adrenergic receptors was dichloroisoproterenol (DCI) (Powell and Slater, 1958). It antagonized the inotropic and chronotropic actions of catecholamines and of sympathetic nervous activity and the dilator effect of isoproterenol on the blood vessels of muscle, and it did not block alpha adrenergic activity (Glover et al., 1962). However, it possessed intrinsic sympathomimetic activity (Moran and Perkins, 1958). Next, pronethalol was synthesized, which was relatively free from complicating sympathomimetic activity (Black and Stephenson, 1962). This compound was found to induce malignant tumors

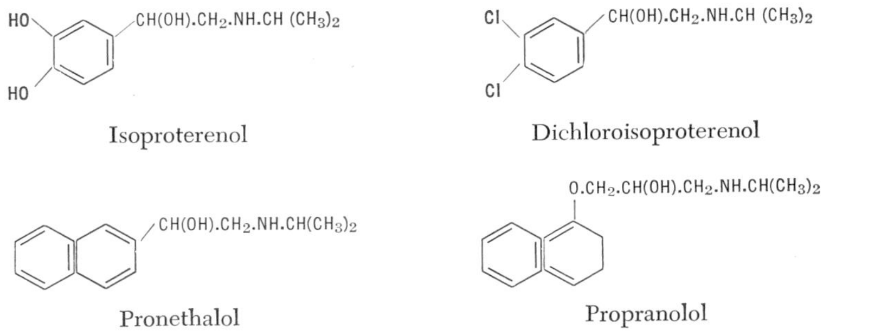

HO, HO — $CH(OH).CH_2.NH.CH(CH_3)_2$

Isoproterenol

Cl, Cl — $CH(OH).CH_2.NH.CH(CH_3)_2$

Dichloroisoproterenol

$CH(OH).CH_2.NH.CH(CH_3)_2$

Pronethalol

$O.CH_2.CH(OH).CH_2.NH.CH(CH_3)_2$

Propranolol

FIGURE 6-4. Structures of isoproterenol, dichloroisoproterenol (DCI), pronethalol and propranolol.

in mice and was superseded by propranolol (Black et al., 1964; Fig. 6-4) and various other specific beta adrenergic receptor blockers (Levy and Richards, 1966).

The classification of adrenergic receptors into alpha and beta groups is useful, but it is an oversimplification. For example, although alpha-methyl-dichloroisoproterenol blocks the vasodilator effect of isoproterenol, it exerts only a very mild antagonism to its positive inotropic action. This suggests that beta adrenergic receptors in the heart differ from those in blood vessels (Moran, 1966).

Norepinephrine (Nestel, 1964) and epinephrine (Havel and Goldfien, 1959) mobilize free fatty acids from adipose tissue stores and increase their concentration in plasma. In man, beta adrenergic receptor blocking drugs prevent this mobilization, but alpha adrenergic receptor blockers have no effect; the receptors in adipose tissue may therefore be classified as the beta type. However, there are pronounced inter-species variations; for example, in the dog, both alpha and beta adrenergic receptor blocking drugs prevent the hyperlipidemic response to epinephrine (Mayer et al., 1961). Thus, receptors in adipose tissue generally are less well differentiated, in terms of the Ahlquist classification, than those elsewhere.

MODE OF ACTION OF PRESSOR AMINES. Many pressor amines have been synthesized. Their chemical structures are similar to that of the naturally occurring catecholamines. The basic structure consists of an aromatic group (benzene ring) and an aliphatic side chain with an amino group (ethylamine). The introduction of methyl, hydroxyl or methoxy groups to the aromatic ring or the side chain produces the different compounds. Their modes of action and the intensity and duration of their effects depend upon the type and position of the substitutions. There are two general categories of pressor amines. The first includes the naturally occurring catecholamines norepinephrine, epinephrine and dopamine, together with the synthetic amines phenylephrine and methoxamine. They act directly on receptors in the myocardium and the smooth muscle of vessel walls. Depletion of tissue stores of norepinephrine does not reduce their efficacy; in fact, it may enhance it. The second category comprises compounds that act indirectly on the effector organs through releasing norepinephrine from tissue stores; they include ephedrine, tyramine, methamphetamine and mephentermine. Their effects clearly should resemble those of norepinephrine. When tissue stores of norepinephrine are depleted, they are ineffective. Metaraminol, propadrine and possibly methoxamine have the capacity to act directly as well as to release norepinephrine. Ephedrine may also have a direct in addition to an indirect action (Eckstein and Abboud, 1962).

ACTION OF CATECHOLAMINES ON THE HEART

MYOCARDIUM. The mammalian ventricle is richly supplied with adrenergic nerves. Release of the neurotransmitter, norepinephrine, from these nerves augments cardiac contractility. The stores of norepinephrine are localized within the nerve terminals, in close apposition to the myocardial fibers (Dahlström et al., 1965).

In isolated human papillary muscles, at any given muscle length, inotropic agents such as epinephrine, norepinephrine, ionic calcium and digitalis shift the force-velocity relation, so that the velocity of shortening is greater at any given load, and the maximal velocity of the unloaded muscle is increased (Sonnenblick, 1962; Sonnenblick et al., 1965A; Fig. 6-5).

The administration of certain sympathomimetic amines has been shown to augment the contractile force of the intact ventricle in man. Goldberg et al. (1960), using a Walton-Brodie strain gauge arch, showed that epinephrine, norepinephrine, mephentermine and metaraminol in equal doses caused equal increments in contractile force. On the other hand, methoxamine in doses that considerably increased the arterial blood pressure had virtually no effect. Glick et al. (1965) used cinéradiography to measure the distances between two markers on the external surface of the ventricle. Since 30 frames were obtained per second, it was possible to measure the velocity of movement of the markers. Intraventricular pressure was recorded simultaneously. A beat to beat analysis of the force-velocity relationship was then accomplished by measuring velocity and pressure at a constant distance between the two markers (isolength point). Norepinephrine, isoproterenol, increase in the heart rate induced by electrical pacing, and paired electrical stimulation all augmented velocity at any given pressure.

The finding of a diminished concentration of norepinephrine in the atria of some patients with heart failure suggested that the neurotransmitter store in the heart may be depleted, thus interfering with the activity of the cardiac sympathetic nerves (Chidsey et al., 1963). In dogs with congestive heart failure, caused by creating tricuspid insufficiency and pulmonary stenosis, the concentration and total amount of norepinephrine in both ven-

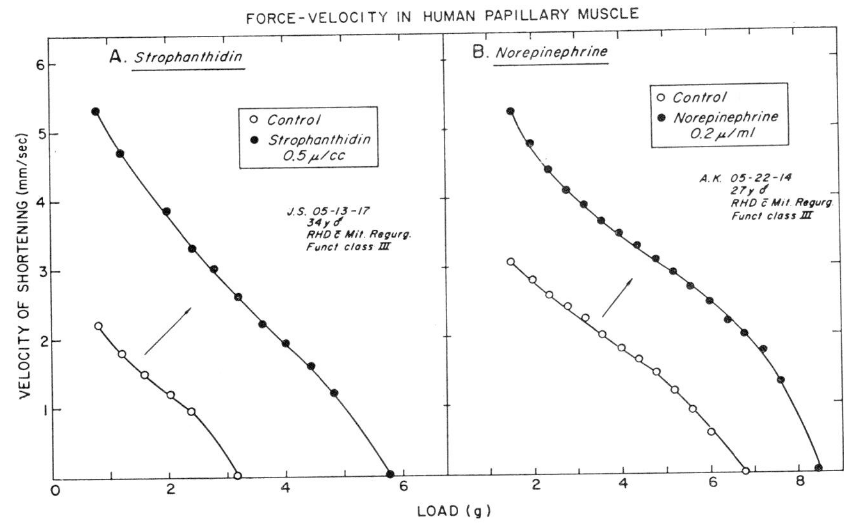

FIGURE 6-5. The addition of *A*, strophanthidin and *B*, norepinephrine increased the maximal velocity of shortening and the maximal isometric force of isolated human papillary muscles. (From Sonnenblick, Braunwald and Morrow, J. Clin. Invest., *44*:966, 1965.)

tricles was reduced. Despite this, the uptake and binding of a tracer dose of radioactive norepinephrine were not significantly reduced. Tyramine, which acts by releasing norepinephrine, produced a maximal increase of 138 per cent in contractile force of papillary muscles from normal dogs and of less than 20 per cent in muscles from dogs with left ventricular failure (Chidsey et al., 1964).

Papillary muscles from the right ventricle of normal cats and of cats with depleted norepinephrine stores due to chronic cardiac denervation or reserpine pretreatment were studied in order to assess the role of norepinephrine stores on the contractile state of non-failing cardiac muscle (Spann et al., 1966). The resting and active length-tension curves, the force-velocity relations and the augmentation of isometric tension achieved by paired electrical stimulation and by increasing frequency of contraction were not depressed in either group of norepinephrine depleted muscles. Similarly, no changes in the absolute refractory period and electrical excitability were observed. It was concluded that cardiac stores of norepinephrine are not fundamental for maintaining the contractile state of the myocardium.

In cardiac tissues exhibiting pacemaker activity, epinephrine alters the shape of the intracellularly recorded action potential. In tissue without pacemaker activity, however, an increase in the concentration of epinephrine sufficient to increase the force of contraction may have no effect at all on the intracellular action potential. The nature of the ionic fluxes underlying the cardiac action potential and of the coupling of the action potential to the contractile process is complex and controversial (Vaughan Williams, 1966). In the intact ventricle, improvement in conduction in Purkinje tissue as well as increase in the speed of the activation processes in individual muscle fibers may contribute to the increased rate of intraventricular pressure development with catecholamines.

CORONARY CIRCULATION. Since extraction of oxygen from the coronary vessels is nearly complete during rest, an increased demand of the myocardium for oxygen is generally met by an increased rate of flow. In order to assess the effects of any event on the coronary circulation, one must measure changes in both the oxygen consumption of the heart and the rate of extraction of oxygen. Much of the oxygen consumed is not related to external work. For example, a heart perfused at a constant pressure and doing no external work, either because of asystole or because it is empty and beating, may consume up to 35 per cent of that used by a heart performing a normal amount of external work.

Norepinephrine and epinephrine given systemically or into the coronary arteries of the normal beating canine heart increase coronary blood flow. However, it is uncertain whether this represents a direct dilator action or whether it is secondary to such factors as extravascular pumping from the augmented cardiac contractions or increased metabolic activity in the myocardium. In the fibrillating canine heart, intracoronary injections caused a brief initial decrease followed by a more prolonged increase in flow associated with a reduction of oxygen tension of blood in the coronary sinus (Berne, 1958). Since the heart was not contracting, the initial decrease was not due to increased extravascular compression. It was concluded that both amines had a primary constrictor effect and, since myocardial oxygen consumption was increased to a greater extent than was coronary blood flow, that their vasodilator action was secondary to their stimulation of myocardial metabolism. In unanesthetized dogs with both normal conduction and ventricular pacing, intracoronary injection of catecholamines (isoproterenol, epinephrine or norepinephrine) generally increased coronary flow and decreased late diastolic coronary resistance before there were any effects on the myocardium or systemic circulation. Beta adrenergic blockade generally decreased coronary blood flow. After such blockade, intracoronary injections of epinephrine, norepinephrine or phenylephrine further reduced coronary blood flow, and the dilator effect of isoproterenol was abolished. These results are consistent with the presence of both alpha and beta adrenergic receptors in the coronary vessels, with the latter predominant (Gregg and Fisher, 1963). Zuberbuhler and Bohr (1965) provided evidence that the small coronary arteries contain beta and the large arteries, alpha adrenergic receptors.

Yurchak et al. (1964) found that infusions of norepinephrine in 21 subjects with normal or failing left ventricles increased both perfusion pressure and coronary blood flow by 16 per cent. Despite an increase in myocardial oxygen consumption, coronary vascular resistance was unchanged. Although the responses of the normal and failing left ventricles were qualitatively similar, the latter showed a greater tendency to meet increased oxygen needs by an increased rate of extraction. On the other hand, isoproterenol increased flow out of proportion to demand, so that the oxygen content of the coronary sinus increased, in contrast with the decreased oxygen content during infusions of epinephrine.

SYSTEMIC EFFECTS

When catecholamines are given intravenously, their local actions are modified by cardiovascular reflexes evoked by the changes in pressure in the vascular system, and by the metabolic and humoral changes that they induce.

NOREPINEPHRINE. In intravenous doses of 10 to 20 μg. per minute, norepinephrine slowed the heart and increased the systolic and diastolic blood pressures (Barcroft and Konzett, 1949; Fig. 6-6). Stroke volume and systemic vascular resistance increased (Goldenberg et al., 1948; Fowler et al., 1951; Tuckman and Finnerty, 1959), and there was no change or a slight decrease in cardiac output. The bradycardia is of reflex origin, mediated by the vagus nerve. Thus, after atropine or blockade of the autonomic ganglia, norepinephrine infusion causes tachycardia, due to its direct action on the pacemaker, and the cardiac output is increased (Wilber and Brust, 1958).

In patients with hypotension, the increase in systemic arterial blood pressure during infusion of norepinephrine was usually accompanied by a slight increase in heart rate and by a moderate increase in cardiac output (Cohn and Luria, 1965). Thus, an increase in arterial pressure from low to normal levels does not induce reflex cardiac slowing.

Infusion of norepinephrine increased the pressures in the pulmonary artery and pulmonary artery wedge (Fowler et al., 1951). These increases were attributed to congestion of the pulmonary vessels secondary to constriction of systemic veins. Infusions decreased plasma volume by about 10 per cent and increased the arterial hematocrit by 2.7 per cent (Cohn, 1966). The response of blood vessels in the hand or forearm to intravenous norepinephrine is complex; it is a result of the direct constrictor action and of the reflexly induced dilator action (Barcroft et al., 1954). After blockade of baroreceptor reflexes, norepinephrine not only causes an exaggerated increase in blood presure, but also increases constriction of the limb vessels, since reflex dilatation no longer opposes the direct constrictor effect. Although norepinephrine stimulates predominantly alpha adrenergic receptors in the resistance vessels, this is not its sole action. When alpha receptor blockade is produced by infusing phentolamine into the brachial artery,

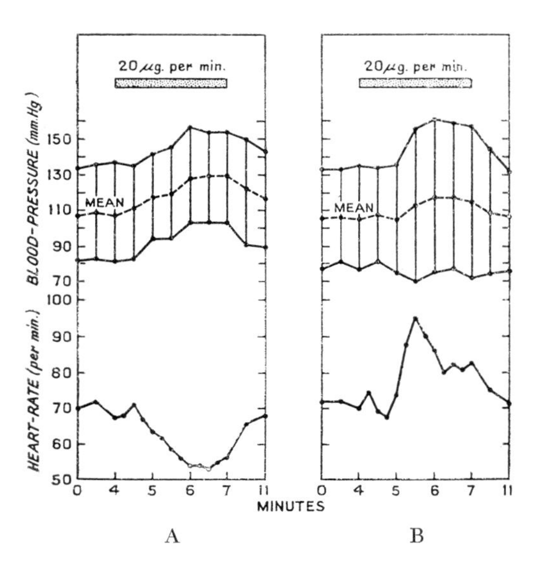

FIGURE 6-6. Systemic arterial blood pressure and heart rate during infusions of *A*, norepinephrine and *B*, epinephrine. (From Barcroft and Konzett, Lancet, *i*:147, 1949.)

norepinephrine causes vasodilatation rather than constriction of the forearm vessels. The dilator response is due to stimulation of beta receptors, since prior blockade of these with propranolol prevents it (Brick et al., 1966B). Renal (Smythe et al., 1952; Corcoran et al., 1956; King and Baldwin, 1956), splanchnic (Bearn et al., 1951) and cerebral (King et al., 1952; Sensenbach et al., 1953) blood flows also decrease during intravenous infusions of norepinephrine.

In normal subjects, a period of hypotension lasting 15 minutes to two hours followed the termination of prolonged infusions of norepinephrine in doses sufficient to maintain the systolic blood pressure at 160 to 190 mm. Hg. Lever et al. (1961) concluded from their experiments in dogs and rabbits that vasodilatation occurs in muscle and intestine during the latter part of the infusion, persists into the hypotensive period and is probably responsible for at least part of the fall in blood pressure. They suggested that the production of an unknown circulating vasodilator substance might be responsible.

In fasting man, plasma triglycerides are derived from free fatty acids (Havel, 1961). Since the flux of free fatty acids from adipose tissue stores is, to a large extent, determined by the activity of the sympathetic nervous system (Havel and Goldfien, 1959), it seems possible that the level of plasma triglycerides in a given individual may be related to the responsiveness of the adipose tissue to catecholamines. Nestel (1964) found a significant relationship between the plasma triglyceride concentration and the absolute and percentile increments in free fatty acids after a 15 minute infusion of norepinephrine in normal subjects and patients with coronary heart disease.

DOPAMINE. This may have physiological functions in addition to its role as an immediate precursor of norepinephrine (Fig. 6-1). It has an inotropic effect on the myocardium and does not constrict peripheral vessels. Indeed, the renal and mesenteric vascular beds are dilated; this dilatation is not opposed by known adrenergic blocking agents. It increased cardiac output, renal blood flow and sodium excretion in normal subjects and patients with congestive heart failure, and it improved the peripheral circulation and increased urine output in patients with hypotension and shock (MacCannell et al., 1966).

TYRAMINE. Tyramine exerts its sympathomimetic effects by liberating norepinephrine from peripheral stores. Much evidence has accumulated that norepinephrine in nerve terminals belongs to two separate metabolic pools (Crout et al., 1962), even though both moieties appear to exist within the granules and cannot be separated anatomically. The smaller pool has a rapid rate of turnover and can be released by tyramine (Trendelenburg, 1961). The larger pool has a slow rate of turnover, is not readily released by tyramine, by other indirectly acting sympathomimetic amines or by stimulation by sympathetic nerves, and it is metabolized within the nerve by monoamine oxidase. On injection, tyramine causes an increase in arterial blood pressure and in circulating catecholamine levels. In patients free from cardiovascular disease, pretreatment with reserpine caused a significant reduction in the pressor response to tyramine. Similarly, the increase in total peripheral resistance produced by tyramine was less marked after pretreatment with reserpine. The resting level of cardiac output was not altered by the dose of reserpine used (0.06 mg. per Kg.), but the resting mean arterial blood pressure was significantly decreased (Mahon and Mashford, 1963).

The observations of Gaffney et al. (1962) suggested that most of the cardiac effects of tyramine result from release of myocardial catecholamines. However, the precise role played by release of catecholamines from different tissues in the total biological response to tyramine has yet to be determined.

EPINEPHRINE. In normal subjects, intravenous infusion of epinephrine at 10 to 15 μg per minute shortened the period of isometric contraction, accelerated the speed of contraction, increased the systolic emptying of the left ventricle, decreased the diastolic arterial blood pressure, increased the pulse pressure and usually increased the heart rate (Kjellberg et al., 1952). Goldenberg et al. (1948) found an increase in cardiac output during infusion of epinephrine. The systolic pressure increased, and the diastolic pressure remained unchanged or decreased slightly. There was a moderate increase in mean blood pressure, and the total systemic vascular resistance decreased. The blood flow through skeletal muscle usually shows two well defined phases. A transient increase to about four times the control value is followed by a return toward resting values; subsequently, there is a sustained increase in flow, which usually is about twice the control value (Barcroft and Swan, 1953). The blood flow through skin and mucous membranes decreases (Barnett et al., 1950). Venous constriction in the extremities (Eckstein and Hamilton, 1957B; Glover et al., 1958) may shift appreciable quantities of blood centrally. The increased pressures in the atria (Ranges and Bradley, 1943), resulting in part from venous constriction, aid ventricular filling. Coronary (Corday et al., 1959), cerebral (King et al., 1952; Sensenbach et al., 1953) and splanchnic (Bearn et al., 1951) blood flows increase, whereas renal blood flow decreases (Smythe et al., 1952). Intravenous infusions at 14 to 40 μg per minute decreased the plasma volume by 13 per cent, while the hematocrit increased by 3.3 per cent (Cohn, 1966).

Changes in cardiac output, stroke volume and systemic blood pressure were correlated with changes in muscle blood flow during the periods of initial transient and subsequent sustained vasodilatation due to intravenous infusions of epinephrine at 10 μg per minute (Allwood et al., 1962). In the initial phase, the mean arterial blood pressure decreased slightly, while forearm blood flow increased by 308 per cent, cardiac output by 50 per cent and stroke volume by 10 per cent (average values). During the sustained phase, the systolic blood pressure increased; corresponding increases for the other measurements were 87, 47 and 25 per cent, respectively (Table 6-1). The lack of correlation between these changes in cardiac output and forearm blood flow suggested that in the transient phase, vasodilatation did not occur simultaneously in all muscle groups. Stroke volume made a greater contribution to the increased output during the sustained phase.

The effects of epinephrine on blood vessels may represent a balance between dilator and constrictor actions. Most observations have been made on the vessels of skeletal muscle. In them, blood flow is increased during

TABLE 6-1. Effects of Intravenous Infusion of Epinephrine Bitartrate (10 μg. per min.) (Average Values from Seven Normal Subjects)*

	CONTROL	DURING TRANSIENT INCREASE IN FOREARM BLOOD FLOW	DURING SUSTAINED INCREASE IN FOREARM BLOOD FLOW
Cardiac output (L./min.)	6.8	10.2	10.0
Heart rate (beats/min.)	62	85	75
Stroke volume (ml.)	110	121	138
Blood pressure (mm. Hg)	138/70	130/65	151/67
Forearm blood flow (ml./100 ml. tissue/min.)	3.9	15.9	7.3

* Adapted from Allwood, Keck, Marshall and Shepherd, J. Appl. Physiol., *17*:71, 1962.

an infusion of epinephrine after alpha adrenergic blockade (de la Lande and Whelan, 1959) and decreased after beta adrenergic blockade (Brick et al., 1966A). There is no evidence to date that the metabolic effect of epinephrine alters blood flow (de la Lande and Whelan, 1962). Its calorigenic action may be related to its ability to increase the rate of mobilization of free fatty acids (Steinberg et al., 1964).

ISOPROPYLNOREPINEPHRINE. Intravenous infusion of isopropylnorepinephrine (isoproterenol) increases the heart rate and systolic blood pressure and decreases the diastolic blood pressure. Weissler et al. (1959) found that a small dose of isoproterenol (1 μg per minute) increased the cardiac output of normal recumbent subjects from 2.9 to 4.4 liters per $M.^2$ per minute; this was achieved through moderate increases in both heart rate and stroke volume. When the subjects were tilted head upwards at a 60 degree angle, there was a similar increase in heart rate, but the changes in stroke volume and cardiac output were much less, possibly because of depletion of the thoracic reservoir of blood.

Both infusion of isoproterenol and muscular exercise produce tachycardia, increased cardiac output, relatively little increase in stroke volume, decreased systemic vascular resistance and decreased systolic ejection time (Bruce et al, 1958). Rushmer and Smith (1959) also commented on the similarity of response to these stimuli. Moss and Duffie (1963) made use of this observation by infusing isoproterenol in order to simulate the effects of physical exercise in patients undergoing cardiac catheterization for assessment of congenital defects. It was found to be of particular value in the appraisal of obstructive valvular lesions.

Krasnow et al. (1964) studied the effects of isoproterenol on the dynamics of cardiac contraction and on myocardial metabolism in patients with normal and with diseased but compensated left ventricles. The left ventricular mean volume tended to decrease without any change in systolic mean pressure. Despite the tachycardia, stroke volume was maintained. Myocardial oxygen consumption increased by 57 per cent and coronary blood flow by 72 per cent, so that the oxygen saturation of coronary venous blood was also increased.

The technique of cinéradiography using radiopaque markers on the ventricles to measure myocardial segment lengths was used to assess the effect of isoproterenol on cardiac dimensions in man (Harrison et al., 1964). The end-systolic dimensions of both ventricles were consistently reduced (Fig. 6-7). Smaller and less consistent decreases occurred in end-diastolic dimensions. Abolition of these changes in patients pretreated with pronethalol provided confirmation that isoproterenol acts on beta adrenergic receptors.

Blood flow in the forearm and calf shows a marked though transient increase followed by a lesser but sustained increase when isoproterenol is given. Blood flow in the hand and foot shows a small and transient initial

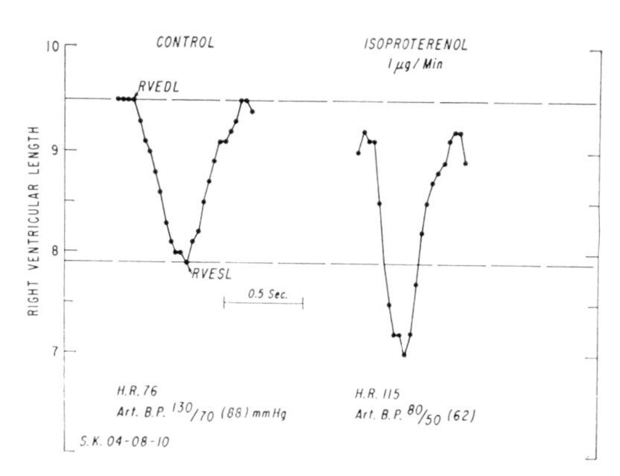

FIGURE 6-7. Distances between two clips sutured to the surface of the right ventricle during a complete cardiac cycle. *Left*: control. *Right*: during infusion of isoproterenol. Note that the infusion caused a marked decrease in right ventricular end-systolic length and a moderate decrease in right ventricular end-diastolic length. (From Harrison, Glick, Goldblatt and Braunwald, Circulation, 29:186, 1964.)

increase only. The increase in blood flow in the forearm and calf is probably due to dilatation of the blood vessels of skeletal muscle. The vasodilator effect is abolished after administration of beta adrenergic blocking agents (Brick et al., 1966A). The capacitance vessels of the forearm apparently lack beta adrenergic receptors and are therefore unaffected by isoproterenol. They do contain alpha adrenergic receptors that are stimulated by epinephrine (Eckstein et al., 1965).

Table 6-2 contrasts the effects of norepinephrine, epinephrine and isoproterenol in man.

METARAMINOL. The effects of metaraminol (Aramine) in man resemble those of norepinephrine more closely than do those of many of the other pressor amines. It has an inotropic effect on the heart (Goldberg et al., 1960). When given intravenously, it increases both systolic and diastolic arterial pressures and slows the heart. Cardiac output shows little change, although peripheral resistance increases. When bradycardia is prevented by atropine, metaraminol increases cardiac output (Livesay et al., 1954). In this respect, it also resembles norepinephrine. It reduces renal blood flow in normal subjects.

TABLE 6-2. The Contrasting Effects of Norepinephrine, Epinephrine and Isopropylnorepinephrine (Isoproterenol) in Man*

	L-NOREPINEPHRINE	L-EPINEPHRINE	DL-ISOPROPYL-NOREPINEPHRINE
Muscle blood flow	Decrease	Increase	Large increase
Skin blood flow	Decrease	Decrease	Small increase
Heart rate	Decrease	Transient increase	Sustained increase
Systolic pressure	Rise	Rise	Marked rise
Diastolic pressure	Rise	Fall	Marked fall
O_2 consumption	Small increase	Increase	Increase
Pulmonary ventilation	Small increase	Increase	Large increase
Blood sugar	Small increase	Increase	Moderate increase
Blood lactate	No change	Increase	No change

* Adapted from Cobbold, Ginsburg and Paton, J. Physiol., *151*:539, 1960.

Metaraminol acts both directly on the receptors and indirectly by releasing norepinephrine from tissue stores; Harrison et al. (1963) showed that the latter action predominates. Prolonged administration of metaraminol or of any other indirectly acting sympathomimetic amine may be accompanied by a gradual diminution and finally a loss of responsiveness (tachyphylaxis). The reason is that the tissue stores of available norepinephrine have become depleted (Potter et al., 1962). Responsiveness may be regained by an infusion of norepinephrine.

MEPHENTERMINE. This increases the force of myocardial contraction (Goldberg et al., 1960) and increases cerebral blood flow without changing cerebral vascular resistance (Richardson et al., 1957). After intravenous injection of moderate doses, there is an initial decrease in forearm blood flow, but it returns to control levels within 10 minutes. Blood pressure and peripheral resistance increase (Horsley and Eckstein, 1960).

EPHEDRINE. The cardiovascular effects of ephedrine are similar to those of epinephrine, but its onset of action is slower and its effects are more prolonged (Ranges and Bradley, 1943). After intramuscular injection, there are increases in cardiac output and systolic blood pressure, without much change in diastolic pressure. Peripheral resistance may increase or decrease. The heart rate changes little with therapeutic doses, although reflex bradycardia may occur at the peak of the pressor response. The stroke volume usually increases. The venous pressure increases, and the veins of the forearm constrict sufficiently to push blood from the extremities (Eckstein et al., 1961). It has only a mild or insignificant vasoconstrictor effect on the kidney in therapeutic doses (Ranges and Bradley, 1943). It increases blood flow in the forearm and constricts finger vessels (Allen, 1948).

METHAMPHETAMINE. Methamphetamine (Methedrine) is structurally similar to ephedrine. It increases cardiac output, systolic blood pressure and total peripheral resistance and decreases muscle blood flow slightly (Churchill-Davidson and Swan, 1952). It constricts veins in the forearm (Eckstein and Hamilton, 1957). The bradycardia which may occur initially can be prevented by atropine. After atropine, methamphetamine increases blood flow through muscle (Allen, 1948). In anesthetized subjects, it increases renal blood flow; under the same conditions, epinephrine and norepinephrine cause a decrease (Churchill-Davidson et al., 1951).

PHENYLEPHRINE. Phenylephrine (Neosynephrine) is a potent vasoconstrictor. It increases both systolic and diastolic blood pressures and peripheral resistance (Horvath and Knapp, 1954) and causes marked bradycardia and a decrease in cardiac output. In the atropinized subject, the heart rate increases and the pressor effect is augmented. Its effect on the contractile force of the dog's heart is minimal, as is its direct cardioaccelerator action. In man it causes a moderate decrease in renal blood flow and constricts vessels in the finger (Eckstein and Abboud, 1962).

METHOXAMINE. The pressor effect of methoxamine (Vasoxyl) also

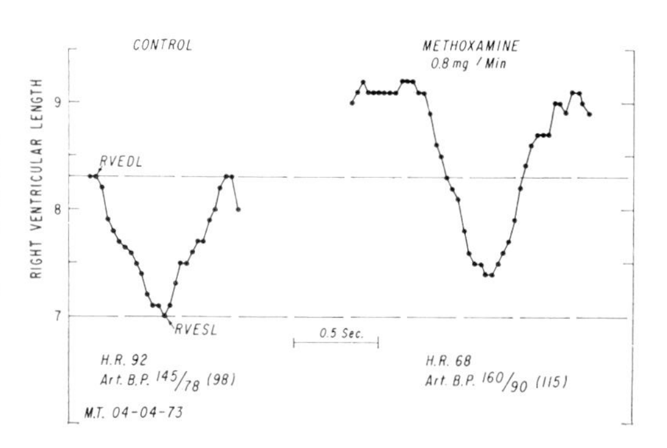

FIGURE 6-8. The effect of an infusion of methoxamine on right ventricular dimension. Note the increases in end-systolic and end-diastolic length. (From Harrison, Glick, Goldblatt and Braunwald, Circulation, *29*:186, 1964.)

is due principally to vasoconstriction. It has no significant inotropic effect on the human heart (Goldberg et al., 1960). It increases end-systolic and end-diastolic ventricular dimensions (Harrison et al., 1964; Fig. 6-8). It causes more renal vasoconstriction for a given increase in blood pressure than does either norepinephrine or metaraminol (Mills and Moyer, 1957). It has little effect on venous tone in the forearm (Eckstein and Hamilton, 1957).

BETA ADRENERGIC RECEPTOR BLOCKADE

In normal subjects resting in the supine position, beta adrenergic blockade with propranolol reduced the heart rate by 10 beats per minute, the cardiac output by 0.7 liters per $M.^2$ per minute and the stroke volume by 4 ml. per $M.^2$ per beat. The systemic arterial pressure was unchanged, whereas the mean right atrial pressure and systemic vascular resistance were increased (Harris et al., 1966). These changes could have been due to suppression of adrenergic activity in the heart, or to a non-specific depressant effect of the drug. They differed from those of previous studies in normal subjects resting in the supine position in which pronethalol caused no significant hemodynamic changes (Dornhorst and Robinson, 1962; Chamberlain and Howard, 1964; Schröder and Werkö, 1964). The explanation for the difference may be that pronethalol is not devoid of intrinsic sympathomimetic activity (Donald et al., 1964A).

Sonnenblick et al. (1965B) also noted decreases in heart rate and cardiac output following injection of propranolol. However, the contractility of the myocardium was not impaired, as judged by only a minor decrease in the velocity of shortening at an isolength point and by little alteration in the rate of pressure development in the ventricle. Therefore, sympathetic nervous activity is not essential for adequate cardiac performance during rest in the supine position. In elderly patients with complete heart block, whose hearts were being driven at fixed rates by internal pacemakers, cardiac output and the rate of pressure development in the left ventricle were both reduced following propranolol (Donoso et al., 1966). Thus, the importance of sympathetic activity for optimal cardiac performance during rest becomes manifest when cardiac reserve is diminished.

The effects of exercise before and after beta adrenergic blockade were studied by Epstein et al. (1965) in normal subjects at rest and during submaximal and maximal work on a treadmill. During maximal work, the heart rate was reduced by 19 per cent, the cardiac output by 22 per cent, the systemic arterial pressure by 15 per cent, the left ventricular minute work by 34 per cent and the oxygen consumption by six per cent, after as compared with before blockade (mean values). The arteriovenous difference in oxygen content was increased by 12 per cent and the central venous pressure by 3 mm. Hg. During submaximal work, quantitatively similar changes were noted; the decrease in cardiac output was balanced by the increase in the arteriovenous difference in oxygen content, so that oxygen consumption remained constant. Patients with heart disease, like normal subjects, had less marked increases in heart rate and cardiac output during exercise in the blocked state (Epstein et al., 1965; Hamer and Sowton, 1965). These results indicated that sympathetic stimulation plays a role in the cardiovascular adaptation to exercise.

In further studies, Robinson et al. (1966) compared the hemodynamic effects of beta adrenergic blockade (with propranolol), parasympathetic blockade (with atropine) and both combined, in normal subjects during rest and exercise in the supine position. During rest, parasympathetic restraint dominated over sympathetic stimulation in the control of the heart rate. This was also true of mild exercise. With increasingly severe exercise, sympathetic stimulation became the dominant factor in the attainment of rapid heart rates.

Cumming and Carr (1966) found that left ventricular end-diastolic pressure increased from 8 to 19 mm. Hg in patients during exercise following blockade with propranolol. When atropine was given in addition, there was a greater increase in cardiac output, and the increase in end-diastolic pressure was less pronounced, probably because the atropine corrected the relative bradycardia due to the blockade.

The reduction of cardiac output during exercise in subjects with beta adrenergic blockade appears to be due to interference with two processes. First, the increase in heart rate is less pronounced. Second, the normal augmentation of myocardial contractility is impaired. Evidence for the latter was provided by Sonnenblick et al. (1965B) who showed that propranolol abolished the shift of the myocardial force-velocity curve that normally occurs during exercise. In these experiments, the heart was paced at fixed rates in order to avoid the complication of propranolol induced changes in rate per se on the force-velocity curve.

It is of interest that when the heart is deprived of its normal sympathetic stimulation, cardiac performance is so well maintained during exercise. Thus, chronic cardiac denervation only slightly reduced the racing speed of greyhounds (Donald et al., 1964B). While the role of sympathetic stimulation of the heart as an important component of the response cannot be denied, other physiological changes are also important and, at least in normal subjects and in those with only mild impairment of cardiovascular reserve, they permit compensation to be achieved. Among them, changes in the peripheral circulation are preeminent; for example, the metabolic vasodilatation in the active muscles decreases peripheral resistance and increases venous return, while the constriction of systemic veins and the pumping action of the skeletal muscles force feed the heart. The heart deprived of extrinsic nerves has sufficient strength to pump out all the blood it receives, even during severe exercise. However, integrity of the sympathetic nerves is necessary if the heart is to make rapid adjustments to changes in demand. Thus, Donald and Shepherd (1964) showed that in dogs with cardiac denervation, both the heart rate and cardiac output increased less abruptly than normal as exercise started, even though the final level of cardiac output achieved was not significantly reduced. These dogs achieved their maximal levels of cardiac output during exercise through equal increments in heart rate and stroke volume. The increases in heart rate were unaltered following adrenalectomy and following blockade of circulating catecholamines. They could not be attributed to a change in intravascular temperature. They must have resulted from some local chemical change at the pacemaker (Donald and Shepherd, 1963).

As has already been pointed out, withdrawal of vagal restraint may be partly responsible for the tachycardia that occurs during exercise following beta adrenergic receptor blockade; also, it is possible that the blockade of endogenous sympathetic nerve stimuli may be less than the 90 per cent blockade of the effects of infused catecholamines.

From the study of Epstein et al. (1965), it seems likely that the contractile activity of the sympathetically denervated heart is augmented by an increase in end-diastolic filling pressure and fiber length; that is, through the Frank-Starling mechanism. The evidence for this is the increase of 2 to 3 mm. Hg in venous filling pressure during exercise in all six subjects with beta adrenergic blockade. Further support for this is provided by the studies of Chamberlain (1966) who used cinéradiography to study changes in heart size in normal subjects during exercise on a bicycle ergometer before and after treatment with pronethalol. Before blockade, the heart size (frontal projection) usually increased at the start of exercise but showed little further change as exercise continued. After blockade, the heart size was greater during exercise than it had been previously.

Thus, the evidence summarized here indicates that sympathetic stimulation is only one of a number of mechanisms whereby cardiac performance is augmented during exercise.

REFERENCES

Abboud, F. M., and Eckstein, J. W.: Vasodilatory action of guanethidine. Circ. Research, *11*:788, 1962.

Ahlquist, R. P.: A study of the adrenotropic receptors. Am. J. Physiol., *153*:586, 1948.

Allen, W. J.: The action of adrenaline, ephedrine and Methedrine on the circulation in man. Clin. Sci., *6*:269, 1948.

Allwood, M. J., Keck, E. W., Marshall, R. J., and Shepherd, J. T.: Correlation of hemodynamic events during infusion of epinephrine in man. J. Appl. Physiol., *17*:71, 1962.

Axelrod, J.: Purification and properties of phenylethanolamine-N-methyl transferase. J. Biol. Chem., *237*:1657, 1962.

Barcroft, H., Gaskell, P., Shepherd, J. T., and Whelan, R. F.: The effect of noradrenaline infusions on the blood flow through the human forearm. J. Physiol., *123*:443, 1954.

Barcroft, H., and Konzett, H.: Action of noradrenaline and adrenaline on human heart rate. Lancet, *i*:147, 1949.

Barcroft, H., and Swan, H. J. C.: Sympathetic Control of Human Blood Vessels. London, Arnold, 1953.

Barnett, A. J., Blacket, R. B., Depoorter, A. E., Sanderson, P. H., and Wilson, G. M.: The action of noradrenaline in man and its relation to phaeochromocytoma and hypertension. Clin. Sci., *9*:151, 1950.

Bearn, A. G., Billing, B., and Sherlock, S.: The effect of adrenaline and noradrenaline on hepatic blood flow and splanchnic carbohydrate metabolism in man. J. Physiol., *115*:430, 1951.

Berne, R. M.: Effect of epinephrine and norepinephrine on coronary circulation. Circ. Research, *6*:644, 1958.

Black, J. W., Crowther, A. F., Shanks, R. G., Smith, L. H., and Dornhorst, A. C.: New adrenergic betareceptor antagonist. Lancet, *i*:1080, 1964.

Black, J. W., and Stephenson, J. S.: Pharmacology of a new adrenergic beta-receptor-blocking compound (Nethalide). Lancet, *ii*:311, 1962.

Boura, A. L. A., and Green, A. F.: Actions of bretylium: adrenergic neurone blocking and other effects. Brit. J. Pharmacol., *14*:536, 1959.

Brick, I., Glover, W. E., Hutchinson, K. J., and Roddie, I. C.: Effects of propranolol on peripheral vessels in man. Am. J. Cardiol., *18*:329, 1966A.

Brick, I., Hutchinson, K. J., and Roddie, I. C.: The vasodilator properties of noradrenaline. J. Physiol., *185*:42P, 1966B.

Bruce, R. A., Cobb, L. A., Katsura, S., and Morledge, J.: Comparative hemodynamic effects of isoproterenol and exercise (walking) in cardiac patients. J. Clin. Invest., *37*:881, 1958 (Abstract).

Chamberlain, D. A.: Effects of beta adrenergic blockade on heart size. Am. J. Cardiol., *18*:321, 1966.

Chamberlain, D. A., and Howard, J.: The haemodynamic effects of beta-sympathetic blockade. Brit. Heart J., *26*:213, 1964.

Chidsey, C. A., Braunwald, E., Morrow, A. G., and Mason, D. T.: Myocardial norepinephrine concentration in man: Effects of reserpine and of congestive heart failure. New Eng. J. Med., *269*:653, 1963.

Chidsey, C. A., Kaiser, G. A., Sonnenblick, E. H., Spann, J. F., and Braunwald, E.: Cardiac norepinephrine stores in experimental heart failure in the dog. J. Clin. Invest., *43*:2386, 1964.

Churchill-Davidson, H. C., and Swan, H. J. C.: Noradrenaline and Methedrine: comparison of their circulatory actions. Anesthesia, *7*:4, 1952.

Churchill-Davidson, H. C., Wylie, W. D., Miles, B. E., and de Wardener, H. E.: The effects of adrenaline, noradrenaline, and Methedrine on the renal circulation during anaesthesia, Lancet, *ii*:803, 1951.

Cobbold, A. F., Ginsburg, J., and Paton, A.: Circulatory, respiratory and metabolic responses to isopropylnoradrenaline in man. J. Physiol., *151*:539, 1960.

Cohn, J. N.: Relationship of plasma volume changes to resistance and capacitance vessel effects of sympathomimetic amines and angiotensin in man. Clin. Sci., *30*:267, 1966.

Cohn, J. N., and Luria, M. H.: Studies in clinical shock and hypotension. II Hemodynamic effects of norepinephrine and angiotensin. J. Clin. Invest., *44*: 1494, 1965.

Corcoran, A. C., Wagner, W. E., and Page, I. H.: Renal participation in enhanced pressor responses to noradrenaline in patients given hexamethonium. J. Clin. Invest., *35*:868, 1956.

Corday, E., Williams, J. H., de Vera, L. B., and Gold, H.: Effect of systemic blood pressure and vasopressor drugs on coronary blood flow and the electrocardiogram. Am. J. Cardiol., *3*:626, 1959.

Crout, J. R.: Substitute adrenergic transmitters. A newly appreciated mechanism of action of antihypertensive drugs. Circ. Research, *18* (Suppl. I):120, 1966.

Crout, J. R., Muskus, A. J., and Trendelenburg, U.: Effect of tyramine on isolated guinea-pig atria in relation to their noradrenaline stores. Brit. J. Pharmacol., *18*:600, 1962.

Crout, J. R., Pisano, J. J., and Sjoerdsma, A.: Urinary excretion of catecholamines and their metabolites in pheochromocytoma. Am. Heart J., *61*:375, 1961.

Crout, J. R., and Sjoerdsma, A.: Turnover and metabolism of catecholamines in patients with pheochromocytoma. J. Clin. Invest., *43*:94, 1964.

Cumming, G. R., and Carr, W. G.: Hemodynamic response to exercise after beta-adrenergic and parasympathetic blockade. Circulation, *34* (Suppl. III):82, 1966 (Abstract).

Dahlström, A., Fuxe, K., Mya-Tu, M., and Zetterström, B. E. M.: Observations on adrenergic innervation of dog heart. Am. J. Physiol., *209*:689, 1965.

Dale, H. H.: On some physiological actions of ergot. J. Physiol., *34*:163, 1906.

de la Lande, I. S., and Whelan, R. F.: The effect of antagonists on the response of the forearm vessels to adrenaline. J. Physiol., *148*:548, 1959.

de la Lande, I. S., and Whelan, R. F.: The role of lactic acid in the vasodilator action of adrenaline in the human limb. J. Physiol., *162*:151, 1962.

Donald, D. E., Kvale, J., and Shepherd, J. T.: The effect of an adrenergic beta-receptor antagonist on the cardiovascular system of the dog. J. Pharm. Exp. Therap., *143*:344, 1964A.

Donald, D. E., Milburn, S. E., and Shepherd, J. T.: Effect of cardiac denervation on the maximal capacity for exercise in the racing greyhound. J. Appl. Physiol., *19*:849, 1964B.

Donald, D. E., and Shepherd, J. T.: Response to exercise in dogs with cardiac denervation. Am. J. Physiol., *205*:393, 1963.

Donald, D. E., and Shepherd, J. T.: Initial cardiovascular adjustment to exercise in dogs with chronic cardiac denervation. Am. J. Physiol., *207*:1325, 1964.

Donoso, E., Cohn, L. J., Newman, B. J., Bloom, H. S., Stein, W. G., and Friedberg, C. K.: Effects of propranolol in patients with complete heart block and implanted pacemakers. Circulation, *34* (Suppl. III):89, 1966 (Abstract).

Dornhorst, A. C., and Robinson, B. F.: Clinical pharmacology of a beta-adrenergic-blocking agent (nethalide). Lancet, *ii*:314, 1962.

Eckstein, J. W., and Abboud, F. M.: Circulatory effects of sympathomimetic amines. Am. Heart J., *63*:119, 1962.

Eckstein, J. W., and Hamilton, W. K.: Effects of sympathomimetic amines on forearm venous distensibility, pressure and volume. Circulation, *16*:875, 1957 (Abstract).

Eckstein, J. W., Hamilton, W. K., and McCammond, J. M.: The effect of thiopental on peripheral venous tone. Anesthesiology, *22*:525, 1961.

Eckstein, J. W., Wendling, M., and Abboud, F. M.: Forearm venous responses to stimulation of adrenergic receptors. J. Clin. Invest., *44*:1151, 1965.

Engelman, K., and Sjoerdsma, A.: Inhibition of catecholamine biosynthesis in man. Circ. Research, *8* (Suppl. I):104, 1966.

Epstein, S. E., Robinson, B. F., Kahler, R. L., and Braunwald, E.: Effects of beta-

adrenergic blockade on the cardiac response to maximal and submaximal exercise in man. J. Clin. Invest., *44*:1745, 1965.
Eränkö, O.: Cell types in adrenal medulla. In: Ciba Foundation Symposium on Adrenergic Mechanisms. Eds. Wolstenholme and O'Connor. Boston, Little, Brown, 1962.
Fewings, J. D., Hodge, R. L., Scroop, G. C., and Whelan, R. F.: The effects of bethanidine on the peripheral circulation in man. Brit. J. Pharmacol., *23*:115, 1964.
Fowler, N. O., Westcott, R. N., Scott, R. C., and McGuire, J.: The effect of norepinephrine upon pulmonary arteriolar resistance in man. J. Clin. Invest., *30*:517, 1951.
Gaffney, T. E., Morrow, D. H., and Chidsey, C. A.: The role of myocardial catecholamines in the response to tyramine. J. Pharm. Exp. Therap., *137*:301, 1962.
Gitlow, S. E., Mendlowitz, M., Wilk, E. K., Wilk, S., Wolf, R. L., and Naftchi, N. E.: Plasma clearance of dl-β-H^3 norepinephrine in normal human subjects and patients with essential hypertension. J. Clin. Invest., *43*:2009, 1964.
Glick, G., Sonnenblick, E. H., and Braunwald, E.: Myocardial force-velocity relations studied in intact unanesthetized man. J. Clin. Invest., *44*:978, 1965.
Glover, W. E., Greenfield, A. D. M., Kidd, B. S. L., and Whelan, R. F.: The reactions of the capacity blood vessels of the human hand and forearm to vasoactive substances infused intra-arterially. J. Physiol., *140*:113, 1958.
Glover, W. E., Greenfield, A. D. M., and Shanks, R. G.: Effect of dichloroisoprenaline on the peripheral vascular responses to adrenaline in man. Brit. J. Pharmacol., *19*:235, 1962.
Goldberg, L. I., Bloodwell, R. D., Braunwald, E., and Morrow, A. G.: The direct effects of norepinephrine, epinephrine, and methoxamine on myocardial contractile force in man. Circulation, *22*:1125, 1960.
Goldenberg, M., Pines, K. L., Baldwin, E. deF., Greene, D. C., and Roh, C. E.: Hemodynamic response of man to norepinephrine and epinephrine and its relation to the problem of hypertension. Am. J. Med., *5*:792, 1948.
Goodall, McC.: Sympathoadrenal responses to gravitation stress. J. Clin. Invest., *41*:197, 1962.
Goodall, McC., Kirshner, N., and Rosen, L.: Metabolism of noradrenaline in the human. J. Clin. Invest., *38*:707, 1959.
Goodall, McC., and Rosen, L.: Urinary excretion of noradrenaline and its metabolites at ten-minute intervals after intravenous injection of dl-noradrenaline-2-C^{14}. J. Clin. Invest., *42*:1578, 1963.
Goodall, McC., Stone, C., and Haynes, B. W., Jr.: Urinary output of adrenaline and noradrenaline in severe thermal burns. Ann. Surg., *145*:479, 1957.
Gregg, D. E., and Fisher, L. C.: In: Handbook of Physiology. Section 2: Circulation, Volume 2. Washington, D.C., American Physiological Society, 1963.
Hamer, J., and Sowton, E.: Cardiac output after beta-adrenergic blockade in ischaemic heart disease. Brit. Heart J., *27*:892, 1965.
Harris, W. S., Schoenfeld, C. D., Brooks, R. H., and Weissler, A. M.: Effect of beta adrenergic blockade on the hemodynamic responses to epinephrine in man. Am. J. Cardiol., *17*:484, 1966.
Harrison, D. C., Chidsey, C. A., Goldman, R., and Braunwald, E.: Relationships between the release and tissue depletion of norepinephrine from the heart by guanethidine and reserpine. Circ. Research, *12*:256, 1963.
Harrison, D. C., Glick, G., Goldblatt, A., and Braunwald, E.: Studies on cardiac dimensions in intact unanesthetized man. IV. Effects of isoproterenol and methoxamine. Circulation, *29*:186, 1964.
Havel, R. J.: The conversion of plasma free fatty acids into triglycerides of plasma lipoprotein fractions in man. Metabolism, *10*:1031, 1961.
Havel, R. J., and Goldfien, A.: The role of the sympathetic nervous system in the metabolism of free fatty acids. J. Lipid Res., *1*:102, 1959.
Horsley, A. W., and Eckstein, J. W.: Effect of mephentermine on venomotor tone, blood flow and arterial pressure in forearm of man. Proc. Soc. Exp. Biol. Med.. *105*:569, 1960.

Horvath, S. M., and Knapp, D. W.: Hemodynamic effects of Neosynephrine. Am. J. Physiol., *178*:387, 1954.
King, B. D., Sokoloff, L., and Wechsler, R. L.: The effects of l-epinephrine and l-norepinephrine upon cerebral circulation and metabolism in man. J. Clin. Invest., *31*:273, 1952.
King, S. E., and Baldwin, D. S.: Production of renal ischemia and proteinuria in man by adrenal medullary hormones. Am. J. Med., *20*:217, 1956.
Kjellberg, S. R., Rudhe, V., and Sjöstrand, T.: Effect of adrenaline on contraction of human heart under normal circulatory conditions. Acta Physiol. Scand., *24*: 333, 1952.
Kopin, I. J.: Storage and metabolism of catecholamines: role of monoamine oxidase. Pharm. Rev., *16*:179, 1964.
Krasnow, N., Rolett, E. L., Yurchak, P. M., Hood, W. B., Jr., and Gorlin, R.: Isoproterenol and cardiovascular performance. Am. J. Med., *37*:514, 1964.
La Brosse, E. H., Axelrod, J., and Kety, S.: O-Methylation, the principle route of metabolism of epinephrine in man. Science, *128*:593, 1958.
Lever, A. F., Mowbray, J. F., and Peart, W. S.: Blood flow and blood pressure after noradrenaline infusions. Clin. Sci., *21*:69, 1961.
Levy, J. V., and Richards, V.: Inotropic and chronotropic effects of a series of β-adrenergic blocking drugs: some structure-activity relationships. Proc. Soc. Exp. Biol. Med., *122*:373, 1966.
Livesay, W. R., Moyer, J. H., and Chapman, D. W.: The cardiovascular and renal hemodynamic effects of Aramine. Am. Heart J., *47*:745, 1954.
MacCannell, K. L., McNay, J. L., Mayer, M. B., and Goldberg, L. I.: Dopamine in the treatment of hypotension and shock. New Eng. J. Med., *275*:1389, 1966.
Mahon, W. A., and Mashford, M. L.: The pressor effect of tyramine in man and its modification by reserpine pretreatment. J. Clin. Invest., *42*:338, 1963.
Mayer, S., Moran, N. C., and Fain, J.: The effect of adrenergic blocking agents on some metabolic actions of catecholamines. J. Pharm. Exp. Therap., *134*:18, 1961.
Mills, L. C., and Moyer, J. H.: Methoxamine: effect on blood pressure and renal hemodynamics. Am. J. Med. Sci., *233*:409, 1957.
Moran, N. C.: Adrenergic receptors, drugs and the cardiovascular system. Mod. Concepts Cardiovasc. Dis., *35*:93, 1966.
Moran, N. C.: Pharmacological characterization of adrenergic receptors. Pharmacol. Rev., *19*(Part 1):503, 1966.
Moran, N. C., and Perkins, M. E.: Adrenergic blockade of the mammalian heart by a dichloro analogue of isoproterenol. J. Pharm. Exp. Therap., *124*:223, 1958.
Moss, A. J., and Duffie, E. R.: The use of isoproterenol (Isuprel) in the evaluation of congenital cardiac defects. Circulation, *27*:51, 1963.
Nagatsu, T., Levitt, M., and Udenfriend, S.: Tyrosine hydroxylase, the initial step in norepinephrine biosynthesis. J. Biol. Chem., *239*:2910, 1964.
Nestel, P. J.: Plasma triglyceride concentration and plasma free fatty acid changes in response to norepinephrine in man. J. Clin. Invest., *43*:77, 1964.
Potter, L. T., and Axelrod, J.: Subcellular localization of catecholamines in tissues of rat. J. Pharm. Exp. Therap., *142*:291, 1963.
Potter, L. T., Axelrod, J., and Kopin, I. J.: Differential binding and release of norepinephrine and tachyphylaxis. Biochem. Pharmacol., *11*:254, 1962.
Powell, C. E., and Slater, I. H.: Blocking of inhibitor adrenergic receptors by a dichloro analogue of isoproterenol. J. Pharm. Exp. Therap., *122*:480, 1958.
Ranges, H. A., and Bradley, S. E.: Systemic and renal circulatory changes following the administration of adrenin, ephedrine, and paredrinol to normal man. J. Clin. Invest., *22*:687, 1943.
Richardson, D. W., Ferguson, R. W., and Patterson, J. L., Jr.: Effects of mephentermine on cerebral metabolism and circulation. J. Pharm. Exp. Therap., *119*: 219, 1957.
Robinson, B. F., Epstein, S. E., Beiser, G. D., and Braunwald, E.: Control of the heart rate by the autonomic nervous system. Studies in man on the interrela-

tion between baroreceptor mechanisms and exercise. Circ. Research, *19*:400, 1966.

Rushmer, R. F., and Smith, O. A., Jr.: Cardiac control. Physiol. Rev., *39*:41, 1959.

Schröder, G., and Werkö, L.: Nethalide, a beta adrenergic blocking agent. Clin. Pharmacol. & Therap., *5*:159, 1964.

Sensenbach, W., Madison, L., and Ochs, L.: Comparison of effects of l-norepinephrine synthetic l-epinephrine, and U.S.P. epinephrine upon cerebral blood flow and metabolism in man. J. Clin. Invest., *32*:226, 1953.

Shanks, R. G.: The pharmacology of beta sympathetic blockade. Am. J. Cardiol., *18*:308, 1966.

Smythe, C. McC., Nickel, J. F., and Bradley, S. E.: Effect of epinephrine (U.S.P.), l-epinephrine and l-norepinephrine on glomerular filtration rate, renal plasma flow, and the urinary excretion of sodium, potassium, and water in normal man. J. Clin. Invest., *31*:499, 1952.

Sonnenblick, E. H.: Force-velocity relations in mammalian heart muscle. Am. J. Physiol., *202*:931, 1962.

Sonnenblick, E. H., Braunwald, E., and Morrow, A. G.: The contractile properties of human heart muscle: Studies on myocardial mechanics of surgically excised papillary muscles. J. Clin. Invest., *44*:966, 1965A.

Sonnenblick, E. H., Braunwald, E., Williams, J. F., Jr., and Glick, G.: Effects of exercise on myocardial force-velocity relations in intact unanesthetized man: Relative roles of changes in heart rate, sympathetic activity, and ventricular dimensions. J. Clin. Invest., *44*:2051, 1965B.

Spann, J. F., Jr., Sonnenblick, E. H., Cooper, T., Chidsey, C. A., Willman, V. L., and Braunwald, E.: Cardiac norepinephrine stores and the contractile state of heart muscle. Circ. Research, *19*:317, 1966.

Spector, S., Sjoerdsma, A., and Udenfriend, S.: Blockade of endogenous norepinephrine synthesis by α-methyl-tyrosine, an inhibitor of tyrosine hydroxylase. J. Pharm. Exp. Therap., *147*:86, 1965.

Spector, S., Sjoerdsma, A., Zaltzman-Nirenberg, P. Levitt, M., and Udenfriend, S.: Norepinephrine synthesis from tyrosine -C^{14} in isolated perfused guinea pig heart. Science, *139*:1299, 1963.

Steinberg, D., Nestel, P. J., Buskirk, E. R., and Thompson, R. H.: Calorigenic effect of norepinephrine correlated with plasma free fatty acid turnover and oxidation. J. Clin. Invest., *43*:167, 1964.

Sutherland, E. W., and Rall, T. W.: The relation of adenosine -3′, 5′ phosphate and phosphorylase to the actions of catecholamines and other hormones. Pharm. Rev., *12*:265, 1960.

Trendelenburg, U.: Modification of effect of tyramine by various agents and procedures. J. Pharm. Exp. Therap., *134*:8, 1961.

Tuckman, J., and Finnerty, F. A., Jr.: Cardiac index during intravenous levarterenol infusion in man. Circ. Research, *7*:988, 1959.

Udenfriend, S.: Biosynthesis of the sympathetic neurotransmitter, norepinephrine. The Harvey Lectures. Series 60. New York and London, Academic Press, 1964-1965.

Vaughan Williams, E. M.: Mode of action of beta receptor antagonists on cardiac muscle. Am. J. Cardiol., *18*:399, 1966.

Vendsalu, A.: Studies on adrenaline and noradrenaline in human plasma. Acta Physiol. Scand., *49*(Suppl. 173):1, 1960.

von Euler, U. S.: A specific sympathomimetic ergone in adrenergic nerve fibers (sympathin) and its relation to adrenaline and noradrenaline. Acta Physiol. Scand., *12*:73, 1946.

von Euler, U. S., Franksson, C., and Hellström, J.: Adrenaline and noradrenaline output in urine after unilateral and bilateral adrenalectomy in man. Acta Physiol. Scand., *31*:1, 1954.

von Euler, U. S., and Hellner, S.: Excretion of noradrenaline and adrenaline in muscular work. Acta Physiol. Scand., *26*:183, 1952.

Weissler, A. M., Leonard, J. J., and Warren, J. V.: The hemodynamic effect of isoproterenol in man with observations on the role of the central blood volume. J. Lab. Clin. Med., *53*:921, 1959.

Wilber, J. A., and Brust, A. A.: The circulatory and metabolic effects in man of histamine, mecholyl, tetraethylammonium and atropine in the presence of circulating epinephrine and norepinephrine. J. Clin. Invest., *37*:476, 1958.
Wurtman, R. J.: Catecholamines. New Eng. J. Med., *273*:637, 1966.
Yurchak, P. M., Rolett, E. L., Cohen, L. S., and Gorlin, R.: Effects of norepinephrine on the coronary circulation in man. Circulation, *30*:180, 1964.
Zuberbuhler, R. C., and Bohr, D. F.: Responses of coronary smooth muscle to catecholamines. Circ. Research, *16*:431, 1965.

Chapter 7

DIGITALIS GLYCOSIDES

- Fundamental Effects
- Effects on Heart and Circulation in Man

The primary action of the cardiac glycosides appears to be on the contractile apparatus rather than on the energy yielding metabolism. However, the means by which they increase the contractile power of heart muscle, in the doses used in clinical practice, is still uncertain.

Despite the diversity of their origins, the glycosides all have similar basic structures and pharmacological actions. They differ in their potency, rate of absorption, duration of action and elimination. Their structure comprises a basic steroid nucleus, a 5- or 6-membered unsaturated lactone ring attached in beta orientation to C_{17} of the steroid nucleus and a sugar such as digitoxose or rhamnose (Fig. 7-1). When the sugar is removed and replaced by a hydroxyl group, the compound is known as an aglycone or genin. The genin moiety is responsible for the physiological activity of the glycosides; the sugar alone has no effect on the myocardium. However, the affinity of the compounds for heart muscle is conferred by glycosidic linkage with one or more sugars.

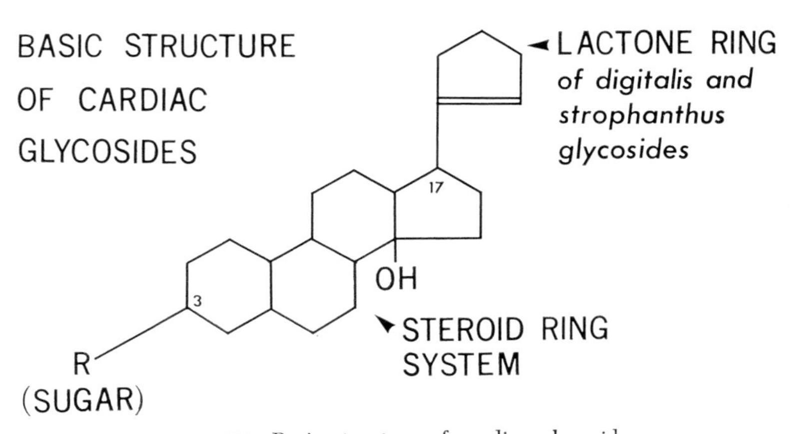

FIGURE 7-1. Basic structure of cardiac glycosides.

FUNDAMENTAL EFFECTS

Attempts have been made to deduce the local effects of the glycosides on cardiac contractility from studies in intact man and animals. However, the many variables inherent in such studies make it difficult to draw conclusions about the effects on individual muscle cells. Thus, alterations in the heart rate, in the initial fiber length due to changes in intraventricular end-diastolic pressure, in the load applied to the heart muscle during contraction due to changes in aortic pressure, and in the activity of cardiac autonomic nerves, all modify the contractile response of individual cells. For this reason, isolated preparations of heart muscle (usually thin strips of papillary muscle) have been used to investigate the local effects of digitalis preparations.

ISOLATED HEART MUSCLE PREPARATIONS. The functional behavior of the contractile apparatus may be represented by an active contractile unit in series with a passive, undamped elastic element (see page 3). The cardiac glycosides improve the ability of the contractile element to exert tension, so that the velocity of shortening is increased; that is, they have a positive inotropic action on heart muscle. They do not change the compliance of the elastic element. The increase in intensity of the active state is accompanied by a shorter duration. The net result is potentiation of the amplitude of isometric contraction together with reduction of the time required to develop peak tension and reduction of the total duration of contraction. Thus, a change in the intensity of the active state at a given rest length is accompanied by a proportionate change in the maximal speed of shortening (Edman, 1965).

Similar changes in the contractile state of mammalian myocardium may result from increasing the rate of electrical stimulation, from increasing concentration of ionic calcium, and from norepinephrine (Sonnenblick, 1962). The synergistic effects of cardiac glycosides and of an increased rate of contraction on the intensity of the active state and on the force-velocity relation suggests that these two inotropic influences may have a common mode of action (Edman, 1965).

Siegel and Sonnenblick (1963) calculated the ratio of the maximal rate of development of isometric tension to the integrated systolic isometric tension in papillary muscles from cats and in innervated isovolumic heart preparations. Using this ratio as an index of myocardial contractility, they found that it changed only when there was an alteration of the maximal intrinsic shortening velocity. Their results suggested that cardioactive drugs such as strophanthin and norepinephrine, in addition to increasing the total mechanical energy available in a contraction (as represented by the integrated systolic isometric tension), caused a relative increase in the rate of delivery of this mechanical energy (Edman, 1965).

The presence of norepinephrine in cardiac muscle is not essential for the development of a positive inotropic response to the digitalis glycosides (Spann et al., 1966).

MYOCARDIAL CELLS. It is now accepted that heart muscle is not a syncytium but consists of discrete cells (Sjöstrand and Andersson-Cedergren, 1960). Measurements of the function of cardiac muscle reflect the integrated activity of countless individual cells. Three subcellular systems must function sequentially before a muscle cell can contract: (1) The cell membrane, which regulates the chemical and ionic composition of the solution inside the cell; (2) Excitation-contraction coupling, by which the electrical events occurring at the cell surface are transmitted to the contractile elements; (3) The contractile elements (or myofibrils) that contain the contractile proteins. It is still uncertain whether the inotropic effect of digitalis is a membrane phenomenon or occurs inside the cell (Page, 1964).

The cell membrane may be regarded as a porous structure, with interstices containing an aqueous salt solution. Through these interstices, sodium and potassium ions are continually leaking into and out of the cell. The expulsion of sodium from the cell must take place against both the concentration gradient and the gradient of electrical potential; it is therefore an energy consuming process. Digitalis in sufficiently high concentrations inhibits the transport of sodium and potassium across the cell membrane (Holland, 1964). This may be due to inhibition of the activity of cell membrane adenosine triphosphatase (ATPase), the probable source of energy for the sodium pump (Glynn, 1957), with a resulting net loss of cell potassium and some gain of cell sodium. High extracellular concentrations of potassium inhibit, and low extracellular concentrations enhance this effect of digitalis (Page, 1964). ATPase activity, which is required for splitting of the energy rich phosphate bond of adenosine triphosphate, is accelerated by potassium ions and inhibited by digitalis glycosides.

The administration of lanatoside increases the venous concentration of potassium relative to its arterial concentration in the heart-lung preparation. This could be correlated with an increase in the mechanical efficiency of cardiac contraction (Wood and Moe, 1940). Correlations have been demonstrated between the potassium depleting and inotropic effects of cardiac glycosides (Sarnoff et al., 1964; Müller, 1965), but the available evidence suggests that a change in the distribution of sodium and potassium is not the cause of the increased contractility (Holland, 1964). Therapeutic doses of digitalis which produce a definite inotropic action do not decrease, and may slightly increase, the concentration of potassium within heart muscle cells (Bliss and Adolph, 1963). Also, digitalis has been shown to augment contractility prior to the demonstration of any change in potassium flux.

The calcium concentration in the immediate environment of the myofibril appears to be regulated by the membrane limited system of tubules and vesicles known as the sarcoplasmic reticulum. Since tritiated digoxin is localized in the transverse tubular system of the sarcoplasmic reticulum (the site of excitation-contraction coupling), it may have an action here (Sonnenblick et al., 1964). This portion of the sarcoplasmic reticulum is in direct continuity with the sarcolemma. Calcium ions are essential for excitation-contraction coupling, and a calcium binding factor in the sarcoplasmic reticulum is necessary for cardiac relaxation. Like the reactions between the contractile proteins, the uptake of calcium by the reticulum depends on the splitting of the energy rich phosphate bond of adenosine triphosphate. Depolarization of the cell membrane leads to an increased inflow of calcium, thereby activating the contractile elements. The positive inotropic effects of the cardiac glycosides are associated with increased uptake and  release of calcium, but the total calcium content of the tissue is unaltered. Thus, the intensification of the active state caused by digitalis may be due to an increase in the quantity of activator calcium being released into the cells at the moment of excitation; that is, the cardiac glycosides cause a further mobilization of calcium that is known to occur with each heart beat (Holland, 1964).

Changes of calcium mobility within the myocardial cell also account for the positive inotropic changes produced by excess of calcium and by increased frequency of contraction; they also account for the negative inotropic effects produced by acetylcholine (Edman, 1965). It is possible that calcium has a direct effect on the contractile elements, either by activating interaction between the myofilaments by a process involving ATPase, or by inhibiting a relaxing system in the myocardium (Holland, 1964). Digitalis may inhibit the ATPase activity of the sarcotubular relaxing factor which is necessary for binding calcium (Weber et al., 1963). The released calcium may then become available for ATPase activity of myosin, for which an adequate concentration of calcium is essential; this then leads to interaction between the contractile proteins.

The failure by Sonnenblick et al. (1964) to find radioactive digoxin localized in the contractile filaments is in keeping with the evidence of Kay and Green (1964) that the inotropic effect of ouabain is not mediated through direct alteration of the contractile protein. Nor is any alteration produced in the ATPase active site of myosin that results in either an increased or decreased rate of hydrolysis of ATP. The digitalis glycosides cause slight changes in the intracellular ionic environment, mediated by reversible binding of ions such as potassium and sodium by actomyosin; in this respect, they exert an indirect effect on the contractile proteins (Kay and Green, 1964).

CARDIAC RATE AND RHYTHM. In addition to their inotropic effects, the digitalis glycosides and ouabain influence the rate and the rhythm of the heart. They have a direct depressant action on the sinuatrial node (McLain et al., 1959). Infusion of acetylstrophanthidin and digoxin

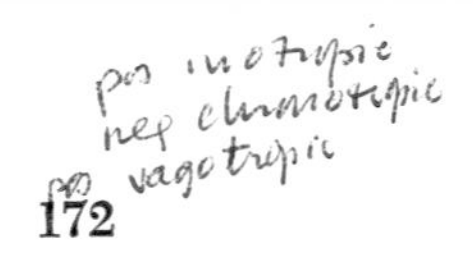

into the artery supplying the sinus node of the dog was followed commonly by sinus bradycardia and occasionally by sinus arrest and atrioventricular (A-V) nodal escape rhythm (James and Nadeau, 1963); prior administration of atropine or bilateral cervical vagotomy did not prevent the negative chronotropic effect. The glycosides increase the sensitivity of the heart to normal vagal activity (Trautwein, 1963), although the chronotropic effect of sympathetic stimulation or epinephrine on the sinuatrial and A-V nodes is reduced (Mendez et al., 1961).

The rates of conduction through the A-V node, determined by measuring conduction time from a stimulating electrode on the atrium to a recording electrode on the surface of the ventricle, and through the Purkinje fiber system are slowed to a greater degree than conduction through either atrium or ventricle. Thus, in atrial fibrillation, the depressant action of digitalis on A-V conduction reduces the number of atrial excitations conducted to the ventricle, thereby slowing the ventricular rate (Moe and Mendez, 1951).

In the presence of ouabain, the resting potential is not appreciably affected, but the action potential is diminished and its rate of rise is reduced. No theoretical relation can be seen between the positive inotropic effect of digitalis and the shortening of the action potential, the inhibition of active transport or the increase or decrease of potassium conductance (Trautwein, 1963). Tuttle et al. (1961) suggested that positive inotropic effects may occur before changes of potassium flux or of intracellular potassium concentrations can be detected. Thus, although loss of potassium or a combination of potassium loss and sodium gain does not explain the inotropic effect of cardiac glycosides, their effects on the electrical activity of the heart including their propensity to induce arrhythmias are mediated in great part through alterations in the movement and the intracellular distribution of these ions. The Purkinje cells are much more susceptible than the myocardial cells to digitalis induced alterations in electrical activity (Conn and Luchi, 1964). It has been suggested that ouabain may have a high affinity for receptors for calcium within the membrane and thereby exert an inotropic effect similar to that of a high intracellular concentration of calcium or a low intracellular concentration of sodium (Trautwein, 1963).

In experiments on Purkinje fibers in which both membrane potential and potassium flux as well as intracellular concentrations of potassium were measured, arrhythmias caused by a toxic dose of ouabain could be attributed to loss of intracellular potassium. When the intracellular potassium concentration was restored, the arrhythmias disappeared (Müller, 1963).

The influence of autonomic innervation and of myocardial catecholamine stores on the response to ouabain of myocardial contractile force and of the functional refractory period of the A-V conduction system was determined in anesthetized dogs with open chests (Morrow et al., 1963). The mean increase in contractile force produced by ouabain in groups of dogs that had been vagotomized, pretreated with reserpine, acutely cardiac denervated or chronically cardiac denervated was not significantly different from the mean increase produced by ouabain in control dogs. Also, the mean cumulative doses of ouabain required to produce multiple ventricular premature contractions did not differ significantly among the groups. Although the inotropic and arrhythmogenic effects of ouabain appeared to be independent of the state of autonomic innervation or of myocardial stores of catecholamine, a major portion of the prolongation of the functional refractory period of the A-V conduction system produced by ouabain was dependent upon the integrity of autonomic innervation. Following chronic cardiac denervation and myocardial catecholamine depletion, ouabain had only a minor direct effect on the functional refractory period (Morrow et al., 1963).

CELL METABOLISM. The energy inherent in the terminal phosphate bond of adenosine triphosphate (ATP) or some closely related intermediate compound can be used to perform work, whether this be the work of active ion or other transport, of muscular contraction or of chemical synthesis of cellular constituents (Page, 1964). The enzymes that synthesize ATP during the oxidation of fatty acids, lactate and other substances to carbon dioxide and water are found predominantly in the membranes of numerous intracellular organelles (mitochondria). A smaller but significant fraction of ATP is synthesized during the breakdown of glucose to lactic acid by enzymes dissolved in the cytoplasmic solution. When cellular oxidation is arrested by depriving the cell of nutrients or oxygen, and when energy conservation is interfered with by uncoupling oxidation from phosphorylation, cellular depletion of energy rich phosphate compounds results. The active transport mechanism is deprived of its energy supply, and the myocardial cell takes up sodium, loses potassium and swells in the same manner as when active transport is inhibited with cardiac glycosides (Page, 1964). However, it has not been convincingly demonstrated that cardiac glycosides in intact muscle affect either mitochondrial and cytoplasmic oxidative reactions or the reactions by which oxidative energy is conserved as ATP (oxidative phosphorylation) (Page, 1964).

METABOLISM OF DIGITALIS GLYCOSIDES. The metabolism and excretion of digoxin labeled with tritium has been extensively studied in patients with congestive heart failure (Doherty and Perkins, 1962, 1965). The half-time (time required for half the administered dose to disappear from the blood) was 30 to 40 hours, whether it was given orally, intramuscularly or intravenously. After seven days, 80 per cent had been recovered unchanged from the urine and 10 per cent from the feces. In patients with renal failure, renal excretion was impaired and the half-time prolonged (Doherty and Perkins, 1964). Tritiated digoxin was given to 11 patients who were anephric prior to renal transplantation (Doherty et al.,

1967). They had high serum levels and greatly increased blood half-times. Excretion in the feces was increased, but insufficiently to compensate for the absence of renal excretion.

The metabolism and excretion of C^{14} labeled digitoxin is different from that of digoxin (Okita, 1957). Ninety per cent of an administered dose is metabolized in the liver, and the end products are mainly excreted in the urine. Small amounts are excreted unchanged in the urine for a prolonged period. The biliary tract and intestinal mucosa also excrete small quantities (Conn and Luchi, 1964).

The distribution of cardiac glycosides among the various organs and tissues is variable. The heart does not selectively bind digitoxin, since greater concentrations may be found in liver and kidney. Digoxin, however, has a selective affinity for heart muscle. When a plateau concentration of digoxin had been attained in the serum following its injection into dogs, there was a heart to serum concentration ratio of 43:1 (Doherty and Perkins, 1966).

EFFECTS ON HEART AND CIRCULATION IN MAN

The administration of digitalis to patients with congestive heart failure from many causes improves the performance of the cardiovascular system. The increase in output of the failing ventricles, combined with the reduction in their end-diastolic pressures attests to its positive inotropic action. The 13 patients studied by Ferrer et al. (1960) had severe pulmonary and systemic venous congestion due to both left and right ventricular failure. Digoxin given intravenously increased the cardiac output. Since the heart rate decreased, the increased output was accounted for by an increased stroke volume (Fig. 7-2). Thus, the major effect of digitalis in relieving congestive heart failure results from an increase in the force of contraction of the failing myocardium. Although other substances such as norepinephrine also increase the force of cardiac contraction, their inotropic effect is accompanied by a measurable increase in oxygen consumption of the intact heart, whereas that due to cardiac glycosides is not (Bing et al., 1950). Hence, in contrast with the catecholamines, digitalis increases the efficiency of myocardial contraction. Digitalis glycosides do cause an increase in the oxygen consumption of slices of human myocardium, which is dependent on calcium ions and accounted for by activation of glycolysis (Crevasse and Wheat, 1962). They also increase the oxygen consumption of papillary muscle from cats (Coleman, 1967). However, this cannot be detected in the intact heart by methods at present available. Lanatoside C, although it improved the work capacity of the failing heart, did not affect the utilization of substrate (Blain et al., 1956).

The increased cardiac output reverses the sequence of events that lead to the accumulation of edema fluid. The glomerular filtration rate in-

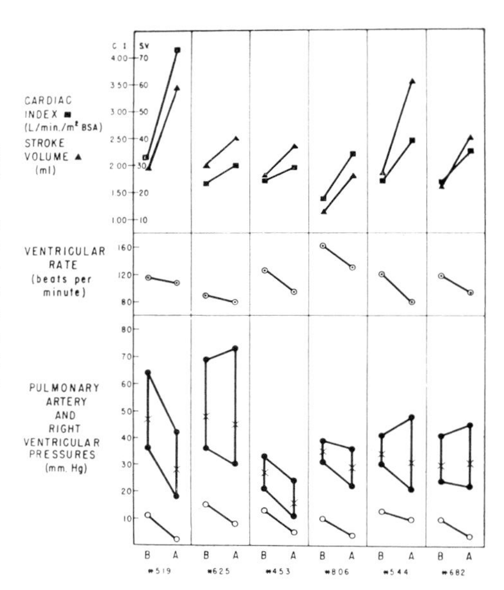

FIGURE 7-2. Effects of intravenous digoxin in patients with left and right ventricular failure. Symbols: squares, cardiac index; triangles, stroke volume; targets, heart rate; black dots, pulmonary arterial systolic and diastolic pressures; white dots, right ventricular end-diastolic pressures. B represents values before and A values after digoxin. The first two patients had sinus rhythm; the remainder had atrial fibrillation. (From Ferrer, Conroy and Harvey, Circulation, *21*:372, 1960.)

creases, the tubular reabsorption of sodium decreases, and the resultant negative sodium balance results in diuresis of obligated intercellular water. Relief of pulmonary edema fluid diminishes dyspnea and cyanosis. Digitalis also has a direct renal action that, presumably through inhibition of tubular reabsorption of sodium, induces a saliuresis and diuresis. This direct effect, as opposed to the indirect effects of increased renal blood flow, is probably insignificant clinically (Strickler and Kessler, 1961).

In congestive failure, the heart rate is more rapid than normal. This may result in part from stimulation of chemoreceptors secondary to hypoxia. Relief of hypoxia, due to improvement in cardiac function from digitalis, leads to reflex slowing of the heart. This slowing is mediated by the vagus and can be blocked by atropine. The direct effect of digitalis on autonomic nerve fibers supplying the heart and on the sinuatrial node, which can slow the heart in experiments in animals, probably is of little significance with the doses normally used in clinical practice.

Excessive doses of digitalis may slow the heart through a direct action on the A-V node. In patients with normal sinus rhythm, the PR interval is prolonged, but as long as a one to one relationship continues between atria and ventricles, the latter are not slowed below the sinus rate. Further depression of the A-V node, however, may lead to second or third degree A-V block.

In patients with atrial fibrillation, the rapid and irregular input to the A-V node leads to an irregular rate of ventricular contraction. The ventricular contractions vary in intensity depending on their time relationships to the immediately preceding contractions and on the relative refractory state of the conduction system and ventricular myocardium. As in patients with sinus rhythm, the improvement in cardiac output from the inotropic effect of therapeutic doses of digitalis enhances the oxygenation of the systemic tissues; there follows a *reflex* slowing of the ventricles mediated by increased vagal activity on the A-V node. The ventricular rate is still capable of acceleration during exercise, due to decreased vagal and increased sympathetic activity. The *direct* action of larger doses of digitalis on the conduction system gradually slows the ventricles, and with toxic doses, the ventricles may be incapable of acceleration during exercise or with other stimuli. The administration of sufficient digitalis to have a direct effect on the A-V node, thereby reinforcing the reflex slowing, may be beneficial in atrial fibrillation, provided that acceleration can still occur during exercise. This direct effect seems to be useful only in this arrhythmia.

The cardiac glycosides either do not change or slightly reduce the cardiac output in normal subjects and in patients with fully compensated cardiac disease (Bing et al., 1950; Harvey et al., 1951; Selzer et al., 1959; Dresdale et al., 1959; Rodman et al., 1961). Digoxin diminishes the total postexercise oxygen debt of patients with compensated heart disease; this emphasizes the value of the cardiac glycosides in the management of such patients (Kahler et al., 1962). In the eight normal resting subjects studied by Williams et al. (1958), the mean systemic arterial blood pressure increased on the average from 95 to 109 mm. Hg following therapeutic doses of digitalis. Cardiac output, determined by the indicator dilution technique, decreased by 12 per cent, heart rate by five per cent and stroke volume by nine per cent (average values). Thus, there was an increase in systemic vascular resistance. During supine leg exercise (average oxygen consumption about 1.3 liters per minute, average cardiac output about 14 liters per minute) cardiac ouput, pulse rate and stroke volume were 18, six and nine per cent less, respectively, after digitalization. It was concluded that any improvement of contractility was overshadowed in these measurements by the action of the glycosides on the peripheral circulation.

Using a strain gauge arch sutured to the right ventricle to record the

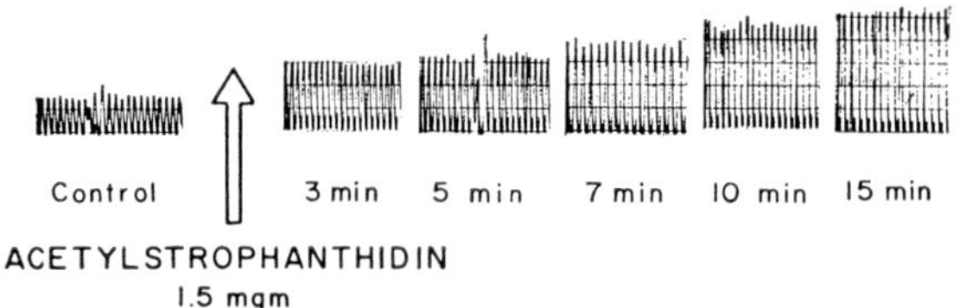

FIGURE 7-3. Recordings of myocardial contractile force before and at intervals after a dose of 1.5 mg. acetylstrophanthidin in a 28 year old woman with atrial septal defect. Augmentation is evident three minutes after the injection. (From Braunwald, Bloodwell, Goldberg and Morrow, J. Clin. Invest., *40*:52, 1961.)

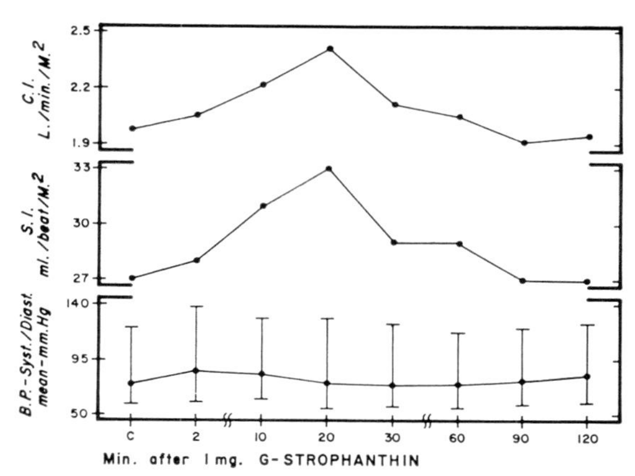

FIGURE 7-4. Cardiac index, stroke volume index and systemic arterial pressure before and after 1 mg. strophanthin G. (average values from six patients with complete heart block). (From Benchimol, Palmero, Liggett and Dimond, Circulation, *32*: 84, 1965.)

isometric tension of the subjacent cardiac fibers, Braunwald et al. (1961) showed that acetylstrophanthidin and lanatoside C considerably augmented the force of ventricular contraction at the time of operation with cardiopulmonary bypass in patients who were not in heart failure (Fig. 7-3). It is uncertain to what extent these results can be extrapolated to the normal hearts of intact unanesthetized man. Benchimol et al. (1965) described the effects of digitalis in patients with complete heart block resulting from coronary artery disease, in whom the ventricular rate was maintained constant with an electronic pacemaker. Cardiac output and stroke volume increased by about 20 per cent from control values that approximated 2 liters per M.^{2} per minute and 27 ml. per M.^{2} per beat, respectively. There was no significant change in systemic arterial blood pressure; therefore, the systemic vascular resistance decreased (Fig. 7-4). The increased stroke volume was accompanied by decreases in the duration of ventricular ejection time and of mechanical systole, due to the direct effect of the drug on the myocardium. The importance of the atrial contribution to ventricular filling was less after treatment with digitalis.

Nine patients, three with left ventricular failure and six with left ventricular enlargement but no clinical manifestations of failure, were studied by means of right and transseptal left heart catheterization before and after an intravenous dose of acetylstrophanthidin. In the compensated group, there were no significant changes in cardiac index, stroke volume index or mean systolic ejection rate. There were minor increases in stroke work and stroke power and moderate decreases in left ventricular diastolic pressures. The most notable finding was augmentation of the rate of increase of left ventricular systolic pressure. In the decompensated group, acetylstrophanthidin decreased the heart rate and increased the stroke volume index, stroke work, mean stroke power, mean systolic ejection rate and the rate of increase of systolic pressure in the left ventricle. Left ventricular end-diastolic pressures were markedly lowered after digitalization (Murphy et al., 1964).

There is ample evidence from experiments with animals that, under well controlled conditions, the rate at which ventricular pressure increases during systole is a function of myocardial contractility (Patterson et al., 1914; Wiggers, 1927; Reeves et al., 1960; Daggett and Weisfeldt, 1965). A cardiac catheter with a high fidelity micromanometer mounted at its tip (Laurens et al., 1959) was linked to an electronic differentiating circuit (Gleason and Braunwald, 1962) and used to measure the rate of increase of pressure during systole in both ventricles of subjects without heart disease (Mason and Braunwald, 1964). Digoxin and ouabain increased the maximal rate of development of pressure in both ventricles (Fig. 7-5). Since these drugs did not appreciably alter the heart rate, the ventricular end-diastolic pressure or volume, or arterial diastolic pressure, changes in which parameters could have influenced the measurement (Wallace et al., 1963), the finding was thought to support the view that the contractility of both ventricles was increased. There was also evidence to suggest that the glycosides stimulated the force of atrial contraction. Weissler et al. (1964) showed that, in normal young adults, deslanoside (Cedilanid-D) shortened the duration of all phases of mechanical systole in the absence of a change in cardiac output. Indeed, measurement of changes in ejection time, corrected for variations in heart rate, offers a relatively simple and semiquantitative approach to the assessment of the cardiac response to digitalis in normal man (Weissler et al., 1966).

Thus, the cardiac glycosides do produce a change in the contractile system of the non-failing human heart, leading to increased velocity of shortening of the contractile elements. Such an increase in contractility is of no importance in normal subjects, since their base line contractility is perfectly adequate for all purposes. The increase in contractility is not accompanied by an increase of cardiac output in normal subjects or those with compensated heart disease, because of concomitant changes in the peripheral circulation, involving both resistance and capacity vessels.

CORONARY VESSELS. Strophanthin had no significant effect on coronary blood flow or myocardial oxygen consumption in the failing heart (Bing et al., 1950), although it increased the cardiac output. In dogs with induced ventricular fibrillation, acetylstrophanthidin caused an initial increase in coronary vascular resistance and a decrease in coronary blood flow (Waldhausen et al., 1965). This was followed by a significant decrease of resistance and a concomitant and sustained increase in coronary blood flow. The ventricular fibrillation eliminated most of the effects of ventricular contraction on coronary blood flow. The initial vasoconstriction was due to

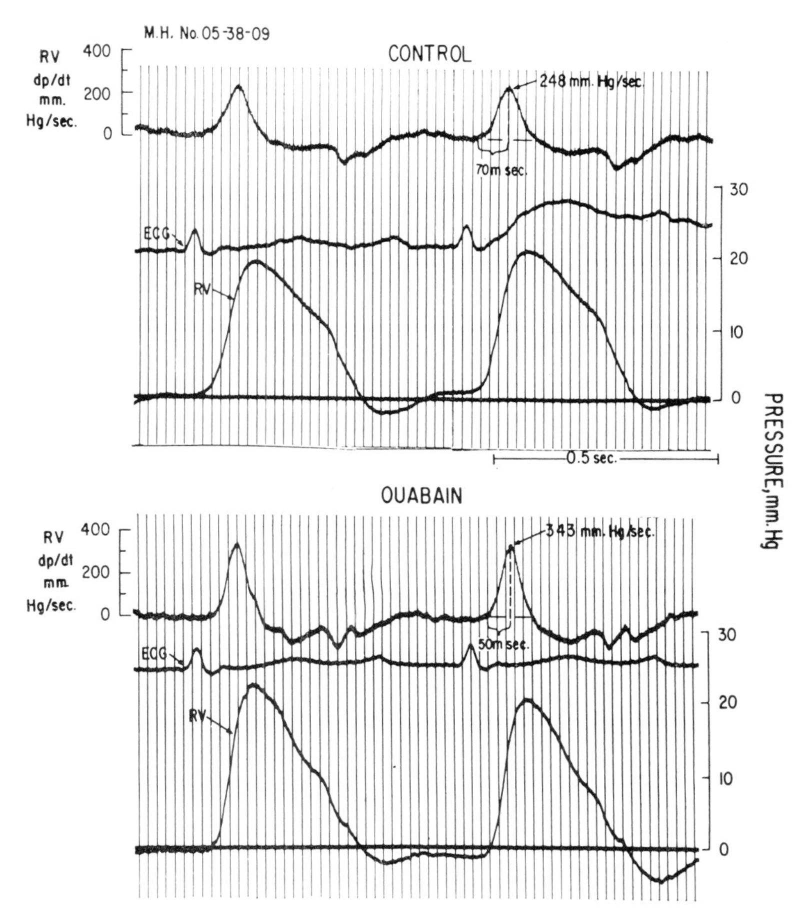

FIGURE 7-5. Records of absolute right ventricular pressure and of the rate of change of this pressure (dp/dt) before and after ouabain in a patient after repair of an uncomplicated atrial septal defect. Ouabain increased the maximal rate of change of pressure from 248 to 343 mm. Hg per second. It also shortened the time interval between the onset of contraction and the maximal rate of contraction from 70 to 50 m.sc. (From Mason, Clin. Pharmacol. & Therap., 7:1, 1966.)

a direct stimulant action of digitalis on the smooth muscle of the coronary vessels. The subsequent increase in flow was associated with an increase in the myocardial oxygen consumption; the vasodilatation may therefore have been due to the effects of myocardial metabolites acting directly on the coronary vessels. In dogs with normally beating hearts, after the initial constriction of the coronary vessels, there were only small changes in coronary blood flow and resistance, although the myocardial oxygen consumption was increased. This may have been due to an increased mechanical resistance secondary to the augmented force of contraction caused by the drug (Waldhausen et al., 1965). As with all animal experiments, it is difficult to predict from these findings whether similar changes would occur in man with therapeutic doses of digitalis.

EXTRACARDIAC EFFECTS. Excised strips of arteries and veins contract when exposed to digitalis glycosides (Leonard, 1957; Lendle and Mercker, 1961). Generalized systemic arteriolar and venous constriction were induced by digitalis in anesthetized dogs with open chests undergoing cardiopulmonary bypass (Ross et al., 1960A and B). Increased renal vascular resistance is also due to a direct effect of digitalis on vascular smooth muscle (Waldhausen and Herendeen, 1964). In normal man, digitalis glycosides increase the systemic vascular resistance (Williams et al., 1958). In patients undergoing cardiopulmonary bypass at a constant perfusion rate, acetylstrophanthidin and lanatoside C caused a brief increase in systemic vascular resistance (Braunwald et al., 1961). Ouabain, given in the usual clinical doses to normal unanesthetized subjects, caused an increase in systemic arterial blood pressure and a simultaneous decrease in forearm blood flow, indicative of constriction of resistance vessels in the

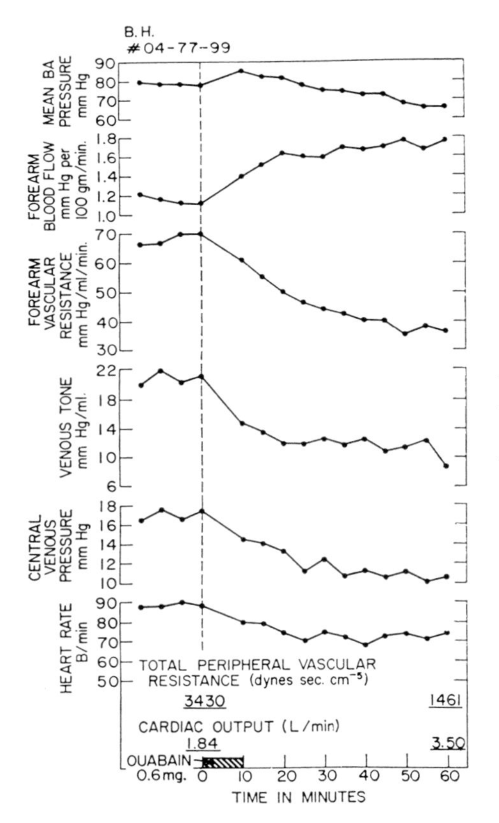

FIGURE 7-6. Serial measurements before and after ouabain in a patient with congestive heart failure. (From Mason and Braunwald, J. Clin. Invest., *43*:532, 1964.)

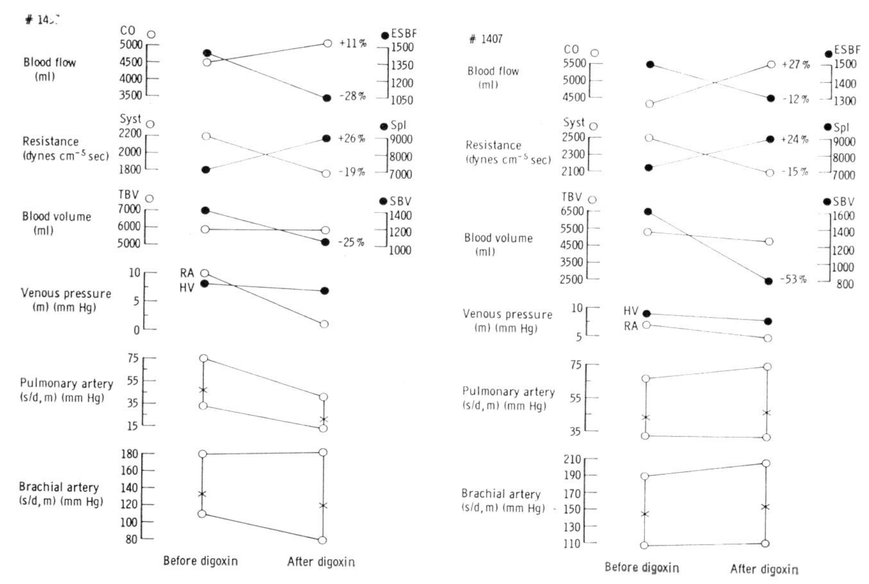

FIGURE 7-7. Effects of intravenous digoxin on the systemic and splanchnic circulations in patients with combined ventricular failure (*left*) and with right ventricular failure due to chronic lung disease (*right*). In both, there was an increase in cardiac output (CO), a decrease in right atrial pressure (RA), a decrease in systemic resistance, a decrease in splanchnic blood flow (ESBF), a decrease in splanchnic blood volume (SBV) and an increase in splanchnic vascular resistance. Hepatic venous pressure (HV) did not change. (From Ferrer, Bradley, Wheeler, Enson, Preisig and Harvey, Circulation, 32:524, 1965.)

forearm. The forearm capacity vessels were also constricted. Ouabain continued to increase forearm vascular resistance and venous tone after prolonged adrenergic blockade; thus, it acts directly on vascular smooth muscle.

Forearm vascular resistance and venous tone were greater in untreated patients with congestive heart failure than in normal subjects. They decreased after ouabain was given, while cardiac output increased, and heart rate, central venous pressure and systemic vascular resistance decreased (Mason and Braunwald, 1964; Benchimol et al., 1965; Fig. 7-6). It has been suggested that the peripheral vasoconstriction in patients with congestive failure results from increased sympathetic nervous activity (Chidsey et al., 1962). The increase in cardiac output caused by ouabain in such patients may, for reasons unknown, cause reflex diminution of sympathetic activity. In congestive failure, this reflex inhibition of vasoconstrictor tone overrides the direct constrictor effect of the drug on vascular smooth muscle. The fact that digitalis causes dilatation of systemic veins in congestive heart failure accounts for the clinical observation that rapid digitalization of patients with heart failure leads to a decrease in systemic venous pressure before the onset of diuresis (Mason and Braunwald, 1964).

Ferrer et al. (1965) measured splanchnic blood flow in 22 patients with heart failure. Intravenous digoxin further intensified the constriction of the splanchnic vascular bed, and the estimated splanchnic blood flow and splanchnic blood volume diminished at a time when systemic blood flow increased and peripheral vascular resistance decreased (Fig. 7-7). The mechanism for the splanchnic vasoconstriction with digoxin (that is, local, humoral, or nervous) was not defined. The decrease in splanchnic blood volume means that a substantial quantity of blood must have been transferred to other systemic veins at a time when cardiac function would best be served by a reduced venous return. The fact that central and peripheral venous pressures usually decrease despite this autotransfusion is additional evidence for the efficacy of the inotropic action of digitalis glycosides and suggests that the central (extrasplanchnic) venous reservoir has been increased sufficiently to accommodate the added volume with ease. The site to which the splanchnic venous blood is transferred is unknown.

In dogs, digitalis appears to constrict hepatic veins, resulting in a trapping of blood in the splanchnic bed and an increase in portal venous pressure (Ross et al., 1960A). The resulting decrease in ventricular filling pressure prevents the increased contractility from expressing itself as an increase in cardiac output. It is possible that a similar sequence occurs in normal subjects or patients with compensated heart disease and accounts for the dissociation between myocardial contractile force and cardiac output. Indeed, Baschieri et al. (1957) have shown that in man, digitalis increases hepatic vein wedge pressure, increases the pressure gradient between the hepatic venous wedge and the inferior vena cava, and decreases splanchnic blood flow, thus producing a substantial augmentation of hepatic vascular resistance.

REFERENCES

Baschieri, L., Ricci, P. D., Mazzuoli, G. F., and Vassale, M.: Studi su la portata epatica nell'uomo: Modificazioni del flusso epatica da digitale. Cuore e Circol., *41*:103, 1957.

Benchimol, A., Palmero, H. A., Liggett, M. S., and Dimond, E. G.: Influence of digitalization on the contribution of atrial systole to the cardiac dynamics at a fixed ventricular rate. Circulation, *32*:84, 1965.

Bing, R. J., Marais, F. M., Dammann, J. F., Jr., Draper, A., Jr., Heimbecker, R., Daley, R., Gerard, R., and Calazel, P.: Effect of strophanthus on coronary blood flow and cardiac oxygen consumption of normal and failing human hearts. Circulation, *2*:513, 1950.

Blain, J. M., Eddleman, E. E., Siegel, A. L., and Bing, R. J.: Studies on myocardial metabolism. V. The effects of lanatoside-C on the metabolism of the human heart. J. Clin. Invest., *35*:314, 1956.

Bliss, H. A., and Adolph, R. J.: Effect of experimental congestive heart failure and acetyl strophanthidin on myocardial electrolyte and water content. Circ. Research, *13*:207, 1963.

Braunwald, E., Bloodwell, R. D., Goldberg, L. I., and Morrow, A. G.: Studies on digitalis. IV. Observations in man on the effects of digitalis preparations on the contractility of the non-failing heart and on total vascular resistance. J. Clin. Invest., *40*:52, 1961.

Chidsey, C. A., Harrison, D. C., and Braunwald, E.: Augmentation of the plasma norepinephrine response to exercise in patients with congestive heart failure. New Eng. J. Med., *267*:650, 1962.

Coleman, H. N.: Role of acetylstrophanthidin in augmenting myocardial oxygen consumption: Relation of increased O_2 consumption to changes in velocity of contraction. Circ. Research, *21*:487, 1967

Conn, H. L., and Luchi, R. J.: Cellular basis for regulation of the circulation by digitalis and quinidine. Circ. Research, *15*(Suppl. II):153, 1964.

Crevasse, L., and Wheat, M. W., Jr.: Role of calcium and lanatoside C in increasing oxygen consumption in human myocardial tissue slices. Circ. Research, *11*:721, 1962.

Daggett, W. M., and Weisfeldt, M. L.: Influence of the sympathetic nervous system on the response of the normal heart to digitalis. Am. J. Cardiol., *16*:394, 1965.

Doherty, J. E., Flanigan, W. J., Perkins, W. H., and Ackerman, G. L.: Studies with tritiated digoxin in anephric human subjects. Circulation, *35*:298, 1967.

Doherty, J. E., and Perkins, W. H.: Studies with tritiated digoxin in human subjects after intravenous administration. Am. Heart J., *63*:528, 1962.

Doherty, J. E., and Perkins, W. H.: Studies with tritiated digoxin in renal failure. Am. J. Med., *37*:536, 1964.

Doherty, J. E., and Perkins, W. H.: Studies following intramuscular tritiated digoxin in human subjects. Am. J. Cardiol., *15*:170, 1965.

Doherty, J. E., and Perkins, W. H.: Tissue concentration and turnover of tritiated digoxin in dogs. Am. J. Cardiol., *17*:47, 1966.

Dresdale, D. T., Yuceoglu, Y. Z., Michtom, R. J., Schultz, M., and Lunger, M.: Effects of lanatoside C on cardiovascular hemodynamics; acute digitalizing doses in subjects with normal hearts and with heart disease without failure. Am. J. Cardiol., *4*:88, 1959.

Edman, K. A. P.: Drugs and properties of heart muscle. Ann. Rev. Pharmacol., *5*:99, 1965.

Ferrer, I. M., Bradley, S. E., Wheeler, H. O., Enson, Y., Preisig, R., and Harvey, R. M.: The effect of digoxin in the splanchnic circulation in ventricular failure. Circulation, *32*:524, 1965.

Ferrer, I. M., Conroy, R. J., and Harvey, R. M.: Some effects of digoxin upon the heart and circulation in man. Circulation, *21*:372, 1960.

Friedberg, C. K.: Diseases of the Heart. Third edition. Philadelphia and London, Saunders, 1966.

Gleason, W. L., and Braunwald, E.: Studies on the first derivative of the ventricular pressure pulse in man. J. Clin. Invest., *41*:80, 1962.

Glynn, I. M.: The action of cardiac glycosides on sodium and potassium movement in human red cells. J. Physiol., *136*:148, 1957.

Harvey, R. M., Ferrer, M. I., Cathcart, R. T., and Alexander, J. K.: Some effects of digoxin on the heart and circulation in man; digoxin in enlarged hearts not in clinical congestive failure. Circulation, *4*:366, 1951.

Holland, W. C.: Ion distribution and myocardial metabolism as affected by cardiac glycosides. Circ. Research, *15*(Suppl. II):85, 1964.

James, T. N., and Nadeau, R. A.: The chronotropic effect of digitalis studied by direct perfusion of the sinus node: J. Pharm. Exp. Therap., *139*:42, 1963.

Kahler, R. L., Thompson, R. H., Buskirk, E. R., Frye, R. L., and Braunwald, E.: Studies on digitalis. VI. Reduction of the post-exercise oxygen debt with digoxin in patients with cardiac disease without heart failure. Circulation, *27*:397, 1962.

Kay, C. M., and Green, W. A.: Physiochemical and enzymatic studies on cardiac myosin A. Circ. Research, *15*(Suppl. II):38, 1964.

Laurens, P., Bouchard, P., Brail, E., Cornu, C., Basculard, P., and Soulié, P.: Bruits et pressions cardio-vasculaires enregistrés in situ à l'aide d'un micromanomètre. Arch. Mal. Coeur, *52*:121, 1959.

Lendle, L., and Mercker, H.: Extrakardiale Digitalis-Wirkungen. Ergebn. f. Physiol., *51*:199, 1961.
Leonard, E.: Alteration of contractile response of artery strips by a potassium free solution, cardiac glycosides and changes in stimulation frequency. Am. J. Physiol., *189*:185, 1957.
Mason, D. T.: The cardiovascular effects of digitalis in normal man. Clin. Pharmacol. & Therap., *7*:1, 1966.
Mason, D. T., and Braunwald, E.: Studies on digitalis. IX. Effects of ouabain on the nonfailing human heart. J. Clin. Invest., *42*:1105, 1963.
Mason, D. T., and Braunwald, E.: Studies on digitalis. X. Effects of ouabain on forearm vascular resistance and venous tone in normal subjects and in patients in heart failure. J. Clin. Invest., *43*:532, 1964.
McLain, P. L., Kruse, T. K., and Redick, T.: The effect of atropine on digitoxin bradycardia in cats. J. Pharm. Exp. Therap., *126*:76, 1959.
Mendez, C., Aceves, J., and Mendez, R.: Inhibition of adrenergic cardiac acceleration by cardiac glycosides. J. Pharm. Exp. Therap., *131*:191, 1961.
Moe, G. K., and Mendez, R.: The action of several cardiac glycosides on conduction velocity and ventricular excitability in the dog heart. Circulation, *4*:729, 1951.
Morrow, D. H., Gaffney, T. E., and Braunwald, E.: Studies on digitalis. VIII. Effect of autonomic innervation and of myocardial catecholamine stores upon the cardiac action of ouabain. J. Pharm. Exp. Therap., *139*:236, 1963.
Müller, P.: Kalium und Digitalistoxizität. Cardiologia, *42*:1, 1963.
Müller, P.: Ouabain effects on cardiac contraction, action potential and cellular potassium. Circ. Research, *17*:57, 1965.
Murphy, G. W., Schreiner, B. F., Bleakley, P. L., and Yu, P. N.: Left ventricular performance following digitalization in patients with and without heart failure. Circulation, *30*:358, 1964.
Okita, G. T.: Selected studies on the metabolic fate of radioactive digitoxin in man. In: Digitalis, Ed. Dimond. Springfield, Ill., Thomas, 1957.
Page, E.: The actions of cardiac glycosides on heart muscle cells. Circulation, *30*:237, 1964.
Patterson, S. W., Piper, H., and Starling, E. H.: The regulation of the heart beat. J. Physiol., *48*:465, 1914.
Reeves, T. J., Hefner, L. L., Jones, W. B., Coghlan, C., Prieto, G., and Carroll, J.: The hemodynamic determinants of the rate of change in pressure in the left ventricle during isometric contraction. Am. Heart J., *60*:745, 1960.
Rodman, T., Gorczyca, C. A., and Pastor, B. H.: The effect of digitalis on the cardiac output of the normal heart at rest and during exercise. Ann. Int. Med., *55*:620, 1961.
Ross, J., Jr., Braunwald, E., and Waldhausen, J. A.: Studies on digitalis. II. Extracardiac effects on venous return and on the capacity of the peripheral vascular bed. J. Clin. Invest., *39*:937, 1960A.
Ross, J., Jr., Waldhausen, J. A., and Braunwald, E.: Studies on digitalis. I. Direct effects on peripheral vascular resistance. J. Clin. Invest., *39*:930, 1960B.
Sarnoff, S. J., Gilmore, J. P., Wallace, A. G., Skinner, N. S., Mitchell, J. H., and Daggett, W. M.: Effect of acetylstrophanthidin therapy on cardiac dynamics, oxygen consumption and efficiency in the isolated heart with and without hypoxia. Am. J. Med., *37*:3, 1964.
Selzer, A., Hultgren, H. N., Ebnother, C. L., Bradley, R. W., and Stone, A. O.: Effect of digoxin on the circulation in normal man. Brit. Heart J., *21*:335, 1959.
Siegel, J. H., and Sonnenblick, E. H.: Isometric time-tension relationships as an index of myocardial contractility. Circ. Research, *12*:597, 1963.
Sjöstrand, F. S., and Andersson-Cedergren, E.: Intercalated discs of heart muscle. In: The Structure and Function of Muscle. Ed. Bourne. New York, Academic Press, 1960.
Sonnenblick, E. H.: Force-velocity relations in mammalian heart muscle. Am. J. Physiol., *202*:931, 1962.
Sonnenblick, E. H., Spotnitz, H. M., and Spiro, D.: Role of the sarcomere in ventricu-

lar function and the mechanism of heart failure. Circ. Research, *15*(Suppl. II): 70, 1964.
Spann, J. F., Sonnenblick, E. H., Cooper, T., Chidsey, C. A., Willman, V. L., and Braunwald, E.: Studies on digitalis. XIV: Influence of cardiac norepinephrine stores on the response of isolated heart muscle to digitalis. Circ. Research, *19*: 326, 1966.
Strickler, J. C., and Kessler, R. H.: Direct renal action of some digitalis steroids. J. Clin. Invest., *40*:311, 1961.
Trautwein, W.: Generation and conduction of impulses in the heart as affected by drugs. Pharm. Rev., *15*:277, 1963.
Tuttle, R. S., Witt, P. N., and Farah, A.: The influence of ouabain on intracellular sodium and potassium concentrations in the rabbit myocardium. J. Pharm. Exp. Therap., *133*:281, 1961.
Waldhausen, J. A., and Herendeen, T. L.: Direct effects of digitalis on renal blood flow. Surgery, *56*:540, 1964.
Waldhausen, J. A., Kilman, T. W., Herendeen, T. L., and Abel, F. L.: Effects of acetylstrophanthidin on coronary vascular resistance and myocardial oxygen consumption. Circ. Research, *16*:203, 1965.
Wallace, A. G., Skinner, N. S., and Mitchell, J. H.: Hemodynamic determinants of the maximal rate of rise of left ventricular pressure. Am. J. Physiol., *205*:30, 1963.
Weber, A., Herz, R., and Reiss, I.: On mechanism of the relaxing effect of fragmented sarcoplasmic reticulum. J. Gen. Physiol., *46*:679, 1963.
Weissler, A. M., Gamel, W. G., Grode, H. E., Cohen, S., and Schoenfeld, C. D.: The effect of digitalis on ventricular ejection in normal human subjects. Circulation, *29*:721, 1964.
Weissler, A. M., Snyder, J. R., Schoenfeld, C. D., and Cohen, S.: Assay of digitalis glycosides in man. Am. J. Cardiol., *17*:768, 1966.
Wiggers, C. J.: Studies on the cardiodynamic actions of drugs. 1. The application of the optical methods of pressure registration in the study of cardiac stimulants and depressants. J. Pharm. Exp. Therap., *30*:217, 1927.
Williams, M. H., Jr., Zohman, L. R., and Ratner, A. C.: Hemodynamic effects of cardiac glycosides on normal human subjects during rest and exercise. J. Appl. Physiol., *13*:417, 1958.
Wood, E. H., and Moe, G. K.: Correlation between serum potassium changes in the heart-lung preparation and the therapeutic and toxic effects of digitalis glucosides. Am. J. Physiol., *129*:499, 1940.

Chapter 8

CORONARY CIRCULATION

CORONARY BLOOD FLOW

ANATOMICAL CONSIDERATIONS. Most of the blood passing through the coronary arteries traverses the myocardial capillary network and drains via the coronary sinus. However, as James (1963) has emphasized, alternative pathways of blood flow exist (Fig. 8-1). Thus, blood entering a coronary artery may pass through an interarterial anastomosis into a second artery. On reaching the arteriolar bed, it may bypass the capillaries to enter the venules (Provenza and Scherlis, 1959). From the venules, it may enter the right atrium through either the coronary sinus or the anterior cardiac veins; the anastomoses between these two venous systems are so large and numerous that the direction of flow may reverse from moment to moment. Finally, a small fraction of the coronary blood flow passes through the venae cordis minimae (Thebesian veins) to enter any of the four chambers; through direct arteriocameral channels (Vieussens); and through extracardiac coronary anastomoses. Wearn (1928) showed that, under certain conditions, up to 60 per cent of the total coronary blood flow could drain into the lumina of the heart chambers by routes other than the coronary sinus.

The presence of these anatomical variations emphasizes the need for cautious interpretation of experiments in which the composition of blood in the coronary sinus is used as an index of metabolic changes in the myocardium, or in which the flow in the coronary sinus is assumed to represent consistently the flow through an identical portion of the heart. For example, a decrease in the arteriovenous difference of oxygen content (between aorta and coronary sinus) could be the result of increased myocardial capillary blood flow, but it could also result from increased precapillary shunting of blood. Similarly, a decrease in calculated coronary vascular

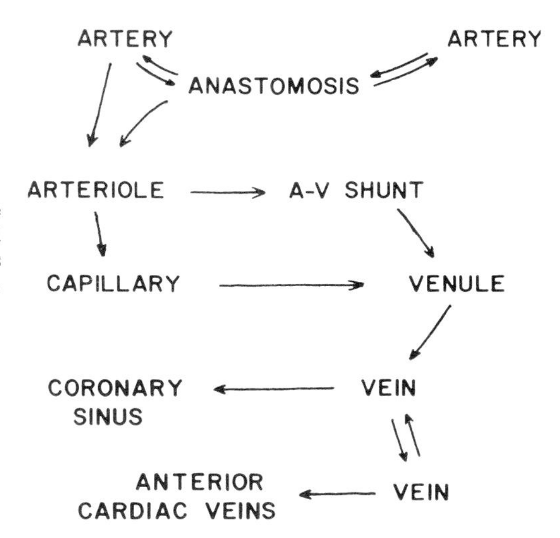

FIGURE 8-1. Schema of the possible routes whereby blood entering the coronary arteries may reach the right atrium. (From James, Circulation, *32*: 1027, 1963.)

resistance could be due either to arteriolar dilatation with increased capillary flow, or to increased shunting between arterioles and venules.

Further anatomical factors will be referred to later in this chapter.

DIRECT MEASUREMENT. Blood flow in the coronary circulation is phasic. This has been demonstrated from measurements in open chest dogs using rotameters and other devices, and more recently in closed chest dogs using electromagnetic flow meters. During systole, the increased intramyocardial pressure resulting from ventricular contraction opposes forward flow in the arteries and increases venous drainage by compressing the coronary sinus and other veins. These effects are more marked in the left ventricle owing to the higher pressure and the increased thickness of muscle. Thus, in the left coronary artery there may be transient retrograde flow during the period of isometric contraction, when mechanical compression is greatest and aortic pressure is least, although some forward flow occurs throughout most of the systolic ejection period (Gregg and Green, 1940). With the onset of isometric relaxation, immediately after closure of the aortic valve, the rate of flow rapidly increases to attain a maximal level in early diastole, from which it gradually declines during the remainder of diastole (Fig. 8-2).

In the right coronary artery, the phasic changes in flow are much less striking; the pattern resembles the simultaneous pressure pulse in the aorta. Retrograde flow does not occur, since the intramural tension of the right ventricle is only moderate.

Because of anatomical differences in the coronary arteries, caution is indicated in the extrapolation of these results to man. The left coronary artery is invariably dominant in the dog, accounting for about 85 per cent of the total coronary blood flow. In man, there is wide variation in the relative distribution of the right and left coronary arteries. According to Schlesinger (1940), the right artery was dominant in 48 per cent of a series of 225 hearts, the left artery was dominant in 18 per cent, and the distribution of the two arteries was balanced in the remaining 34 per cent. Therefore, it is likely that in most cases, the rates of flow through the two coronary arteries are more nearly equal in man than in the dog.

INDICATOR DILUTION CURVES. To avoid the necessity for cardiac catheterization, attempts have been made to quantitate the passage of radioactive substances through the coronary circulation. Thus, a radioactive isotope may be injected intravenously, and radioactivity measured continuously by means of a monitoring device positioned over the chest wall (Sevelius and Johnson, 1959). The resultant time-concentration curve has well defined peaks, corresponding to the passage of the indicator through the right and left sides of the heart, respectively. In addition, a

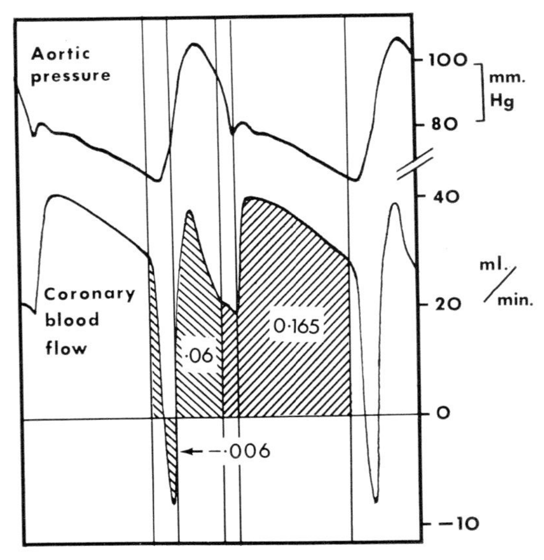

FIGURE 8-2. Aortic pressure (*above*) and blood flow in anterior descending coronary artery of a dog. Forward flow reaches a rate of 40 ml. per minute in early diastole and declines to a rate of 28 ml. per minute at end-diastole. During the period of isometric ventricular contraction (*between first pair of vertical lines*), it decreases abruptly and there is transient backflow. With the onset of ejection, the rate rapidly increases to a peak at 38 ml. per minute. During protodiastole (*between second pair of vertical lines*), the rate of flow was about 20 ml. per minute. After closure of the aortic valve, it increased to its early diastolic value of 40 ml. per minute. The actual flow per beat may be calculated from the integrated areas shown in crosshatching. Thus, during systole, there was a forward flow of 0.06 ml., a backward flow of 0.006 ml., with a net forward flow of 0.054 ml. During the longer diastole, the forward flow was 0.165 ml. Systolic blood flow was 33 per cent of diastolic flow. Since the heart rate was 131 beats per minute, total forward flow per minute was 28.7 ml. (Redrawn from Gregg, Coronary Circulation in Health and Disease. Philadelphia, Lea and Febiger, 1950.)

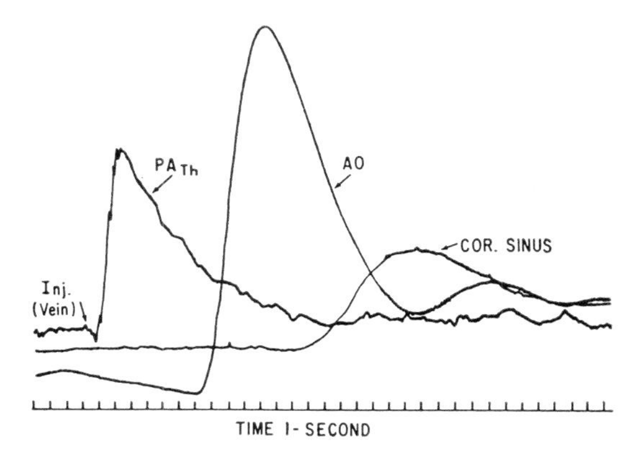

FIGURE 8-3. Dilution curves obtained from pulmonary artery (using a thermistor) and from aorta and coronary sinus (using densitometers) following injection of cold dye into a peripheral vein. The three peaks correspond in time to the three peaks obtained by precordial monitoring following intravenous injection of radioactive isotopes. Note that the curve from the coronary sinus is superimposed upon the latter part of the primary component of the aortic curve and upon its early recirculation phase. In other experiments, the curve from the coronary sinus also coincided in time with curves recorded from both venae cavae. (From Tsagiris, Koehler, Kuida and Hecht, J. Clin. Invest., *42*:10, 1963.)

smaller third peak can sometimes be discerned. This peak has been attributed to passage of the isotope through the coronary circulation. Unfortunately, however, this third peak is superimposed upon the delay slope of the peak related to passage through the left side of the heart. Tsagiris et al. (1963) recorded dilution curves from multiple sites within the heart and the great vessels following intravenous injections of indicator, and showed that indicator emerging from the coronary circulation via the coronary sinus was spread over a wide time base and was temporally inseparable both from the tails of curves recorded from the right and left sides of the heart and from the early parts of curves recorded from the superior and inferior venae cavae (Fig. 8-3). It is therefore unlikely that the third peak of precordial dilution curves represents only coronary blood flow. They concluded that this temporal overlap, together with the smallness of the fraction of the injected dye that passed through the coronary bed, precluded the quantitation of coronary blood flow by precordial monitoring methods. Similar conclusions have been reached by Marchioro et al. (1961), Forte et al. (1961) and Conn (1962).

OTHER ISOTOPE METHODS. Most of the attempts to measure coronary blood flow with the use of radioactive isotopes have been based on quantitation of the myocardial uptake of Rb^{86} (rubidium), an element which the heart handles like potassium (Love and Burch, 1957). Bing et al. (1958) attempted to measure flow from a knowledge of the rate of uptake by the heart and of the coronary arteriovenous difference in concentration.

However, the rate of extraction of Rb^{86} from blood by the myocardium is not constant but varies from 40 to 70 per cent with variations in coronary blood flow and in the duration of perfusion (Mack et al., 1959). Difficulties in determining the uptake by the heart alone, separated from surrounding organs, and the reduction of myocardial extraction with time have prevented development of this approach into a practical technique (Donato et al., 1966).

More recently, clearance techniques using xenon-133 and other diffusible indicators are being evaluated (Linder, 1966; Bernstein et al., 1966).

CORONARY ARTERIOGRAPHY. Coronary arteriography has been extensively used for examination of the arteries in patients suspected of having coronary artery disease. It may be performed by injecting contrast material rapidly into the root of the aorta, preferably when the cardiac output has been reduced through performance of the Valsalva maneuver, or when the heart has been arrested for a few seconds by the prior injection of acetylcholine through the catheter. Alternatively, selective opacification of the coronary arteries may be achieved by injecting contrast material directly into their ostia (Sones and Shirey, 1962).

Although its main application has been in the demonstration of anatomical changes, coronary arteriography has also been applied to assess the effects of vasodilator drugs. Again, the results must be interpreted with caution. For example, angiographic studies in animals and man have demonstrated that nitrites are capable of dilating the coronary arteries. Yet these drugs do not increase coronary blood flow, measured by the nitrous oxide method, in either normal subjects or patients with coronary artery disease. The reason for this apparent discrepancy is that the drugs cause a decrease in arterial blood pressure. Thus, a change in the caliber of vessels does not necessarily imply a change in the blood flow.

Contrast media are hypertonic solutions and, when introduced rapidly and in high concentration, have profound effects on vascular smooth muscle (Marshall and Shepherd, 1959; Read et al., 1960). Several mechanisms may be involved including dehydration of the vessel wall, ionic shifts across the vessel (Friedman et al., 1958) and the release of vasodilator material from erythrocytes agglutinated and disrupted by the hypertonic medium (Deyrup, 1951). The net result is vasodilatation, the occurrence of which after angiocardiography or aortography is obvious from simple inspection of patients and from hemodynamic measurements (Rahimtoola et al., 1966). It follows that, when coronary arteriography is performed before and after administration of a drug, an increased caliber of the arteries in the second arteriogram could be due to persistent effects of the first injection of contrast medium rather than to the drug.

Lehan et al. (1963) studied changes in the coronary circulation of dogs following injections of Hypaque into the coronary arteries. Immediately after each injection, there was a decrease by 35 to 50 per cent in the hematocrit of blood in the coronary sinus, indicative of a transfer of tissue water to the capillaries. After the radiopaque medium had left the vessels, the coronary arteries were dilated, and the hematocrit of blood in the coronary sinus exceeded normal, suggesting that water was being restored to the myocardium. They concluded, from their demonstration of compartmental water shifts and of variations in coronary vascular resistance, that contrast angiography could not be applied to assess the effects of drugs on the coronary circulation.

NITROUS OXIDE METHOD. The nitrous oxide method, originally applied to the measurement of cerebral blood flow (Kety and Schmidt, 1945) has been adapted to the measurement of flow in the coronary sinus (Bing et al., 1949). It is an application of the Fick principle. Blood flow per unit weight of myocardium is calculated from the amount of nitrous oxide taken up per minute, divided by the coronary arteriovenous difference of nitrous oxide content. The amount taken up per minute is the product of the concentration in venous blood after equilibrium has been attained and of the partition coefficient (relative solubility) between myocardium and blood, which is assumed to be approximately 1.0. The arteriovenous difference across the coronary circulation is the averaged difference from several pairs of samples drawn over a period of ten minutes, or else, the difference between a single pair of samples drawn slowly and at a uniform rate from the coronary sinus and an artery during the entire period of inhalation of the mixture of 15 per cent nitrous oxide in air. Since the coronary sinus does not drain the entire heart, the flow measured is that through the portion drained by the coronary sinus. Fortunately for the validity of the method, the blood that drains via the coronary sinus originates almost exclusively from the left ventricle, when care is taken to avoid sampling too near to the ostium of the sinus. Messer et al. (1962) showed that, both in normal subjects and in patients with coronary artery disease, the saturation in the distal and middle portions of the sinus was usually almost identical over a wide range of saturations (13 to 42 per cent). The proximal portion of the sinus is likely to be contaminated with more highly saturated blood from the middle cardiac vein or the right atrium (Fig. 8-4).

The nitrous oxide method has certain disadvantages. Flow is measured per 100 g. of myocardium rather than in absolute terms; a single determination must be made over a period of minutes, so that rapid fluctuations in flow cannot be measured; a state of equilibrium must exist between concentrations in blood and tissues; it is uncertain whether the partition coefficient is the same in healthy and diseased hearts and whether it remains constant from time to time in the same heart. Nevertheless, the method is free from the more serious theoretical problems of the other indirect methods described before and is the most widely used method for measurement of coronary blood flow in man.

OXYGEN EXTRACTION. The coefficient of oxygen extraction is the

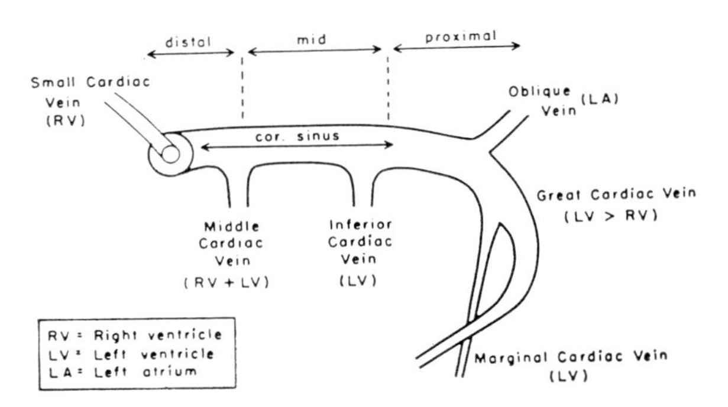

FIGURE 8-4. Dominant pattern of coronary venous drainage. RV, right ventricle; LV, left ventricle; LA, left atrium. The proximal and middle portions of the coronary sinus receive blood predominantly from the left ventricle. (From Messer, Wagman, Levine, Neill, Krasnow and Gorlin, J. Clin. Invest., *41*:725, 1962.)

fraction of the available oxygen removed from the coronary vessels by the myocardium. The value of the coefficient is that it permits comparisons to be made between subjects with various levels of hemoglobin in the blood. In the resting subject, it is approximately 70 per cent, whereas the coefficient of oxygen extraction for the body as a whole is about 20 per cent. The extraction coefficient (and hence the percentage saturation of coronary venous blood) alters little with various types of stress, such as anemia, hypoxia and muscular exercise.

CORONARY RESISTANCE. The calculation of coronary vascular resistance is subject to more reservations than is the calculation of resistance in most other vascular beds, since the small vessels in the left ventricle are compressed or even occluded during systole, while those in the right ventricle remain open. Gorlin (1960) has suggested the following as an empirical formula for calculation of the resistance during diastole in the small vessels of the left ventricle:

$$\mathrm{CVR} = \frac{\mathrm{P} \times \mathrm{DFT} \times 1332}{\mathrm{CBF} \times 0.75}$$

where *CVR* is coronary vascular resistance during diastole (dynes sec. cm.$^{-5}$); *P* is mean arterial pressure during diastole minus coronary venous pressure (mm. Hg); *DFT* is coronary diastolic filling time (seconds per minute); *CBF* is coronary blood flow; 0.75 is ratio of flow in diastole to total flow.

CARDIAC WORK. The heart performs work by creating pressure and applying kinetic energy to the blood. The latter is a negligible proportion of the total. The work performed by either ventricle may be calculated from the following expression:

$$\mathrm{W} = \underset{\text{(static)}}{\mathrm{QR}} + \underset{\text{(kinetic)}}{\tfrac{1}{2}\frac{\mathrm{QV}^2}{\mathrm{g}}}$$

where Q is the output of the ventricle per beat (ml.); R is the resistance to outflow, or mean pressure in aorta or pulmonary artery (mm. Hg); V is the mean velocity of blood in aorta or pulmonary artery (M. per second); g is the acceleration due to gravity (9.8 M. per second^2). Representative values for the left ventricle of a normal adult are: Q, 80 ml.; R, 100 mm. Hg (or 1.36 M. H_2O); V, 0.5 M. per second; Work, $80 \times 1.36 + \frac{1}{2}\ (20/9.8) = 109 + 1 = 110$ gram-meter per beat. At a heart rate of 70 per minute, minute work = 7.7 Kg.-M.

Since each ml. oxygen used by the heart is equivalent to about 2.06 Kg.-M., the left ventricular minute work of 7.7 Kg.-M. is equivalent to about 3.7 ml. oxygen. The normal right ventricle has to generate much less pressure, its minute work is considerably less, and the combined work of the two ventricles is equivalent to the expenditure of about 4.5 ml. oxygen. The total oxygen consumption of the heart is, however, much greater than this, being approximately 30 ml. per minute. The ratio of the quantity of oxygen equivalent to the mechanical work performed to the total quantity used per minute represents the *mechanical efficiency* of the heart. In the example chosen, it is 4.5/30, or 15 per cent.

OXYGEN UTILIZATION. The coefficient of oxygen utilization was used by Gorlin et al. (1959) as an expression of the consumption of oxygen by the left ventricle in the performance of mechanical work. When other factors remain constant, the oxygen consumption of the left ventricle increases in direct proportion to the number of seconds per minute spent in systole. Therefore, oxygen consumption per minute may be divided by the number of seconds per minute occupied by systole to give the consumption per second of systole. This permits comparison of data obtained at different heart rates. The coefficient of oxygen utilization is calculated by dividing the oxygen consumption per 100 g. left ventricle per systolic second by the left ventricular pressure work index (Kg.-M. per M.^{2} per minute). In a group of normal subjects, its value was 0.075 ± 0.05 (Gorlin, 1960).

NORMAL CORONARY CIRCULATION

VALUES DURING REST. In nine apparently healthy men resting in the fasting state (Regan et al., 1961), myocardial blood flow was 74 to 96 (mean 82) ml. per 100 g. per minute, the arteriovenous difference in oxygen content across the left ventricle was 8.9 to 12.6 (mean 10.4) ml. per 100 ml., the coefficient of oxygen extraction was 60 to 72 (mean 68) per cent, and the myocardial oxygen consumption was 7.2 to 9.6 (mean 8.5) ml. per 100 g. per minute. Table 8-1, which summarizes results from eight different studies, illustrates the consistency of values obtained by the use of the nitrous oxide method in normal subjects or patients with minor cardiac lesions. Since the weight of the left ventricle in normal adults of medium build is about 150 g., coronary blood flow to the left ventricle averages about 120 ml. per minute.

TABLE 8-1. Normal Values for Coronary Blood Flow Measured by the Nitrous Oxide Method (Corrected to Partition Coefficient of 1 for Uniformity)

	NO. OF SUBJECTS	CORONARY BLOOD FLOW (ML./100G./MIN.)	CORONARY SINUS O_2 (ML./100 ML.)	CORONARY A-V O_2 DIFF. (ML./100 ML.)	LV O_2 CONSUMPTION (ML./100G./MIN.)
Bing (1951)	18	77		12.0	9.4
Goodale et al. (1953)	5	86			
Calazel et al. (1954)	8	78	4.9	12.2	9.2
Ito et al. (1956)	15	69		10.5	7.1
Leight et al. (1956)	8	93		10.3	9.5
Rowe et al. (1959)	30	85	5.7	11.6	9.7
Brachfeld et al. (1959)	10	66	5.3	12.5	8.3
Regan et al. (1961)	9	74		10.4	8.5

The values summarized above were obtained under controlled conditions in the laboratory. In the course of normal activities, however, the coronary circulation is influenced by many factors, such as changes in heart rate, cardiac output and blood pressure, alterations in autonomic nervous activity, and hormonal and other chemical influences.

ARTIFICIAL CHANGES IN HEART RATE. In dogs, myocardial oxygen consumption and coronary blood flow both increase as the heart rate increases (Duff et al., 1955; Berglund et al., 1958). Gorlin (1958) measured blood flow and myocardial oxygen consumption in six patients before and after giving atropine intravenously. The heart rate increased from 70 to 97 beats per minute. Despite a decrease in the diastolic time from 37 to 31 seconds per minute, the blood flow increased from 74 to 102 ml. per 100 g. per minute, and the oxygen consumption from 8.9 to 11.9 ml. per 100 g. per minute. The cardiac output did not change.

EXERCISE. Coronary blood flow was monitored during exercise in dogs with an electromagnetic flowmeter chronically implanted around an internal mammary artery anastomosed to the left circumflex coronary artery (Khouri et al., 1960). The increase in flow was slightly less than the increase in heart rate; that is, the coronary stroke flow was slightly diminished during exercise. This was in contrast to an increase in coronary stroke flow at a similarly rapid heart rate during spontaneous excitement (Rayford et al., 1961).

During mild exercise in man, Lombardo et al. (1953) found increases of 45 per cent in coronary blood flow per 100 g. left ventricle, of 63 per cent in cardiac output, and of 65 per cent in oxygen consumption per 100 g. left ventricle. Since cardiac work increased more than did oxygen consumption, it was concluded that left ventricular efficiency was enhanced. In nine normal subjects, Regan et al. (1961) found that moderate exercise increased the cardiac output from 3.2 to 5.1 liters per $M.^2$ per minute and the coronary

TABLE 8-2. Effects of Exercise on the Coronary and Systemic Circulations in Normal Subjects*

	REST	EXERCISE
Total O_2 consumption (ml./M.^{2}/min.	129	279
Tension-time index	2440	3360
Systemic mean arterial pressure (mm. Hg)	114	133
Heart rate (beats/min.)	80	102
Cardiac index (L./M.^{2}/min.)	3.0	4.7
Coronary flow (ml./100 g./min.)	66	90
Myocardial O_2 cons. (ml./M.^{2}/min.)	7.8	10.8
Coronary venous O_2 (ml./100 ml.)	4.6	4.7

* Adapted from Messer, Wagman, Levine, Neill, Krasnow and Gorlin, J. Clin. Invest., *41*:725, 1962.

blood flow from 82 to 113 ml. per 100 g. per minute. The coefficient of oxygen extraction during exercise (70 per cent) was almost identical with that during rest. Messer et al. (1962) also found that, in their normal subjects, the increased demand of the left ventricle for oxygen during mild exercise was met by increased coronary blood flow rather than by an increased coefficient of extraction of oxygen (Table 8-2 and Fig. 8-5). Studies

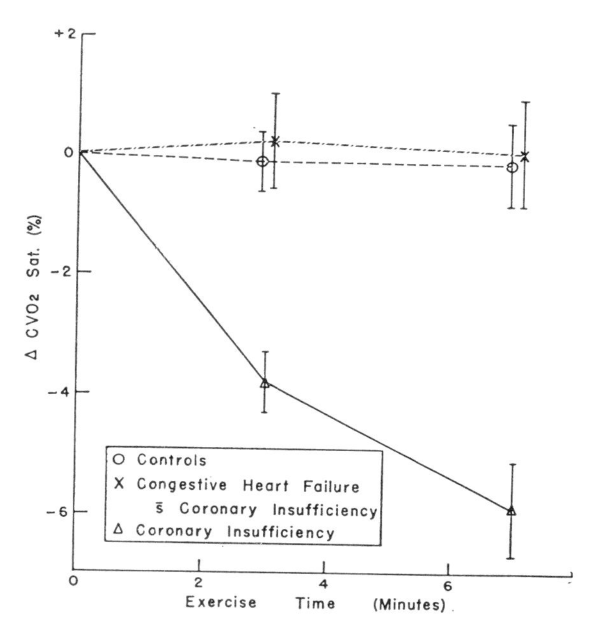

FIGURE 8-5. The saturation of coronary venous blood in normal subjects and in patients with heart failure but without coronary insufficiency is no less during exercise than at rest. In patients with coronary insufficiency, it decreases progressively during exercise ($p<0.001$ at both three and seven minutes). Vertical lines standard error of the mean. (From Messer, Wagman, Levine, Neill, Krasnow and Gorlin, J. Clin. Invest., *41*:725, 1962.)

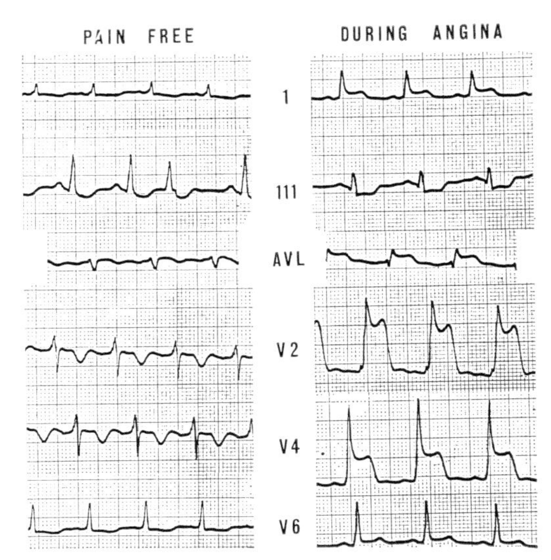

FIGURE 8-6. Electrocardiogram (ECG) from a patient with intractable angina pectoris associated with chronic disease of the gallbladder. While he was free from pain, the ECG showed scooping of the *ST* segments and inversion of the *T* waves. During angina, there was elevation of the *ST* segment in leads I, aVL and V_{1-6}, the elevation at times being as much as 15 mm. in certain leads (Prinzmetal's variant form.)

of coronary flow and myocardial oxygen consumption during strenuous exercise would be of great interest but are not as yet available.

NEURAL CONTROL. The effects of nervous stimuli on the coronary circulation are difficult to analyze, since the autonomic nerves also influence myocardial function. Physiological activities of the coronary vessels and the myocardium are so intimately related that a change in the behavior of one alters the behavior of the other.

Stimulation and section of the vagus nerves have little or no demonstrable effect on coronary blood flow. Stimulation of the stellate ganglion increases flow in both coronary arteries of the dog, an increase that persists after changes in heart rate and blood pressure have returned to normal. The increase may be due, in part at least, to shortening of systole (Eckstein et al., 1950). However, as indicated above, the increased flow could be due to vasodilatation induced by the increased production of vasodilator metabolites as a result of the heart's contracting more rapidly and more vigorously. No observations are available in man.

There have been many suggestions that coronary blood flow may be influenced reflexly by stimuli originating in various distant organs, particularly the gastrointestinal tract (DeMey et al., 1959) and gallbladder (Gilbert et al., 1940). Ravdin et al. (1943) caused angina in patients thus predisposed by increasing the pressure inside their bile ducts, and Cullen and Reese (1952) demonstrated reduction in coronary blood flow in dogs with intact vagi following rapid distension of the common bile duct.

Figure 8-6 shows electrocardiograms from a patient with intractable angina pectoris when he was free from pain (*left*) and during a prolonged attack (*right*). In the latter situation, he was pallid, sweating profusely, and had protodiastolic gallop rhythm; nitroglycerin had no effect on the pain, which could be relieved only by intravenous morphine. Following removal of a chronically inflamed gallbladder that contained stones, he has remained free from angina, and his electrocardiogram is now normal.

Although doubt exists concerning the importance of such reflexes (Fishman and Cournand, 1953), their existence appears to be beyond dispute.

In the dog, ligation of one coronary artery is said to induce reflex constriction in the other (LeRoy et al., 1942), and cinéangiographic studies have shown that, after selective embolization of one coronary artery, there is marked constriction of the unembolized artery and reduction of flow in the coronary sinus (Guzman et al., 1962). There are no data concerning the possible role of intercoronary reflexes in man.

Certain other stimuli may also induce coronary vasoconstriction. For example, the inhalation of cold air often induces an attack of angina pectoris in persons predisposed to this (Murray, 1962). The precipitating factor may be a nervous reflex (Murray, 1965), the release of catecholamines with a consequent increase in cardiac work (Arnett and Watts, 1960), or both.

CHEMICAL CONTROL. One of the most potent stimuli leading to coronary vasodilatation is hypoxemia. Maximal dilatation occurs when the arterial saturation is about 20 per cent and the oxygen content of arterial blood about 4 ml. per 100 ml. In this situation, increased flow is mandatory for survival, since the maximal possible arteriovenous difference in oxygen content is less than 4 ml. per 100 ml., as compared with a normal difference of about three times this level. In fact, coronary blood flow in dogs increases by about threefold during severe hypoxemia.

Hellems et al. (1957) studied the effects of inhaling 10 per cent oxygen in normal human subjects. This caused a decrease in arterial oxygen saturation to levels of 42 to 83 per cent and an average increase in cardiac output from 3.6 to 4.8 liters per $M.^2$ per minute. The coronary blood flow increased from 81 to 150 ml. per 100 g. per minute. Myocardial oxygen consumption was unchanged at 9.0 ml. per 100 g. per minute. Whether the coronary vasodilatation was due to the direct effects of the reduced pO_2 on the vessels or to metabolites is uncertain.

The effects of changes in pH on coronary blood flow are much less consistent and less marked, probably because of their complex actions on the heart. Hypercapnia directly depresses myocardial contractility and the smooth muscle of the coronary arteries but indirectly has a stimulant effect through the release of catecholamines from the sympathoadrenal system.

Various metabolic products, particularly ATP and ADP, have marked coronary vasodilator properties. Although these vasoactive products have not been identified in coronary venous blood, degradation products have been identified in blood from the coronary sinus in hypoxic hearts. These observations are compatible with the concept that adenosine is formed during myocardial hypoxia and diffuses out of the myocardial cell to reach the resistance vessels and induce vasodilatation. Also in support of this notion are the direct relationships between coronary blood flow, the concentration of the adenosine, inosine and hypoxanthine in the perfusates, and the degree of hypoxia. Myocardial oxygen tension may well be the factor responsible for adenosine release, but it remains to be established that the adenosine released and the coronary dilatation observed with hypoxia do indeed represent a cause and effect relationship (Katori and Berne, 1966).

The effects of catecholamines are also complex. Berne (1958) showed that epinephrine and norepinephrine have a direct constrictor effect and an indirect dilator effect secondary to increased myocardial metabolic activity. Most investigators have noted a moderate increase in coronary blood flow (Lewis et al., 1961; Siegel et al., 1961). However, since there is an increase in the extraction coefficient of oxygen, the increase in metabolic activity is greater. This could account for the occurrence of angina in some patients with coronary artery disease when they are given catecholamines. Further details of the effects of catecholamines on coronary blood vessels are discussed in Chapter 6.

Cigarette smoking is accompanied by increases in heart rate, cardiac output, arterial blood pressure and left ventricular work (Pentecost and Shillingford, 1964). These effects are mediated through the release of catecholamines by nicotine (Westfall and Watts, 1964). Coronary blood flow is increased after smoking in normal subjects (Bargeron et al., 1957), whereas Regan et al. (1960) noted no change in blood flow in patients with coronary artery disease.

CORONARY ARTERY DISEASE

Resting levels of coronary blood flow in patients with coronary arteriosclerosis are within normal limits. Messer et al. (1962) found a mean value of 70 ml. per 100 g. per minute as compared with 66 ml. in a group of apparently normal subjects of similar ages (Table 8-3). Although there was considerable individual variation, mean values for the coefficient of oxygen extraction were lower, and for the saturation of coronary venous blood were higher, in the patients than in the normal subjects. While the explanation for this unexpected finding was not clear, one possibility was that arteriovenous shunts might occur through recanalized vessels in areas of scar tissue.

In contrast, whereas the coronary venous saturation did not decrease during mild exercise in the normal subjects, it fell by four per cent after three minutes and by six per cent after seven minutes in the patients. If abnormal shunts do exist in the patients with coronary artery disease, then the effects of these shunts may be reduced during exercise because of the

TABLE 8-3. Physiological Data at Rest and During Exercise in Patients with Coronary Artery Disease*

	EXERCISE	REST
Total O_2 consumption (ml./M.^{2}/min.)	137	306
Tension-time index	2765	3800
Systemic mean arterial pressure (mm. Hg)	113	136
Heart rate (beats/min.)	78	100
Cardiac index (L./M.^{2}/min.)	2.5	3.5
Coronary flow (ml./100 g./min.)	70	100
Myocardial O_2 cons. (ml./M.^{2}/min.)	8.8	13.8
Coronary venous O_2 (ml./100 ml.)	5.5	4.7

* Adapted from Messer, Wagman, Levine, Neill, Krasnow and Gorlin, J. Clin. Invest., *41*:725, 1962.

decreased resistance to flow in the normal vessels supplying healthy myocardium.

Most other investigators have confirmed that total coronary blood flow is within normal limits in resting subjects with coronary artery disease. Thus, the total coronary blood flow or the mean coronary blood flow per unit of left ventricular weight measured at rest is not a helpful guide in assessing the extent or severity of pathological lesions. Such lesions are usually focal, and reduced flow through them may readily be concealed in the sum total of myocardial blood flow as it is measured by the nitrous oxide method.

Improved discrimination between normal subjects and patients with coronary artery disease is provided by measurements of lactate levels in arterial and coronary venous blood. The normal heart is an aerobic organ, deriving most of its energy from metabolism of fatty acids, glucose, lactate and pyruvate. It extracts lactate from the coronary circulation. In the presence of severe hypoxia (Hackel et al., 1954) or ischemia (Evans et al., 1933), anaerobic metabolism occurs. The rate of extraction of lactate is reduced or excess lactate is produced by the heart.

ANGINA PECTORIS. Krasnow and Gorlin (1963) studied 34 patients with heart disease but without angina pectoris, and 31 with classical angina pectoris. Observations were made during rest, during exercise, and during infusion of isoproterenol. Twenty-nine of the former group had consistently normal rates of extraction of lactate, while in 15 of the latter group, extraction was either absent or reversed during at least one phase of the study.

The presence of normal extraction of lactate in about half the patients with angina pectoris is again probably explained by the fact that the ischemic lesions are focal. Thus, excess lactate production in these focal lesions may readily be concealed, since their effluent blood is mixed with blood from which normal myocardium has extracted lactate. It is possible that in such patients, studies of discrete areas drained by individual tributaries of the coronary sinus (Harman et al., 1966) might reveal an abnormal lactate balance.

Excess lactate production is more readily demonstrable during an episode of angina pectoris (Cohen et al., 1965).

EFFECT OF DRUGS. Nitroglycerin is the most effective drug for the relief of angina pectoris. When given in therapeutic doses to normal persons, it increased coronary blood flow and myocardial oxygen consumption, each by about 50 per cent; thus, the coronary arteriovenous difference in oxygen saturation was unchanged (Brachfeld et al., 1959). There were decreases in aortic pressure, coronary diastolic vascular resistance, pulmonary artery wedge and right atrial pressures, and left ventricular work. The mechanical efficiency of the heart was decreased. In contrast, in patients with coronary artery disease, nitroglycerin decreased coronary blood flow from 82 to 69 ml. per 100 g. per minute and myocardial oxygen consumption from 9.0 to 7.5 ml. per 100 g. per minute (Gorlin et al., 1959). The arteriovenous difference in oxygen saturation was unchanged. As in the normal group, the filling pressures and cardiac work were decreased. Most other workers have confirmed that nitroglycerin fails to increase myocardial blood flow in patients with coronary artery disease and angina pectoris.

Any vasodilator drug that is given by mouth exerts its effect on the total systemic vascular bed and has more effect on normal vessels. Therefore, it is scarcely surprising that nitroglycerin does not selectively dilate diseased coronary vessels. Experiments in which nitroglycerin has been shown to have a marked dilator effect when introduced directly into the coronary arteries of normal dogs or man (Bernstein et al., 1966) are irrelevant to the situation in which it is given by mouth to man.

Thus, nitroglycerin must confer its benefit by some means other than increasing myocardial blood flow. Williams et al. (1965) measured left and right ventricular dimensions in 11 patients without clinical evidence of coronary artery disease by cinéradiography using radiopaque markers previously sutured to the surface of the ventricles. After 0.6 mg. nitroglycerin, end-diastolic and end-systolic dimensions decreased. The diminution of end-diastolic ventricular dimensions approximated 30 per cent of the stroke volume. Systolic, mean and diastolic arterial pressures decreased, while cardiac output fell from 5.6 to 5.0 liters per minute and stroke volume from 65 to 55 ml. (average values). Thus, in addition to the decreased systemic vascular resistance, the decrease in ventricular size and the consequent decreases in the development of myocardial tension and myocardial oxygen consumption could at least partly account for the effectiveness of the drug in angina pectoris.

Certain other drugs such as erythrityl tetranitrate that are also beneficial in angina pectoris reduce left ventricular work but do not increase coronary blood flow (Rowe et al., 1961). The saliuretic agent chlorothiazide and ganglion blocking drugs, by reducing systemic arterial blood pressure and left ventricular work, often relieve angina in patients with hypertensive heart disease.

On the other hand, there are some drugs which do appear to increase coronary blood flow when given by mouth to patients with coronary artery disease and angina pectoris. Thus, Peel et al. (1961), Elliot (1961) and Kinsella et al. (1962) all demonstrated increased saturation of coronary venous blood following parenteral administration of dipyridamole (Persantin). Yet carefully controlled therapeutic studies have failed to show any benefit from this drug (Peel et al., 1961; Kinsella et al., 1962). It may be that the flow through normal vascular beds in the heart is increased, but that flow through the inadequately perfused areas that are presumably responsible for the sensation of pain is not increased. Indeed, it is possible that flow through the narrowed vessels supplying ischemic areas may be diminished because of diversion of flow through adjacent normal vessels that become dilated under the influence of the drug. The occurrence of such diversion or redistribution phenomena has been demonstrated in ischemic limbs (Marshall and Whelan, 1956; Hyman and Winsor, 1959; Gillespie, 1959).

It is unlikely that any significant additional dilatation of the vessels to the ischemic areas can occur once an attack of angina has developed (Sandler et al., 1963). Probably the vasodilatation in ischemic areas is caused by the liberation of metabolites such as the adenine nucleotides from anoxic cells (Katori and Berne, 1966). Since these metabolites in the concentration present locally are extremely powerful, it is unlikely that drugs can have any additional dilator action.

Effect of exercise. Foster and Reeves (1964) compared the hemodynamic response to mild exercise in two groups of middle aged men, one normal and the other with angina pectoris. With oxygen consumptions of about 400 ml. per M.^{2} per minute, the cardiac output was 5.0 and 4.0 liters per M.^{2} per minute, the heart rates were 95 and 101 per minute, and the stroke volumes were 53 and 40 ml. per M.^{2} respectively.

MYOCARDIAL INFARCTION. Numerous studies have been made of the hemodynamic effects of acute myocardial infarction. Variations in the reported results are to some extent attributable to differences in the techniques used for measuring cardiac output and to the difficulties in obtaining repeated studies in these often critically ill patients. There is general agreement, however, that the cardiac output and stroke volume are reduced, and that there is a moderate correlation between the extent of the reduction and the patient's clinical state (Table 8-4).

Mackenzie et al. (1964) investigated 15 patients, with particular reference to the effects of cardiogenic shock. The criteria used for the diagnosis of shock included arterial hypotension together with cold clammy skin and apathy or restlessness. As in previous reports, the cardiac output tended to be lower in the presence of shock, although in some cases without shock,

TABLE 8-4. Hemodynamic Studies During First Four Days Following Myocardial Infarction

AUTHOR AND YEAR	CLINICAL SEVERITY	NO. OF PATIENTS	CARDIAC INDEX (L./M.^{2}/MIN.)	MEAN ART BP (MM. HG)
Freis et al. (1952)	Mild	4	3.4	95
	Severe	4	2.9	89
	Shock	3	1.8	79
Smith et al. (1954)	Mild	9	2.4	86
	Shock	7	1.6	70
Gilbert et al. (1954)	Mild	7	2.6	106
	Severe	6	1.9	101
	Shock	7	1.0	73
Gammill et al. (1955)	Mild	11	4.3	—
	Severe	12	3.2	—
	Shock	14	2.9	—
Lee (1957)	All cases	11	3.7	98
Broch et al. (1959)	Mild	18	3.0	—
	Severe & Shock	17	2.0	—
Murphy et al. (1963)	All cases	13	2.9	—
MacKenzie et al. (1964)	No shock	9	2.6	94
	Shock	6	1.7	75

equally low values were found. However, there was virtually no overlap between the two groups in values for stroke volume. Thus it appeared that, in some of the shocked patients, inability of the left ventricle to maintain an adequate stroke volume was partially compensated by tachycardia. Serious impairment of left ventricular function in cardiogenic shock was also apparent from other measurements, including the maximal rate of increase of pressure in the aorta, mean ejection flow rate and mean stroke power index. Although the primary factor in cardiogenic shock was impairment of the heart's performance as a pump, the absence of a reflex increase in systemic vascular resistance, possibly related to acidosis and arterial hypoxemia, was contributory.

Murphy et al. (1963) used a precordial radioisotope indicator dilution method for serial measurements of cardiac output. There was a considerable overlap in the initial values among those who ultimately died (1.7 to 3.4, mean 2.5 liters per M.^{2} per minute) and those who survived (2.6 to 3.8, mean 3.0 liters per M.^{2} per minute). Serial measurements provided improved discrimination. Thus, a persistently low value for stroke volume, or a persistently low or progressively decreasing value for cardiac output, generally indicated a fatal outcome.

Malmcrona and Varnauskas (1964) found that the cardiac output soon after infarction was reduced in patients who had no fever, whereas in patients whose temperature exceeded 38 degrees C., the cardiac output was within normal limits. The peripheral resistance was decreased in both groups of patients.

The inhalation of oxygen is a common form of treatment in acute infarction. The rationale for its use is that it may improve oxygenation of the peripheral zones of the infarcted area (Sayen et al., 1951) through facilitating more complete saturation of arterial blood. However, Thomas et al. (1965) found that, although the inhalation of a 40 per cent oxygen mixture increased the arterial pressure, it was accompanied by a decrease in cardiac output. The cardiac output usually, but not invariably, decreased slightly during the inhalation of oxygen in the patients studied by MacKenzie et al. (1964). Cameron et al. (1966) noted a decrease in cardiac output and increases in mean arterial pressure and systemic vascular resistance in patients receiving oxygen at 1 atmosphere. There were slight additional changes in these values during hyperbaric oxygen administration (2 atmospheres), but they did not attain statistical significance.

The arterial oxygen tension is reduced in many patients with acute myocardial infarction. In the uncomplicated cases of MacKenzie et al. (1964), the arterial pO_2 while breathing air varied from 47 to 77 mm. Hg and the oxygen saturation from 83 to 94 per cent. After breathing 82 to 96 per cent oxygen, the pO_2 increased to between 330 and 465 mm. Hg and the saturation to 99 per cent. In the shocked patients, the pO_2 while breathing air was only 37 to 66 mm. Hg, and in two patients, it was less than 70 mm. Hg (saturation less than 90 per cent) after prolonged inhalation of oxygen. Thus, in the shocked patients, there was functional shunting of about one quarter of the cardiac output through vessels in the lungs inaccessible for the exchange of gases, probably secondary to collapse, congestion or edema of basal segments of the lung (Fig. 8-7).

Whereas the uncomplicated cases had no demonstrable metabolic abnormalities, the shocked patients had metabolic acidosis and lactic acidemia. Metabolic acidosis has been shown in animals to depress myocardial function and diminish responsiveness to catecholamines (Thrower et al., 1961).

The occurrence of arterial hypoxemia and metabolic acidosis, which has been confirmed by others (McNicol et al., 1965; Cameron et al., 1966; Valentine et al., 1966; Pain et al., 1967), indicates the need for oxygen therapy in patients who are severely ill from acute myocardial infarction, despite its slight depressant effect on cardiac output.

Gunnar et al. (1966) compared the effects of methoxamine and norepinephrine in a group of patients with cardiogenic shock, who had values of 0.6 to 4.0 liters per minute for cardiac output. Methoxamine, the action of which is confined to stimulation of the alpha adrenergic receptors, increased peripheral resistance and caused a further decrease in cardiac output whereas norepinephrine, which has a positive inotropic effect on the heart, increased cardiac output. The possible role of angiotensin II in cardiogenic shock has also been considered (Derrick et al., 1962). Although it has a positive inotropic action on mammalian heart muscle (Koch-Weser, 1964), this effect may be masked in intact animals or man by intense peripheral vasoconstriction, so that cardiac output (Finnerty et al., 1961) and

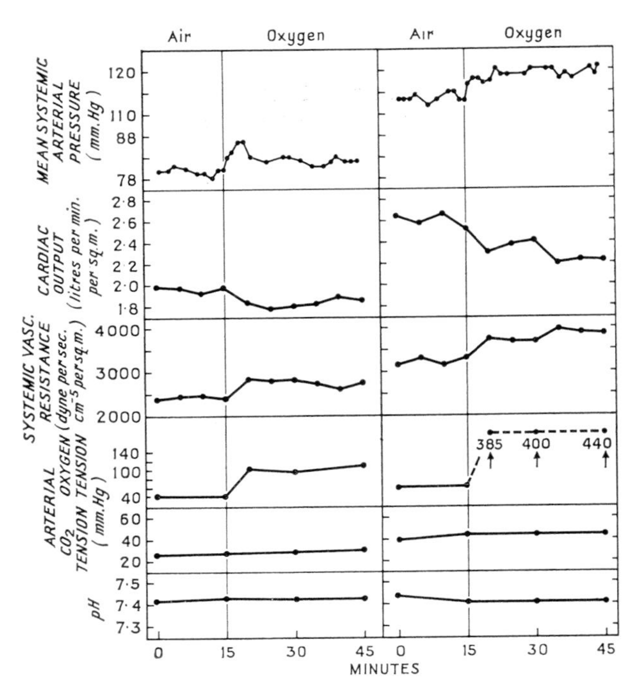

FIGURE 8-7. Effects of inhaling air and 100 per cent oxygen in two cases of acute myocardial infarction: (a) with shock (*left*), and (b) without shock (*right*). (From MacKenzie, Flenley, Taylor, McDonald, Staunton and Donald, Lancet, *ii*:825, 1964.)

urine flow (Udhoji and Weil, 1963) may be decreased. Therefore, it seems doubtful whether angiotensin II has any advantage over norepinephrine in attempts to reverse the effects of cardiogenic shock.

Left ventricular function is impaired following healing of a myocardial infarct. Often, however, the impairment is insufficient to become clinically manifest, so that special techniques are required for its demonstration. Measurement of precordial movement (kinetocardiography) has shown the occurrence of abnormal outward motion in two thirds of patients with recent or old myocardial infarction (Harrison, 1965). A similar abnormality may become manifest in patients without infarction during attacks of angina (Skinner et al., 1961), with changes diminishing or disappearing as the pain subsides.

Herman et al. (1966) used ciné left ventriculography to study the time sequence of contraction. In 42 of 70 cases of ischemic heart disease, proven by coronary arteriography, there was evidence of asynergy that led to dissipation of the contractile effort, to decreases in cardiac output and to reduced rates of pressure rise in the isovolumic phase of contraction. The zones of abnormal contractility corresponded with the areas of distribution of the diseased arteries.

Repeated stretching of the non-contracting scar tissue following an extensive transmural infarct may result in the formation of a saccular dilatation or aneurysm. Greenwood et al. (1965) investigated the hemodynamic effects of such aneurysms. In all cases, the left ventricular end-diastolic pressure was increased (17 to 35 mm. Hg), probably because of increased end-diastolic volume and of diminished diastolic compliance of the wall of the aneurysm. Increased time-tension index and decreased left ventricular work were indicative of ineffectual energy expenditure. These measurements reverted to normal following successful resection of a large aneurysm.

Other complications may result. Perforation of the interventricular septum leads to a left-to-right shunt and to congestive heart failure. Rupture of a papillary muscle results in the acute onset of mitral valve regurgitation which is poorly tolerated (Robinson et al., 1965); occasionally, patients survive but have chronic congestive heart failure (Breneman and Drake, 1962). In addition, mitral regurgitation may be due to malfunction of the papillary muscle from necrosis and scarring rather than to actual rupture (Phillips et al., 1963).

CORONARY CIRCULATION IN OTHER DISEASES

VALVULAR HEART DISEASE. In aortic stenosis, the hypertrophy of the left ventricle necessitates an increase in the total coronary blood flow if the flow per 100 g. is to be maintained at an adequate level. The valvular obstruction results in a pressure gradient, so that the intraventricular systolic pressure exceeds that in the coronary arteries. It is therefore presumed that forward flow in the coronary arteries cannot occur during systole.

In severe aortic regurgitation, the muscle bulk of the left ventricle is also greatly increased. Since there is no systolic pressure gradient, forward flow can occur in the coronary vessels during systole. However, the low aortic diastolic pressure probably impairs perfusion during this portion of the cycle.

Gorlin et al. (1959) found that coronary blood flow per 100 g. left ventricle remained within normal limits in a small group of patients with chronically increased left ventricular work due to mitral regurgitation, aortic stenosis or aortic regurgitation. The patients were not in cardiac failure. Total left ventricular flow was as great as 250 to 600 ml. per minute and total left ventricular oxygen consumption as great as 79 ml. per minute, or about 25 per cent of the total oxygen consumption. Regan et al. (1956) reported similar changes in patients with aortic regurgitation and Rowe et al. (1965) in patients with aortic stenosis. Data are not available for coronary flow in patients with cardiac failure caused by these lesions.

In uncomplicated mitral stenosis, the left ventricle is not enlarged, and coronary blood flow is not likely to be impeded. Nevertheless, Read et al. (1955) found that coronary flow averaged 69 ml. per 100 g. per minute compared with 96 ml. in normal subjects. The resting cardiac outputs were, respectively, 2.3 and 3.1 liters per M.^{2} per minute. The reduced flow may reflect participation of the coronary vascular bed in the general vasoconstrictor response to the reduced cardiac output (Wade and Bishop, 1962). When myocardial demands for oxygen are increased, as during exercise, the coronary flow is capable of increasing (Gorlin, 1960).

THYROID DISEASE. In thyrotoxicosis, the heart participates in the increased demand for oxygen. The coronary blood flow increases, and coronary vascular resistance is reduced. Myocardial oxygen consumption is increased proportionately more than the heart rate. Thus, the oxygen consumption per beat is also increased, suggesting that the utilization of oxygen by the heart is related to the hypermetabolic state (Rowe et al., 1956; Leight et al., 1956).

Decreased thyroid activity is accompanied by a decrease in coronary blood flow (Rowe et al., 1956). Despite this, therapeutically induced hypothyroidism occasionally relieves angina pectoris in patients in whom this symptom was previously intractable (Blumgart et al., 1957), probably because cardiac work diminishes to a greater degree than does coronary blood flow. However, the possibility cannot be excluded that other factors, such as reduced sensitivity of the heart to the effects of catecholamines, or altered utilization of available oxygen, may play a role.

REFERENCES

Arnett, E. L., and Watts, D. T.: Catecholamine excretion in men exposed to cold. J. Appl. Physiol., *15*:499, 1960.

Bargeron, L. M., Jr., Ehmke, D., Gonlubol, F., Castellano, A., Siegel, A., and Bing, R. J.: Effects of cigarette smoking on coronary blood flow and myocardial metabolism. Circulation, *15*:251, 1957.

Berglund, E., Borst, H. G., Duff, F., and Schreiner, G. L.: Effect of heart rate on cardiac work, myocardial oxygen consumption and coronary blood flow in the dog. Acta Physiol. Scand., *42*:185, 1958.

Berne, R. M.: Effect of epinephrine and norepinephrine on coronary circulation. Circ. Research, *6*:644, 1958.

Bernstein, L., Friesinger, G. C., Lichtlen, P. R., and Ross, R. S.: The effect of nitroglycerin on the systemic and coronary circulation in man and dog. Myocardial blood flow measured with Xenon^{133}. Circulation, *33*:107, 1966.

Bing, R. J.: Coronary circulation in health and disease as studied by coronary sinus catheterization. Bull. N. Y. Acad. Med., *27*:407, 1951.

Bing, R. J., Hammond, M. M., Handelsman, J. C., Powers, S. R., Spencer, F. C., Eckenhoff, J. E., Goodale, W. T., Hafkenschiel, J. F., and Kety, S. S.: The measurement of coronary blood flow, oxygen consumption and efficiency of the left ventricle in man. Am. Heart J., *38*:1, 1949.

Bing, R. J., Mack, R. E., Nolting, D. D., Kirsch, M., Luthy, E., and Choudhury, J. D.: Determination of coronary blood flow with Rb^{86}. Fed. Proc., *17*:101, 1958 (Abstract).

Blumgart, H. L., Freedberg, A. S., and Kurland, G. S.: Radioactive iodine treatment of angina pectoris and congestive heart failure. Circulation, *16*:110, 1957.

Brachfeld, N., Bozer, J., and Gorlin, R.: Action of nitroglycerin on the coronary circulation in normal and mild cardiac subjects. Circulation, *19*:696, 1959.

Breneman, G. M., and Drake, E. H.: Ruptured papillary muscle following myocardial infarction with long survival. Report of two cases. Circulation, *25*:862, 1962.
Broch, O. J., Humerfelt, S., Haarstad, J., and Myhre, J. R.: Hemodynamic studies in acute myocardial infarction. Am. Heart J., *57*:522, 1959.
Calazel, P., Cassagneau, J., Esclavissat, M., Bollinelli, R., Dueuing, J., and Merill, P.: Étude du débit coronaire. 1. Premières resultats chez l'homme normal. Arch. Mal. Coeur, *47*:289, 1954.
Cameron, A. J. V., Hulton, I., Kenmure, A. C. F., and Murdoch, W. R.: Haemodynamic and metabolic effects of hyperbaric oxygen in myocardial infarction. Lancet, *ii*:833, 1966.
Cohen, L. S., Elliot, W. C., Rolett, E. L., and Gorlin, R.: Hemodynamic studies during angina pectoris. Circulation, *31*:409, 1965.
Conn, H. L., Jr.: Use of external counting techniques in studies of the circulation. Circ. Research, *10*:505, 1962.
Cullen, M. L., and Reese, H. L.: Myocardial circulatory changes measured by clearance of Na^{24}—effect of common duct distension on myocardial circulation. J. Appl. Physiol., *5*:281, 1952.
DeMey, D., Cloetens, W., and Romainville, P.: L'avenir de la hernie hiatale dans son incidence sur la pathologie cardiaque. Acta Gastro-Ent. Belg., *22*:19, 1959.
Derrick, J. R., Anderson, J. R., and Ronald, B. J.: Adjunctive use of biological pressor agent, angiotensin, in management of shock. Circulation, *25*:263, 1962.
Deyrup, I. J.: Release of adenine derivatives from mammalian erythrocytes following admixture of blood with strongly hypertonic solutions. Am. J. Physiol., *167*:749, 1951.
Donato, L., Bartolomei, G., Federighi, G., and Torreggiani, G.: Measurement of coronary blood flow by external counting with radioactive rubidium. Circulation, *33*:708, 1966.
Duff, F., Berglund, E., and Borst, H. C.: Effect of heart rate on ventricular function and coronary circulation in dogs. Am. J. Physiol., *185*:611, 1955.
Eckstein, R. W., Stroud, M., III, Eckell, R., Dowling, C. V., and Pritchard, W. H.: Effects of control of cardiac work upon coronary flow and oxygen consumption after sympathetic nerve stimulation. Am. J. Physiol., *163*:539, 1950.
Elliot, E. C.: The effect of Persantin on coronary flow and cardiac dynamics. Canad. Med. Ass. J., *85*:469, 1961.
Evans, C. L., DeGraff, A. C., Kosaka, T., MacKenzie, K., Murphy, G. E., Vacek, T., Williams, D. H., and Young F. G.: Utilization of blood sugar and lactate by the heart-lung preparation. J. Physiol. *80*:21, 1933.
Finnerty, F. A., Jr., Massaro, G. D., Chupkovich, V., and Tuckman, J.: Evaluation of the pressor, cardiac, and renal hemodynamic properties of angiotensin II in man. Circ. Research, *9*:256, 1961.
Fishman, A. P., and Cournand, A.: Heart. Ann. Rev. Physiol., *15*:247, 1953.
Forte, I. E., Schmitthenner, J. E., and Neal, H. S.: Measurement of coronary blood flow using radioactive iodine compared with nitrous oxide. Circ. Research, *9*:547, 1961.
Foster, G. L., and Reeves, T. J.: Hemodynamic responses to exercise in clinically normal middle-aged men and in those with angina pectoris. J. Clin. Invest., *43*: 1758, 1964.
Freis, E. D., Schnafer, H. W., Johnson, R. L., and Schreiner, G. E.: Hemodynamic alterations in acute myocardial infarction. 1. Cardiac output, mean arterial pressure, total peripheral resistance, "central" and total blood volumes, venous pressure and average circulation time. J. Clin. Invest., *31*:131, 1952.
Friedman, S. M., Friedman, C. L., and Nakashima, M.: Effects of aldosterone on blood pressure and electrolyte distribution in the rat. Am. J. Physiol., *195*:621, 1958.
Gammill, J. F., Appelgarth, J. J., Reed, C. E., Fernald, J. D., and Antenucci, A. J.: Hemodynamic changes following acute myocardial infarction using the dye injection method for cardiac output determination. Ann. Int. Med., *43*:100, 1955.

Gilbert, N. C., LeRoy, G. V., and Fenn, G. K.: Effect of distension of abdominal viscera on the blood flow in the circumflex branch of the left coronary artery of the dog. Am. Heart J., *20*:519, 1940.
Gilbert, R. P., Goldberg, M., and Griffin, J.: Circulatory changes in acute myocardial infarction. Circulation, *9*:847, 1954.
Gillespie, J. A.: The case against vasodilator drugs in occlusive vascular disease of the legs. Lancet, *ii*:995, 1959.
Goodale, W. T., and Hackel, D. B.: Measurement of coronary blood flow in dogs and man from rate of myocardial nitrous oxide desaturation. Circ. Research, *1*:502, 1963.
Gorlin, R.: Studies on the regulation of the coronary circulation in man. 1. Atropine-induced changes in cardiac rate. Am. J. Med., *25*:37, 1958.
Gorlin, R.: Measurement of coronary blood flow in health and disease. In: Modern Trends in Cardiology. Ed. Morgan Jones. London, Butterworth, 1960.
Gorlin, R., Brachfeld, N., MacLeod, C., and Bopp, P.: Effect of nitroglycerin on the coronary circulation in patients with coronary artery disease or increased left ventricular work. Circulation, *19*:705, 1959.
Greenwood, W. F., Aldridge, H. E., and Wigle, E. D.: The nature of the disorder of function in chronic postinfarction aneurysm of the left ventricle. Canad. Med. Ass. J., *92*:611, 1965.
Gregg, D. E.: The Coronary Circulation in Health and Disease. Philadelphia, Lea and Febiger, 1950.
Gregg, D. E., and Green, H. D.: Registration and interpretation of normal phasic inflow into a left coronary artery by an improved differential manometric method. Am. J. Physiol., *130*:114, 1940.
Gunnar, R. M., Cruz, A., Boswell, J., Co, B. S., Pietras, R. J., and Tobin, J. R., Jr.: Myocardial infarction with shock. Hemodynamic studies and results of therapy. Circulation, *33*:753, 1966.
Guzman, S. V., Swenson, E., and Jones, M.: Intercoronary reflex: demonstration by coronary angiography. Circ. Research, *10*:739, 1962.
Hackel, D. B., Goodale, W. T., and Kleinerman, J.: Effects of hypoxia on the myocardial metabolism of intact dogs. Circ. Research, *2*:169, 1954.
Harman, M. A., Markov, A., Lehan, P. H., Oldewurtel, H. A., and Regan, T. J.: Coronary blood flow measurements in the presence of arterial obstruction. Circ. Research, *19*:632, 1966.
Harrison, T. R.: Some unanswered questions concerning enlargement and failure of the heart. Am. Heart J., *69*:100, 1965.
Hellems, H. K., Ord, J. W., Talmers, F. N., and Christensen, R. C.: Effects of hypoxia on coronary blood flow and myocardial metabolism in normal human subjects. Circulation, *16*:893, 1957 (Abstract).
Herman, M. V., Heinle, R. A., Klein, M. D., and Gorlin, R.: Localized disorders in myocardial contraction. Asynergy and its role in congestive heart failure. New Eng. J. Med., *277*:222, 1967.
Hyman, C., and Winsor, T.: Symposium on peripheral vascular disorders. Blood flow distribution in the human extremity. The Diversion Phenomenon. Am. J. Cardiol., *4*:566, 1959.
Ito, I., Kobayashi, T., Ito, Y., Nakanishi, A., Murao, S., Shiba, M., Kato, K., Takeuchi, Y., Yasuda, H., and Mikamo, Y.: Studies on coronary circulation in man by method of coronary sinus catheterization. Jap. Circ. J., *20*:229, 1956.
James, T. N.: Anatomy of the coronary arteries in health and disease. Circulation, *32*:1020, 1963.
Katori, M., and Berne, R. M.: Release of adenosine from anoxic hearts. Relationship to coronary flow. Circ. Research, *19*:420, 1966.
Kety, S. S., and Schmidt, C. F.: Determination of cerebral blood flow in man by the use of nitrous oxide in low concentrations. Am. J. Physiol., *143*:53, 1945.
Khouri, E. M., Gregg, D. E., Hall, R. J., and Rayford, C. R.: Regulation of coronary flow during treadmill exercise in the dog. Physiologist, *3*:93, 1960 (Abstract).
Kinsella, D., Troup, W., and McGregor, M.: Studies with a new coronary vasodilator drug: Persantin. Am. Heart J., *63*:146, 1962.

Koch-Weser, J.: Myocardial actions of angiotensin. Circ. Research, *14*:377, 1964.
Krasnow, N., and Gorlin, R.: Myocardial lactate metabolism in coronary insufficiency. Ann. Int. Med., *59*:781, 1963.
Lee, G. de J.: Total and peripheral blood flow in acute myocardial infarction. Brit. Heart J., *19*:117, 1957.
Lehan, P. H., Harman, M. A., and Oldewurtel, H. A.: Myocardial water shifts induced by coronary arteriography. J. Clin. Invest., *42*:950, 1963 (Abstract).
Leight, L., DeFazio, V., Talmers, F. N., Regan, T. J., and Hellems, H. K.: Coronary blood flow, myocardial oxygen consumption and myocardial metabolism in normal and hyperthyroid human subjects. Circulation, *14*:90, 1956.
LeRoy, G. V., Fenn, G. K., and Gilbert, N. C.: The influence of xanthine drugs and atropine on the mortality rate after experimental occlusion of a coronary artery. Am. Heart J., *23*:637, 1942.
Lewis, F. B., Coffman, J. D., and Gregg, D. E.: Effect of heart rate and intracoronary isoproterenol, levarterenol and epinephrine on coronary flow and resistance. Circ. Research, *9*:89, 1961.
Linder, E.: Measurements of normal and collateral coronary blood flow by close-arterial and intra-myocardial injection of $Krypton^{85}$ and $Xenon^{133}$. Acta Physiol. Scand., *68* (Suppl. 272):5, 1966.
Lombardo, T. A., Rose L., Taeschler, M., Tuluy, S., and Bing, R. J.: The effect of exercise on coronary blood flow, myocardial oxygen consumption and cardiac efficiency in man. Circulation, *7*:71, 1953.
Love, W. D., and Burch, G. E.: A study in dogs of methods suitable for estimating the rate of myocardial uptake of Rb^{86} in man, and the effect of l-norepinephrine and pitressin on Rb^{86} uptake. J. Clin. Invest., *36*:468, 1957.
Mack, R. E., Nolting, D. D., Hogancamp, C. E., and Bing, R. J.: Myocardial extraction of Rb^{86} in the rabbit. Am. J. Physiol., *197*:1175, 1959.
MacKenzie, G. J., Flenley, D. C., Taylor, S. H., McDonald, A. H., Staunton, H. P., and Donald, K. W.: Circulatory and respiratory studies in myocardial infarction and cardiogenic shock. Lancet, *ii*:825, 1964.
Malmcrona, R., and Varnauskas, E.: Hemodynamics in acute myocardial infarction. Acta Med. Scand., *175*:1, 1964.
Marchioro, T., Feldman, A., Owens, C. J., and Swan, H.: Measurement of myocardial blood flow: indicator dilution technique. Circ. Research, *9*:541, 1961.
Marshall, R. J., and Shepherd, J. T.: Effect of injections of hypertonic solutions on blood flow through the femoral artery of the dog. Am. J. Physiol., *197*:951, 1959.
Marshall, R. J., and Whelan, R. F.: Intra-arterial oxygen in peripheral vascular disease. Brit. Med. J., *ii*:1448, 1956.
McNicol, M. W., Kirby, B. J., Bhoola, K. D., Everest, M. E., Price, H. V., and Freedman, S. F.: Pulmonary function in acute myocardial infarction. Brit. Med. J., *ii*:1270, 1965.
Messer, J. V., Wagman, R. J., Levine, H. J., Neill, W. A., Krasnow, N., and Gorlin, R.: Patterns of human myocardial oxygen extraction during rest and exercise. J. Clin. Invest., *41*:725, 1962.
Murphy, G. W., Glick, G., Schreiner, B. F., Jr., and Yu, P. N.: Cardiac output in acute myocardial infarction. Serial determination by precordial radio-isotope dilution curves. Am. J. Cardiol., *11*:587, 1963.
Murray, M. J.: Effect of inspiration of cold air on electrocardiograms of normal humans with angina pectoris. Circulation, *26*:765, 1962 (Abstract).
Murray, M. J.: The effect of inhalation of cold air on the circulation in dogs. Am. J. Cardiol., *15*:141, 1965.
Pain, M. C. F., Stannard, M., and Sloman, G.: Disturbances of pulmonary function after acute myocardial infarction. Brit. Med. J., *i*:591, 1967.
Peel, A. A. F., Blum, K., Lancaster, W. M., Dall, J. L. C., and Chalmers, G. L.: Observations on the coronary vasodilator effect of Persantin. Scot. Med. J., *6*:403, 1961.
Pentecost, B., and Shillingford, J.: The acute effects of smoking on myocardial per-

formance in patients with coronary arterial disease. Brit. Heart J., *26*:422, 1964.

Phillips, J. H., Burch, G. E., and De Pasquale, N. P.: The syndrome of papillary muscle dysfunction. Ann. Int. Med., *59*:508, 1963.

Provenza, D. V., and Scherlis, S.: Demonstration of muscle sphincters as a capillary component in the human heart. Circulation, *20*:35, 1959.

Rahimtoola, S. H., Duffy, J. P., and Swan, H. J. C.: Hemodynamic changes associated with injection of angiocardiographic contrast medium in assessment of valvular lesions. Circulation, *33*:52, 1966.

Ravdin, I. S., Royster, H. P., and Sanders, G. B.: Reflexes originating in the common duct giving rise to pain simulating angina pectoris. Ann. Surg., *115*:1055, 1943.

Rayford, C. R., Havos, A., Khouri, E. M., and Gregg, D. E.: Some determinants of coronary flow in intact dogs. Physiologist, *4*:92, 1961 (Abstract).

Read, J. L., Porter, R. R., Bond, E. G., and Bradford, S. C.: Coronary blood flow and myocardial metabolism in valvular heart disease. Circulation, *12*:762, 1955 (Abstract).

Read, R. C., Johnson, J. A., Vick, J. A., and Meyer, M. W.: Vascular effects of hypertonic solutions. Circ. Research, *8*:538, 1960.

Regan, T. J., Hellems, H. K., and Bing, R. J.: Effect of cigarette smoking on coronary circulation and cardiac work in patients with arteriosclerotic coronary disease. Ann. N. Y. Acad. Sci., *90*:186, 1960.

Regan, T. J., Talmers, F. N., Christensen, R. C., Wada, T., and Hellems, H. K.: Coronary blood flow and myocardial metabolism in aortic insufficiency. Circulation, *14*:987, 1956 (Abstract).

Regan, T. J., Timmis, G., Gray, M., Binak, K., and Hellems, H. K.: Myocardial oxygen consumption during exercise in fasting and lipemic subjects. J. Clin. Invest., *40*:624, 1961.

Robinson, J. S., Stannard, M. M., and Long, M.: Ruptured papillary muscle after acute myocardial infarction. Am. Heart J., *70*:233, 1965.

Rowe, G. G., Alfonso, S., Lugo, J. E., Castillo, C. A., Boake, W. C., and Crumpton, C. W.: Coronary blood flow and myocardial oxidative metabolism at rest and during exercise in subjects with severe aortic valve disease. Circulation, *32*: 251, 1965.

Rowe, G. G., Castillo, C. A., Maxwell, G. M., and Crumpton, C. W.: Comparison of systemic and coronary hemodynamics in normal human male and female. Circ. Research, *7*:728, 1959.

Rowe, G. G., Chelius, C. J., Alfonso, S., Gurtner, H. P., and Crumpton, C. W.: Systemic and coronary hemodynamic effects of erythrol tetranitrate. J. Clin. Invest., *40*:1217, 1961.

Rowe, G. G., Huston, J. H., Weinstein, A. B., Tuchman, H., Brown, J. F., and Crumpton, C. W.: The hemodynamics of thyrotoxicosis in man with special reference to coronary blood flow and myocardial oxygen metabolism. J. Clin. Invest., *35*:272, 1956.

Sandler, G., Ilahi, M. A., and Lawson, C. W.: Glyceryl trinitrate in angina pectoris. Lancet, *i*:1130, 1963.

Saÿen, J. J., Sheldon, W. F., Horvitz, O., Kuo, P. T., Pierce, G., Zinsser, H. F., and Mead, J., Jr.: Studies of coronary disease in the experimental animal. II. Polarographic determinations of local oxygen availability in the dog's left ventricle during coronary occlusion and pure oxygen breathing. J. Clin. Invest. *30*:932, 1951.

Schlesinger, M. J.: Significant variations in the anatomic pattern of the coronary vessels. In: Blood, Heart and Circulation. Amer. Assoc. Adv. Sci., 61-72, Publ. No. 13. Washington, D.C., Science Press, 1940.

Sevelius, G., and Johnson, P. C.: Myocardial blood flow determined by surface counting and ratio formula. J. Lab. Clin. Med., *54*:669, 1959.

Siegel, J. H., Gilmore, J. P., and Sarnoff, S. J.: Myocardial extraction and production of catecholamines. Circ. Research, *9*:1336, 1961.

Skinner, N. S., Jr., Leibeskind, R. S., Phillips, H. L., and Harrison, T. R.: Angina pectoris: effect of exertion and of nitrites on precordial movements of patients with angina pectoris. Am. Heart J., *61*:250, 1961.

Smith, W. W., Wikler, N. S., and Fox, A. C.: Hemodynamic studies of patients with myocardial infarction. Circulation, *9*:352, 1954.

Sones, F. M., Jr., and Shirey, E. K.: Ciné coronary arteriography. Mod. Concepts Cardiovasc. Dis., *31*:735, 1962.

Thomas, M., Malmcrona, R., and Shillingford, J.: Haemodynamic effects of oxygen in patients with acute myocardial infarction. Brit. Heart J., *27*:401, 1965.

Thrower, W. B., Darby, T. D., and Aldinger, E. E.: Acid-base derangements and myocardial contractility. Effects as a complication of shock. A.M.A. Arch. Surg., *82*:56, 1961.

Tsagiris, T. J., Koehler, J. A., Kuida, H., and Hecht, H. H.: Studies of coronary blood flow by multiple dye dilution curves. J. Clin. Invest., *42*:10, 1963.

Udhoji, V. N., and Weil, M. H.: Circulatory effect of angiotensin, norepinephrine and metaraminol in the treatment of hypotension (shock). Clin. Res., *11*:176, 1963 (Abstract).

Valentine, P. A., Fluck, D. C., Mounsey, J. P. D., Reid, D., Shillingford, J. P., and Steiner, R. E.: Blood-gas changes after acute myocardial infarction. Lancet, *ii*:837, 1966.

Wade, O. L., and Bishop, J. M.: Cardiac Output and Regional Blood Flow. Philadelphia, Davis, 1962.

Wearn, J. T.: The role of the Thebesian vessels in the circulation of the heart. J. Exper. Med., *47*:293, 1928.

Westfall, T. C., and Watts, D. T.: Catecholamine excretion in smokers and nonsmokers. J. Appl. Physiol., *19*:40, 1964.

Williams, J. F., Jr., Glick, G., and Braunwald, E.: Studies on cardiac dimensions in intact unanesthetized man. V. Effects of nitroglycerin. Circulation, *32*:767, 1965.

Chapter 9

CARDIAC FAILURE

- Cardiac Metabolism
- Ventricular Function
- Circulatory Dynamics
- Blood Volume
- Water and Electrolyte Balance

The definition of heart failure presents problems. Wood (1956) suggested that it is "a state in which the heart fails to maintain an adequate circulation for the needs of the body despite a satisfactory venous filling pressure," thereby excluding extracardiac causes of circulatory failure such as vasovagal syncope and shock. This definition is adequate for the common clinical syndrome of cardiac failure.

Although failure sometimes develops suddenly from such causes as acute myocardial infarction or a rapid arrhythmia complicating valve disease, it often develops gradually. In the latter instance, it is difficult to decide at what point in time failure may be said to exist. Thus, the circulation may be adequate during rest but become inadequate when stressed by exercise. The reserve mechanisms of the heart and circulation are such that compensation is often maintained for months or years in the presence of extensive myocardial disease or of increased pressure or volume loads on the heart.

Diseases such as hypertension and aortic stenosis lead initially to left ventricular failure. This causes venous and capillary engorgement in the lungs, and the symptoms and signs are those of capillary congestion. Similarly, right sided failure results from impaired pumping of the right ventricle secondary to such conditions as chronic pulmonary emphysema and pulmonary stenosis. There is venous and capillary engorgement of the systemic organs and tissues, and the symptoms and signs are directly related to these. Although one ventricle may be primarily affected, the output of the other ventricle must follow suit, since they are in series in a closed system. Left ventricular failure is often followed by right ventricular failure, so that both the pulmonary and systemic circulations are congested. Alternatively, right and left ventricular failure may develop simultaneously. Reduction of the cardiac output during rest is characteristic of congestive heart failure. However, congestive heart failure complicating such conditions as thyrotoxicosis, severe anemia, beriberi and peripheral arteriovenous fistulae may be accompanied by a greater than normal output; even though the output is increased, it may be inadequate to satisfy the needs of the tissues (Eichna, 1960). Thus, in thyrotoxicosis, the metabolic rate is increased; in severe anemia, the oxygen capacity of the blood is greatly reduced; in beriberi, the flow is inadequate for the tissues in which oxidative metabolism is impaired; and in arteriovenous fistulae, the shunted blood is not available for metabolic exchange.

Abnormal retention of salt and water occurs in all forms of cardiac failure. Over the years, there has been much debate as to whether this is due primarily to venous congestion behind the failing ventricle (backward failure) or to an inadequate output of blood by the failing ventricle (forward failure). Protagonists of the backward failure theory attributed the retention of salt and water to renal venous hypertension. According to the forward failure theory, the manifestations of failure are related to inadequate blood flow to the various organs and tissues in relation to their needs, with the major emphasis on impaired blood supply to the kidneys. Neither the backward failure nor the forward failure theory by itself provides an adequate explanation for cardiac failure. Retention of the terms leads to confusion rather than clarification.

CARDIAC METABOLISM

Metabolic processes in heart muscle occur in three general phases: (1) energy liberation, (2) energy conservation and (3) energy utilization (Olson, 1964). Energy is liberated as a result of glycolysis, oxidation of fatty acids and pyruvic acid and the dehydrogenation of the Krebs tricarboxylic acid cycle. Glycolysis, which results in the formation of pyruvate and lactate from glucose, takes place in the cytoplasm, whereas most of the other activity occurs in the mitochondria. Energy conservation is achieved through the activity of hydrogen transport enzymes located in the mitochondrial membranes; in the process of oxidative phosphorylation, the energy of hydrogen is converted into the terminal bond energy of adenosine triphosphate (ATP) and, via creatine kinase, to creatine phosphate (CP). In the phase of energy utilization, the terminal high energy phosphate bond of ATP is channeled into the contractile process that results in mechanical work. In cardiac muscle, the contractile events occur in the myofibrils, which lie side by side with mitochondria. Shortening of the myofibril is thought to result from ATP activated sliding of filaments to account for the approximation of the Z membranes towards one another. This appears to be achieved by the rapid making and breaking of actomyosin bonds between the thick myosin-containing and thin actin-containing filaments.

These three phases have been extensively studied, both in congestive heart failure in man and in its experimental counterpart in animals. Most studies of energy liberation in patients with cardiac failure have necessarily been based on measurement of arteriovenous differences across the coronary circulation and have the inherent assumption that these differences accurately reflect myocardial activity. More direct observations can be made on specimens of heart muscle obtained from failing hearts in animal preparations. However, since no animal preparation precisely resembles congestive heart failure in man, caution is needed in the extrapolation of results.

In patients with congestive heart failure, myocardial uptake of glucose, pyruvate, fatty acids and ketones was measured by the technique of coronary sinus catheterization and found to be normal (Kako and Bing, 1958). Energy liberation also appeared to be normal in dogs with low output congestive heart failure caused by tricuspid regurgitation or stenosis of the pulmonary artery (Olson, 1964). Further, oxygen consumption per 100 g. of heart muscle was normal during rest in patients with heart disease both with and without congestive heart failure (Olson, 1959; Danforth et al., 1960). Lombardo et al. (1953) found that the failing heart could increase its oxygen consumption during moderate exercise. In more recent studies, there was some evidence that patients with failure due to ischemic heart disease developed myocardial hypoxia and anaerobic metabolism during exercise (Stock et al., 1962). The normal utilization of substrates and oxygen in low output congestive heart failure makes it unlikely that energy liberation is a basic defect.

Data concerning a possible defect in the phase of energy conservation have been more conflicting. For example, Lamprecht and Hockerts (1959) found that the production of high energy phosphate by the failing heart was impaired. Schwartz and Lee (1962) found evidence for uncoupling of oxidative phosphorylation in the mitochondria. However, in other studies, there was no diminution in the levels of either ATP or phosphocreatine in failing heart muscle (Furchgott and De Gubareff, 1958; Lee et al., 1960) or in acute hypoxic heart failure (Pool et al., 1965). Failure could still occur in the heart-lung preparation (Wollenberger, 1949) and in dogs with congestive heart failure (Olson and Piatnek, 1959) in the presence of normal or even increased stores of high energy phosphate. Oxidative phosphorylation was normal in the hearts of guinea pigs with chronic congestive heart failure (Plaut and Gertler, 1959). Thus, the balance of evidence favored the view that if there was a fundamental defect in cardiac metabolism, this was more likely to be in the phase of energy utilization (by the contractile proteins) rather than in the storage phase (Danforth et al., 1960).

Chidsey et al. (1966B) studied the structure and function of mitochondria from left ventricular papillary muscles of patients with rheumatic heart disease and severe heart failure who were having their mitral valves replaced. There was no morphological alteration in the mitochondria, in contrast with reports of loss of cristae from the mitochondria of failing canine hearts (Wollenberger and Schulze, 1961). Further, normal oxygen consumption, coupled phosphorylation and adenosine triphosphatase activity testified to their functional integrity.

A defect in the phase of energy utilization could involve either excitation-contraction coupling or the contractile elements of the myocardium.

EXCITATION-CONTRACTION COUPLING. The addition of ATP in vitro to a protein suspension of actomyosin in the presence of calcium and magnesium leads to shortening of the actomyosin. Although these ingredients are all present in intact resting skeletal muscle, they do not interact to contract the muscle until excitation of the cell occurs. The reason appears to be that in skeletal muscle, the concentration of ionic calcium near the contractile protein is very low, most of the calcium being sequestered in intracellular organelles or relaxing factor vesicles. It is postulated that excitation of the cell causes sudden release of calcium from the vesicles, thus leading to contraction (Weber et al., 1964); relaxation follows return of calcium to the vesicles. Contraction-relaxation cycles can occur when the bathing medium contains a negligible concentration of calcium.

In contrast, extracellular ionic calcium is essential for the contraction of heart muscle. The strength of contraction is increased by increase in the concentration of extracellular calcium and by prolongation of the duration of depolarization, both of which factors permit more calcium to enter the cell during that period of permeability of its membrane to calcium. Relaxation is dependent upon the presence of an active transport system in the cell membrane that restores the calcium to the extracellular fluid. Relaxing factor vesicles, however, are also present in heart muscle and probably play an essential role, since the amount of extracellular calcium that enters the cell is much less than that required for full activation of the contractile protein (Winegrad, 1961).

The presence of a system for regulating cardiac contractile force by altering the amount of calcium entering the cell might be anticipated. Cardioglobulin may play a role by releasing its protein bound calcium into the cell (Leonard and Hajdu, 1961; Hajdu and Leonard, 1965). It is possible that disturbances in the control mechanisms for calcium entry and exit, leading to impaired regulation of myocardial contractility, may be responsible for certain forms of heart failure (Leonard, 1966).

CONTRACTILE ELEMENTS. The contractility of actomyosin bands from patients dying from congestive heart failure was found to be impaired; a combination of digoxin and calcium was required to restore contractility (Kako and Bing, 1958). Both the concentration and the viscosity of actomyosin were reduced in dogs with chronic failure secondary to surgically created valve defects (Benson, 1955), and the contractility of glycerol extracted bundles from failing canine hearts was impaired (Benson et al., 1958). Suggestions that in the failing canine heart, myosin undergoes polymerization to a less active form (Olson et al., 1961) have not been confirmed, however, by other studies (Davis et al., 1960; Mueller et al., 1964). Thus, the role of alterations in the contractile proteins remains to be elucidated.

Bing et al. (1964) measured enzyme levels in hearts obtained shortly after death. There were marked reductions in the levels of isocitric dehydrogenase, lactic dehydrogenase and aldolase in hearts that had been in failure, in comparison with those that had been fully compensated. Although the significance of these findings is uncertain, it is possible that enzyme deficiencies could, in the course of time, impair the synthesis of contractile protein.

VENTRICULAR FUNCTION

The nature of the Frank-Starling mechanism, its ultrastructural basis and its applicability to man were discussed in Chapter 1. It provides the failing heart with an important compensatory mechanism. The ventricle, through an increase in its end-diastolic volume, is capable of ejecting a normal or nearly normal stroke volume, despite depression of its function. As myocardial contractility is further impaired, the ventricle continues to dilate. This is theoretically advantageous in that a much less degree of shortening of individual myocardial fibers is required to expel a given quantity of blood (Burch et al., 1952). However, this mechanical advantage is annulled by the fact that the ventricle must develop more tension in order to generate pressure inside its cavity. The law of Laplace, $P = T\left(\frac{1}{R_1} + \frac{1}{R_2}\right)$, defines the relationship between pressure (P), tension (T, per unit length of ventricular wall) and the principal radii of curvature of the ventricular wall at any point (R_1 and R_2) (Burton, 1957). In a normal ventricle, which ejects about 50 per cent of its end-diastolic volume, the change in wall radius is considerable. The effect of decreasing radius may outweigh that of increasing intracavitary pressure, so that myocardial tension may begin to decrease early in the ejection phase. In a dilated ventricle, the change in radius is relatively slight, so that tension increases during the early ejection phase. The increased tension required to generate the pressure inside the cavity leads to a decreased rate of fiber shortening (Fry et al., 1964; Levine and Britman, 1964).

In studies of normal canine hearts in which ventricular end-diastolic pressure was held constant, increases in the afterload resulted in decreases in the velocity of ejection, and an inverse relationship was demonstrated between wall tension and fiber or contractile element velocity (Ross et al., 1966). During acute failure, the curve relating contractile velocity to tension was shifted to the left, resulting in decreased velocity at any given tension. Although there is no direct evidence of impaired maximal velocity of fiber shortening in the failing human heart, indirect evidence suggests that this may occur. Thus, the maximal rate of increase of pressure in the left ventricle is impaired (Miller et al., 1965), the mean rate of left ventricular ejection during exercise fails to increase normally (Levine et al., 1962), and the mean rate of circumferential shortening is reduced (Gorlin et al., 1964).

In addition to physical factors, such as the Frank-Starling mechanism and the law of Laplace, nervous and humoral factors are of great importance in the control of cardiac function. The urinary excretion of norepinephrine averaged 22 μg. per day in normal subjects and in patients with heart disease who were fully compensated, whereas in patients with heart failure, it averaged 46 μg. per day. The fact that the excretion of epinephrine was unaltered suggested that the increased norepinephrine excretion reflected increased activity of the adrenergic sympathetic nerve terminals rather than of the adrenal medulla (Chidsey et al., 1965). Plasma levels of norepinephrine tended to be higher in patients with heart failure during rest, although there was some overlap of values. During exercise, however, there was a much more striking increase in the levels in the patients with failure, suggesting that there was a marked augmentation of sympathetic activity in this circumstance (Chidsey et al., 1962; Fig. 9-1).

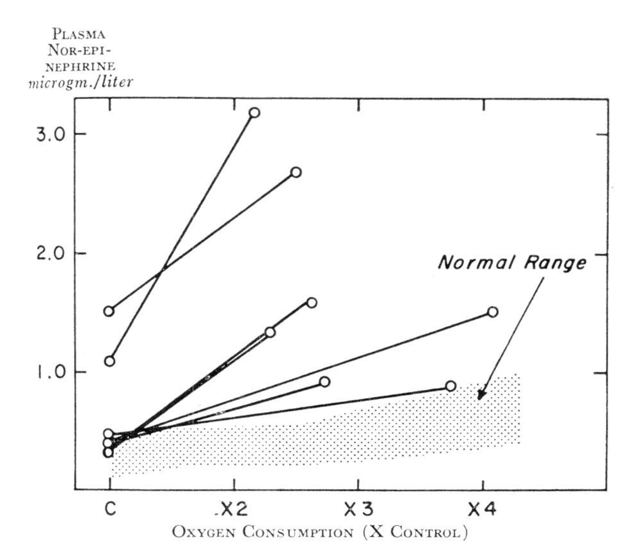

FIGURE 9-1. Plasma levels of norepinephrine at rest and during mild exercise in patients with heart failure The stippled area represents the normal range. (From Chidsey, Harrison and Braunwald, New Eng. J. Med., *267*:650, 1962.)

Cardiac norepinephrine stores are depleted in heart failure both in man (Chidsey et al., 1966A) and animals (Chidsey et al., 1964). This does not alter the intrinsic contractile properties of the myocardium (Spann et al., 1965). Failing heart muscle still responds normally to exogenous norepinephrine. However, dogs with heart failure have reduced chronotropic and inotropic responses to stimulation of the cardiac sympathetic nerves, due to diminished release of intrinsic norepinephrine (Covell et al., 1966). Thus, in conditions such as exercise, which are accompanied by increased sympathetic nervous activity, the failing heart loses an important mechanism for increasing its contractility.

Other observations have illustrated the importance of adrenergic nervous activity for optimal myocardial performance. For example, guanethidine, by depleting catecholamine stores, precipitated cardiac failure in some patients with hypertensive heart disease (Braunwald et al., 1963).

Pool et al. (1967) demonstrated that tyrosine hydroxylase activity in homogenates of hearts from dogs with congestive heart failure is markedly reduced. Since tyrosine hydroxylase has been shown to be the rate limiting step in the biosynthesis of norepinephrine, the depression of cardiac norepinephrine stores in congestive heart failure may be related to a reduction in norepinephrine synthesis.

EFFECTS OF PAIRED PULSE STIMULATION. When the heart is driven electrically so that each regular beat is followed by a very premature beat (immediately after completion of the refractory period), the latter is mechanically ineffective; thus, the electrical rate is twice the rate of effective mechanical contraction (Lopez et al., 1963). It has also been known for many years that the strength of cardiac contraction is enhanced during the cycle following an extrasystole (postextrasystolic potentiation) (Koch-Weser and Blinks, 1963; Cranefield, 1965). Therefore, it seemed that paired pulse stimulation might also be of value in maintaining prolonged enhancement of myocardial contractility. Sonnenblick et al. (1965) found that paired pulse stimulation had a powerful inotropic effect on the papillary muscles of cats and also in norepinephrine depleted papillary muscles from patients with congestive heart failure; the effect greatly exceeded that of the inotropic drugs, digitalis, catecholamines and calcium.

In acute right ventricular failure in dogs produced by constricting the pulmonary artery and injecting an adrenergic blocking drug, paired pulse stimulation restored cardiac output toward control levels; it did not alter the cardiac output of normal dogs (Cranefield et al., 1964; Lopez and Petkovich, 1965). In dogs with opened chests and non-failing hearts, it doubled myocardial contractility and increased energy expenditure (Chardack et al., 1965). When the effective ventricular rate, stroke volume and mean arterial pressure were held constant, paired pulse stimulation increased the oxygen consumption, the rate of rise of intraventricular pressure, the speed of ventricular contraction and the velocity of blood flow in the ascending aorta; the duration of ejection, tension-time index and left ventricular end-diastolic pressure were reduced. In experimental heart failure, as few as 10 successive pairs of stimuli were required to reduce ventricular end-diastolic pressure from 35 mm. Hg to normal levels (Ross et al., 1965).

Paired pulse stimulation is feasible in man, and it has potential applications in situations such as acute heart failure, failure of the heart to recover mechanical force following cardiac surgery, and shock secondary to myocardial infarction (Hoffman et al., 1965). However, its effect in augmenting cardiac output in patients with cardiac failure has been less consistent than in dogs with acute heart failure. Also, the increased oxygen consumption of the heart is a contraindication to its application in patients with ischemic heart disease, unless the ventricular rate is simultaneously reduced, as by the technique of coupled pacemaking (Frommer, 1965). Since the second stimulus of the pair arrives during or near the vulnerable period, the induction of a serious arrhythmia is a theoretical possibility. Although in patients with rheumatic heart disease, paired pulse pacemaking may enhance ventricular contractility, any benefit from this may be annulled through accentuation of valvular regurgitation (Meijler and Durrer, 1965).

DILATATION AND HYPERTROPHY. Ventricular dilatation, in theory, confers a mechanical advantage to the damaged heart and may be regarded as an early compensatory mechanism. As has been noted, it increases the contractile force of the heart through the Frank-Starling mechanism and, for a time, permits compensation to be maintained. However, the increase in chamber size is accompanied by increases in mural tension and energy expenditure. Therefore, a point is reached at which the mechanical advantage from dilatation is lost.

Chronic dilatation has been thought to be due to stretching of the individual contractile elements of heart muscle (sarcomeres). However, Linzbach (1960) concluded from a microscopic study that the sarcomeres in chronically dilated hearts are no longer than those in normal hearts. Thus, the dilatation may result from rearrangement of the sarcomeres rather than from their being stretched. This concept offers an explanation for the fact that the large residual (end-diastolic) volume in these hearts cannot be mobilized, since the muscle fibers lack the stimulus that would be provided by increased stretching.

Another compensatory mechanism is provided by myocardial hypertrophy. This takes more time to develop. Diseases associated with increased pressure work, such as aortic and pulmonary stenosis and arterial hypertension, are accompanied predominantly by hypertrophy, whereas those associated with volume overload, such as aortic and mitral regurgitation, are accompanied predominantly by dilatation. Myocardial hypertrophy has been generally thought to result from an increase in the size of individual fibers, with no increase in their number. Undoubtedly, the fibers do increase in thickness, from a normal diameter of about 15 μ up to 25 to 30 μ. Linzbach (1960), however, concluded that hyperplasia (an increase in the total number) can also occur, probably from longitudinal splitting of fibers. This is accompanied by an increase in the number of myocardial capillaries. The mechanism of hypertrophy is unknown.

CIRCULATORY DYNAMICS

Some patients with symptoms and signs indicative of cardiac failure have resting values for cardiac output that are within normal limits. When they are stressed, for example, when they perform muscular exercise, their disability becomes apparent. Although the cardiac output increases, the increase is subnormal in relation to the energy expenditure as assessed by the increase in oxygen consumption. The ratio between the increase in oxygen consumption and that in cardiac output, however, has not provided a clearcut distinction between normal subjects and those with various degrees of impairment of cardiac performance. A better separation may be obtained by plotting hemodynamic data in other ways (Epstein et al., 1966): (1) at a saturation of 30 per cent in the pulmonary artery (mixed venous blood), all normal subjects had cardiac outputs exceeding 7 liters per M.^{2} per minute, whereas no patients with moderate or severe disability attained values as high as 5 liters per M.^{2} per minute; (2) the quantity of unextracted oxygen returned to the lungs was calculated as the product of cardiac output and oxygen content in the pulmonary artery. In normal subjects, this averaged 375 ml. per M.^{2} per minute at rest and 519 ml. during maximal exercise. In the same group of patients, it averaged 210 ml. at rest and decreased to 181 ml. during maximal exercise.

In more severe grades of cardiac failure, particularly those associated with obstructive valvular lesions such as mitral stenosis, not only is the cardiac output reduced at rest, but it increases only very slightly, or may even fail to increase, with exercise (Donald et al., 1954). As compensation is regained, improvement in cardiac output would be anticipated. This has generally (Howarth et al., 1946; Eichna et al., 1953), but not invariably been the case when studies were made in resting subjects. More clearcut evidence of improvement is apparent during the stress of exercise. However, the correlation with improvement in symptoms is not close; clearly, factors other than cardiac output are implicated.

The mean pressures in the right and left atria normally average 4 and 8 mm. Hg, respectively. In the absence of disease of the atrioventricular valves, the diastolic pressures in the ventricles are equivalent to the atrial pressures. The end-diastolic pressures correspond to the *a* waves of the atrial pressure pulses. Cardiac failure is accompanied by increases in atrial and in ventricular diastolic pressures in the affected side(s) of the heart.

However, some reservations are necessary (Braunwald and Ross, 1963): (1) the shape of the curves relating ventricular work to end-diastolic pressure, and end-diastolic volume to end-diastolic pressure, are such that when end-diastolic pressure is normal or slightly increased, it is a poor index of end-diastolic volume and of ventricular function; (2) when compliance is greatly reduced, as in the concentrically hypertrophied left ventricle with normal end-systolic and end-diastolic volumes that one finds in aortic stenosis, or in constrictive pericarditis, the end-diastolic pressure may be greatly increased in the absence of any evidence of impaired contractility or failure.

Since the ventricular end-diastolic volume is increased in the failing heart, the ratio of stroke volume to end-diastolic volume becomes very small. With exercise, the stroke volume may diminish further, so that the ratio becomes even smaller. This contrasts with the increase in the ratio in normal subjects during supine exercise. When failure is secondary to mitral or aortic valve regurgitation, the total stroke volume may be greatly increased, but the effective (forward) stroke volume is diminished because of the large regurgitant fraction.

The mechanical efficiency of the normal left ventricle is about 30 per cent during rest (Bing and Michal, 1959; Levine et al., 1963), and it increases with muscular exercise, probably because of decreases in end-systolic and end-diastolic volumes. During exercise, the oxygen consumption of the dilated failing ventricle is considerably increased, the end-systolic volume may also increase, and there is no improvement in its mechanical efficiency (Levine et al., 1963; Lombardo et al., 1953).

In left ventricular failure and in pulmonary congestion from mitral stenosis, the pulmonary venous pressure is moderately or markedly increased, and there is a concomitant increase in pulmonary artery pressure, so that the perfusion pressure is maintained. Pulmonary venous hypertension is sometimes accompanied by arteriolar constriction, so that there is a disproportionate increase in pulmonary arterial pressure and a high value for pulmonary vascular resistance. Exercise usually increases pulmonary vascular resistance, whereas the injection of acetylcholine into the pulmonary artery (Wood et al., 1957) or inhalation of oxygen often decreases it.

CHANGES IN THE PERIPHERAL CIRCULATION. The increased venous pressure in congestive heart failure is related to the inability of the heart to increase its output and to decreased distensibility of the venous capacity vessels of the systemic circulation. Increase of the blood volume (Samet et al., 1957), much of which is accommodated in the postcapillary vessels, may contribute to the increased venous pressure. However, since acute hypervolemia causes only transient increases of venous pressure in normal subjects (Warren et al., 1948), its importance is subsidiary to that of the changes in cardiac function and venous tone.

The decreased venous distensibility with congestive heart failure has been demonstrated by Burch (1954), Sharpey-Schafer (1961), Wood (1962) and Mason and Braunwald (1964). With recovery from failure, the distensibility increases again (Wood et al., 1956). Autonomic ganglionic blockade with intravenous hexamethonium in patients with congestive heart failure due to hypertension, ischemic heart disease and aortic regurgitation reduced the venous pressure (Kelly et al., 1953); the reduction was not accompanied by a significant change in total blood volume (Lewis et al., 1959). Although this would indicate that the increased venomotor tone at rest is mediated by adrenergic nerves, it is not proof of this, since the hemodynamic changes following ganglionic blockade are complex and are not confined to inhibition of nervous activity to the venous system. Mason (1966) found a slight positive correlation between the reduction in the compliance of the forearm veins and central venous pressure in patients with heart failure; with digitalis therapy, the cardiac output and venous compliance increased, and venous pressure decreased. By contrast, the intravenous administration of ouabain may cause venoconstriction in normal subjects (Mason and Braunwald, 1964); to explain the opposite response in the patients, they suggested that in them, the improvement in cardiac function due to ouabain results in a diminution of the reflex venoconstriction, so that the resultant decrease in tone exceeds the increase due to the direct effect of ouabain on the vessels.

Normal subjects have a reflex increase in venomotor tone in the limbs during exercise, which is proportional to the severity of the exercise. When patients with heart failure exercise, their venomotor tone is further augmented, even with a work load that is too mild to elicit venoconstriction in normal subjects (Wood, 1962).

With the exception of causative conditions such as aortic valve regurgitation and systemic hypertension that inherently alter the arterial blood pressure, low output heart failure is generally associated with a mean arterial pressure within the normal range. The increased venous pressure may result in a slightly reduced systemic perfusion pressure (mean arterial – mean venous pressure). However, since there is a more marked decrease in cardiac output, systemic vascular resistance (cardiac output divided by systemic perfusion pressure) is increased. As mentioned previously, the renal blood flow is reduced. Myers and Hickam (1948), Rapaport et al. (1958) and Ferrer et al. (1965) found that splanchnic blood flow estimated by the sulfobromophthalein method was usually reduced to the same extent as cardiac output despite maintenance of, or even elevation of, arterial blood pressure. The degree of splanchnic vasoconstriction was equivalent to that of the body as a whole but much less than that in the kidney. Splanchnic blood volume was disproportionately increased with respect to total blood volume in patients having visceral congestion with right ventricular failure and combined ventricular failure. There was a significant relationship between central venous pressure and splanchnic blood volume; the greater elevation of the former than of the latter suggested the presence of splanchnic venoconstriction (Ferrer et al., 1965).

The blood flow to the limbs is also reduced. Lundsgaard (1918) found a decreased oxygen saturation of forearm venous blood, and Weiss and Ellis (1935) found increased arteriovenous differences in oxygen saturation in both upper and lower limbs. In patients with rheumatic heart disease, the reduction in total blood flow through the upper limb correlated with the decrease in cardiac output (Donald et al., 1955). The patients studied by Mason (1966) all had heart failure with venous pressures above 15 cm. H_2O, cardiac outputs less than 2.5 liters per $M.^2$ per minute, and Class III or IV disability (criteria of New York Heart Association). Resting values for forearm blood flow were generally below the normal range, and the decrease in flow was proportionately greater than that in cardiac output. Forearm vascular resistance was consistently increased. Peak values for forearm blood flow during the period of reactive hyperemia following release of arterial occlusion averaged only 4.3 ml. per 100 ml. per minute compared with 15.1 ml. per 100 ml. per minute in normal patients. The latter finding cannot readily be attributed to increased sympathetic vasoconstrictor tone, since one would expect that the powerful vasodilator metabolites formed in ischemic tissues would be capable of overcoming this. Thus, congestive heart failure is accompanied by complex changes in the peripheral circulation. Some of these changes result from increased sympathetic activity in the resistance vessels and the veins, but the stimulus for this and the receptors concerned are unknown. Humoral and local interactions are also involved. Congestive heart failure may increase systemic vascular resistance directly, by altering the mechanical properties and reducing the dilating ability of the resistance vessels (Zelis et al., 1967).

BLOOD VOLUME

Plasma volume, measured by Evans blue dye, was found to be increased in congestive heart failure (Gibson and Evans, 1937; Meneely and Kaltreider, 1943). Reported changes in the red blood cell volume were less consistent, probably because of differences in the peripheral and whole body hematocrits (Schreiber and Rothschild, 1962). Simultaneous measurements of red cell and plasma volumes have shown consistent increases in both (Samet et al., 1957). As compensation is regained, the blood volume decreases, and it is usually within normal limits in patients with heart disease who have not been in failure. The increase in plasma volume results from retention of sodium and water by the kidney; it amounts to about 15 per cent in moderate and 30 per cent in severe congestive failure. This increase is small in relation to that in interstitial fluid. The reason for the increase in red cell volume is unknown.

Accompanying the increased distending pressure in the pulmonary vessels in left ventricular failure is an increase in the volume of blood in the lungs measured by the indicator dilution method. This may be less than has commonly been thought. Thus, Schreiner et al. (1966) found mean values for pulmonary blood volume of 271 ml. per M.[2] in normal subjects and 292 ml. per M.[2] in patients with left ventricular or biventricular failure from causes other than rheumatic heart disease. The reduction in pulmonary compliance and the increase in minute ventilation during exercise together probably provide a basis for the dyspnea (Bates and Christie, 1964).

WATER AND ELECTROLYTE BALANCE

Abnormal renal retention of sodium is the main factor responsible for the accumulation of excessive quantities of water in the body. Several mechanisms are probably involved.

GLOMERULAR FILTRATION. Merrill (1946) showed that the glomerular filtration rate was reduced in congestive cardiac failure and suggested that this was responsible for the sodium retention. Acute decreases in glomerular filtration rate both in dogs (Barger et al., 1961) and in man (Farber et al., 1953) are accompanied by temporary increases in salt and water retention; chronic decreases often fail to promote retention. Shannon (1942) suggested that the decreased rate of flow in the renal tubules permitted more nearly complete tubular reabsorption of sodium. Davis (1965) felt that the initial retention of salt and water, following an acute reduction of glomerular filtration rate, might inhibit secretion of aldosterone and that this, in turn, might lead to less tubular reabsorption of sodium. This would account for the transience of the increased rate of salt and water retention.

Many patients with chronic cardiac failure have a glomerular filtration rate within normal limits (Sinclair-Smith et al., 1949), and compensation may be regained through the ability to excrete sodium in the absence of any significant change in the glomerular filtration rate. In hypertension and some intrinsic renal diseases, the glomerular filtration rate is often reduced, yet salt and water are not retained abnormally. In certain forms of experimental cardiac failure (Davis et al., 1957B) and in chronic constriction of the inferior vena cava (Davis and Howell, 1953) associated with retention of salt and water, the glomerular filtration rate is increased. Hence, reduced glomerular filtration rate probably plays a minor role, at most, in salt and water retention.

RENAL BLOOD FLOW. Vasoconstriction is more intensive in the kidney than in any other vascular bed. The reason for this is unknown. Renal vasoconstriction can still occur in the absence of sympathetic nervous

TABLE 9-1. Renal Circulation in Normal Subjects, Compensated Heart Disease, and Congestive Heart Failure*

	RENAL BLOOD FLOW (ML./M.²/MIN.)		RENAL A-V O_2 DIFFERENCE (ML./100 ML.)		RENAL FRACTION OF OUTPUT (%)	
	NO.	MEAN	NO.	MEAN	NO.	MEAN
Normal subjects	169	660	30	1.29	37	15.3
Compensated heart disease	124	411	9	2.04	88	14.8
Congestive heart failure	109	231	33	3.37	63	11.1

* From Wade and Bishop, Cardiac Output and Regional Blood Flow. Oxford, Blackwell, 1962.

activity in the kidneys (Mokotoff and Ross, 1948). Merrill (1946) found a mean renal blood flow of only 199 ml. per M.² per minute in 31 patients with congestive failure from causes other than hypertension. This has been confirmed in numerous subsequent investigations. Wade and Bishop (1962) compared values for renal blood flow, renal arteriovenous difference in oxygen content and renal fraction of the cardiac output in groups of normal subjects, patients with compensated cardiac disease and patients with congestive heart failure with low cardiac output, collected from published reports (Table 9-1). The renal blood flow was reduced, on the average, by one third in patients with organic heart disease (mainly valvular) while compensation was retained, and by about two thirds in patients with failure. Sequential measurements have shown an increase in renal blood flow as compensation is regained (Eichna et al., 1953).

Since the renal blood flow or renal plasma flow is reduced more markedly and more consistently than the glomerular filtration rate, the filtration fraction is increased. Vander et al. (1958) suggested that the relatively high glomerular filtration rate (in relation to the renal plasma flow), by resulting in an increased oncotic pressure in peritubular capillary blood, might induce an oncotic pressure gradient across the proximal tubule. This would lead to increased reabsorption of water and secondarily of sodium. However, the available evidence is that the reabsorption of sodium in the proximal tubule is the primary event. Further, there are numerous situations in which a high filtration fraction is not accompanied by increased retention of sodium. These include essential hypertension, in which there is decreased retention of sodium in response to an acute load (Baldwin et al., 1958; Cottier et al., 1958), and organic heart disease (Werkö et al., 1954) or chronic pulmonary disease (Fishman et al., 1951), prior to the onset of abnormal sodium retention.

Thus, it is likely that the decrease in renal plasma flow, rather than the increase in the filtration fraction, may be an important factor in initiating the events that lead to accumulation of sodium and water.

RENAL VENOUS PRESSURE. The pressure in the renal veins, as in other systemic veins, is increased in congestive heart failure. There has therefore been debate as to whether renal venous hypertension is causally related to the abnormal retention of sodium and water. Acute compression of a renal vein in the dog was accompanied by decreased sodium and water excretion by the corresponding kidney (Blake et al., 1949). Similarly, acute elevation of pressure in the renal veins induced by inflating a balloon in the inferior vena cava of normal subjects led to retention of sodium and water (Farber et al., 1953). However, chronic constriction of the inferior vena cava below the hepatic and above the renal veins did not result in retention of sodium and water (Ball and Davis, 1957), even though venous hypertension persisted in the kidneys; and, in nephrectomized dogs with a kidney transplanted to the neck, marked sodium retention followed constriction of the inferior vena cava above the hepatic veins, even though the venous pressure in the cervical kidney was normal (Carpenter et al., 1961). Thus, it appears that an increase in renal venous pressure, like a reduction in the glomerular filtration rate, has only a relatively transient effect on the ability of the kidney to handle sodium and water.

TUBULAR REABSORPTION. Both in experimental preparations and in congestive heart failure in man, excessive tubular reabsorption of sodium may occur independently of any changes in glomerular filtration rate or renal plasma flow. This evidence has accumulated particularly since the isolation and identification of aldosterone, the potent salt retaining adrenal cortical hormone (Simpson et al., 1954). It is now apparent that aldosterone

plays a major role in the retention of salt and water in congestive failure, although evidence is accumulating that the relationship is not a simple one (Luetscher, 1962), and that some extra-adrenal factor is necessary (Davis et al., 1964A).

Numerous reports of changes in the electrolyte composition of body fluids (White et al., 1950) and of increased sodium retaining ability of urine (Singer and Wener, 1953) preceded the demonstration of increased levels of aldosterone in urine of patients with congestive heart failure (Luetscher and Johnson, 1954). Increased levels of aldosterone have also been demonstrated in the plasma of patients with congestive failure. In experimental cardiac failure with both low (Davis et al., 1957A) and high (Davis et al., 1964B) levels of cardiac output, increased secretory levels of aldosterone have been documented. Evidence in congestive failure in man is less clearcut. The studies of Laragh (1962) indicated a moderate increase in plasma levels that became more apparent following the ingestion of salt. Increased plasma levels could be due to impaired inactivation by the congested liver (Yates et al., 1958) as an alternative to increased rate of secretion. There is evidence that this is a factor in patients with congestive failure (Luetscher et al., 1963), and in patients in whom hepatic blood flow is considerably reduced (Myers and Hickam, 1948) and venous pressure increased. It is likely that there are usually both an increased rate of secretion and a decreased rate of degradation.

Other observations render improbable a simple cause and effect quantitative relationship between increased secretion rate of aldosterone and tubular reabsorption of sodium. Thus, plasma levels are much higher in hepatic cirrhosis (Laragh, 1962) and in nephrosis than in congestive heart failure. In primary hyperaldosteronism (Conn and Louis, 1956), edema is not a usual feature. Spironolactone, a specific antagonist of aldosterone, is frequently ineffective in reversing sodium and water retention in congestive failure.

ALDOSTERONE AND SODIUM REABSORPTION. Aldosterone increases reabsorption in the distal tubule by augmenting active transport mechanisms (Sonnenblick et al., 1961). In normal subjects, large daily doses cause sodium retention for several days, but when the dosage is maintained, a readjustment occurs and normal sodium balance is regained. The explanation for this is not clear, but it seems likely that an extra-adrenal factor is involved (Davis et al., 1964A). This factor may be humoral; it is not related to venous hypertension or to the integrity of renal nerves.

The mechanism for the release of aldosterone is uncertain. Since completely denervated adrenal glands produce aldosterone at a normal rate, the intermediate stimulus for its release is humoral rather than nervous. Cross circulation experiments in sheep (Denton et al., 1959) and dogs (Yankopoulos et al., 1959) provided evidence for a circulating aldosterone stimulating hormone elaborated by the kidney. This hormone is thought to be identical with renin. Following are some of the reasons for this belief. Intravenous infusions of synthetic angiotensin II stimulate the secretion of aldosterone in man (Biron et al., 1961). The concentration of renin in renal venous blood is increased in patients with congestive heart failure (Merrill et al., 1946). Peripheral venous blood contains increased quantities of renin (Peart, 1963) and angiotensin II (de Champlain et al., 1963) in congestive heart failure; the concentration of angiotensin II lessens as compensation is regained. Thus, the relation of aldosterone to the renin-angiotensin system is established (Davis et al., 1962).

Tobian (1960) demonstrated a relationship between the granularity of the juxtaglomerular cells and the renin content of the kidney. In hyperaldosteronism secondary to experimental cardiac failure or high constriction of the inferior vena cava, these cells have increased granularity, and the kidney has more renin (Davis et al., 1962). Renin may be released from the juxtaglomerular cells during cardiac failure. This would increase the production of angiotensin II, and this, in turn, would stimulate the secretion of aldosterone from the zona glomerulosa of the adrenal cortex.

OTHER HORMONES. Antidiuretic hormone is not a prerequisite for the abnormal retention of water in congestive failure. Dogs with experimental cardiac failure or with high inferior vena caval constriction form ascites and peripheral edema following ablation of the posterior lobe of the pituitary gland. In normal subjects, antidiuretic hormone leads to fluid retention but does not cause edema. However, it may play a secondary role in fluid retention. There is no evidence that norepinephrine is involved. Although the administration of estrogen does not cause edema in normal subjects, it has been shown to facilitate sodium and water retention in patients with congestive failure (Preedy and Aitken, 1956), possibly because it is inadequately inactivated by the congested liver. However, endogenous estrogen is likely to be of only minor importance in the accumulation of edema fluid in patients with failing hearts.

OTHER ASPECTS OF SODIUM RETENTION. The increased excretion of sodium in dogs (Barger et al., 1959) and patients (Brod et al., 1954) following the use of sympatholytic drugs suggested that adrenergic nervous activity may be partly responsible for sodium and water retention. Patients with autonomic neuropathy have enhanced sodium excretion in response to an acute load (Wagner, 1957). Also, sodium excretion in normal subjects in response to acute loads was 50 to 300 per cent greater after adrenergic blockade with guanethidine (Gill et al., 1964). This latter finding is of interest, in view of the tendency of some patients with heart disease to develop congestive failure during treatment with guanethidine. It appears that in them, loss of adrenergic nervous activity in the heart (Chidsey et al., 1962) may outweigh the potential advantage of reduced sympathetic activity in the kidney.

There are distinctive alterations of body water and electrolyte content in patients with congestive cardiac failure. The total body water and the total exchangeable sodium and chloride, expressed as a percentage of body weight, are increased, whereas the total exchangeable potassium, cell mass and body fat are reduced (Moore et al., 1956; Edelman et al., 1958; Moore et al., 1963). Retention of water in excess of sodium contributes to the hyponatremia found in cardiac edema (Welt, 1952).

Braunwald et al. (1965) studied the ability of normal subjects and patients with heart disease to handle sodium. Following an intake of 10 mEq. sodium daily for four days, a total of 920 mEq. was given over the next eight days to some normal subjects and to patients free from failure (plan A), while other normal subjects and patients with congestive failure received an eight day total of 320 mEq. (plan B). Normal subjects excreted 644 ± 54 mEq. (plan A) and 130 ± 35 mEq. (plan B). Of the 41 patients tested with plan A, 31 excreted less than 550 mEq., and 10 excreted normal amounts. The type and severity of the heart disease, intracardiac pressures, cardiac index and mean diastolic gradient across the mitral valve did not correlate with the degree of impairment of sodium excretion. The ability to excrete sodium was improved in patients receiving spironolactone, and in others following corrective cardiac surgery. Six of eight patients tested with plan B had impaired excretion of sodium (less than 75 mEq.) In two of these, excretion increased after insertion of a prosthetic valve to correct mitral regurgitation.

REFERENCES

Baldwin, D. S., Biggs, A. W., Goldring, W., Hulet, W. H., and Chasis, H.: Exaggerated natriuresis in essential hypertension. Am. J. Med., *24*:893, 1958.

Ball, W. C., Jr., and Davis, J. O.: Failure of chronic adrenal venous congestion to produce sodium retention and increased aldosterone excretion in the dog. Am. J. Physiol., *191*:339, 1957.

Barger, A. C., Muldowney, F. P., and Liebowitz, M. R.: Role of the kidney in the pathogenesis of congestive heart failure. Circulation, *20*:273, 1959.

Barger, A. C., Yates, F. E., and Rudolph, A. M.: Renal hemodynamics and sodium excretion in dogs with graded valvular damage, and in congestive failure. Am. J. Physiol., *200*:601, 1961.

Bates, D. V., and Christie, R. V.: Respiratory Function in Disease. Philadelphia and London, Saunders, 1964.

Benson, E. S.: Composition and state of protein in heart muscle of normal dogs and dogs with experimental myocardial failure. Circ. Research, *3*:221, 1955.

Benson, E. S., Hallaway, B. E., and Turbak, C. E.: Contractile properties of glycerol-extracted muscle bundles from the chronically failing canine heart. Circ. Research, *6*:122, 1958.

Bing, R. J., and Michal, G.: Myocardial efficiency. Ann. N.Y. Acad. Sci., *72*:555, 1959.

Bing, R. J., Wu, C., and Gudbjarnason, S.: Mechanism of heart failure. Circ. Research, *15* (Suppl. II):64, 1964.

Biron, P., Koiw, E., Nowaczynski, W., Brouillet, J., and Genest, J.: Effects of intravenous infusion of valine-5-angiotensin II and other pressor agents on urinary electrolytes and corticosteroids, including aldosterone. J. Clin. Invest., *40*:338, 1961.

Blake, W. D., Wégria, R., Keating, R. P., and Ward, H. P.: Effect of increased venous pressure on renal function. Am. J. Physiol., *157*:1, 1949.

Braunwald, E., Chidsey, C. A., Harrison, D. C., Gaffney, T. E., and Kahler, R. L.: Studies on the function of the adrenergic nerve endings in the heart. Circulation, *28*:958, 1963.

Braunwald, E., Plauth, W. H., Jr., and Morrow, A. G.: A method for the detection and quantification of impaired sodium excretion. Results of an oral sodium tolerance test in normal subjects and in patients with heart disease. Circulation, *32*:223, 1965.

Braunwald, E., and Ross, J., Jr.: The ventricular end-diastolic pressure. Appraisal of its value in the recognition of ventricular failure in man. Editorial. Am. J. Med., *34*:147, 1963.

Brod, J., Fejfar, Z., and Fejfarova, M. H.: The role of neuro-humoral factors in the genesis of renal haemodynamic changes in heart failure. Acta Med. Scand., *148*:273, 1954.

Burch, G. E.: A method for measuring venous tone in digital veins of intact man. Evidence for increased digital venous tone in congestive heart failure. Arch. Int. Med., *94*:724, 1954.

Burch, G. E., Ray, C. T., and Cronvich, J. A.: Certain mechanical peculiarities of the human cardiac pump in normal and diseased states. Circulation, *5*:504, 1952.

Burton, A. C.: The importance of the size and shape of the heart. Am. Heart J., *54*:801, 1957.

Carpenter, C. C. J., Davis, J. O., Holman, J. E., Ayers, C. R., and Bahn, R. C.: Studies on the response of the transplanted adrenal gland to thoracic inferior vena cava constriction. J. Clin. Invest., *40*:161, 1961.

de Champlain, J., Boucher, R., and Genest, J.: Arterial angiotensin levels in edematous patients. Proc. Soc. Exp. Biol. Med., *113*:932, 1963.

Chardack, W. M., Gage, A. A., and Dean, D. C.: Paired and coupled electrical stimulation of the heart. Bull. N.Y. Acad. Med., *41*:462, 1965.

Chidsey, C. A., Braunwald, E., and Morrow, A. G.: Catecholamine excretion and cardiac stores of norepinephrine in congestive heart failure. Am. J. Med., *39*: 442, 1965.

Chidsey, C. A., Harrison, D. C., and Braunwald, E.: Augmentation of the plasma norepinephrine response to exercise in patients with congestive heart failure. New Eng. J. Med., *267*:650, 1962.

Chidsey, C. A., Kaiser, G. A., Sonnenblick, E. H., Spann, J. F., and Braunwald, E.: Cardiac norepinephrine stores in experimental heart failure in the dog. J. Clin. Invest., *43*:2386, 1964.

Chidsey, C. A., Sonnenblick, E. H., Morrow, A. G., and Braunwald, E.: Norepinephrine stores and contractile force of papillary muscle from the failing human heart. Circulation, *33*:43, 1966A.

Chidsey, C. A., Weinbach, E. C., Pool, P. E., and Morrow, A. G.: Biochemical studies of energy metabolism in the failing human heart. J. Clin. Invest., *45*:40, 1966B.

Conn, J. W., and Louis, I. H.: Primary aldosteronism, a new clinical entity. Ann. Int. Med., *44*:1, 1956.

Cottier, P. T., Weller, J. M., and Hoobler, S. W.: Effect of intravenous sodium chloride load on renal hemodynamics and electrolyte excretion in essential hypertension. Circulation, *17*:750, 1958.

Covell, J. W., Chidsey, C. A., and Braunwald, E.: Reduction of the cardiac response to postganglionic sympathetic nerve stimulation in experimental heart failure. Circ. Research, *19*:51, 1966.

Cranefield, P. F.: The force of contraction of extrasystoles and the potentiation of force of the postextrasystolic contraction: a historical review. Bull. N.Y. Acad. Med., *41*:419, 1965.

Cranefield, P. F., Scherlag, B. J., Yeh, B. K., and Hoffman, B. F.: Treatment of acute cardiac failure by maintained postextrasystolic potentiation. Bull. N.Y. Acad. Med., *40*:903, 1964.

Danforth, W. H., Ballard, F. B., Kako, K., Choudhury, J. D., and Bing, R. J.: Metabolism of the heart in failure. Circulation, *21*:112, 1960.

Davis, J. O.: The physiology of congestive heart failure. In: Handbook of Physiology. Section 2: Circulation, Volume 3. Washington, D.C. American Physiological Society, 1965.

Davis, J. O., Carroll, W. R., Trapasso, M., and Yankopoulos, N. A.: Chemical characterization of cardiac myosin from normal dogs and from dogs with chronic congestive heart failure. J. Clin. Invest., *39*:1463, 1960.

Davis, J. O., Goodkind, M. J., and Ball, W. C., Jr.: Functional changes during high output failure produced by daily hemorrhage in dogs with pulmonic stenosis. Circ. Research *5*:388, 1957A.

Davis, J. O., Hartroft, P. M., Titus, E. O., Carpenter, C. C. J., Ayers, C. R., and Spiegel, H. E.: The role of the renin-angiotensin system in the control of aldosterone secretion. J. Clin. Invest., *41*:378, 1962.

Davis, J. O., Holman, J. E., Carpenter, C. C. J., Urquhart, J., and Higgins, J. T., Jr.: An extra-adrenal factor essential for chronic renal sodium retention in presence of increased sodium-retaining hormones. Circ. Research, *14*:17, 1964A.

Davis, J. O., and Howell, D. S.: Mechanisms of fluid and electrolyte retention in experimental preparations in dogs. II. With thoracic inferior vena cava constriction. Circ. Research, *1*:171, 1953.

Davis, J. O., Pechet, M. M., Ball, W. C., Jr., and Goodkind, M. J.: Increased aldosterone secretion in dogs with right-sided congestive heart failure and in dogs with thoracic inferior vena cava constriction. J. Clin. Invest., *36*:689, 1957B.

Davis, J. O., Urquhart, J., Higgins, J. T., Jr., Rubin, E., and Hartroft, P. M.: Hypersecretion of aldosterone in dogs with chronic aortic-caval fistula and high output heart failure. Circ. Research, *14*:471, 1964B.

Denton, D. A., Goding, J. R., and Wright, R. D.: Control of adrenal secretion of electrolyte-active steroids. Brit. Med. J., *ii*:337 and 552, 1959.

Donald, K. W., Bishop, J. M., and Wade, O. L.: Study of minute to minute changes of arteriovenous oxygen content difference, oxygen uptake and cardiac output and rate of achievement of a steady state during exercise in rheumatic heart disease. J. Clin. Invest., *33*:1146, 1954.

Donald, K. W., Bishop, J. M., and Wade, O. L.: Changes in the oxygen content of axillary venous blood during leg exercise in patients with rheumatic heart disease. Clin. Sci., *14*:531, 1955.

Edelman, I. S., Leibman, J., O'Meara, M. P., and Birkenfeld, L. W.: Interrelations between serum sodium concentration, serum osmolarity and total exchangeable sodium, total exchangeable potassium and total body water. J. Clin. Invest., *37*:1236, 1958.

Eichna, L. W.: Circulatory congestion and heart failure. Circulation, *22*:864, 1960.

Eichna, L. W., Farber, S. J., Berger, A. R., Earle, D. P., Rader, B., Pellegrino, E., Albert, R. E., Alexander, J. E., Taube, H., and Youngswirth, S.: Cardiovascular dynamics, blood volumes, renal functions and electrolyte excretions in the same patients during congestive heart failure and after recovery of cardiac compensation. Circulation, *7*:674, 1953.

Epstein, S. E., Beiser, G. D., Stampfer, M., Robinson, B. F., and Braunwald, E.: Two new and sensitive indices of cardiac performance: the cardiac output at a mixed venous O_2 saturation of 30% and the quantity of unextracted O_2 returned to the lungs. Circulation, *34* (Suppl. III):97, 1966 (Abstract).

Farber, S. J., Becker, W. H., and Eichna, L. W.: Electrolyte and water excretion and renal hemodynamics during induced congestion of the superior and inferior vena cava of man. J. Clin. Invest., *32*:1145, 1953.

Ferrer, M. I., Bradley, S. E., Wheeler, H. O., Enson, Y., Preisig, R., and Harvey, R. M.: The effect of digoxin in the splanchnic circulation in ventricular failure. Circulation, *32*:524, 1965.

Fishman, A. P., Maxwell, M. H., Crowder, C. H., and Morales, P.: Kidney function in cor pulmonale. Particular consideration of changes in renal hemodynamics and sodium excretion during variation in level of oxygenation. Circulation, *3*:703, 1951.

Frommer, P. L.: Studies on coupled pacing technique and some comments on paired electrical stimulation. Bull. N.Y. Acad. Med., *41*:670, 1965.

Fry, D. L., Griggs, D. M., Jr., and Greenfield, J. C., Jr.: Myocardial mechanics. Tension-velocity-length relationships of heart muscle. Circ. Research, *14*:73, 1964.

Furchgott, R. F., and De Gubareff, T.: High energy phosphate content of cardiac muscle under various experimental conditions which affect contractility. J. Pharm. Exp. Therap., *124*:203, 1958.

Gibson, J. G., and Evans, W. A., Jr.: Clinical studies of the blood volume. III. Changes in blood volume, venous pressure and blood velocity rate in chronic congestive heart failure. J. Clin. Invest., *16*:851, 1937.

Gill, J. R., Jr., Mason, D. T., and Bartter, F. C.: Adrenergic nervous system in sodium metabolism: effects of guanethidine and sodium-retaining steroids in normal man. J. Clin. Invest., *43*:177, 1964.

Gorlin, R., Rolett, E. L., Yurchak, P. M., and Elliott, W. C.: Left ventricular volume in man measured by thermodilution. J. Clin. Invest., *43*:1203, 1964.

Hajdu, S., and Leonard, E.: Binding of cardioglobulin-C-Ca^{45} to cardiac muscle and release by cardioglobulin-A. Am. J. Physiol., *209*:1, 1965.

Hoffman, B. F., Bartelstone, H. J., Scherlag, B. J., and Cranefield, P. F.: Effects of postextrasystolic potentiation on normal and failing hearts. Bull. N.Y. Acad. Med. *41*:498, 1965.

Howarth, S., McMichael, J., and Sharpey-Schafer, E. P.: Effects of venesection in low output heart failure. Clin. Sci., *6*:41, 1946.

Kako, K., and Bing, R. J.: Contractility of actomyosin bands prepared from normal and failing human hearts. J. Clin. Invest., *37*:465, 1958.

Kelly, R. T., Freis, E. D., and Higgins, T. F.: The effects of hexamethonium on certain manifestations of congestive heart failure. Circulation, 7:169, 1953.
Koch-Weser, J., and Blinks, J. R.: The influence of the interval between beats on myocardial contractility. Pharm. Rev., *15*:60, 1963.
Lamprecht, W., and Hockerts, T. (1959). Quoted by Bing, R. J., Wu, C., and Gudbjarnason, S. (1964) (q.v.).
Laragh, J. H.: Hormones and the pathogenesis of congestive heart failure: vasopressin, aldosterone and angiotensin II. Circulation, *25*:1015, 1962.
Lee, K. S., Yu, D. H., and Burstein, R.: Effect of ouabain on the oxygen consumption, the high energy phosphates and the contractility of the cat papillary muscles. J. Pharm. Exp. Therap., *129*:115, 1960.
Leonard, E. J.: Excitation-contraction coupling and control of cardiac contractility. Circulation, *33*:673, 1966.
Leonard, E., and Hajdu, S.: Cardioglobulin. Clinical correlations. Circ. Research, *9*:891, 1961.
Levine, H. J., and Britman, N. A.: Force-velocity relations in the intact dog heart. J. Clin. Invest., *43*:1383, 1964.
Levine, H. J., Neill, W. A., Wagman, R. J., Krasnow, N., and Gorlin, R.: The effect of exercise on mean left ventricular ejection rate in man. J. Clin. Invest., *41*:1050, 1962.
Levine, H. J., Neill, W. A., Wagman, R. J., Krasnow, N., and Gorlin, R.: The effect of exercise on cardiac performance in human subjects with congestive heart failure. Am. Heart J., *66*:731, 1963.
Lewis, D. H., Cardenas, M., and Sandberg, H.: The effect of ganglionic blockade on venous pressure and blood volume. Further evidence in favor of increased venomotor tone in congestive heart failure. Am. Heart J., *57*:897, 1959.
Linzbach, A. J.: Heart failure from the point of view of quantitative anatomy. Am. J. Cardiol., *5*:370, 1960.
Lombardo, T. A., Rose, L., Taeschler, M., Tuluy, S., and Bing, R. J.: The effect of exercise on coronary blood flow, myocardial oxygen consumption and cardiac efficiency in man. Circulation, *7*:71, 1953.
Lopez, J. F., Edelist, A., and Katz, L. N.: Slowing of the heart rate by artificial electrical stimulation with pulses of long duration in the dog. Circulation, *28*:759, 1963.
Lopez, J. F., and Petkovich, N. J.: Effects of paired electrical stimulation in acute right ventricular failure in dogs. Bull. N.Y. Acad. Med., *41*:546, 1965.
Luetscher, J. A.: Symposium on the role of hormones in heart failure. Circulation, *25*:1001, 1962.
Luetscher, J. A., Canarge, C. A., Colin, A. P., Dowdy, A. J., and Callaghan, A. M.: Observations on metabolism of aldosterone in man. Ann. Int. Med., *59*:1, 1963.
Luetscher, J. A., and Johnson, B. B.: Observations on the sodium-retaining corticoid (aldosterone) in the urine of children and adults in relation to sodium balance and edema. J. Clin. Invest., *33*:1441, 1954.
Lundsgaard, C.: Studies of oxygen in the venous blood. Studies of the oxygen unsaturation in the venous blood of a group of patients with circulatory disturbances. J. Exper. Med., *27*:179, 1918.
Mason, D. T.: Failure and blood flow in the forearm. In: Clinical Staff Conference. Congestive heart failure. Biochemical and Physiological Considerations. Ann. Int. Med., *64*:920, 1966.
Mason, D. T., and Braunwald, E.: Studies on digitalis. X. Effects of ouabain on forearm vascular resistance and venous tone in normal subjects and in patients in heart failure. J. Clin. Invest., *43*:532, 1964.
Meijler, F. L., and Durrer, D.: Physiological and clinical aspects of paired stimulation. Bull. N.Y. Acad. Med., *41*:575, 1965.
Meneely, G. R., and Kaltreider, N. L.: A study of the volume of the blood in congestive failure. Relation to other measurements in fifteen patients. J. Clin. Invest., *22*:521, 1943.
Merrill, A. J.: Edema and decreased renal blood flow in patients with chronic conges-

tive heart failure. Evidence of "forward failure" as the primary cause of edema. J. Clin. Invest., *25*:389, 1946.

Merrill, A. J., Morrison, J. L., and Brannon, J. S.: Concentration of renin in renal venous blood in patients with chronic heart failure. Am. J. Med., *1*:468, 1946.

Miller, G. A. H., Kirklin, J. W., and Swan, H. J. C.: Myocardial function and left ventricular volumes in acquired valvular insufficiency. Circulation, *31*:374, 1965.

Mokotoff, R., and Ross, G.: The effect of spinal anesthesia on the renal ischemia in congestive heart failure. J. Clin. Invest., *27*:335, 1948.

Moore, F. D., McMurrey, J. D., Parker, H. V., and Magnus, I. C.: Body composition; total body water and electrolytes; intravascular and extravascular phase volumes. Metabolism, *5*:447, 1956.

Moore, F. D., Olesen, K. H., McMurrey, J. D., Parker, H. V., Ball, M. R., and Boyden, I. C. M.: The Body Cell Mass and Its Supporting Environment. Body Composition in Health and Disease. Philadelphia and London, Saunders, 1963.

Mueller, H., Franzen, J., Rice, R. V., and Olson, R. E.: Characterization of cardiac myosin from the dog. J. Biol. Chem., *239*:1447, 1964.

Myers, J. D., and Hickam, J. B.: Estimation of hepatic blood flow and splanchnic oxygen consumption in heart failure. J. Clin. Invest., *27*:620, 1948.

Olson, R. E.: Myocardial metabolism in congestive heart failure. J. Chron. Dis., *9*:442, 1959.

Olson, R. E.: Abnormalities of myocardial metabolism. Circ. Research, *15* (Suppl. II): 109, 1964.

Olson, R. E., Ellenbogen, E., and Iyengar, R.: Cardiac myosin and congestive heart failure in the dog. Circulation, *24*:471, 1961.

Olson, R. E., and Piatnek, D. A.: Conservation of energy in cardiac muscle. Ann. N.Y. Acad. Sci., *72*:466, 1959.

Peart, W. S.: Estimation of renin in body fluids. International Symposium on Aldosterone. Prague, Czechoslovakia, 1963.

Plaut, G. W. E., and Gertler, M. M.: Oxidative phosphorylation studies in normal and experimentally produced congestive heart failure in guinea pigs: a comparison. Ann. N.Y. Acad. Sci., *72*:515, 1959.

Pool, P. E., Covell, J. W., Chidsey, C. A., and Braunwald, E.: Myocardial high energy phosphate stores in acutely induced, hypoxic heart failure. Clin. Res., *13*:528, 1965 (Abstract).

Pool, P. E., Covell, J. W., Levitt, M., Gibb, J., and Braunwald, E.: Reduction of cardiac tyrosine hydroxylase activity in experimental congestive heart failure; its role in the depletion of cardiac norepinephrine stores. Circ. Research, *20*: 349, 1967.

Preedy, J. R. K., and Aitken, E. H.: The effect of estrogen on water and electrolyte metabolism. III. Cardiac and renal disease. J. Clin. Invest., *35*:443, 1956.

Rapaport, E., Weisbart, M. H., and Levine, M.: The splanchnic blood volume in congestive heart failure. Circulation, *18*:581, 1958.

Ross, J., Jr., Covell, J. W., Sonnenblick, E. H., and Braunwald, E.: Contractile state of the heart characterized by force-velocity relations in variably afterloaded and isovolumic beats. Circ. Research, *18*:149, 1966.

Ross, J., Jr., Sonnenblick, E. H., Kaiser, G. A., Frommer, P. L., and Braunwald, E.: Electroaugmentation of ventricular performance and oxygen consumption by repetitive application of paired electrical stimuli. Circ. Research, *16*:332, 1965.

Samet, P., Fritts, H. W., Fishman, A. P., and Cournand, A.: The blood volume in heart disease. Medicine, *36*:211, 1957.

Schreiber, S. S., and Rothschild, M. A.: Blood volume and heart disease. Prog. Cardiovasc. Dis., *4*:565, 1962.

Schreiner, B. F., Murphy, G. W., and Yu, P. N.: Pulmonary blood volume in congestive heart failure. Circulation, *34*:249, 1966.

Schwartz, A., and Lee, K. S.: Study of heart mitochondria and glycolytic metabolism in experimentally induced cardiac failure. Circ. Research, *10*:321, 1962.

Shannon, J. A.: The control of the renal excretion of water. J. Exper. Med., *76*:371, 1942.

Sharpey-Schafer, E.: Venous tone. Brit. Med. J., *ii*:1589, 1961.

Simpson, S. A., Tait, J. F., Wettstein, A., Neher, R., Euw, J. V., Schindler, O., and Reichstein, T.: Aldosteron Isolierung und Eigenschaften. Über Bestandteile der Nebennierenrinde und verwandt Stoffe. Helvet. Chim. Acta, *37*:1163, 1954.

Sinclair-Smith, B. C., Kattus, A. A., Genest, J., and Newman, E. V.: The renal mechanism of electrolyte excretion and the metabolic balances of electrolytes and nitrogen in congestive cardiac failure; the effects of exercise, rest and aminophyllin. Bull. Johns Hopkins Hosp., *84*:369, 1949.

Singer, B., and Wener, J.: Excretion of sodium-retaining substances in patients with congestive heart failure. Am. Heart J., *45*:795, 1953.

Sonnenblick, E. H., Cannon, P. J., and Laragh, J. H.: The nature of the action of intravenous aldosterone. Evidence for a role of the hormone in urinary dilution. J. Clin. Invest., *40*:903, 1961.

Sonnenblick, E. H., Frommer, P. L., and Braunwald, E.: Electroaugmentation of human and cat papillary muscle produced by paired electrical stimulation. Bull. N.Y. Acad. Med., *41*:554, 1965.

Sonnenblick, E. H., Spotnitz, H. M., and Spiro, D.: Role of the sarcomere in ventricular function and the mechanism of heart failure. Circ. Research, *15* (Suppl. II):70, 1964.

Spann, J. F., Jr., Sonnenblick, E. H., Cooper, T., Chidsey, C. A., Willman, V. L., and Braunwald, E.: Role of norepinephrine stores in determining the contractile state of myocardium and its responsiveness to glycosides and norepinephrine. Circulation, *32* (Suppl. II):201, 1965.

Stock, T. B., Wendt, V. E., Bruce, T. A., and Bing, R. J.: New concepts of angina pectoris. Med. Clin. N. Amer., *46*:1497, 1962.

Tobian, L.: Interrelationship, of electrolytes, juxtaglomerular cells and hypertension. Physiol. Rev., *40*:280, 1960.

Vander, A. J., Malvin, R. L., Wilde, W. S., and Sullivan, L. P.: Re-examination of salt and water retention in congestive heart failure. Am. J. Med., *25*:497, 1958.

Wade, O. L., and Bishop, J. M.: Cardiac Output and Regional Blood Flow. Oxford, Blackwell, 1962.

Wagner, H. N., Jr.: The influence of autonomic vasoregulatory reflexes on the rate of sodium and water excretion in man. J. Clin. Invest., *36*:1319, 1957.

Warren, J. V., Brannon, E. S., Weens, H. S., and Stead, E. A., Jr.: Effect of increasing the blood volume and right atrial pressure on the circulation of normal subjects by intravenous infusion. Am. J. Med., *4*:193, 1948.

Weber, A., Herz, R., and Reiss, I.: Role of calcium in contraction and relaxation of muscle. Fed. Proc., *23*:896, 1964 (Abstract).

Weiss, S., and Ellis, L. B.: Oxygen utilization and lactic acid production in the extremities during rest and exercise. A.M.A. Arch. Int. Med., *55*:665, 1935.

Welt, L. G.: Edema and hyponatremia. A.M.A. Arch. Int. Med., *89*:931, 1952.

Werkö, L., Varnauskas, E., Eliasch, H., Ek, J., Bucht, H., Thomasson, B., and Bergström, J.: Studies on the renal circulation and renal function in mitral valvular disease. I. Effect of exercise. Circulation, *9*:687, 1954.

White, A. G., Gordon, H., and Leiter, L.: Studies in edema. II. The effect of congestive heart failure on saliva electrolyte concentration. J. Clin. Invest., *29*:1445, 1950.

Winegrad, S.: The possible role of calcium in excitation-contraction coupling of heart muscle. Circulation, *24*:523, 1961.

Wollenberger, A.: The energy metabolism of the failing heart and the metabolic action of the cardiac glycosides. J. Pharm. Exp. Therap., *97*:311, 1949.

Wollenberger, A., and Schulze, W. J.: Mitochondrial alterations in the myocardium of dogs with aortic stenosis. Biophys. Biochem. Cytol., *10*:285, 1961.

Wood, J. E.: The mechanism of the increased venous pressure with exercise in congestive heart failure. J. Clin. Invest., *41*:2020, 1962.

Wood, J. E., Litter, J., and Wilkins, R. W.: Peripheral venoconstriction in human congestive heart failure. Circulation, *13*:524, 1956.

Wood, P.: Diseases of the Heart and Circulation. Second edition. Philadelphia, Lippincott, 1956.

Wood, P., Besterman, E. M., Towers, M. K., and McIlroy, M. B.: The effect of acetylcholine on pulmonary vascular resistance and left atrial pressure in mitral stenosis. Brit. Heart J., *19*:179, 1957.

Yankopoulos, N. A., Davis, J. O., Kliman, B., and Peterson, R. E.: Evidence that a humoral agent stimulates the adrenal cortex to secrete aldosterone in experimental secondary hyperaldosteronism. J. Clin. Invest., *38*:1278, 1959.

Yates, F. E., Urquhart, J., and Herbst, A. L.: Impairment of the enzymatic inactivation of adrenal cortical hormones following passive venous congestion of the liver. Am. J. Physiol., *194*:65, 1958.

Zelis, R., Mason, D. T., and Braunwald, E.: Abnormal peripheral vascular dynamics in patients with congestive heart failure: diminished response to vasodilator drugs. Clin. Res., *15*:227, 1967 (Abstract).

Chapter 10

ARRHYTHMIAS

- Effects of Pacemaking
- Supraventricular Tachyarrhythmias
- Ventricular Tachyarrhythmias
- Complete Heart Block

Paroxysms of rapid heart action of supraventricular origin may occur in otherwise normal persons (Orgain et al., 1936). Long sustained rapid heart action, (usually atrial fibrillation) almost always occurs as a complication of heart disease, or of other conditions such as uncontrolled thyrotoxicosis that directly influence cardiac function. The effects of supraventricular tachyarrhythmias are dependent on many factors. These include the nature of the arrhythmia, its duration, the rate and regularity of the ventricular response, the patient's age and the nature and severity of the underlying heart disease, if such is present. Thus, for example, atrial fibrillation occurring in an otherwise normal heart may be remarkably well tolerated for months, years or even decades (Levine, 1963), whereas its onset in a pregnant woman with mitral stenosis is likely to precipitate pulmonary congestion or edema. Knowledge of the effects of increasing heart rates on cardiovascular dynamics has been increased by recent studies during artificial pacemaking both in normal subjects and in patients with various types of heart disease.

EFFECTS OF PACEMAKING

Stein et al. (1966) found that pacing the atrium in normal subjects at various rates up to about 160 per minute caused no alteration in cardiac output, mean arterial blood pressure, peripheral resistance or left ventricular work, as compared with values in the control state. This was true for studies carried out during both rest and mild exercise. The tension-time index (Sarnoff et al., 1958) alone increased; from this, it was inferred that myocardial oxygen consumption increased at the higher rates of pacing.

In another study (Ross et al., 1965), cardiac output remained unchanged at 3.7 liters per $M.^2$ per minute, when the heart rates of 17 resting patients were increased by atrial pacing from average values of 80 to 121 beats per minute. A further increase in the rate to 148 beats per minute was associated with a small reduction in cardiac output to 3.2 liters per $M.^2$ per minute. When exercise was undertaken by, or isoproterenol infused into, subjects being paced at fast heart rates, the increases in cardiac output were achieved by increases in stroke volume. Therefore, it was concluded that when metabolic demands are constant, cardiac output changes little, despite induced wide variations in heart rate, but that when metabolic demands are increased by exercise or the circulation stimulated by isoproterenol, cardiac output can increase through an increase in stroke volume, when alterations in heart rate are prevented from occurring.

In contrast, Benchimol et al. (1965A) found that the cardiac output of normal resting subjects was greater during atrial pacing at 110 per minute than it was under control conditions. A similar increase occurred during ventricular pacing at 110 per minute. Changes in the tension-time index, ventricular power and ventricular ejection time were also similar with the two types of pacing. Thus, the reserve of the normal circulation is such that under these conditions, loss of the contribution of normally coordinated atrial systole was not manifest. In patients with heart disease of various types, increase in the rate of atrial pacing again resulted in increases of cardiac output, tension-time index, systolic ejection rate and ventricular power. With comparable rates of ventricular pacing in the same subjects, all these functions were decreased. The differences were more marked at the higher rates of pacing (Benchimol and Liggett, 1966). In one patient, angina pectoris developed and was relieved by slowing the heart to the control level. Thus, when cardiovascular reserve is diminished, the importance of the normal sequence of atrial and ventricular contraction becomes evident.

Samet et al. (1965B) confirmed the decreased efficiency of ventricular as opposed to atrial pacemaking in 54 patients, most of whom had either rheumatic heart disease or obstructive pulmonary emphysema with or without cor pulmonale (Table 10-1). Their initial measurements of cardiac output were made within two minutes of the start of pacing; almost identical values were obtained up to eight minutes after pacing started. However, Sowton (1964) found that when the ventricular rate was suddenly increased by a catheter pacemaker, serial measurements with the patient in the same resting state revealed an initial increase in cardiac output, with a subsequent decline. When the rate was then suddenly further increased, the cardiac output again increased but returned to its previous level in three to seven minutes.

Samet et al. (1965B) also demonstrated the presence of very prominent *v* waves in the left atrial pressure pulse during ventricular pacing in man. Figure 10-1 shows pressure pulses from a patient with a Starr-Edwards mitral prosthesis. During sinus rhythm, there was a prominent

TABLE 10-1. Cardiac Index During Atrial and Ventricular Pacemaking at Various Rates in 54 Patients with Rheumatic Heart Disease or Chronic Emphysema*

	CARDIAC INDEX (L./M.^{2}/MIN.)	
PACEMAKING RATE/MIN.	ATRIAL PACEMAKING	VENTRICULAR PACEMAKING
60- 89	2.66	2.13
90-109	2.70	2.24
110-140	2.80	2.27

* Adapted from Samet, Bernstein, Levine and Lopez, Am. J. Med., 39:905, 1965.

a wave in the left atrium, and the arterial pressure was 135/70 mm. Hg. During ventricular pacing, a tall *v* wave, with a peak pressure of 25 mm. Hg, appeared in the left atrium, and the arterial pressure decreased. The belief that these changes indicated mitral regurgitation was supported by the observation, at operation, of a systolic regurgitant thrill over the left atrium during ventricular pacing.

A greater cardiac output during atrial as opposed to ventricular pacemaking could be due either to the normal time sequence of atrial and ventricular contraction in the former, or to less effective ventricular contraction due to the aberrant pattern of ventricular depolarization in the latter. Samet et al. (1966) showed that the proper timing of atrial systole was the more important factor. They used a paired pulsemaking unit to stimulate both atrium and ventricle at preset *PR* intervals (sequential pacing). Al-

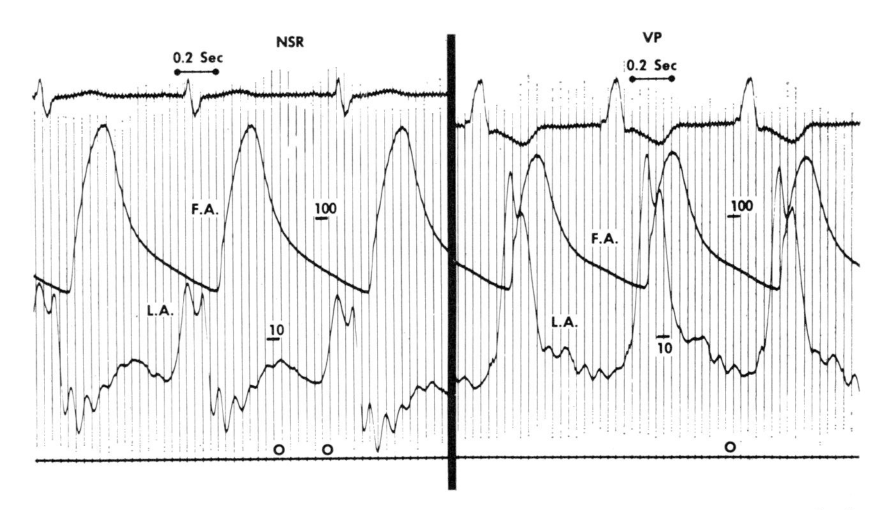

FIGURE 10-1. Femoral artery and left atrial pressures during normal sinus rhythm (*left panel*) and ventricular pacing (*right panel*) in patient with Starr-Edwards mitral prosthesis. Ventricular pacing results in a prominent *v* wave in the left atrium, indicative of mitral regurgitation (From Samet, Bernstein, Levine, and Lopez, Am. J. Med., 39:905, 1965.)

though, in this circumstance, ventricular depolarization was aberrant, in a group of normal subjects the cardiac index of 3.1 liters per $M.^2$ per minute during sequential pacing was comparable with that during atrial pacing (3.2 liters per $M.^2$ per minute) and greater than that during ventricular pacing (2.7 liters per $M.^2$ per minute). In patients with rheumatic heart disease, the findings were similar, the values for cardiac index averaging 2.7, 2.8 and 2.3 liters per $M.^2$ per minute, respectively.

Sonnenblick et al. (1966) studied the effects of alterations of heart rate on the dynamics of force development in the human right ventricle during thoracotomy by the use of Walton-Brodie strain gauge arches. With increasing rate, from 72 to 145 per minute, peak contractile force did not alter, but the time required to attain it decreased, and the maximal rate of change of force increased. An inverse relationship between the maximal rate of change of force and the time to peak force was implied, since these factors reflect the intensity and duration of the active state, respectively. Sudden changes in rate were accompanied by transient changes in peak force, attributable to differences in the rates with which the maximal rate of change of force and the time to peak force reached new constant levels. Thus, in man, a "velocity staircase" rather than a "force staircase" occurs with changes in heart rate; this apparently permits the ventricle to maintain its force of contraction and an adequate diastolic interval with changes in rate.

SUPRAVENTRICULAR TACHYARRHYTHMIAS

SUPRAVENTRICULAR TACHYCARDIA. Saunders and Ord (1962) observed three patients in whom paroxysms of supraventricular tachycardia could be readily induced by manipulation of a catheter. There was no evidence of heart disease, apart from the presence of Wolff-Parkinson-White complexes in the electrocardiogram. At rest, the cardiac output during spells of tachycardia was similar to that during normal sinus rhythm. However, in one subject, limitation of cardiac reserve was demonstrable during exercise. This led to a smaller increase in cardiac output and to a greater increase in the arteriovenous difference in oxygen content during tachycardia than during sinus rhythm.

When paroxysmal tachycardia develops in a patient with heart disease, the cardiac output decreases, the arterial blood pressure falls, and angina pectoris may occur. Nitroglycerin is ineffective in relieving the angina, since it causes a further decrease in the already low blood pressure and thereby further compromises coronary blood flow (O'Rourke et al., 1964). Prolonged tachycardia may lead to shock or to congestive heart failure.

The site of the ectopic focus may have some influence on the hemodynamic effects of the tachycardia. Thus, tachycardia originating in the lower portions of the atrioventricular node leads to nearly simultaneous contraction of atria and ventricles, with consequent loss of the atrial contribution to ventricular filling. In atrial tachycardia, the normal sequence of contraction is retained.

Spontaneously occurring atrial tachycardia differs in some respects from equally rapid heart rates induced by electrical pacing of the atria. In the former, the PR interval is short, and the atrial contraction is an important factor in ventricular filling. In the latter, the *PR* interval does not shorten and may actually lengthen, resulting in a considerable attenuation of the atrial contribution to ventricular filling.

ATRIAL FIBRILLATION. The cardiac output of anesthetized dogs decreased by 20 to 62 per cent with the onset of atrial fibrillation (Stewart et al., 1926). Such decreases could have been due to: (1) the tachycardia associated with fibrillation resulting in very short diastolic periods, and hence in inadequate time for ventricular filling; or (2) a separate deleterious effect of the arrhythmia on cardiac function. The latter possibility was investigated by Skinner et al. (1964). Complete heart block was produced by tying a suture around the bundle of His, and cardiac function was assessed in two sets of circumstances: (1) stimulation of the right atrium and right ventricle at identical rates by means of a relay circuit, the PR interval being set at any desired value; and (2) stimulation of the ventricle at the same rate while atrial fibrillation was being maintained by rapidly repeated atrial stimulation. Atrial fibrillation was accompanied by an increase in mean left atrial pressure and by decreases in left ventricular end-diastolic pressure and cardiac output. This impairment of function was attributed partly to loss of the contribution of atrial systole to ventricular filling, and partly (based on evidence from indicator dilution curves) to regurgitation of blood from ventricle to atrium before closure of the valve cusps occurred (Daley et al., 1955).

In patients with atrial fibrillation in the absence of demonstrable heart disease, the resting cardiac output is normal, although the response to exercise is impaired (Killip and Boer, 1964). Atrial fibrillation, however, is more commonly a complication of underlying heart disease. The hemodynamic changes, therefore, are in large part a reflection of the pathological changes in the heart. The introduction of synchronized direct current shock for conversion of atrial fibrillation to sinus rhythm (Lown et al., 1962) has provided an opportunity to assess the relationship of the arrhythmia itself, as opposed to the pathological changes in the heart, to the altered hemodynamics. However, electrical conversion of an arrhythmia is usually performed under general anesthesia; if cardiac output is measured too soon after cardioversion, it may be influenced by the anesthesia. If it is measured much later, compensatory mechanisms may have come into play to mask an earlier change. Problems also exist when conversion of rhythm is achieved by quinidine, since this drug is a cardiac depressant.

Kory and Meneely (1951) and Hecht et al. (1951) found an increase in cardiac output following conversion of fibrillation to sinus rhythm by means of quinidine, but others noted little (Storstein and Tveten, 1955) or no change (Hansen et al., 1952). Rowe (1966) measured cardiac output before and 20 minutes after cardioversion performed without anesthesia. There was an increase of nine per cent in output both in those successfully converted and in those who did not respond. The failure to demonstrate a greater increase in the successful group could have been due to persistent depression of myocardial contractility resulting from the electrical shock. Montgomery et al. (1966) also concluded that, although cardioversion immediately restores normal electrical activity, restoration of more nearly normal mechanical function is delayed. Oram et al. (1963) found no increase in output immediately after conversion to sinus rhythm but a definite increase three to 16 days later. The lack of an early increase was attributed to persistent effects of general anesthesia. Halmos and Patterson (1965) found a mean increase in cardiac output from 4.1 to 6.1 liters per minute in 20 patients, most of whom had rheumatic heart disease, studied before and a week after cardioversion. Those patients who maintained sinus rhythm subsequently also maintained an increase in cardiac output, whereas in those in whom relapse occurred, the cardiac output decreased towards its original level. Increases in resting levels of cardiac output following cardioversion have also been reported by Kahn et al. (1964) and Reale

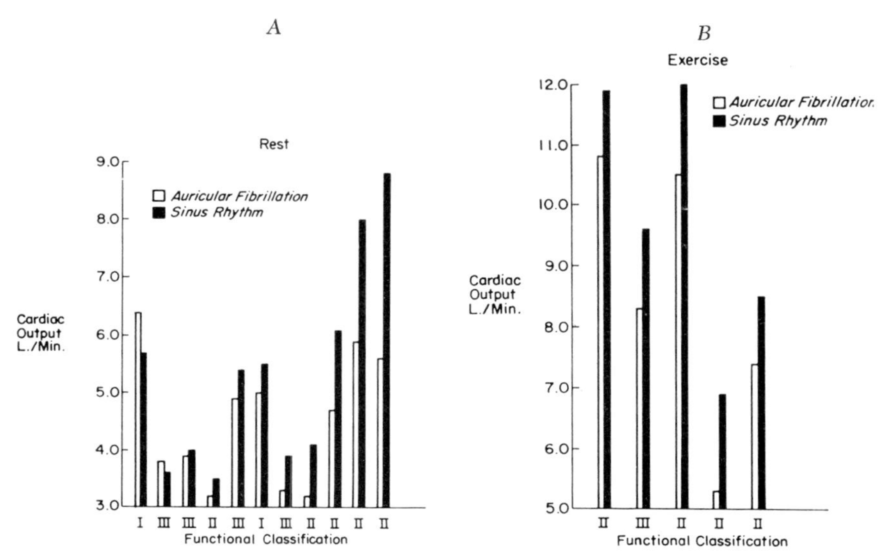

FIGURE 10-2. Cardiac output during atrial fibrillation (white bars) and following reversion to sinus rhythm (black bars). *A*, during rest; *B*, during exercise. (From Morris, Entman, North, Kong and McIntosh, Circulation, *31*:670, 1965.)

TABLE 10-2. Hemodynamic Effects of Changes in Ventricular Rate After Conversion from Atrial Fibrillation to Sinus Rhythm*

	REST		MILD EXERCISE	
Group A†	AF	SR	AF	SR
O_2 consumption (ml./M.^{2}/min.)	143	143	278	259
Cardiac output (L./M.^{2}/min.)	2.13	2.59	3.10	3.65
Stroke volume (ml./M.^{2})	15	29	19	34
Heart rate (beats/min.)	152	96	157	104
Group B‡				
O_2 consumption (ml./M.^{2}/min.)	135	133	207	196
Cardiac output (L./M.^{2}/min.)	2.39	2.51	2.92	2.95
Stroke volume (ml./M.^{2})	27	31	28	32
Heart rate (beats/min.)	89	82	106	94

* Adapted from Graettinger, Carleton and Muenster, J. Clin. Invest., *43*:2290, 1964.
†Group A: decrease in ventricular rate more than 30 beats/min.
‡ Group B: decrease in ventricular rate less than 30 beats/min.

(1965). The cardiac output was higher following conversion to sinus rhythm than it was during atrial fibrillation, when identical muscular exercise was undertaken (Morris et al. 1965, Fig. 10-2).

The most obvious mechanism for the improvement in cardiac output with restoration of sinus rhythm is the addition of the atrial pump for increasing the diastolic volume of the ventricle (Morris et al., 1965). An additional mechanism is the slowing of the ventricular rate, with consequent enhancement of the opportunity for diastolic filling. Graettinger et al. (1964) found an increase in cardiac output one to two hours after cardioversion only in those patients in whom the ventricular rate, initially rapid, decreased by more than 30 beats per minute (Table 10-2, Group A). They concluded that, if the ventricular rate was adequately controlled (Table 10-2, Group B), the presence of atrial fibrillation was of only slight importance in determining the level of the cardiac output.

Lown (1966), among others, has drawn attention to the occasional deterioration of cardiac performance following cardioversion. These patients fail to develop a sustained sinus rhythm; instead, they have erratic mechanisms which may include sinuatrial standstill, sinuatrial block with nodal escape, wandering atrial pacemaker and paroxysms of atrial tachycardia or flutter. In most cases, atrial fibrillation recurs. In some, a slow nodal rhythm supervenes. Persistence of such a rhythm, especially in patients with severe underlying valvular disease, may result in heart failure.

The cardiac output is lower in patients with mitral stenosis who have atrial fibrillation than in others with comparable grades of disability who have sinus rhythm (Wade and Bishop, 1962). Although the arrhythmia per se could account for the lower output, a difference in the severity or duration of the rheumatic damage to the heart in the two groups is undoubtedly a contributory factor.

ATRIAL FLUTTER. Few detailed studies on atrial flutter have been made. The cardiac output was below normal limits at rest in 11 of 12 patients with atrial flutter complicating compensated heart disease (Harvey et al., 1955). Following restoration of normal sinus rhythm, it increased by about 35 per cent. Leguime (1941) found that the cardiac output was 35 per cent less during atrial flutter with 2:1 ventricular response than during subsequent sinus rhythm.

VENTRICULAR TACHYARRHYTHMIAS

Ventricular flutter and fibrillation are life threatening arrhythmias, and therefore the opportunity does not exist for making hemodynamic measurements. In the dog, the atria may continue to contract, despite ventricular fibrillation, and may propel small amounts of blood forward (McIntosh and Morris, 1966). However, this is inadequate to maintain an effective circulation. Ventricular flutter has a rate exceeding 250 per minute and generally occurs in a severely diseased heart. Unless it is rapidly reversed, unconsciousness and death supervene.

Ventricular tachycardia is often sufficiently slow to permit a diminished but adequate circulation to be sustained. Occasionally, in the precardioversion era, ventricular tachycardia was tolerated for periods of many weeks (Mathieu et al., 1958). Nevertheless, it is a potentially serious arrhythmia, sometimes leading to ventricular fibrillation. Therefore, when it occurs, for example during cardiac catheterization, attention is necessarily devoted to its termination rather than to measuring its effects on the heart and circulation. Observations, therefore, are few and incomplete. Since it generally occurs in hearts with serious organic disease, since the pattern of ventricular depolarization is abnormal, and since there is asynchrony of atrial and ventricular contraction, one would anticipate a greater reduction in cardiac output than during supraventricular arrhythmias with comparable ventricular rates.

Nakano (1964) studied the effects of experimental ventricular tachycardia in dogs. The transition from sinus tachycardia at 124 beats per minute to ventricular tachycardia at 200 beats per minute was associated with sudden increases in pressure in the left atrium and pulmonary artery. The systemic arterial blood pressure and cardiac output decreased rapidly at first and then increased gradually to approach control values. With termination of the ventricular tachycardia, there was a transient overshoot in arterial blood pressure and cardiac output, while left atrial and pulmonary artery pressures returned to normal.

The most convenient opportunity to study the effects of ventricular tachycardia in man is provided by the use of artificial pacemakers in patients with complete heart block.

COMPLETE HEART BLOCK

The development of electronic pacemaking devices has renewed interest in the response of the cardiovascular system to the presence of complete heart block. In congenital heart block, adaptation to the slow ventricular rate commences in intrauterine life, and the heart is usually normal in all other respects. When other defects are absent, the prognosis is good (Wright et al., 1959), at least in those surviving infancy (Landegren and Biörck, 1963). Acquired heart block occurs in an older age group, is usually associated with myocardial fibrosis from coronary artery disease or other more obscure causes (Lenègre and Moreau, 1962), and is sometimes accompanied by congestive heart failure. In other instances, heart block results from surgical operations for the relief of congenital defects or of diseased mitral or aortic valves; if it persists or recurs following the early postoperative period, the prognosis is also unfavorable (McGoon et al., 1964). Therefore, it is expedient to consider isolated congenital heart block and acquired heart block separately.

CONGENITAL HEART BLOCK. The resting ventricular rate is usually between 40 and 80 per minute during childhood and early adult life. In some patients, it gradually decreases with advancing age (Burchell et al., 1964). The cardiac output is maintained within the normal range by an increase in stroke volume which may be up to twice the normal value of 45 ml. per $M.^2$ or even more. The increase in stroke volume is facilitated by the prolonged diastolic interval available for ventricular filling and by the enlargement of the heart (Ikkos and Hanson, 1960). There is a moderate increase in systolic arterial pressure, little change in diastolic pressure and therefore, an increase in pulse pressure, again reflecting the increased stroke volume. Similar changes occur in the pulmonary artery pressure. When a left-to-right shunt such as a secundum variety of atrial septal defect coexists, the hemodynamic effects of congenital heart block are further exaggerated, and in one such case, a resting right ventricular stroke output of 240 ml. per $M.^2$ has been recorded (Scarpelli and Rudolph, 1964).

The *QRS* complex of the electrocardiogram has a normal configuration and duration. This indicates that the ventricular pacemaker is situated proximally to the bifurcation of the bundle of His, and that the sequence of ventricular excitation is normal or relatively normal. In contrast, the ventricular pacemaker in cases of acquired heart block is usually located peripherally; the *QRS* complex has a bizarre contour and is prolonged, indicating an abnormal sequence of excitation. The difference in the efficiency of ventricular excitation between congenital and acquired heart block is probably one of the reasons why myocardial function is superior in the former. Other and probably more important reasons include the absence of intrinsic myocardial disease and the increased responsiveness of the

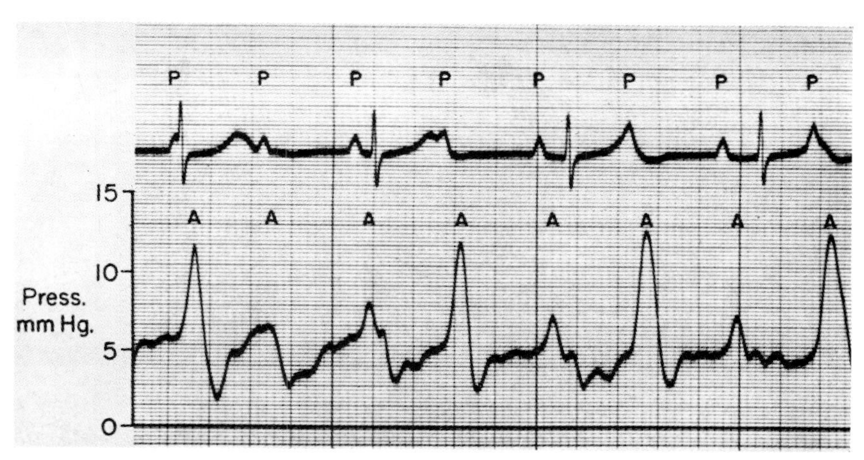

FIGURE 10-3. Right atrial pressure pulse in congenital complete heart block. Giant *a* waves occur when the atrium contracts during ventricular systole. Note also the normal contour and duration of the *QRS* complexes in the electrocardiogram. (From Ayers, Boineau and Spach, Am. Heart J., 72:381, 1966.)

idioventricular pacemaker to physiological and pharmacological stimuli in congenital heart block.

Asynchronous contraction of the atria and ventricles results in the appearance of tall *a* waves in the right atrial pressure pulse and of cannon waves in the jugular veins (Fig. 10-3). The asynchrony also leads to characteristic variations in the intensity of the first heart sound at the apex of the heart. The increased stroke volume may cause an early systolic ejection sound followed by an ejection murmur that at times may suggest the presence of organic valvular disease. A greater than normal rate of flow across the mitral valve in early diastole may result in a prominent third heart sound followed by a short diastole rumble.

EFFECTS OF EXERCISE. Ikkos and Hanson (1960) measured the heart rate at rest and at various work loads up to the limit of tolerance in 11 children and young adults with isolated congenital heart block. At rest, the atrial rates were 43 to 109 per minute and during maximal exercise, they were 143 to 185 per minute. The ventricular rates increased from 43 to 60 per minute at rest to 64 to 130 per minute during maximal exercise. There was a modest correlation between the individuals' increases in atrial and ventricular rates. The working capacity was equal, or nearly equal, to that of normal persons of similar ages. Five of the subjects engaged in athletics, including ice hockey.

Table 10-3 shows the effects of exercise on cardiac output and stroke volume in six subjects, collected from the literature. The exercise was not maximal in all cases. In all four adults the cardiac output approximately

TABLE 10-3. Effects of Exercise in Congenital Heart Block

	CASE NO.	AGE	SEX	HEART RATE (BEATS/MIN.)		CARDIAC OUTPUT (L./MIN.)		STROKE VOL. (ML.)	
				R	E	R	E	R	E
Holmgren et al. (1959)	1	23	M	44	88	6.7	13.4	150	152
	2	30	M	36	70	6.3	12.7	174	182
Ikkos & Hanson (1960)	5	15	F	48	67	4.8	10.5	100	156
	7	12	F	54	110	4.8	8.8	90	80
Marshall & Shepherd (1963)		24	M	36	59	8.3	14.5	230	248
Burchell et al. (1964)		23	M	36	61	7.2	14.4	200	236

doubled; the increase, as in normal subjects, was achieved almost entirely by an increase in heart rate, with only a minor contribution from an increase in stroke volume. In one of the children the stroke volume increased by 28 per cent, whereas in the second it decreased slightly.

ACQUIRED HEART BLOCK. The hemodynamic changes in acquired heart block are principally due to the low ventricular rate, both at rest and during stress, but the underlying heart disease is often an important contributory factor. Immediately after the conduction tissue is severed or destroyed in the dog, there are decreases in cardiac output and coronary blood flow and increases in stroke volume, arteriovenous difference in oxygen content and right atrial pressure (Starzl et al., 1955A). The arterial systolic pressure is scarcely altered, but the diastolic pressure decreases, sometimes to less than 40 mm. Hg. The left ventricular end-diastolic diameter is considerably increased; thus, the immediate compensation for the effects of heart block is cardiac dilatation (Brockman, 1965A). Hypertrophy then gradually develops and becomes the main basis for cardiac adjustment to the chronically increased diastolic load. Some animals develop congestive heart failure immediately after creation of the block (Starzl et al., 1955B), whereas others develop failure several months later.

The effects of ventricular pacemaking at different rates were studied by Miller et al. (1962) in dogs with surgically induced heart block, none of which showed signs of cardiac failure. At the idioventricular rates of 24 to 42 per minute, the stroke volumes were great. Increasing the ventricular rate to 60 per minute led to an increase in cardiac output with no change in stroke volume; the right atrial and right ventricular end-diastolic pressures decreased. At ventricular rates of 60 to 90 per minute, there was a further slight increase in cardiac output; at rates of 90 to 150 per minute, no further change occurred; at rates exceeding 150 per minute, cardiac output sometimes decreased, and right atrial and right ventricular end-diastolic pressures tended to increase.

In dogs with complete heart block, vagal stimulation caused only a very slight decrease in ventricular rate and had no direct effect on ventricular contractility (Brockman, 1965B). In contrast, the ventricle was

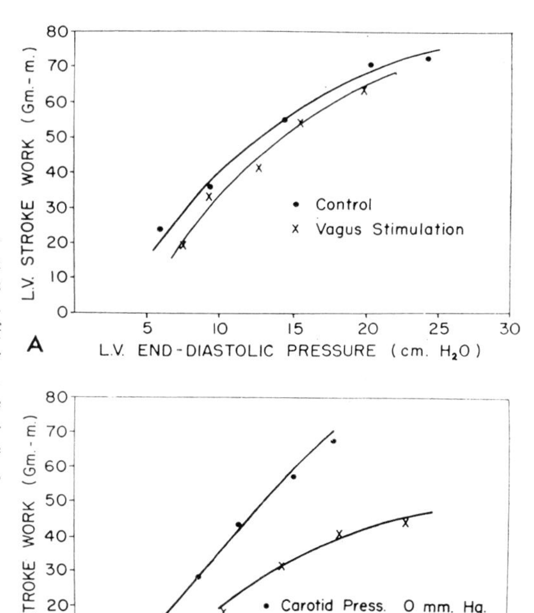

FIGURE 10-4. Ventricular function curves obtained in dogs with complete A-V block. *A*, Vagus stimulation. The curve is unchanged, indicating the lack of any inotropic effect. *B*, At low and high carotid sinus pressures. The shift to the right during the high carotid sinus pressure indicates a reflexly induced negative inotropic effect. (From Brockman, Am. J. Cardiol., *16*:84, 1965.)

profoundly influenced by increased activity of the sympathetic nervous system (Fig. 10-4). Stimulation of the carotid sinus caused marked slowing of the idioventricular rate, both in neurally intact animals and in those with bilateral vagotomy. Occasionally, prolonged asystole and even death occurred, suggesting that sudden reflex diminution in cardiac sympathetic tone may occasionally be responsible for Adams-Stokes seizures.

The hemodynamic effects of chronic acquired heart block in man have been studied extensively. Segel et al. (1964) found that the cardiac output in 13 patients, aged 42 to 77 years, at rest in the supine position was 1.4 to 3.4 (mean 2.1) liters per $M.^2$ per minute. The idioventricular rates were in the range of 27 to 44 beats per minute. Values for stroke volume were highly variable, ranging from 36 to 113 ml. per $M.^2$, but the mean value (63 ml. per $M.^2$) was significantly higher than in normal persons. The cardiac output ranged from 1.5 to 2.7 liters per $M.^2$ per minute in the patients of Samet et al. (1964) and from 1.3 to 2.3 liters per $M.^2$ per minute in those of Levinson et al. (1959). In both of these series, the stroke volume was also highly variable but was usually increased.

Pressures in the right atrium, right ventricle (systolic), pulmonary artery and pulmonary artery wedge are slightly to moderately increased at slow idioventricular rates. Pressure in the atrium tends to increase towards the end of the long ventricular diastolic interval. Cannon waves occur when the atrium contracts synchronously with the ventricle. The systemic arterial systolic and pulse pressures are increased, partly due to the increased stroke volume and partly to the loss of arterial resilience in these middle aged or elderly patients.

Winters et al. (1965) found surprisingly low values for oxygen consumption of 54 to 125 (mean 90) ml. per M.^{2} per minute, as compared with values of 90 to 143 (mean 120) ml. per M.^{2} per minute for normal subjects of comparable age, but this may have been due to heavy premedication. Levinson et al. (1959) also found low values ranging from 82 to 96 ml. per M.^{2} per minute and, since there was no evidence of hypothyroidism, postulated that the tissues in some way had adapted their metabolic requirements to the low cardiac output. In contrast, Segel et al. (1964) reported values of 95 to 180 ml. per M.^{2} per minute in their larger series of patients, with a mean value of 6.3 ml. per 100 ml. for the arteriovenous difference in oxygen content. Stack et al. (1958) had comparable results.

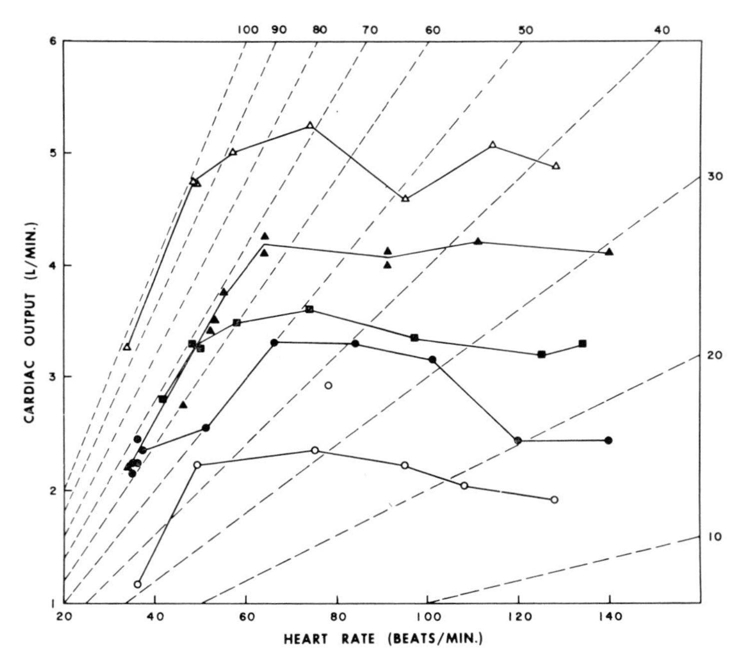

FIGURE 10-5. Cardiac output at the idioventricular rate (*values at extreme left*) and at various ventricular rates during short periods of endocardial pacemaking in five patients with complete heart block. The oblique interrupted lines are isopleths for stroke volume (milliliters). Note the consistent increase in cardiac output which tends to reach a plateau at rates of about 60 to 80 per minute. However, at optimal pacing rates, the cardiac output is below normal in four of the five patients.

Endocardial electrode catheters may be used to drive the ventricles at various rates, thereby permitting the assessment of changes in heart rate alone on cardiac output and other parameters of cardiovascular function. In most cases, cardiac output increases with an increase in the ventricular rate, maximal values being attained in the general range of 60 to 90 beats per minute. At rates above 90 per minute, there is often no further change in cardiac output, but in some patients, it tends to decline gradually (Fig. 10-5). The extent to which the cardiac output increases during pacemaking depends on its value at the initial (idioventricular) rate. When this is low (less than 2.0 liters per $M.^2$ per minute), as in the five cases illustrated in Fig. 10-5, a moderate increase can be expected. With increasing rates of pacemaking between the idioventricular values of 34 to 42 per minute and about 60 per minute, the stroke volume remained relatively constant; at faster rates, as the cardiac output approached a plateau, the stroke volume diminished reciprocally as the rate increased. The effects of the increased cardiac output are at times dramatic. At the start of the study, the patient with the cardiac output of 1.2 liters per minute (0.7 liters per $M.^2$ per minute) had a rightsided hemiparesis and severe dysphasia; within 90 seconds of pacemaking at 48 beats per minute, he was able to move his limbs and to talk coherently. On temporarily ceasing pacemaking, he rapidly reverted to his previous state. Dalessio et al. (1965) have also noted improvement in cerebral function resulting from prolonged pacemaking.

When the cardiac output at the idioventricular rate is less severely depressed, pacemaking results in a less pronounced increase, as might be expected, and the stroke volume decreases at all rates in excess of the idioventricular rate. This is illustrated in Fig. 10-6 (Carleton et al. 1966B). Even at optimal rates, the cardiac output does not usually attain normal values. This may be due to coexisting or causative lesions in the heart, although the possibility of chronic adaptation to a subnormal output cannot be excluded.

Table 10-4 shows results at three different levels of pacemaking in the study of Segel et al. (1964). At the optimal rate of pacing, cardiac

TABLE 10-4. Observations Made at Various Ventricular Rates in Thirteen Patients with Acquired Complete Heart Block*

	IVR†	50-65	70-83	85-100
Ventricular rate (beats/min.)	35	55	77	92
O_2 consumption (ml./$M.^2$/min.)	133	145	151	147
A-V O_2 difference (ml./100 ml.)	6.3	5.9	5.4	5.4
Cardiac output (L./$M.^2$/min.)	2.2	2.6	2.9	2.8
Stroke volume (ml./$M.^2$)	65	47	39	31
Mean arterial pressure (mm. Hg)	129	147	155	159

* Adapted from Segel, Hudson, Harris and Bishop, J. Clin. Invest., *43*:1541, 1964.

† Idioventricular rate.

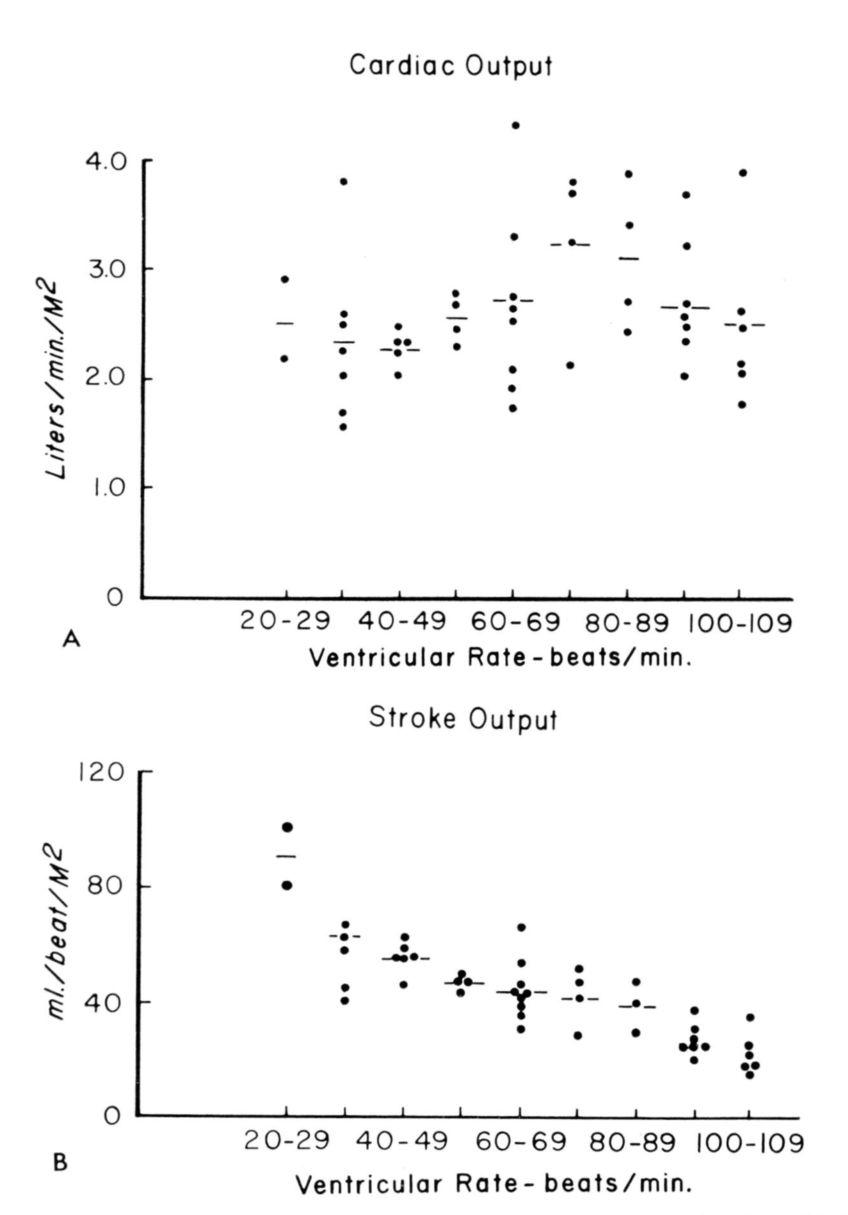

FIGURE 10-6. *A*, Cardiac output at rest in 12 patients with complete heart block. The highest average value occurred at a ventricular rate of 70 per minute. *B*, The progressive decline of stroke volume at increasing ventricular rates. (From Carleton, Sessions and Graettinger, Med. Clin. N. Amer., *50*:325, 1966.)

output increased by one third and the arteriovenous difference in oxygen content was reduced. The increase in mean arterial pressure resulted from the shortening of diastole. Bevegård (1962) and Samet et al. (1964) reported similar findings.

EFFECTS OF EXERCISE. The exercise which patients with acquired complete heart block can perform is limited by their associated heart disease. The patients studied by Segel et al. (1964) were able to increase their oxygen consumption from 130 ml. to only 336 ml. per $M.^2$ per minute during exercise at their idioventricular rates. The arteriovenous difference in oxygen saturation increased from 6.3 to 12.2 ml. per 100 ml. The cardiac output increased from 2.2 to 3.0 liters per $M.^2$ per minute. In two patients, the ventricular rate increased by the same proportion as the cardiac output. In the others, the maximal increase in ventricular rate was 5 beats per minute, and the stroke volume made a greater contribution to the increase of output.

In a patient with heart block, the resting cardiac output increased from 3.3 liters per minute at the idioventricular rate of 36 per minute to 4.0 liters per minute during pacing at 60 per minute, and to 4.6 and 4.8 during two periods of pacing at 108 per minute. During three identical short periods of exercise (atrial rates 140 to 144 per minute), the cardiac outputs were 4.2, 6.2 and 6.3 liters per minute at ventricular rates of 39 (idioventricular), 60 and 108 per minute, respectively. Pacing thus permitted a more effective response to exercise than was possible at the slow intrinsic ventricular rate. Segel et al. (1964) found that their patients attained a cardiac output of 4.0 liters per $M.^2$ per minute during ventricular pacing at 79 per minute; identical exercise at the idioventricular rate (mean 39 per minute) achieved a cardiac output of 3.0 liters per $M.^2$ per minute.

Even with the benefit of ventricular pacemaking, the cardiac response to exercise in heart block is inferior to that in normal persons. The increment in cardiac output is less, the increase in the arteriovenous difference in oxygen content is greater, and the pulmonary artery wedge (indirect left atrial) pressure increases up to as much as 30 mm. Hg. Reasons for this inferior response include the presence of impaired myocardial contractility due to underlying disease, the asynchrony of atrial and ventricular contractions, and perhaps the occurrence of functional tricuspid regurgitation due to stretching of the valve ring (McMichael and Shillingford, 1957). When myocardial failure is present, the stroke volume sometimes fails to increase during exercise; with return of compensation, following several days of continual pacemaking, the response to exercise is improved, and an increase in stroke volume makes a significant contribution (McGregor and Klassen, 1964).

EFFECTS OF DRUGS. Atropine did not alter the cardiac output in five patients who were being paced at a fixed rate (McGregor and Klassen,

1964). Nitroglycerin decreased the arterial blood pressure but did not affect the cardiac output in patients at fixed rates of pacemaking (Benchimol et al., 1964). Isoproterenol infusions usually increase the cardiac output, mainly through an increase in the idioventricular rate. However, during ventricular pacing at relatively high fixed rates, isoproterenol was unable to influence the ventricular rate; the increase in cardiac output in this situation was therefore due to an increase in stroke volume (Benchimol et al., 1965B). Isoproterenol sometimes reduces the degree of heart block and rarely restores normal conduction.

Judge et al. (1964) infused norepinephrine at 4 to 8 μg. per minute into five patients who were being paced at rates of 60, 75, 90 and 110 per minute. The cardiac output was consistently increased (mean increase 40 per cent). This contrasts with the situation in normal subjects in whom the inotropic effect of norepinephrine is countered by reflex bradycardia, so that the cardiac output fails to increase or decreases slightly (Goldenberg et al., 1948).

The effects of digitalization with intravenous infusion of strophanthin G (ouabain) were studied in patients whose ventricular rates were fixed at 70 to 75 beats per minute by means of permanent pacemakers (Benchimol et al., 1965B). The cardiac index increased from 2.0 to 2.4 liters per $M.^2$ per minute (mean values) after 20 minutes, before gradually returning to prior values after two hours. The arterial blood pressure did not change.

PACEMAKER SITE AND CARDIAC PERFORMANCE. Temporary pacemaking is generally achieved by endocardial catheter electrodes placed in the right ventricle, and permanent pacemaking by electrodes implanted in the anterior wall of the left ventricle. The effects of differences in the pacemaker site on cardiac performance have not been systematically studied in patients. However, results of investigations in dogs with surgically created complete heart block may have clinical implications.

It has often been thought that varying the site of the ventricular pacemaker does not alter the cardiac output (Starzl and Gaertner, 1955B; William-Olsson and Anderson, 1963). Lister et al. (1964) paced the hearts of blocked dogs from each of eight different ventricular sites at 90, 120 and 150 per minute. Differences of up to 100 per cent were recorded when the sites were varied in sequence. The more effective left ventricular sites were associated with higher values for cardiac output than were sites anywhere in the right ventricle. The changes in cardiac performance with variations in pacemaker sites were attributed to variations in the degree of synchrony during ventricular contraction and possibly to variations in the position of the atrioventricular valves early in ventricular systole. Vagnini et al. (1966) also showed that, in dogs with complete heart block, the maximal rate of increase in left ventricular pressure was achieved when pacing was undertaken at the anterior aspect of the left ventricular apex.

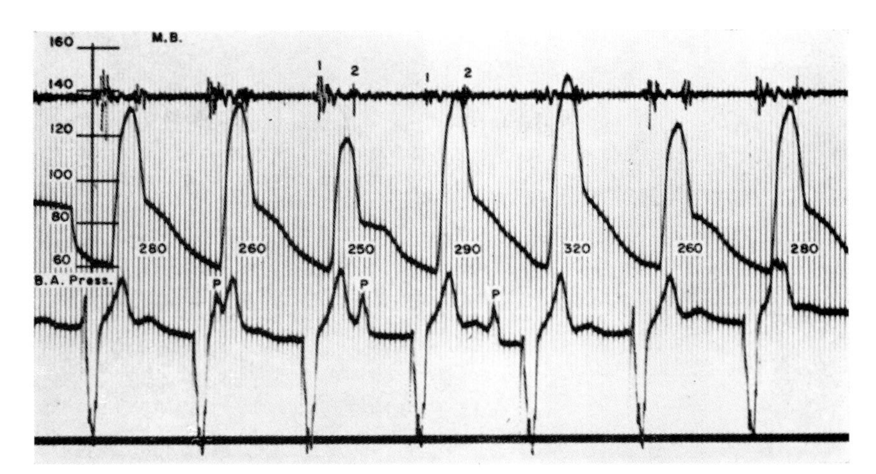

FIGURE 10-7. Brachial artery blood pressure showing variations in systolic and pulse pressures and in ejection time related to variations in the antecedent *PR* intervals. The values printed under the pressure pulses indicate the corresponding systolic ejection times (milliseconds). (From Benchimol, Palmero, Liggett and Dimond, Circulation, 32:84, 1965.)

Wallace (1966) showed, also in dogs, that pacing from the bundle of His, which results in rapid ventricular activation via normal conduction pathways, is associated with more efficient cardiac performance than is direct ventricular pacing. The latter leads to slow activation because the impulse spreads through muscle rather than through the Purkinje system.

Bourassa et al. (1965) had the opportunity to study a patient with sinus rhythm and intermittent left bundle branch block. When this aberration of conduction was present, left ventricular peak systolic pressure, the maximal rate of increase in left ventricular systolic pressure, arterial pulse pressure and cardiac output all decreased.

ATRIAL SYSTOLE AND VENTRICULAR FILLING. Patients with complete heart block and a fixed ventricular rate provide an opportunity to study the contribution of atrial systole to ventricular filling. Ventricular function is enhanced when the *P* wave precedes the *QRS* complex by approximately 100 to 300 m.sec. (Benchimol et al., 1965B). As a result of increased ventricular end-diastolic pressure and volume, the force of the subsequent ventricular contraction is increased, and the systolic ejection time is prolonged (Fig. 10-7). There are variations in systemic arterial systolic and pulse pressures. When the ventricle is driven at a rate considerably in excess of the atrial rate, the arterial pressure varies from beat to beat. When the rates are only slightly different, regular cyclical fluctuations occur in blood pressure, that are related to the phasic alterations in the relative timing of atrial and ventricular systole (Fig. 10-8). Similar fluctuations in

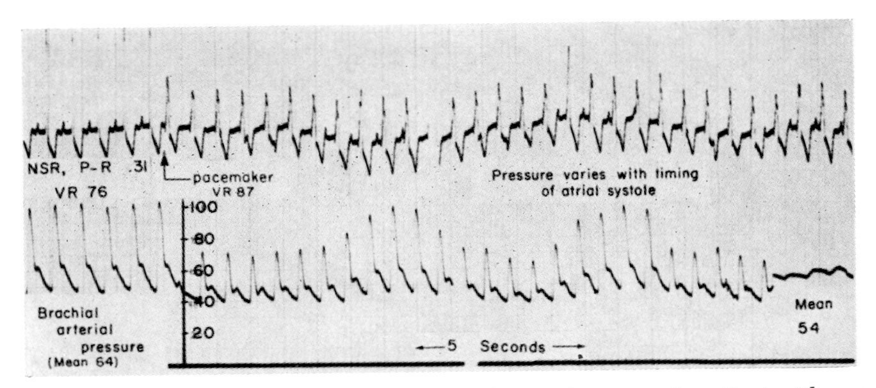

FIGURE 10-8. Electrocardiogram and brachial arterial pressure in patient with cardiac pacemaker. Sinus rhythm (rate 76 per minute) is present for the first six beats, and the arterial pressure is 102/48 mm. Hg. During the remainder of the record, the right ventricle was paced at a rate of 87 per minute, so that there was a variable relationship of the *P* waves to the *QRS* complexes. Corresponding variations are present in the arterial pressure, which is 100/46 mm. Hg when the *PR* interval is optimal, and 65/40 when the *P* wave coincides with ventricular systole. (From Martin and Cobb, J. Lab. Clin. Med., *68*:224, 1966.)

pressure and in the duration of ventricular systole are noted in the right ventricle and pulmonary artery.

Carleton et al. (1966 A and B) studied the relationship between the arterial systolic pressure and the duration of the preceding *PR* interval. Data from an individual patient are shown in Fig. 10-9. At any rate of ventricular pacing, there was a parabolic relationship between the *PR* interval and the corresponding arterial systolic pressure. The optimal *PR* intervals were inversely related to the ventricular rate. The percentage increase between the systolic pressure associated with the least effective atrial systole and that associated with the optimally timed atrial systole was used as an index of the atrial contribution to ventricular performance. This contribution was small at ventricular rates under 60 per minute and important at rates above 90 per minute (Fig. 10-10).

The acute administration of full therapeutic doses of digitalis reduced the systolic ejection time and minimized the variations in ventricular function that resulted from variations in the *PR* interval (Benchimol et al., 1965B).

Judge et al. (1964) were able to adjust the directly paced ventricular rate in two patients with complete heart block until it equaled the atrial rate for periods that permitted the recording of an indicator dilution curve and hence measurement of cardiac output. In both, the cardiac output was greater when the *P* wave preceded the *QRS* complex by approximately 0.20 seconds (6.0 and 6.2 liters per minute, respectively) than when the *P* and *QRS* complexes were out of phase (4.8 and 5.1 liters per minute, respectively).

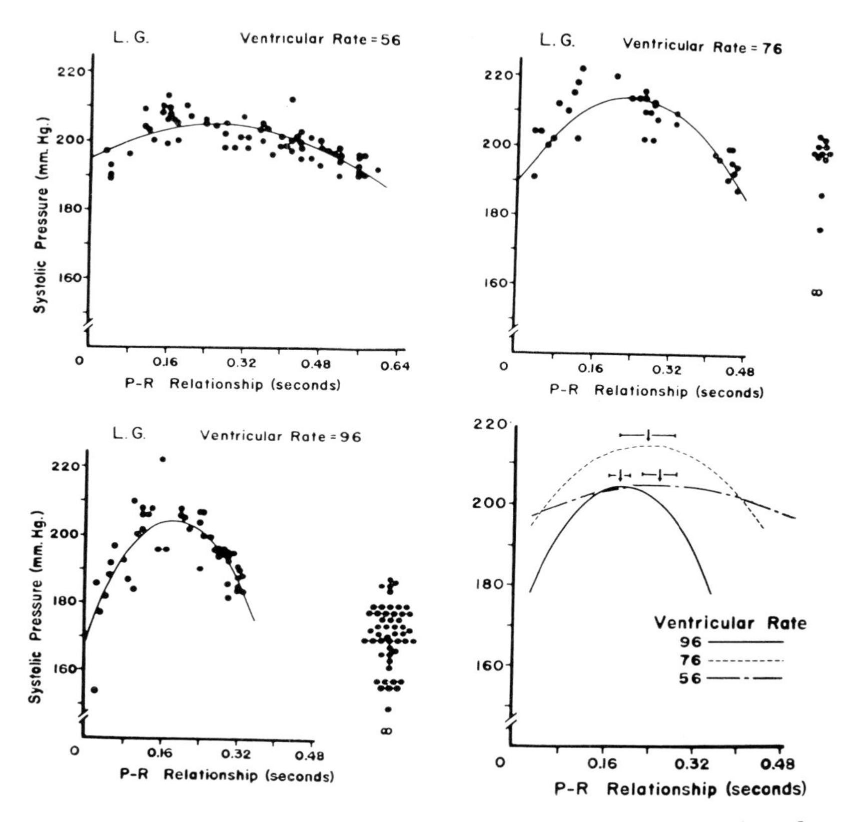

FIGURE 10-9. Patient with acquired heart block. Systolic pressure, on the ordinate, is plotted against *PR* relationship at each of three paced ventricular rates. Points from those cycles with ineffective atrial systoles are clustered above the symbol ∞. Arterial pressure was low at very short or very long *PR* intervals and highest when atrial systole was optimally timed. Parabolas derived by the least squares method are shown in the lower right panel, with arrows indicating the optimal *PR* relationships. (From Carleton, Sessions and Graettinger, Med. Clin. N. Amer., *50*:325, 1966.)

In a patient who had return of his own conduction mechanism subsequent to implantation of a ventricular pacemaker, virtual identity of the sinus rate and the pacemaker rate (81 beats per minute) resulted in the ventricle being continuously under the control of one or the other mechanism for prolonged periods (Sowton, 1965). The cardiac output was consistently greater with sinus (4.3 to 4.6 liters per minute) than with pacemaker (3.2 to 3.5 liters per minute) capture. In a second patient, the atrium was stimulated with a separate electrode at a rate identical to that of a ventricular electrode. In order to suppress sinus activity, the rates had to be set at not less than 90 per minute. The cardiac output was 4.0 liters per minute with a *PR* interval of 0.20 second. When the atrium and ventricle were stimulated simultaneously, the output immediately decreased to 2.8 liters per minute. However, with continued synchronous stimulation of atrium and ventricle, the cardiac output was soon restored to 3.9 liters per minute, indicating that compensatory mechanisms are available to counteract the loss of effectively timed atrial systole.

Samet et al. (1965C) compared the effect of stimulating the right ventricle directly and of stimulating the right atrium and relaying the stimulus via a synchronizing unit to the right ventricle (atrial synchronous pacemaking). In the latter case, the *PR* interval was constant and was generally set at 0.12 second. In the former case, atrial and ventricular systole had no fixed sequence. Thirty four paired measurements were available in six patients. The mean cardiac output during ventricular pacemaking

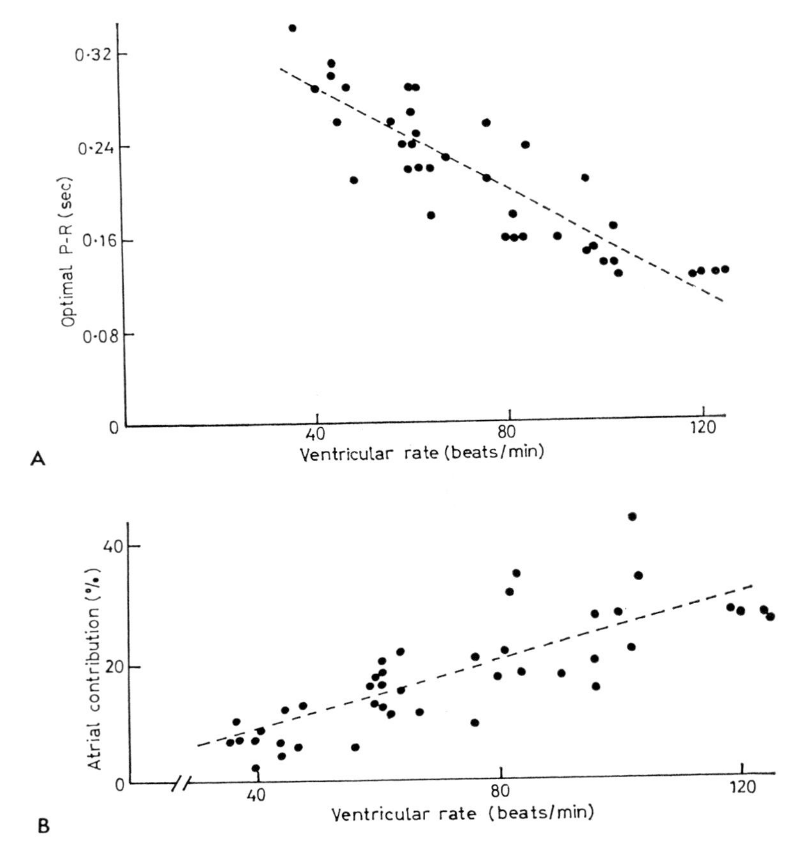

FIGURE 10-10. *A*, Relation of optimal values for the *PR* interval at different rates of ventricular pacing in patients with complete heart block. The least squares regression line is shown. *B*, The percentage increase in systolic arterial blood pressure produced by an optimally timed atrial systole is plotted against the corresponding ventricular rate. (From Carleton, Passovoy and Graettinger, Clin. Sci., *30*:151, 1966.)

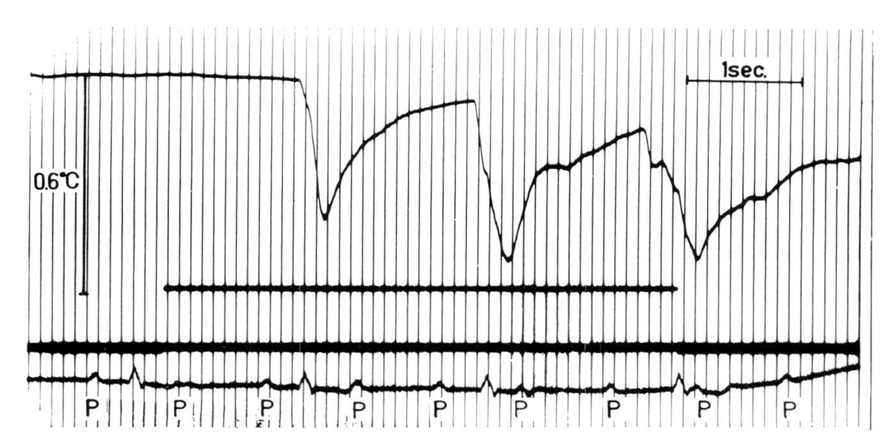

FIGURE 10-11. Demonstration of atriogenic tricuspid valve regurgitation in a patient with complete heart block. *Upper tracing*: right atrial temperature. *Middle tracing*: duration of infusion of 20 ml. cold saline into right ventricle. *Lowest tracing*: ECG. Note that reflux, indicated by a decrease in temperature, occurred after late diastolic *P* waves that were not followed by *QRS* complexes in normal sequence. Atrial contractions occurring during or immediately after ventricular contractions did not cause regurgitation. (From Rutishauser, Wirz, Gander and Lüthy, Circulation, *34*:807, 1966.)

was 2.6 liters per M.^{2} per minute; during atrial synchronous pacing, it was 2.9 liters per M.^{2} per minute.

When the *P* wave coincides with the *QRS* complex, prominent *v* waves appear in the atrial pressure tracing. These suggest that regurgitation is occurring through the atrioventricular valves (Samet et al., 1965B). This is in agreement with the observations of Skinner et al. (1963), based on pressure measurements and an indicator dilution technique, that in dogs improperly timed left atrial systole leads to mitral regurgitation. Rutishauser et al. (1966) used a thermal dilution technique to detect regurgitation of cold saline from right ventricle to right atrium and from left ventricle to left atrium, in five patients with complete heart block. They found that diastolic regurgitation occurred when atrial systoles were not followed by correctly timed ventricular systoles (Fig. 10-11). They supported previous conclusions (Williams et al., 1965; Vandenberg et al., 1965) that only ventricular contraction, whether normal or extrasystolic, leads to efficient closure of the valves.

Left ventricular angiocardiography in a number of patients with various forms of atrioventricular dissociation sometimes failed to show any reflux of contrast medium into the left atrium during ventricular systole (Braunwald, 1964). Thus, it seems that the absence of properly synchronized atrial systole does not necessarily impair closure of the mitral valve to the point of producing clinically or hemodynamically significant degrees of mitral regurgitation. Similar conclusions were reached by Burchell (1964).

REFERENCES

Ayers, C. R., Boineau, J. P., and Spach, M. S.: Congenital complete heart block in children. Am. Heart J., *72*:381, 1966.

Benchimol, A., Dimond, E. G., and Li, Y-B.: The effect of heart rate, exercise and nitroglycerin on the cardiovascular dynamics in patients with complete heart block. Am. J. Cardiol., *13*:96, 1964 (Abstract).

Benchimol, A., Ellis, J. G., and Dimond, E. G.: Hemodynamic consequences of atrial and ventricular pacing in patients with normal and abnormal hearts. Effects of exercise at a fixed atrial and ventricular rate. Am. J. Med., *39*:911, 1965A.

Benchimol, A., and Liggett, M. S.: Cardiac hemodynamics during stimulation of the right atrium, right ventricle, and left ventricle in normal and abnormal hearts. Circulation, *33*:933, 1966.

Benchimol, A., Palmero, H. A., Liggett, M. S., and Dimond, E. G.: Influence of digitalization on the contribution of atrial systole to the cardiac dynamics at a fixed ventricular rate. Circulation, *32*:84, 1965B.

Bevegård, S.: Observations on the effect of varying ventricular rate on the circulation at rest and during exercise in two patients with an artificial pacemaker. Acta Med. Scand., *172*:615, 1962.

Bourassa, M. G., Boiteau, G. M., and Allenstein, B. J.: Hemodynamic studies during intermittent left bundle branch block. Am. J. Cardiol., *10*:792, 1965.

Braunwald, E.: Symposium on cardiac arrhythmias. Introduction. With comments on the hemodynamic significance of atrial systole. Am. J. Med., *37*:655, 1964.

Brockman, S. K.: Cardiodynamics of complete heart block. Am. J. Cardiol., *16*:72, 1965A.

Brockman, S. K.: Reflex control of the heart in complete A-V block, with special reference to the experimental creation of Adams-Stokes disease. Am. J. Cardiol., *16*:84, 1965B.

Burchell, H. B.: A clinical appraisal of atrial transport function. Lancet, *i*:775, 1964.

Burchell, H. B., Connolly, D. C., and Ellis, F. H., Jr.: Indications for and results of implanting cardiac pacemakers. Am. J. Med., *37*:764, 1964.

Carleton, R. A., Passovoy, M., and Graettinger, J. S.: The importance of the contribution and timing of left atrial systole. Clin. Sci., *30*:151, 1966A.

Carleton, R. A., Sessions, R. W., and Graettinger, J. S.: Cardiac pacemakers: clinical and physiological studies. Med. Clin. N. Amer., *50*:325, 1966B.

Dalessio, D. J., Benchimol, A., and Dimond, E. G.: Chronic encephalopathy related to heart block. Its correction by permanent cardiac pacemaker. Neurology, *15*:499, 1965.

Daley, R., McMillan, I. K. R., and Gorlin, R.: Mitral incompetence in experimental auricular fibrillation. Lancet, *ii*:18, 1955.

Goldenberg, M., Pines, K. M., Baldwin, E. deF., Greene, D. G., and Roh, C. E.: Hemodynamic response of man to nor-epinephrine and epinephrine and its relation to problem of hypertension. Am. J. Med., *5*:792, 1948.

Graettinger, J. S., Carleton, R. A., and Muenster, J. J.: Circulatory consequences of changes in cardiac rhythm produced in patients by transthoracic direct-current shock. J. Clin. Invest., *43*:2290, 1964.

Halmos, P. B., and Patterson, G. C.: Effect of atrial fibrillation on cardiac output. Brit. Heart J., *27*:719, 1965.

Hansen, W. R., McClendon, R. L., and Kinsman, J. M.: Auricular fibrillation: hemodynamic studies before and after conversion with quinidine. Am. Heart J., *44*:499, 1952.

Harvey, R. M., Ferrer, M. I., Richards, D. W., and Cournand, A.: Cardiocirculatory performance in atrial flutter. Circulation, *12*:507, 1955.

Hecht, H. H., Osher, W. J., and Samuels, A. J.: Cardiovascular adjustments in subjects with organic heart disease before and after conversion of atrial fibrillation to normal sinus rhythm. J. Clin. Invest., *30*:647, 1951.

Holmgren, A., Karlberg, P., and Pernow, B.: Circulatory adaptation at rest and during

muscular work in patients with complete heart block. Acta Med. Scand., *164*: 119, 1959.
Ikkos, D., and Hanson, J. S.: Response to exercise in congenital complete atrioventricular block. Circulation, *22*:583, 1960.
Judge, R. D., Wilson, W. S., and Siegel, J. H.: Hemodynamic studies in patients with implanted cardiac pacemakers. New Eng. J. Med., *270*:1391, 1964.
Kahn, D. R., Wilson, W. S., Weber, W., and Sloan, H.: Hemodynamic studies before and after cardioversion. J. Thorac. Cardiovasc. Surg., *48*:898, 1964.
Killip, T., and Boer, R. A.: Cardiac function before and after electrical reversion of atrial fibrillation to sinus rhythm. Clin. Res., *12*:175, 1964 (Abstract).
Kory, R. C., and Meneely, G. R.: Cardiac output in auricular fibrillation with observations on the effects of conversion to sinus rhythm. J. Clin. Invest., *30*:653, 1951.
Landegren, J., and Biörck, G.: The clinical assessment and treatment of complete heart block and Adams-Stokes attacks. Medicine, *42*:171, 1963.
Leguime, J.: Circulatory disturbances in pathologic conditions with high heart rates. Cardiologia, *5*:105, 1941.
Lenègre, J., and Moreau, P.: Le bloc auriculo-ventriculaire complet. Ses causes et ses lésions. Bull. Soc. Med. Hôp. Paris, *113*:767, 1962.
Levine, S. A.: Benign atrial fibrillation of forty years' duration with sudden death from emotion. Ann. Int. Med., *58*:681, 1963.
Levinson, D. C., Shubin, H., Gunther, L., and Meehan, J. P.: Hemodynamic findings in heart block with slow ventricular rates. Am. J. Cardiol., *4*:440, 1959.
Lister, J. W., Koltz, D. H., Jomain, S. L., Stuckey, J. H., and Hoffman, B. F.: Effect of pacemaker site on cardiac output and ventricular activation in dogs with complete heart block. Am. J. Cardiol., *14*:494, 1964.
Lown, B.: Electrical reversion of atrial fibrillation. In: Mechanisms and Therapy of Cardiac Arrhythmias. The Fourteenth Hahnemann Symposium. Ed. Dreifus and Likoff. New York and London, Grune & Stratton, 1966.
Lown, B., Amarasingham, A., and Neuman, J.: New method for terminating cardiac arrhythmias; use of synchronized capacitor discharge. J.A.M.A., *182*:548, 1962.
Marshall, R. J., and Shepherd, J. T.: Exercise and the circulation. Circulation, *27*:323, 1963.
Martin, R. H., and Cobb, L. A.: Observations on the effect of atrial systole in man. J. Lab. Clin. Med., *68*:224, 1966.
Mathieu, L., Pernot, C., Metz, J., and Streiff, F.: Tachycardie ventriculaire de longues durée (trois mois) au cours d'un infarctus du myocardie; restauration tardive du rhythme sinusal et guérison. Arch. Mal. Coeur, *51*:389, 1958.
McGoon, D. C., Ongley, P. A., and Kirklin, J. W.: Surgically induced heart block. Ann. New York Acad. Sci., *111*:830, 1964.
McGregor, M., and Klassen, G. A.: Observations on the effect of heart rate on cardiac output in patients with complete heart block at rest and during exercise. Circ. Research, *15*:215, 1964.
McIntosh, H. D., and Morris, J. J., Jr.: The hemodynamic consequences of arrhythmias. Prog. Cardiovasc. Dis., *8*:330, 1966.
McMichael, J., and Shillingford, J. P.: The role of valvular incompetence in heart failure. Brit. Med. J., *i*:537, 1957.
Miller, D. E., Gleason, W. L., Whalen, R. E., Morris, J. J., Jr., and McIntosh, H. E.: Effect of ventricular rate on the cardiac output in the dog with chronic heart block. Circ. Research, *10*:658, 1962.
Montgomery, E. F., Co, B. S., Pietras, R. J., Gunnar, R. M., and Tobin, J. R.: Immediate and delayed hemodynamic changes resulting from the restoration of atrial systole by electroversion. Circulation, *34* (Suppl. III):172, 1966 (Abstract).
Morris, J. J., Jr., Entman, M., North, W. C., Kong, Y., and McIntosh, H.: The changes in cardiac output with reversion of atrial fibrillation to sinus rhythm. Circulation, *31*:670, 1965.
Nakano, J.: Effects of atrial and ventricular tachycardias on the cardiovascular dynamics. Am. J. Physiol., *206*:547, 1964.

Oram, S., Davis, J. P. M., Weinbren, L., Taggert, P., and Kitchen, L. D.: Conversion of atrial fibrillation to sinus rhythm by direct-current shock. Lancet, *ii*:159, 1963.

Orgain, E. S., Wolff, L., and White, P. D.: Uncomplicated auricular fibrillation and auricular flutter. Frequent occurrence and good prognosis in patients without other evidence of cardiac disease. A.M.A. Arch. Int. Med., *57*:493, 1936.

O'Rourke, R., Mann, O., and Harvey, W. P.: Control of coronary pain by prevention of tachycardia. J.A.M.A., *188*:1005, 1964.

Reale, A.: Acute effects of countershock conversion of atrial fibrillation upon right and left heart hemodynamics. Circulation, *32*:214, 1965.

Ross, J., Jr., Linhart, J. W., and Braunwald, E.: Effects of changing heart rate in man by electrical stimulation of the right atrium. Studies at rest, during exercise, and with isoproterenol. Circulation, *32*:549, 1965.

Rowe, G. G.: Personal communication, 1966.

Rutishauser, W., Wirz, P., Gander, M., and Lüthy, E.: Atriogenic diastolic reflux in patients with atrioventricular block. Circulation, *34*:807, 1966.

Samet, P., Bernstein, W. H., Levine, S., and López, A.: Hemodynamic effects of tachycardias produced by atrial and ventricular pacing. Am. J. Med., *39*:905, 1965B.

Samet, P., Bernstein, W. H., Medow, A., and Nathan, D. A.: Effect of alterations in ventricular rate on cardiac output in complete heart block. Am. J. Cardiol., *14*:477, 1964.

Samet, P., Bernstein, W. H., Nathan, D. A., and López, A.: Atrial contribution to cardiac output in complete heart block. Am. J. Cardiol., *16*:1, 1965C.

Samet, P., Castillo, C. A., and Bernstein, W. H.: Hemodynamic effects of sequential atrioventricular pacing. Circulation, *34* (Suppl. III):204, 1966 (Abstract).

Sarnoff, S. J., Braunwald, E., Welch, G., Case, R. B., Stainsby, W. N., and Macruz, R.: Hemodynamic determinants of oxygen consumption of the heart with special reference to the tension-time index. Am. J. Physiol., *192*:148, 1958.

Saunders, D. E., and Ord, J. W.: The hemodynamic effects of paroxysmal supraventricular tachycardia in patients with the Wolff-Parkinson-White syndrome. Am. J. Cardiol., *9*:223, 1962.

Scarpelli, E. M., and Rudolph, A. M.: The hemodynamics of congenital heart block. Prog. Cardiovasc. Dis., *6*:327, 1964.

Segel, N., Hudson, W. A., Harris, P., and Bishop, J. M.: The circulatory effects of electrically induced changes in ventricular rate at rest and during exercise in complete heart block. J. Clin. Invest., *43*:1541, 1964.

Skinner, N. S., Mitchell, J. H., Wallace, A. G., and Sarnoff, S. J.: Hemodynamic effects of altering the timing of atrial systole. Am. J. Physiol., *205*:499, 1963.

Skinner, N. S., Mitchell, J. H., Wallace, A. G., and Sarnoff, S. J.: Hemodynamic consequences of atrial fibrillation at constant ventricular rates. Am. J. Med., *36*:342, 1964.

Sonnenblick, E. H., Morrow, A. G., and Williams, J. F., Jr.: Effects of heart rate on the dynamics of force development in the intact human ventricle. Circulation, *33*:945, 1966.

Sowton, E.: Haemodynamic studies in patients with artificial pacemakers. Brit. Heart J., *26*:737, 1964.

Sowton, E.: Artificial pacemaking and sinus rhythm. Brit. Heart J., *27*:311, 1965.

Stack, M. F., Rader, B., Sobol, B. J., Farber, S. J., and Eichna, L. W.: Cardiovascular hemodynamic functions in complete heart block and the effect of isopropylnorepinephrine. Circulation, *17*:526, 1958.

Starzl, T. E., and Gaertner, R. A.: Chronic heart block in dogs: Method for producing experimental heart failure. Circulation, *12*:259, 1955B.

Starzl, T. E., Gaertner, R. A., and Baker, R. R.: Acute complete heart block in dogs. Circulation, *12*:82, 1955A.

Stein, E., Damato, A. N., Kosowsky, B. D., Lau, S. H., and Lister, J. W.: The relation of heart rate to cardiovascular dynamics. Pacing by atrial electrodes. Circulation, *33*:925, 1966.

Stewart, H. J., Crawford, J. H., and Hastings, A. B.: The effect of tachycardia on the blood flow in dogs: 1. The effect of rapid irregular rhythms as seen in auricular fibrillation. J. Clin. Invest., *3*:435, 1926.

Storstein, O., and Tveten, H.: The hemodynamic effect of restoring normal sinus rhythm in patients with auricular fibrillation. Scand. J. Clin. Lab. Invest., *7*:167, 1955.

Vagnini, F. J., Gourin, A., and Stuckey, J. H.: Ventricular pacemaker sites and myocardial contraction. Am. J. Cardiol., *17*:141, 1966 (Abstract).

Vandenberg, R. A., Sturm, R. E., and Wood, E. H.: Efficiency of closure of the mitral valve by isolated ventricular systoles. Fed. Proc., *24*:704, 1965 (Abstract).

Wade, O. L., and Bishop, J. M.: Cardiac Output and Regional Blood Flow. Oxford, Blackwell, 1962.

Wallace, A. G.: Quoted by McIntosh, H. D., and Morris, J. J., Jr.: The hemodynamic consequence of arrhythmias. Prog. Cardiovasc. Dis., *8*:330, 1966.

William-Olsson, G., and Anderson, M. N.: The effect of pacemaker electrode site on cardiac output. J. Thorac. Cardiovasc. Surg., *45*:618, 1963.

Williams, J. C. P., O'Donovan, T., Osypka, P., and Lambert, E. H.: Efficacy of atriogenic closure of mitral valve in dogs without thoracotomy. Fed. Proc., *24*:704, 1965 (Abstract).

Winters, W. L., Jr., Tyson, R. R., Barrera, F., and Soloff, L. A.: Cardiac pacemaking. II. Physiological studies. Ann. Int. Med., *62*:220, 1965.

Wright, F. S., Adams, P., Jr., and Anderson, R. C.: Congenital atrioventricular dissociation due to complete or advanced atrioventricular heart block. Am. J. Dis. Child., *98*:72, 1959.

Chapter 11

VALVULAR HEART DISEASE

- Assessment of Valvular Stenosis
- Assessment of Valvular Regurgitation
- Mitral Stenosis
- Mitral Regurgitation
- Aortic Stenosis
- Aortic Regurgitation
- Tricuspid Valve Disease
- Pulmonary Valve Disease

ASSESSMENT OF VALVULAR STENOSIS

Normal cardiac valves offer little resistance to the forward flow of blood, and the pressure gradient across them when they are open is too small to be measured by conventional methods. When valve orifices become narrowed, either the pressure in the proximal heart chamber increases, or the quantity of flow across the valve decreases, or both changes occur.

A mathematical relationship exists between the cross sectional area of an orifice, the decrease in pressure across it and the rate of flow through it (Daugherty, 1937). Poiseuille's equation is applicable to those situations in the circulation in which a decrease of pressure results from frictional resistance in tubes rather than from orifice action. Torricelli's orifice equation is concerned with situations in which high losses of kinetic energy at orifices are associated with large volumes of flow. Gorlin and Gorlin (1951) adapted the standard orifice equation for calculation of the areas of the orifices of stenosed cardiac valves.

The general formula for all orifices is:

$$VA = \frac{F}{C \times \sqrt{2g \times (P_1 - P_2)}} = \frac{F}{C \times 44.5 \times \sqrt{(P_1 - P_2)}}$$

where

VA = orifice area (cm.^{2});

F = mean rate of flow during time that the orifice is open;

C = empirical orifice constant based on comparing valve orifice areas at necropsy with data from previous physiological measurements;

g = acceleration due to gravity;

$P_1 - P_2$ = pressure gradient across orifice.

When the stenosis is mild, the pressure gradient ($P_1 - P_2$) is slight and, since it is included in the denominator of the equation, the calculated area may be inaccurate. The greater the pressure gradient, the greater will be the relative accuracy of its measurement, and hence of the calculation of orifice area. Rodrigo and Snellen (1953), while approving of the formula in principle, believed that the introduction of a "constant" could lead to an error as great as 20 to 40 per cent.

For the mitral and tricuspid valves, the specific formula is:

$$\mathrm{VA} = \frac{\text{Valve flow (ml./diastolic sec.)}}{\mathrm{C} \times 44.5 \times \sqrt{(\mathrm{A_{pm}} - \mathrm{V_{pmd}})}}$$

where

$C = 0.7$;

A_{pm} = mean atrial pressure;

V_{pmd} = mean ventricular diastolic pressure.

Since blood traverses the atrioventricular valves only during diastole, the cardiac output (ml. per minute) is divided by the number of seconds of diastole per minute. The latter is calculated by multiplying the diastolic filling period (measured from the arterial or ventricular pressure pulse) by the heart rate.

In tricuspid stenosis, the mean right atrial and right ventricular diastolic pressure are readily measured at catheterization. In mitral stenosis, the pulmonary artery wedge pressure was formerly used instead of left atrial pressure. This was a valid substitution, since the mean pressures are similar (Epps and Adler, 1953; Werkö et al., 1953; Connolly et al., 1954). Also, the left ventricular diastolic pressure was assumed to be 5 mm. Hg. This assumption was less satisfactory, since it is now known that even in pure mitral stenosis, this pressure may range from 3 to 12 mm. Hg (Libanoff and Rodbard, 1966). It was clearly invalid when there were complicating lesions of the aortic valve, or other conditions such as myocardial disease, that might have been accompanied by abnormally high ventricular diastolic pressures. In recent years, transseptal catheterization of the left atrium and retrograde catheterization of the left ventricle have permitted simultaneous or closely sequential measurement of left atrial and left ventricular diastolic pressures, although there is still indecision as to whether one should use the early (Dutrey and Drake, 1961), the mean (Hugenholtz et al., 1962) or the late (Leach et al., 1962) ventricular diastolic pressure.

EXAMPLE

Cardiac output (ml. per minute)		5600
Diastolic filling period (seconds per beat)		0.6
Heart rate (per minute)		70
Diastolic filling period (seconds per minute)		42
Cardiac output (ml. per diastolic second)	$\frac{5600}{42}$	133
Left atrial pressure (mm. Hg)		25
Left ventricular diastolic pressure (mm. Hg)		5
C		0.7

$$\text{Area (cm.}^2\text{)} = \frac{133}{0.7 \times 44.5 \times \sqrt{(25 - 5)}} = \frac{133}{31 \times 4.47} = 0.96 \text{ cm.}^2$$

For the aortic and pulmonary valves, the specific formula is:

$$\text{VA} = \frac{\text{Valve flow (ml./systolic sec.)}}{\text{C} \times 44.5 \times \sqrt{(\text{V}_{\text{psm}} - \text{A}_{\text{psm}})}}$$

where

$C = 1.0$;

V_{psm} = mean ventricular systolic pressure;

A_{psm} = mean arterial systolic pressure.

Flow per systolic second is calculated by dividing the cardiac output (ml. per minute) by the number of seconds of systole per minute. The latter is obtained by multiplying the systolic ejection period per pulse beat by the heart rate per minute.

EXAMPLE

Cardiac output (ml. per minute)	4800
Systolic ejection period (seconds per beat)	0.4
Heart rate (per minute)	60
Systolic ejection period (seconds per minute)	24
Cardiac output (ml. per systolic second)	200
Right ventricular mean systolic pressure (mm. Hg)	120
Pulmonary arterial mean systolic pressure (mm. Hg)	20

$$\text{Area (cm.}^2\text{)} = \frac{200}{44.5 \times \sqrt{(120 - 20)}} = \frac{200}{445} = 0.45 \text{ cm.}^2$$

The standard Gorlin formulae are inapplicable when a significant amount of regurgitation is also occurring through a stenosed valve, unless the amount of regurgitation can be accurately quantitated and an appropriate correction made in the equation (Gorlin et al., 1952; McDonald et al., 1957). The reason is that both the direct Fick and the indicator dilution methods, when used for determining cardiac output, measure net forward flow only. The actual forward flow through the valve is, however, the sum of the net forward flow and of the regurgitant flow. For example, in the case of an aortic valve which permitted regurgitation during diastole of half of the volume ejected during the preceding systole, the numerator of the orifice equation should be twice the net forward flow.

Another inaccuracy may occur when the pressure in the chamber or vessel distal to a severely narrowed valve is measured by means of a catheter traversing the valve. The catheter may then cause a significant additional obstruction to flow and result in an overestimate of the severity of the stenosis. This is of more than theoretical importance; catheter obstruction of a critically small pulmonary valve orifice may cause acute right ventricular failure and even death (Paul and Rudolph, 1958).

Finally, it is pertinent to point out that there are theoretical objections to the application of hydraulic formulae, derived from situations in which there is a constant rate of flow of Newtonian fluids through non-branching rigid tubes, to the human circulation, in which a non-Newtonian fluid (blood) flows in a pulsatile manner through branching elastic tubes and chambers. Despite these objections, much useful information has been gained from the application of formulae to measure areas of orifices or resistances in vascular beds.

ASSESSMENT OF VALVULAR REGURGITATION

Regurgitation through one or more of the cardiac valves leads to an increase in the volume of blood in the heart and to a delayed clearance of blood from the heart. These changes lead to characteristic alterations in the contours of indicator dilution curves recorded from peripheral arterial sites, including a decrease in the peak concentration, prolongation of the disappearance slope and inadequate clearance prior to the onset of recirculation.

From experiments with a model of the circulation, Korner and Shillingford (1955, 1956) felt that the effects of regurgitation could be separated from those of flow and of volume. By treating the indicator dilution curve as a frequency distribution of indicator particles, and regarding the effect of regurgitation as a diminished probability of forward movement of particles, they attempted to assess this probability as a function of the dispersion of the curve. In the presence of valvular regurgitation, the variance and the reciprocal of the disappearance slope (both of which are functions of dispersion) increased, and could be separated into components related to forward flow, volume and regurgitant flow. The regurgitant flow could then be calculated from a regression equation. Although the method gave a good estimate in the model, it soon became clear that in patients it was inconsistent and sometimes misleading (Woodward et al., 1957A; Carleton et al., 1959).

In further studies of a model circulation, Hoffman and Rowe (1959) showed that under certain conditions of size, shape and elasticity of the chamber proximal to the regurgitant valve, the amount of regurgitation could be varied without appreciably affecting the shape of the curve. Warner (1962) pointed out that the ability of empirical indices based upon disproportionate prolongation of the disappearance slope to detect and quantitate mitral regurgitation must depend upon either enlargement of the atrium and left ventricle or upon the occurrence of peculiar mixing patterns. That the latter is less important is suggested by the observation that in dogs with acutely induced mitral regurgitation, in whom the heart chambers have not had time to become enlarged, indicator dilution curves do not show the characteristic distortion noted in patients with long standing mitral regurgitation. Thus, the analysis of arterial dilution curves recorded following injection of indicator into the right side of the heart provides limited information about valvular function.

More precise evaluation is possible when indicator is injected into the chamber distal to the regurgitant valve, and dilution curves are recorded simultaneously from the proximal chamber (upstream sampling) and from a peripheral artery. The area of the curve from the proximal chamber is calculated as a percentage of the area of the arterial dilution curve and termed the regurgitant fraction. The method has been applied to lesions of the mitral (Newcombe et al., 1961; Conn, 1959; Levinson et al., 1961; Gorelick et al., 1962), aortic (Armelin et al., 1963, 1964) and pulmonary and tricuspid (Bajec et al., 1958; Collins et al., 1959) valves.

In dogs with surgically created defects leading to mitral regurgitation, Newcombe et al. (1961) found that measurement of the regurgitant fraction gave results that were in reasonably good agreement with estimates of regurgitation from hydraulic formulae. Results were reproducible when blood was sampled from a region in the left atrium close to the mitral valve. Falsely low estimates would be anticipated with sampling near the entrance of the pulmonary veins. The site of injection in the left ventricle did not appear to influence the regurgitant fraction, despite the fact that the left ventricle is not a perfect mixing chamber (Swan and Beck, 1960; Irisawa et al., 1960). The timing of the injection in relation to the cardiac cycle was also not critical.

The cardiac chambers are much larger in man than in dogs, particularly in patients with long established mitral regurgitation. It might therefore be anticipated that measurement of the regurgitant fraction would be subject to greater inaccuracy. Gorelick et al. (1962), however, found satisfactory agreement in 60 patients between the prediction of regurgitation from the upstream sampling method and subsequent estimates of the severity of regurgitation at surgery or at necropsy. Further, they found that results were reasonably reproducible when successive dilution curves were obtained from the same or even different sampling sites in the left atrium. There were three false positive results. The experience of Levinson et al. (1961) was less favorable. In six of 16 patients, their results were entirely inconsistent with clinical estimates of the severity of regurgitation, and in individual instances, the results were not reproducible. They felt that the principal source of error lay in unrepresentative sampling from the left atrium. Indeed, the problem of non-mixing is sometimes so great that no indicator may be recovered from the left atrium, even after its direct injection, via a second catheter, into a different area of the atrium (Woodward et al., 1957B).

A serious problem in the evaluation of techniques for the assessment of valvular regurgitation is the lack of an independent quantitative method to provide a basis for comparison. Armelin et al. (1963) attempted to circumvent this, in dogs with surgically induced aortic regurgitation, by comparing the results obtained by the regurgitant fraction method with those derived from retrograde perfusion of the aorta at necropsy at appropriate pressure gradients. In most normal dogs, no indicator was detected in the left ventricle. In a few normal dogs, a trivial amount of indicator was detected; presumably, this was due to retrograde flow across the valve in the brief interval between the onset of left ventricular relaxation and the closure of the aortic valve cusps. In the dogs with valve lesions, the regurgitant fraction correlated closely with the severity of regurgitation assessed by retrograde perfusion at necropsy. The position of the sampling catheter in the left ventricle was not an important determinant of the amount of indicator detected. Variations in the timing of brief injections in the cardiac cycle influenced the regurgitant fraction, but when the injection was prolonged to cover all of systole, all of diastole or one or more full cardiac cycles, results were reproducible.

Warner and Toronto (1958) described a method for quantitating aortic regurgitation in man that involved the recording of simultaneous dilution curves from the left radial and femoral arteries following injections of indicator into the descending aorta at and progressively distal to the origin of the left subclavian artery. They determined the distance from the origin of this artery beyond which no indicator, injected during diastole, would return to it. This distance, multiplied by the cross sectional area of the aorta, gave the backflow per stroke for the descending aorta, on the assumption that aortic flow was laminar. Using a similar principle, Braunwald and Morrow (1958) determined the most distal point in the descending aorta from which injected indicator could be detected by an oximeter on the right ear.

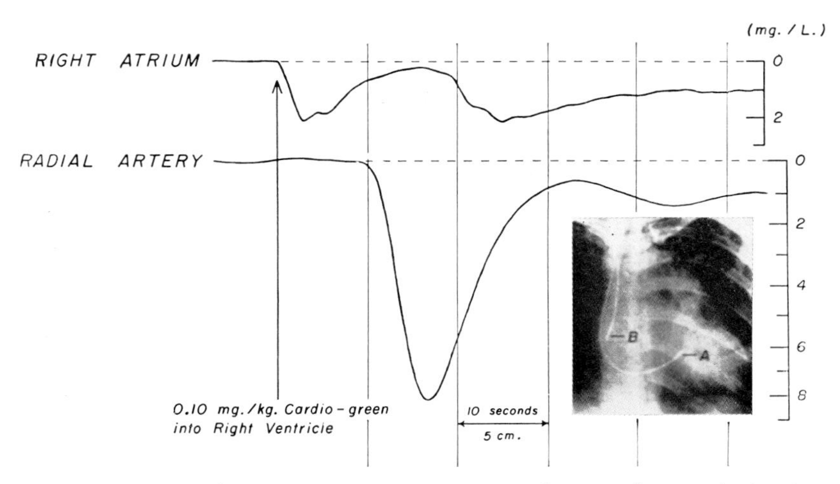

FIGURE 11-1. Demonstration by dilution curves of tricuspid regurgitation in a 42 year old woman with disease of the mitral and tricuspid valves. At the instant indicated by the vertical arrow, dye was injected into the inflow portion of the right ventricle via catheter A, and the resulting dilution curves were recorded from the right atrium via catheter B and from the radial artery. Note the instantaneous appearance of dye in the right atrium, indicating that dye has regurgitated through the tricuspid valve. The regurgitant fraction calculated from these curves was 10 per cent. Note that, despite this amount of tricuspid regurgitation, the curve recorded from the radial artery is apparently normal. (From Bajec, Birkhead, Carter and Wood, Proc. Staff Meet. Mayo Clin., 33:569, 1958.)

Pulmonary or tricuspid regurgitation may be assessed by using two catheters, the tips of which are placed distally (for injection) and proximally (for sampling) to the incompetent valve. Alternatively, a single double lumen catheter may be used. In normal persons, regurgitant indicator is not usually detected; occasional small quantities may be explained by the shaft of the distal catheter preventing perfect apposition of the valve cusps during ventricular systole. In tricuspid (Fig. 11-1) or pulmonary regurgitation, a significant fraction of the injected indicator appears immediately. The regurgitant fraction varies with variations in the sites of both the injection and sampling catheters. The optimal positions for assessing competence of the tricuspid valve are the apex of the right ventricle and the mid right atrium, respectively (Bajec et al., 1958). Collins et al. (1959) emphasized the value of the upstream sampling method in deciding whether an early blowing basal diastolic murmur, unaccompanied by peripheral signs of increased arterial "run off," is due to aortic or pulmonary regurgitation.

Analysis of pressure pulses also helps in the evaluation of both stenotic and regurgitant lesions; this is discussed in connection with individual valve lesions.

MITRAL STENOSIS

Obstruction to the flow of blood through the orifice of the mitral valve leads to an increase of pressure in the left atrium, pulmonary veins, pulmonary capillaries and pulmonary artery. In mild mitral stenosis, the mean pressure in the left atrium is slightly increased in the resting state, and the *a* wave, resulting from atrial contraction, is prominent. With more severe obstruction, the *ac* complex and the *v* wave are about equal in height, and the mean pressure is further increased (Fig. 11-2). The *v* wave is caused by continued flow of blood into the left atrium during left ventricular systole. During early diastole, the rate of decrease in left atrial pressure (*y* descent) is relatively slow, because of the obstruction caused by the narrowed valve orifice. This observation was used by Owen and Wood (1955) in their *Ry/v* ratio, which they found to be of some value in distinguishing between predominant stenosis and predominant regurgitation. However, other workers, including Connolly and Wood (1957), were unable to obtain satisfactory discrimination with the ratio. With the advent of atrial fibrillation, the *a* wave disappears from the left atrial pressure pulse.

The cross sectional area of the mitral valve orifice in normal adults is about 5 cm.[2] In mitral stenosis, the orifice becomes gradually narrowed over many years. The condition is well tolerated, even during strenuous exercise,

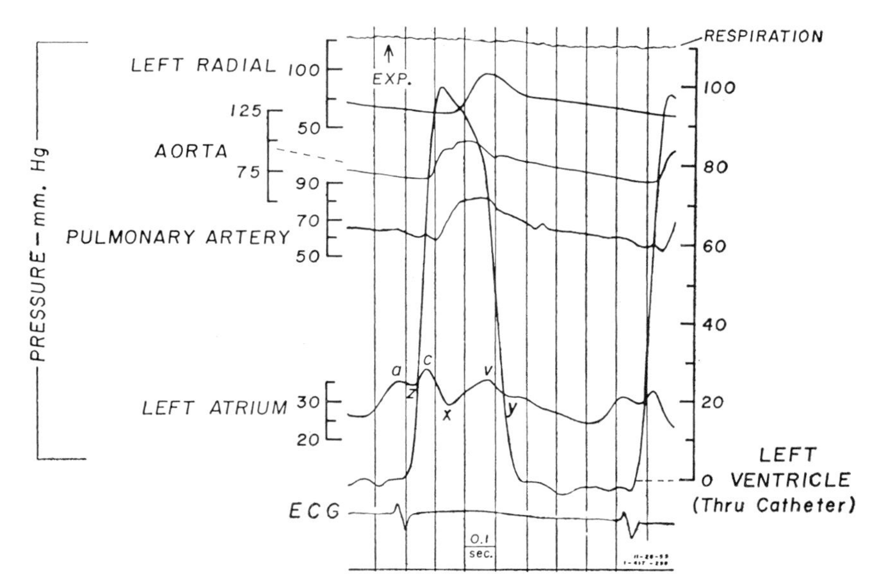

FIGURE 11-2. Simultaneous pressure pulses from various blood vessels and cardiac chambers in a patient with pure mitral stenosis (confirmed at subsequent operation). Individual waves and descents in the left atrial pressure pulse are labeled. (From Marshall, Woodward and Wood, Am. J. Cardiol., 2:24, 1958.)

as long as the area is 2.5 cm.^{2} or more. Characteristically, with areas of 1.5 to 2.5 cm.^{2}, there is dyspnea during moderately severe exercise. As the orifice continues to narrow, exercise tolerance is further impaired, and at the critical size 1 cm.^{2} (Lewis et al., 1952), even mild exercise is poorly tolerated. Such a gradual progression of disability may be interrupted if an unusual stress is laid on the circulation, such as pregnancy, thyrotoxicosis, severe anemia, paroxysmal tachycardia, emotional stress, pulmonary infection or exposure to high altitude.

From the Gorlin formula, it can be shown that a patient with a valve area of 2.5 cm.^{2}, a cardiac output of 6 liters per minute and a heart rate of 70 per minute would have an increase in left atrial pressure of only about 4 mm. Hg. With a valve area of 1 cm.^{2}, a left atrial pressure of about 25 mm. Hg would be anticipated, if flow were to be maintained at its normal level. Usually, however, the adjustment to the stenosis consists of both an increase in pressure gradient and a decrease in blood flow.

Simultaneous measurement of pressures in the left atrium and ventricle confirms the presence of a diastolic gradient. When the stenosis is mild, a significant gradient may be demonstrable only during the phase of rapid ventricular filling that immediately follows opening of the mitral valve, and in late diastole, due to rapid filling associated with atrial systole. With severe stenosis, there is a pressure gradient throughout diastole (Fig. 11-2), even during prolonged cardiac cycles.

The increased left atrial pressure is transmitted via the pulmonary veins to the pulmonary capillaries. When the pulmonary capillary pressure reaches 25 to 35 mm. Hg, it exceeds the oncotic pressure of the blood, and exudation of fluid occurs into the alveoli. If the rate of increase in the pressure has been rapid, such as may occur as a consequence of the increased blood volume (Hytten and Paintin, 1963) and cardiac output (Walters et al., 1966) during pregnancy, pulmonary edema may occur. Usually, however, fluid exudes more slowly and is removed by the lymph vessels which become engorged. Edema of the connective tissue septa and distention of lymph vessels in the septa can be demonstrated regularly as Kerley B lines (Kerley, 1951) in the costophrenic angles in x-ray films of the chest, when the left atrial pressure exceeds 24 mm. Hg (Rossall and Gunning, 1956). Distended lymph vessels can also be demonstrated in sections of lung from patients in whom the pulmonary capillary pressure exceeds 20 mm. Hg, and the mitral valve orifice is less than 1.4 cm.^{2} (Van Waasbergen, 1961). In addition, erythrocytes may pass by diapedesis from the pulmonary capillaries, and venules may rupture, leading to hemoptysis. If such intrapulmonary bleeding continues for long periods, hemosiderosis eventually occurs. There is a poor correlation, however, between the presence and extent of pulmonary hemosiderosis and the pressures in either pulmonary arteries or veins (Wagenvoort et al., 1964).

The mean pressure in the pulmonary artery is normally 5 to 10 mm. Hg

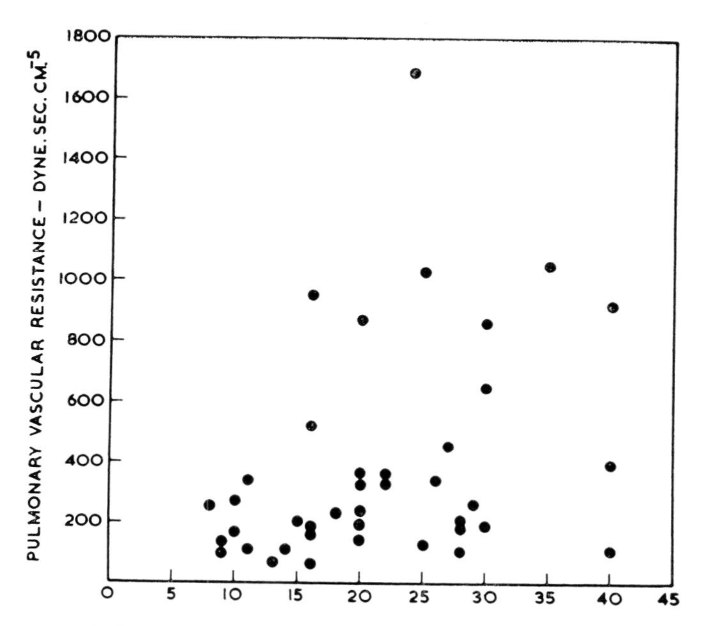

FIGURE 11-3. Pulmonary vascular resistance (ordinate) related to mean pulmonary artery wedge (indirect left atrial) pressure (abscissa, mm. Hg) in 40 patients with mitral stenosis. (From Donald. In: Pulmonary Circulation. Ed. Adams and Veith. New York, Grune & Stratton, 1959.)

higher than that in the left atrium or pulmonary capillaries. In most cases of mitral stenosis, this relationship persists, so that calculated values for pulmonary vascular resistance remain unchanged, or increase slightly if there is a modest decrease in cardiac output. In some patients with severe mitral stenosis in whom the resting left atrial pressure is 20 mm. Hg or more, there is a disproportionate increase in pulmonary artery pressure; occasionally, the pulmonary artery systolic pressure approaches systemic levels. However, the relationship is far from consistent; that is, although a great increase in pulmonary vascular resistance is not found in the absence of high left atrial pressures, there are many other patients with equally high or even higher left atrial pressures in whom the resistance is within normal limits (Fig. 11-3).

The increased vascular resistance or precapillary impedence (Arnott, 1964) to some extent protects the pulmonary capillary bed against further increases in pressure. At the same time, it greatly increases the pressure load on the right ventricle (Taquini et al., 1953), which is poorly adapted to function as a pressure pump. Thus, by this mechanism, early death from pulmonary edema is prevented at the cost of a low cardiac output and ultimately right ventricular failure (Wood, 1956). Such patients have a characteristic clinical course. In earlier years, they have the common complaints of dyspnea on exertion, orthopnea, paroxysmal nocturnal dyspnea and episodes of acute pulmonary congestion and hemoptysis. Later, these symptoms become overshadowed by extreme fatigue and effort intolerance and with the development of right ventricular failure, tricuspid regurgitation, peripheral edema and abdominal swelling.

Although it is still not clear why some patients with severe mitral stenosis develop greatly increased pulmonary vascular resistance and others do not, two mechanisms may account, in varying degrees, for the change in resistance: (1) structural changes in the arteries and arterioles; and (2) abnormal vasoconstrictor responses to various stimuli.

Parker and Weiss (1936) and Larrabee et al. (1949) described medial hypertrophy and intimal fibrosis, and Henry (1952) the presence of a distinct vascular tunica media in the arterioles. The changes are similar to those occurring in pulmonary hypertension complicating various forms of congenital heart disease, except that in mitral stenosis the peculiar dilatation lesions (angiomatoid and plexiform) do not seem to occur (Wagenvoort, 1959), and fibrinoid necrosis is rare. Correlation between the extent of anatomical changes in the arterioles and the degree of pulmonary vascular resistance is slight, and the histological changes are of little or no value in predicting the responses to mitral valvotomy (Edwards et al., 1952; Goyette et al., 1954). Several patients reported by Goodale et al. (1955) had extensive fibrous occlusion of the small muscular arteries, and yet they had a striking decrease in pulmonary vascular resistance after operation.

There are interesting differences in the structure of the larger blood vessels and in the blood flow between the upper and lower lobes of the lungs in severe mitral stenosis. The elastic pulmonary arteries in the upper lobes are dilated or normal, whereas those in the lower parts of the lungs are narrow (Doyle et al., 1957; Harrison, 1958). The muscular arteries in the upper lobes show only slight widening of the tunica media, whereas those in the lower lobes have extremely thick walls (Ferencz and Dammann 1957; Heath and Best, 1958). The veins in the lower lobes also contain more muscle, and in the venous phase of pulmonary angiograms, they seem to be normal or narrow in caliber compared with the dilated veins in the upper lobes (Steiner, 1958). It seems likely that these changes account for the regional redistribution of pulmonary blood flow. In normal persons standing at rest, perfusion of the upper zones of the lungs is less than perfusion of the basal zones, because of the effects of gravity on the relatively low pulmonary vascular pressures (West and Dollery, 1965). In patients with moderately severe mitral stenosis, the difference in perfusion rates is reduced, and when the pulmonary arterial pressure and pulmonary vascular resistance are excessively high, the upper zones may be more effectively perfused than the lower (Dollery and West 1960; Dollery and Hugh-Jones 1965; Fig. 11-4). External scintillation

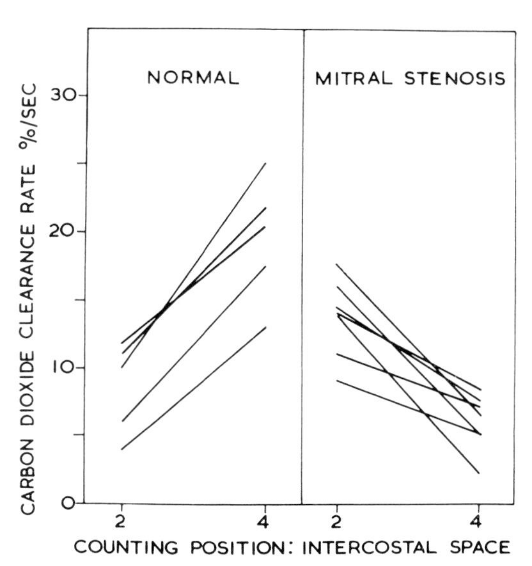

FIGURE 11-4. Carbon dioxide clearance rates at the second and fourth intercostal spaces in five normal subjects (*left*) and seven patients with mitral stenosis and severe pulmonary hypertension (*right*) examined in the upright position. (From Dollery and West, Circ. Research, 8:765, 1960.)

scanning of the upper and lower thirds of the lungs was performed following the intravenous injection of I^{131} labeled albumin, and blood flows in the corresponding areas (U and L) were assessed (Friedman and Braunwald, 1966). The ratio U/L averaged 0.43 in normal subjects; in mitral stenosis, it was less than 0.80 when the left atrial pressure was less than 15 mm. Hg, and exceeded 0.80 with higher atrial pressures.

Many investigators have been concerned with the possible role of increased vasomotor tone in maintaining the increased resistance in the pulmonary vascular bed. Conclusions from studies in which adrenergic and ganglion blocking drugs were used were often in conflict (Scott et al., 1955; Mackinnon et al., 1956; Balchum et al., 1957; Yu et al., 1958), partly because the powerful action of these drugs on the systemic circulation made it difficult to decide whether changes in the pulmonary circulation were actively or passively induced. Acetylcholine, however, is so rapidly inactivated by cholinesterase in the blood that, after injection into the pulmonary artery, it reaches the pulmonary arterioles in high concentration but has no effect on the systemic circulation. Wood et al. (1957), who injected acetylcholine into the pulmonary artery, concluded that constriction of the smooth muscle of the pulmonary vessels contributed to the pulmonary hypertension.

Semler et al. (1959) found a considerable decrease in pulmonary vascular resistance between two and five weeks after mitral valvotomy (Fig. 11-5). They concluded that, since regression of muscular hyertrophy in the arterioles is slow (Ferguson and Varco, 1955), a reduction of tone in smooth muscle was most probably responsible. Little additional change in

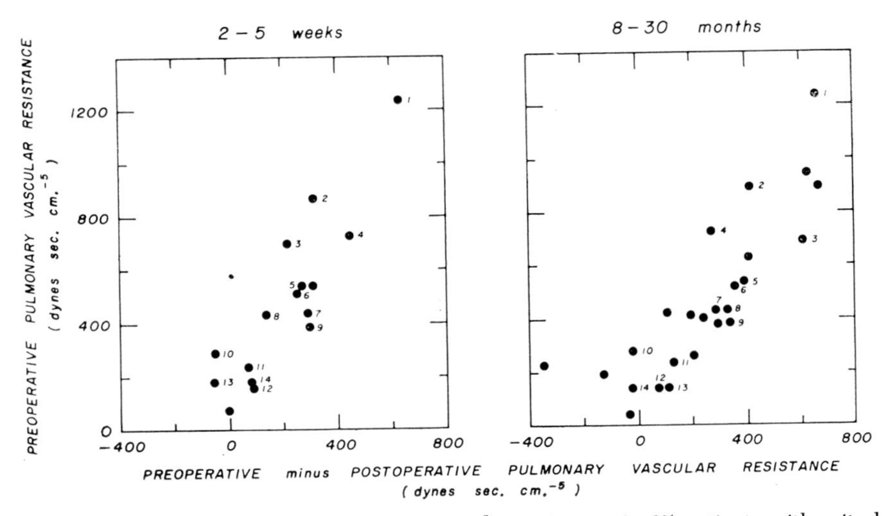

FIGURE 11-5. Changes in pulmonary vascular resistance in 25 patients with mitral stenosis at two to five weeks (*left*) and eight to 30 months (*right*) after mitral valvotomy. The numbered dots represent patients studied during both periods after operation. (From Semler, Shepherd and Wood, Circulation, *19*:386, 1959.)

resistance was noted when measurements were again made eight to 30 months after operation.

It may be that changes in pressure somewhere in the pulmonary vascular bed (or left atrium) provide a stimulus capable of regulating tone in the pulmonary vessels in mitral stenosis (Ferri et al., 1956; Semler et al., 1959). An alternative possibility is that part of the increased vascular resistance may be due to vasoconstriction in those areas in which there is alveolar hypoventilation due to venous congestion and edema. Improvement in the venous circulation could then account for decreased vascular resistance soon after a successful valvotomy, and more extensive congestion and edema developing rapidly during exercise could account for increased resistance (Semler et al., 1959) in the latter circumstance.

There is some correlation between the resting level of cardiac output and the degree of disability, assessed by the criteria of the New York Heart Association. Eliasch (1952) reported a mean cardiac index of 3.8 liters per M.^{2} per minute in patients with Class I or II disability, 2.7 liters per M.^{2} per minute in those with Class III disability and 2.4 liters per M.^{2} per minute in those with Class IV disability. Others, including Gorlin et al. (1951) and Wade and Bishop (1962), found less clear cut differences. In their collective experience, the presence or absence of atrial fibrillation correlated more closely with the level of cardiac output than did the clinical assessment of disability. It is difficult to be certain whether atrial fibrillation is responsible for the reduced output or whether the arrhythmia and the reduced output are merely parallel indications of more advanced cardiac damage. Evidence reviewed in Chapter 10 indicates, however, that the onset of atrial fibrillation can reduce cardiac output and that this can be restored following reversion to sinus rhythm.

The response of the cardiac output to exercise correlates more closely with clinical assessment of disability than do measurements obtained in the resting state (Ferrer et al., 1952). In some, cardiac output fails to increase at all during exercise (Donald et al., 1954). Metabolic demands of the tissues can then be met only by almost complete extraction of oxygen from capillary blood. The saturation of mixed venous blood occasionally decreases to as little as 10 per cent.

Studies after clinically successful closed mitral valvotomy have shown only slight and inconsistent improvement in the hemodynamic response to exercise (Donald et al., 1957); with the passage of further time, no additional improvement occurs, and the response may actually deteriorate due to restenosis of the valve or to progressive muscle damage. Objective evidence of improved pulmonary function, reflecting decreased congestion and stiffness of the lungs, is more readily demonstrable (Arnott, 1964).

There is ample evidence that, when cardiac output is reduced at rest and especially during exercise, there is a reflex redistribution of arterial blood flow in the systemic circulation. The receptors and the afferent pathway for this reflex are unknown; sympathetic adrenergic nerve fibers constitute the efferent pathway. This results in an adequate flow being maintained to the more vital organs (and, in the case of exercise, to the skeletal muscles) while flow elsewhere is curtailed. These changes apply to many cardiac diseases, but they have been studied most extensively in mitral stenosis.

At rest, mean renal blood flow (ml. per $M.^2$ per minute) was 660 in normal subjects, 411 in patients with compensated heart disease and 231 in patients with congestive heart failure (Wade and Bishop, 1962). Values for the arteriovenous difference in oxygen content in the kidney were 1.3, 2.0 and 3.4 ml. per 100 ml. blood for the same three groups. Cerebral blood flow is reduced in proportion to the decrease in cardiac output (Bishop et al., 1958). The coronary blood flow is maintained at a normal level while the heart disease is compensated but decreases with the advent of failure (Blain et al., 1956).

During comparably severe supine leg exercise, the femoral arteriovenous difference in oxygen saturation is greater in mitral stenosis than in normal subjects. Although the total blood flow to the exercising limbs is less than in normal subjects, it constitutes a larger fraction of the total cardiac output. Venous blood from non-exercising vascular beds, such as the splanchnic circulation, the kidneys and both muscle and skin in the arms, is excessively desaturated during even moderate exercise (Donald et al., 1955). Normal levels of venous saturation are sometimes not regained for ten or more minutes after the end of exercise. On the other hand, cerebral blood flow is not further reduced, and coronary blood flow is probably increased (Lombardo et al., 1953).

Earlier studies (Kopelman and Lee, 1951; Rapaport et al., 1956) often failed to show an increase in the central blood volume in mitral stenosis, despite the radiological evidence of enlargement of the heart and congestion of the lungs. However, the central blood volume, measured between an injection site in the right side of the heart and an arterial sampling site, contains a large and ill defined component in vessels of the systemic circulation (Marshall and Shepherd, 1961). Therefore, particularly in view of the redistribution of systemic blood flow that occurs in mitral stenosis, it was impossible to know how much of the measured volume was actually contained in the pulmonary vascular bed. More recently, the use of techniques for leftsided cardiac catheterization has permitted more direct measurement of the volume of blood between the pulmonary artery and left atrium. The mean value for this true pulmonary blood volume was almost identical in normal subjects (230 ml. per $M.^2$) and in patients with mild mitral stenosis (229 ml. per $M.^2$), but in patients with moderate to severe mitral stenosis, it was 359 ml. per $M.^2$ (McGaff et al., 1963). Schreiner et al. (1963) found an increase of 87 ml. per $M.^2$ in true pulmonary blood volume during light exercise in fourteen patients with valvular disease, usually mitral stenosis. The pulmonary capillary blood volume is inconstantly increased (Bates et al., 1960; Hamer, 1965).

Mackenzie's view was that myocardial weakness, rather than valvular obstruction, was the main factor responsible for heart falure in mitral stenosis (Lewis, 1946). Although this view is no longer tenable, there is little doubt that muscular dysfunction is a contributory factor in at least some patients (Fleming and Wood, 1959). The hemodynamic sequelae of myocardiopathy are more difficult to define than are those of mechanical obstruction at valve orifices. The criterion of Harvey et al. (1955) was the inability of cardiac output to increase by the anticipated amount on exercise, despite the presence of relatively normal pulmonary vascular pressures.

Chronic congestion and increased thickness of the alveolar walls lead to a progressive increase in the stiffness of the lungs, a physical change that is reflected in tests of pulmonary function. The vital capacity is reduced. The total work of breathing, both at rest and during exercise, is two to three times that of normal persons (Marshall et al., 1954). The distribution of inspired air is defective at rest; it is even more defective during exercise, perhaps because of increased transudation of fluid into the alveoli (Raine and Bishop, 1963). Ventilation-perfusion relationships are abnormal (Bishop et al., 1962). Impaired membrane diffusing capacity may be due to both reduction of the surface area available for diffusion through obliteration of the pulmonary capillary bed and, perhaps of more importance, to thickening of the alveolar-capillary membrane (McCredie, 1964). Arterial oxygen tension is generally normal (Williams, 1953) whereas carbon dioxide tension is frequently reduced as a result of hyperventilation. In view of these indications of impaired pulmonary function, it is not surprising that dyspnea (the subjective equivalent of increased work of breathing) is the most characteristic symptom of mitral stenosis.

MITRAL REGURGITATION

Mitral regurgitation may result from dilatation of the valve annulus, or from organic disease of the valve cusps or their attachments. Characteristically, the mean pressure in the left atrium is increased, and there is a prominent *v* wave occurring during ventricular systole. The diastolic pressure in the left ventricle is usually normal and, even in the absence of associated mitral stenosis, there is a definite pressure gradient across the valve orifice (McDonald et al., 1957; Nixon and Wooler, 1963). Thus, an increased left atrial pressure is not necessarily indicative of either associated mitral stenosis or left ventricular failure. The *v* wave and the increased mean level of pressure are transmitted to the pulmonary capillary bed. When the regurgitation is severe, it may even be identified as a shoulder just after the systolic peak in the pressure pulse from the pulmonary artery (Radner, 1955). As in mitral stenosis, the increased pressure in the pulmonary veins and capillaries results in an increase in pulmonary artery pressure. Pulmonary vascular resistance is usually normal or only slightly increased. In a minority of cases of long standing, a marked increase in pulmonary vascular resistance results in a disproportionate rise in pulmonary artery pressure and eventually in right ventricular failure.

The left atrial *v* wave results from the stream of blood regurgitating from the left ventricle. Many attempts have been made to quantitate the regurgitation by analyzing the *v* wave, recorded from either the pulmonary artery wedge or from the left atrium. The best discrimination between mitral stenosis and regurgitation (Fig. 11-6) was provided by the ratio of the peak pressure of the *v* wave to the mean left atrial pressure, provided the latter exceeded 20 mm. Hg (Marshall et al., 1958). However, factors apart from the quantity of regurgitant flow may influence the pressure pulse.

Braunwald and Awe (1963) described 10 patients, all with severe and long standing mitral regurgitation, who had normal mean pressures and normal *v* waves in their greatly enlarged left atria. They attributed their findings to increased compliance of the left atrium and pulmonary veins. Increased compliance has been confirmed by the construction of pressure-volume curves for atria obtained at autopsy (Fig. 11-7).

At the other end of the spectrum are those patients who have mitral regurgitation of sudden onset due to ruptured chordae tendineae. Unlike

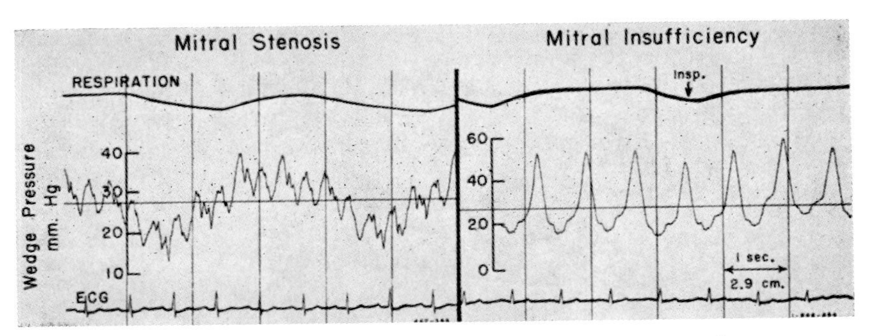

FIGURE 11-6. Comparison of pulmonary artery wedge pressure pulse contours in patients with mitral stenosis (*left*) and mitral regurgitation (*right*). In both, the mean pressure (horizontal line) was 28 mm. Hg, and the pulse rates were similar. In the patient with mitral stenosis, the average peak *v* wave pressure was 34 mm. Hg; in the patient with regurgitation, it was 50 mm. Hg. (From Connolly and Wood, J. Lab. Clin. Med., *49*:526, 1957.)

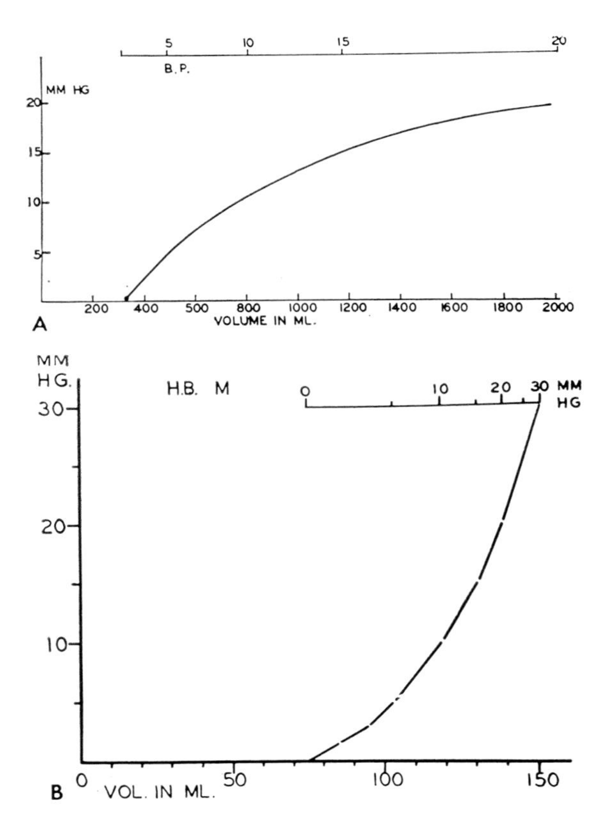

FIGURE 11-7. Pressure-volume curves for the left atrium: *A*, in patients with pure mitral regurgitation; and *B*, in patients with severe mitral stenosis. In the former, the atrium is highly distensible; in the latter, distensibility is limited. (From Liu, Piccirillo and Ellestad, Am. J. Cardiol., *13*:232, 1964.)

patients with chronic rheumatic regurgitation who have had years of adaptation to their lesions, they have striking increases in mean left atrial pressure, usually prominent *v* waves (Fig. 11-8), only a modest enlargement of the left atrium, severe pulmonary arterial hypertension, right ventricular hypertrophy and proliferative changes in the small pulmonary vessels (Roberts et al., 1966). The situation is analogous to that produced in dogs by rupturing a single chorda (Haller and Morrow, 1955); there is an immediate rise in left atrial pressure and rapid development of congestive cardiac failure.

Most patients, however, fall between these two extremes. They have moderate to marked increases in the size of the left atrium and increased left atrial pressures. When the amount of regurgitation is moderate, the left ventricle becomes enlarged, but it is capable of maintaining a normal output into the aorta. With increasing regurgitation, the ventricle has to work harder. Eventually, left ventricular failure occurs, with reduced cardiac output and increased ventricular diastolic pressure. For equivalent grades of clinical disability, cardiac output tends to be lower in mitral regurgitation than in mitral stenosis. The advent of failure is hastened when performance of the ventricle is further compromised by myocardial disease, such as active rheumatic myocarditis, or by increased resistance to outflow caused by such conditions as aortic stenosis and arterial hypertension.

Jose et al. (1964) studied the relationship between systemic arterial pressure and the amount of mitral regurgitation. In patients with combined stenosis and regurgitation or with regurgitation associated with a rigid valve

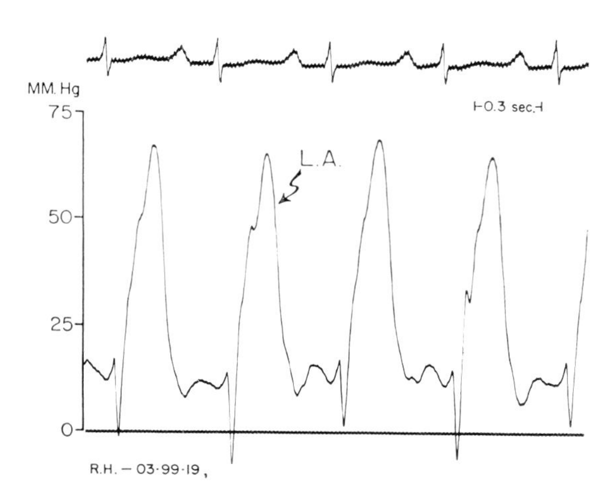

FIGURE 11-8. Left atrial pressure pulse in patient with acute onset of mitral regurgitation secondary to rupture of the chordae tendineae. The mean pressure is increased and the *v* waves are strikingly tall. (From Braunwald and Awe, Circulation, 27:29, 1963.)

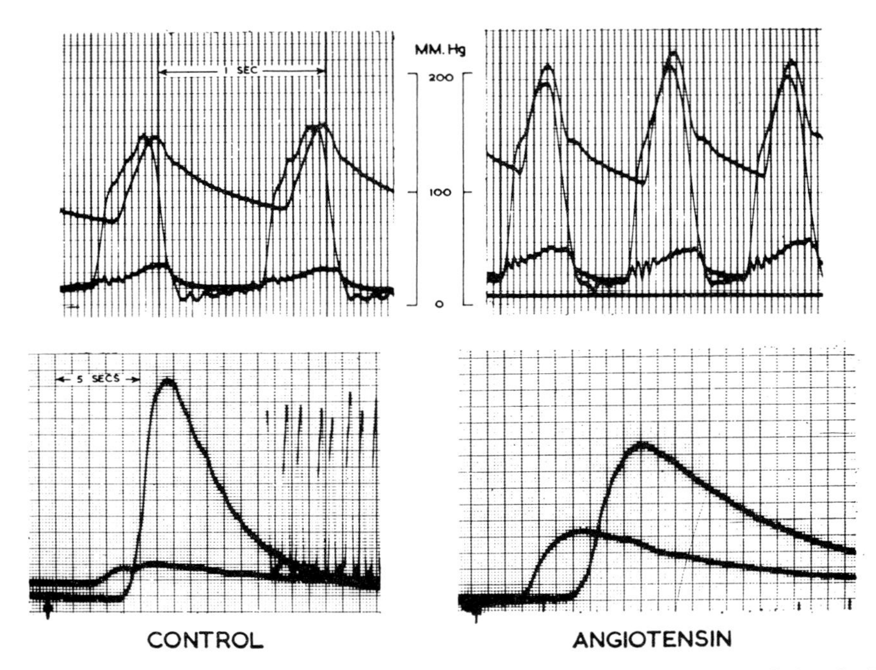

FIGURE 11-9. Pressures recorded from left atrium, left ventricle and brachial artery (*above*), and dilution curves recorded from left atrium and brachial artery following injection of indicator into left ventricle (*below*) in patients with mitral regurgitation. The data on the left were obtained under control conditions; those on the right during intravenous infusion of angiotensin at 1 μg. per minute. The infusion increased the mean arterial pressure from 109 to 137 mm. Hg, reduced the cardiac index from 1.8 to 1.2 liters per M.^{2} per minute, increased the regurgitant fraction from 14 to 47 per cent, and increased the calculated orifice from 0.07 to 0.13 cm.^{2}. (From Jose, Taylor and Bernstein, J. Clin. Invest., *43*:2094, 1964.)

ring, increasing the arterial pressure by vasoconstrictor drugs caused only a moderate increase in the regurgitant fraction, and the calculated valve orifice did not change. In those with severe regurgitation, methoxamine and angiotensin II, which increase the arterial blood pressure but do not stimulate the human myocardium, caused a disproportionate increase in the regurgitant fraction and a substantial increase in the calculated valve orifice (Fig. 11-9).

Angiocardiography is frequently used in the assessment of mitral regurgitation. Injection of contrast medium into the left ventricle is usually accompanied by a brief run of ventricular premature beats. These may be responsible for reflux into the left atrium even in patients whose mitral valves are normally fully competent, but with the return of normal cardiac rhythm, the medium is rapidly washed out. When mitral regurgitation is present, reflux of medium occurs with every heart beat, and it washes out of the left atrium only over periods of several to many beats. The time that contrast medium persists in the left atrium is determined by the severity of the regurgitation, the size of the atrium and the forward output from the left ventricle. When the atrium is small or relatively non-compliant, reflux may also occur into the pulmonary veins. Assessment of the severity of regurgitation is based largely on subjective impressions of the density of contrast and of the duration of its persistence in the left atrium. More precise quantitation by radiological methods awaits the application to man of such techniques as roentgen videodensitometry, the potential of which has already been demonstrated in the dog (Wood et al., 1964).

The application of indicator dilution techniques to the demonstration and quantitation of mitral regurgitation was discussed earlier. They may also be used in the assessment of patients with regurgitation at both mitral and aortic valves (Guidry et al., 1958). Bloomfield et al. (1966) showed that the combined regurgitant fraction across both valves in nine patients equaled the product of the regurgitant fraction at each valve separately. The relationship was then used in eight further patients to predict the degree of regurgitation at one valve when the fraction at the other valve and the combined regurgitant fraction were known. Confirmation of the predicted degrees of regurgitation was provided by cinéangiocardiography and by subsequent inspection at surgery.

AORTIC STENOSIS

The normal aortic valve orifice in adults measures 2.5 to 3.5 $cm.^2$. Although minor degrees of valvular stenosis may be accompanied by loud systolic ejection murmurs, they have little effect upon cardiac function. When aortic stenosis is severe and not associated with regurgitation, the left ventricle becomes hypertrophied. Systolic pressures of up to 250 or even 300 mm. Hg may be generated in order to maintain forward flow. The thick walled chamber is less distensible than the normal, and the diastolic pressure is often increased, even during rest. The left atrium also undergoes hypertrophy; its forceful contraction in late ventricular systole, which results in the appearance of a prominent *a* wave in the ventricular pressure pulse, makes an important contribution to ventricular filling pressure. With the onset of atrial fibrillation, this contribution is lost, and cardiac output may decrease.

The aortic and peripheral arterial pressure pulses show characteristic changes in valvular stenosis. In early systole, the pressure in the aorta rises steeply, but it is soon interrupted by the anacrotic incisura, after which it rises slowly throughout the remainder of systole. With increasingly severe stenosis, the initial rise is less and the anacrotic shoulder lower. No post-dicrotic wave is identifiable (Wright and Wood, 1958). The peak first derivative of the arterial pressure pulse is diminished, its value in the brachial artery (mm. Hg per second) averaging 360 in aortic stenosis,

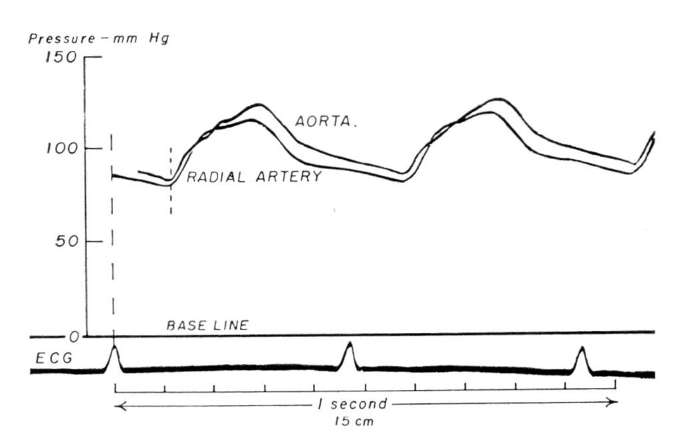

FIGURE 11-10. Simultaneous pressure pulses from aorta and radial artery in a patient with severe valvular aortic stenosis. The contours are similar. (From Marshall, Helmholz and Wood. In: Handbook of Physiology. Section 2: Circulation, Volume 1. Washington, D.C., American Physiological Society, 1962.)

810 in normal subjects and 1740 in patients with pure regurgitation (Mason et al., 1964).

Differences in the contours of central aortic and peripheral arterial pressure pulses are diminished and eventually disappear (Fig. 11-10). The pulse pressure is often diminished, but in older people with coexistent arteriosclerosis and consequently reduced elasticity of the major arteries, it may be normal, even when the aortic stenosis is severe. The changes differ greatly from those characteristic of obstructive cardiomyopathy or idiopathic hypertrophic subaortic stenosis, which is discussed elsewhere.

Usually the stenosis increases slowly, and the cardiac output is maintained until the late stages of the disease. Gorlin et al. (1955) found normal or increased values for cardiac output in 12 of 14 patients with severe acquired valvular stenosis, and Dexter et al. (1958) and Hancock and Fleming (1960) found mean values of 4.2 and 4.0 liters per $M.^2$ per minute, respectively. Of 54 patients with congenital valvular stenosis, the cardiac output was above the upper limits of normal in 28, within normal limits in 20 and reduced in only six (Braunwald et al., 1963). However, the phasic pattern of aortic blood flow is altered. Figure 11-11 shows the blood flow in the ascending aorta in a patient with pure aortic stenosis. The peak is flatter and more delayed than normal; the backflow wave at the time of valve closure is less prominent, reflecting relative immobility of the valve. The flow pulse contour is quite similar to the systolic pressure gradient between left ventricle and aorta (stippled areas).

The response of the cardiac output to muscular exercise, however, is impaired when the stenosis is severe. A large additional increase in left ventricular systolic pressure and work is accompanied by only a slight increase in output. Failure of output to increase adequately, together with the peripheral vasodilatation that occurs with exercise, helps to explain the frequent syncope on effort. Exercise causes an increase in left ventricular diastolic pressure, and if it is maintained, pulmonary edema may result.

Eventually the left ventricle begins to fail, even during rest. As dilatation occurs, contraction of the chamber becomes progressively less efficient. The cardiac output was 1.6 to 2.4 liters per M.[2] per minute in seven patients, studied by Sancetta and Kleinerman (1957), who were in left ventricular failure. Pulsus alternans, which consists of alternating weak and strong ventricular contractions in the presence of a regular rhythm,

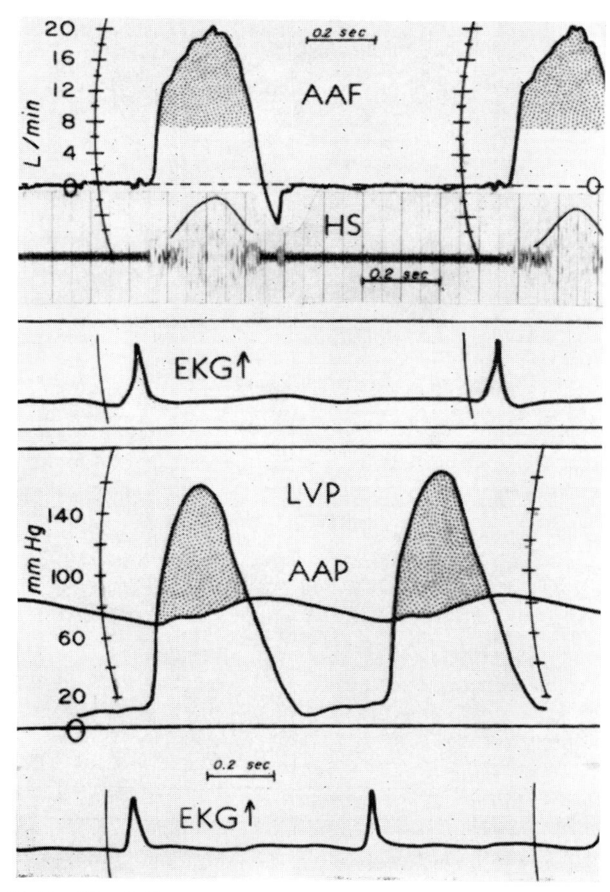

FIGURE 11-11. Blood flow in ascending aorta (electromagnetic flowmeter) and phonocardiogram (*upper panel*); simultaneous pressure from left ventricle and ascending aorta (*lower panel*). The measurements were made during an operation for the repair of aortic stenosis. (From Spencer and Dennison. In: Handbook of Physiology. Section 2: Circulation, Volume 2. Washington, D.C., American Physiological Society, 1963.)

may occur. Cooper et al. (1958) found pulsus alternans in 15 of 28 patients with acquired valvular stenosis who were investigated by leftsided cardiac catheterization. The measurement that provided the best separation between these patients and others with aortic stenosis who were not in failure was the product of the left ventricular systolic pressure and the pulse rate. Since this product correlates closely with the tension-time index, which is thought to reflect myocardial oxygen requirement (Sarnoff et al., 1958), it was suggested that a discrepancy between the oxygen needs of the heart and the supply available may be responsible for the impaired contractility that becomes manifest by alternation in the strength of contraction.

The reserve capacity of the coronary circulation is reduced in aortic stenosis. The coronary arteries arise distal to the obstruction, and therefore the pressure in the branches that traverse the left ventricle is less during systole than the intraventricular pressure. In the normal heart, left ventricular coronary flow is impeded during systole because of mechanical compression of the vessels by the myocardium. In aortic stenosis, the impediment to flow during systole is more complete, and systole is prolonged. Further, the work of the left ventricle, and therefore its requirement of oxygen, is almost twice normal, and when there is a combination of severe stenosis and regurgitation, it may be three to four times normal (Gorlin et al., 1955).

AORTIC REGURGITATION

Minor degrees of regurgitation, caused either by dilatation of the aortic valve ring or by deformity of one or more valve cusps, are associated with the characteristic early diastolic decrescendo murmur but cause neither symptoms nor readily demonstrable hemodynamic changes. More severe regurgitation causes characteristic changes in the arterial pressure pulses and in left ventricular function. Regurgitation and stenosis often coexist in acquired disease of the aortic valve, but for purposes of simplicity, the effects of pure regurgitation will be considered here.

There is a rapid increase of pressure in the aorta with the onset of ventricular systole, and the peak pressure is attained early in systole. The first and second derivatives of the arterial pressure pulses are increased (Mason et al., 1964). The ejection period is shortened, in contrast with its increase in aortic stenosis, and the incisura and dicrotic notch are accentuated. The systolic pressure is increased and the diastolic pressure decreased, with the result that the pulse pressure is wide. These changes are much more pronounced as the pulse wave moves peripherally, and the characteristic collapsing nature of the pulse wave is appreciated by palpation of the radial artery, particularly if the arm is held straight above the head. In peripheral arteries, the dicrotic incisura is diminished or absent. The capillaries may be seen to pulsate. The wide pulse pressure also gives rise to acoustic phenomena, including the pistol shot sound and Duroziez's murmur. Rowe et al. (1965) used cinéarteriography to demonstrate that the characteristic to-and-fro murmur can be explained by the occurrence of a considerable increase in both forward and backward flow in the femoral artery. Although these changes are most pronounced in aortic regurgitation, they also occur in other conditions characterized by a rapid "run off" of blood from the major arteries, such as thyrotoxicosis, systemic arteriovenous aneurysm and beriberi. They are accentuated in the presence of peripheral vasodilatation, for example during fever or following a hot bath.

The peak systolic pressure in the left ventricle often exceeds that in the proximal aorta, even when stenosis of the valve is absent. Presumably, this pressure gradient is due to a relative stenosis, resulting from the high velocity of ejection of blood from the ventricle. Regurgitation of blood during diastole leads to a progressive increase in left ventricular diastolic pressure, and when the regurgitant fraction exceeds 50 per cent and the heart rate is slow, the end-diastolic pressure gradient across the aortic valve may disappear. Because of the wide pressure gradient between the aorta and the left ventricle in early diastole, large volumes of blood may regurgitate into the ventricle within a short period. For example, Gorlin et al. (1955) estimated that there could be a regurgitant flow of 5 liters per minute through an orifice measuring only 0.5 cm.^{2}.

In order to maintain systemic blood flow at an optimal level, the ventricle must eject into the aorta a volume of blood equal to the normal stroke volume plus the volume regurgitated per stroke during diastole. Systemic blood flow is well maintained as long as the progression of the valvular lesion is sufficiently slow to permit the ventricle to adapt to it; eventually, however, as the ventricle becomes greatly enlarged, its efficiency of contraction progressively diminishes, and failure occurs. However, when aortic regurgitation occurs suddenly, as in experimental preparations, there is no time for adaptive phenomena to occur, and systemic blood flow is reduced. Later, the animals become adapted, and forward flow is restored to normal (Schenk et al., 1961).

Studies with electromagnetic flow meters have shown characteristic alterations in the pattern of aortic flow. Acceleration at the onset of systole and deceleration at its end are greater than in normal persons. The valve closure notch is replaced by a sustained negative deflection indicative of backflow. The magnitude of the backflow diminishes in the latter part of diastole (Spencer and Dennison, 1963). Morrow et al. (1965) measured total forward aortic flow and regurgitant flow in eight patients immediately before and after replacement of the aortic valve with a Starr-Ewards prosthesis (Fig. 11-12). Preoperatively, regurgitant flow was 63 to 75 per cent of total stroke volume. Immediately after valve replacement, no regurgitation was demonstrable; net forward flow increased by an average of 60 per cent, mean aortic blood pressure increased by an average of 29 per

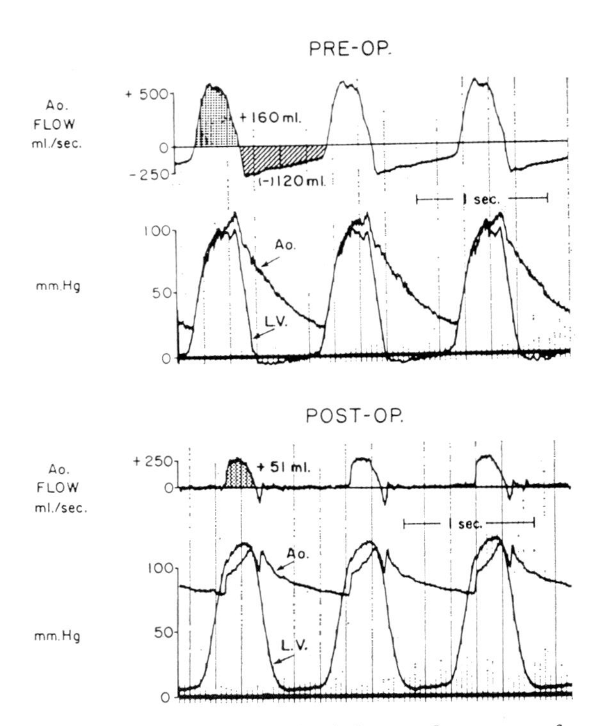

FIGURE 11-12. Instantaneous aortic blood flow and pressures from left ventricle and central aorta before and after aortic valve replacement with a Starr-Edwards prosthesis. Before replacement, 73 per cent of the total left ventricular stroke volume regurgitated during the following diastole; the severity of the regurgitation is also evident from the equality of ventricular and aortic pressures during late diastole. After replacement, there was no regurgitation; the high frequency negative deflection in the flow record at the end of the ejection period was characteristic of the closure of a competent aortic valve. (From Morrow, Brawley and Braunwald, Circulation, *31* [Suppl. 1]:80, 1965.)

cent, and total left ventricular work fell to or remained at normal levels. Kinetic work fell by an average of 73 per cent.

Theoretically, the regurgitant fraction might be diminished during tachycardia, which leads to disproportionate shortening of the diastolic interval. However, since most of the regurgitation occurs in early diastole, the total quantity regurgitated per minute might well be increased. Further, tachycardia increases the work of the left ventricle.

The left ventricle is structurally more suited for the performance of pressure work than for volume work (Rushmer, 1961), since it has a small surface area per unit volume. With the progressive increase in stroke volume, it undergoes dilatation; as it does so, the surface area increases considerably, and less shortening of individual myocardial fibers is required to eject any given volume of blood. At the same time, much more tension must be developed by the myocardial fibers to raise the intraventricular systolic pressure to any given level. The need for increased tension is met by the development of myocardial hypertrophy. Combined dilatation and hypertrophy is thus characteristic of aortic regurgitation. When the left ventricle begins to fail, the the mitral valve ring dilates, mitral regurgitation occurs, and there is a rapid increase in pressure in the left atrium and pulmonary veins, leading to pulmonary congestion and edema. After this has happened, there is little chance of the ventricle recovering, and the subsequent course is one of progressive deterioration.

The increase in the left ventricular end-diastolic volume and in stroke volume has been confirmed by the use of several techniques. Bristow et al. (1964), using thermodilution curves inscribed from the proximal aorta following injection of cold saline into the left ventricle, found a mean value for end-diastolic volume of 218 ml. per M^2. in seven patients with predominant aortic regurgitation. Corresponding values for patients with pure or predominant aortic stenosis and with mitral stenosis were 140 and 116 ml. per M^2., respectively. Sandler et al. (1963) calculated the volume of the left ventricular cavity at end-systole and end-diastole from angiocardiograms, and by subtraction derived values for total stroke volume. This was as high as four times the effective (forward) stroke volume, derived by the Fick method.

Muscular exercise may result in left ventricular decompensation. Gorlin et al. (1955) studied three patients whose pulmonary capillary pressures were within normal limits during rest. With moderate exercise resulting in increases of only 2.0, 0.9 and 1.2 liters per M^2. per minute in systemic blood flow, the pressures increased from 8 to 27, from 12 to 25 and from 8 to 32 mm. Hg, respectively. In patients who already had increased pulmonary vascular pressures at rest, Sancetta and Kleinerman (1957) observed a further increase in left ventricular filling pressure during mild exercise that scarcely altered systemic flow. Regan et al. (1959) increased peripheral resistance by infusing norepinephrine in eight patients with fairly severe regurgitation. The pulmonary artery wedge pressure increased from 8 to 29 mm. Hg.

TRICUSPID VALVE DISEASE

TRICUSPID STENOSIS. Acquired tricuspid stenosis is uncommon, and it almost invariably coexists with rheumatic lesions of other valves, particularly the mitral valve. Kitchin and Turner (1964) found hemodynamically significant degrees of tricuspid stenosis in 17 of 550 consecutive patients undergoing operation for the relief of mitral stenosis. This was similar to the incidence of 3.3 per cent found clinically by Wood (1954) in mitral

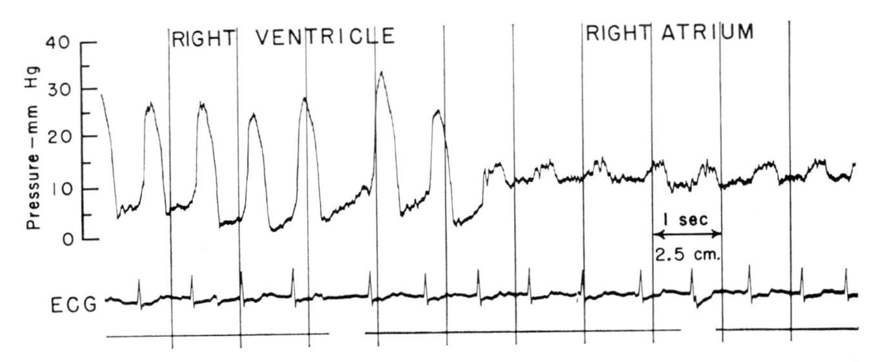

FIGURE 11-13. Pressure pulses during withdrawal of the catheter tip from right ventricle to right atrium in patient with tricuspid stenosis and atrial fibrillation. Even during the longer cardiac cycles, there is an end-diastolic pressure gradient across the valve. The positive pressure waves during systole in the right atrium indicate that tricuspid regurgitation was also present. (From Marshall, Helmholz and Wood. In: Handbook of Physiology. Section 2: Circulation, Volume 1. Washington, D.C., American Physiological Society, 1962.)

stenosis. Serious obstruction is probably present only when the valve orifice is less than 1.5 cm.^{2}; when it exceeds 5 cm.^{2}, the lesion cannot be detected clinically (White, 1944).

The obstruction results in a mean diastolic pressure gradient of 5 mm. Hg or more across the valve (Fig. 11-13). The gradient is best demonstrated by the use of a double lumen catheter. Deep inspiration leads to an increase in the pressure gradient, as does exercise (Yu et al., 1956). The right atrium is hypertrophied and generally dilated, although the correlation between its size and the mean atrial pressure is not close. The *a* wave is prominent in the pressure pulses in right atrium and jugular veins, and the pressure gradient across the valve is maximal at the time of the *a* wave, just before the onset of ventricular systole. A prominent *a* wave in the jugular venous pulse, however, is by no means specific for tricuspid stenosis; equally prominent *a* waves may be found in other situations that lead to right atrial hypertrophy, such as pulmonary valve stenosis, idiopathic pulmonary hypertension and mitral stenosis with severe pulmonary hypertension. The liver may be felt to pulsate coincidentally with the *a* wave. The *y* descent is slow. When the cardiac rhythm is atrial fibrillation or flutter, the *a* wave disappears, there is a dominant systolic or *v* wave even in the absence of gross regurgitation (Reale et al., 1956), and the maximal pressure gradient is present in early diastole. The clinical diagnosis may be difficult, owing to loss of the *a* wave and of the tricuspid presystolic murmur (Sanders et al., 1966). The mean gradient throughout the diastolic filling period, obtained by planimetry, is preferable to other measurements, such as those in early diastole (McCord et al., 1954), at end-diastole (Ferrer et al., 1953) or at the instant at which the gradient is maximal (Gibson and Wood, 1955), since it is less influenced by artifacts or by individual variations in pulse wave contours. However, it has been emphasized that the pressure gradient across the tricuspid valve may be just as great in patients with severe tricuspid regurgitation as it is in those with severe stenosis (Kitchin and Turner, 1964).

In isolated tricuspid stenosis, the pressures in the right ventricle and pulmonary artery are normal. When disease of the mitral valve is present, these pressures are increased accordingly. The cardiac output tends to be less when both tricuspid and mitral stenosis are present than when mitral stenosis of comparable severity exists alone. In addition, the presence of left-sided valvular lesions may overshadow the evidence for tricuspid stenosis, the hemodynamic significance of which may become apparent only after technically successful operations on the mitral (Pantridge and Marshall, 1957) or aortic (Watson and Lowe, 1962) valves have failed to confer the anticipated benefit.

TRICUSPID REGURGITATION. Tricuspid regurgitation, resulting from dilatation of the valve ring, occurs very commonly in congestive heart failure. Several factors are responsible, including: (1) the relative inadequacy of valve tissue, to which Mackenzie (1908) alluded; (2) weakness of the right ventricular muscle, efficient contraction of which is essential for complete closure of the valve; (3) dilatation of the right ventricle with consequent retraction of the chordae tendineae and papillary muscles, and hence with impaired mobility of the valve cusps; and (4) atrial fibrillation, which is often present and which intensifies the regurgitation (Skinner et al., 1964).

McMichael and Shillingford (1957) found a close relationship between the mean systemic venous pressure and the development of functional tricuspid regurgitation in a series of 50 patients with heart failure from various causes. As the venous pressure increased, the *x* descent became impaired and then replaced by a positive systolic pulsation (Fig. 11-14), since the normal fall in pressure in the right atrium during ventricular systole was opposed by the regurgitant stream. The "critical level of pressure was about 8 mm. Hg higher than normal mean pressure" (Lottenbach and Shillingford, 1957). In some patients with severe degrees of regurgitation, the regurgitant flow (assessed by using a double lumen catheter as a Pitot flow meter) was as much as 6 or 7 liters per minute, whereas the net forward flow was only 2 to 3 liters per minute (McMichael and Shillingford, 1957). These large volumes of reflux are accompanied by systolic expansion of the right atrium, the great veins and the liver.

The height of the positive systolic wave or *v* wave in the right atrium does not correlate closely with the severity of the regurgitation. As in the case of the left atrium in mitral stenosis, the compliance of the chamber is a determining factor. Thus, when the right atrium is extremely large, the regurgitant wave will be rapidly dissipated. In contrast, the most striking

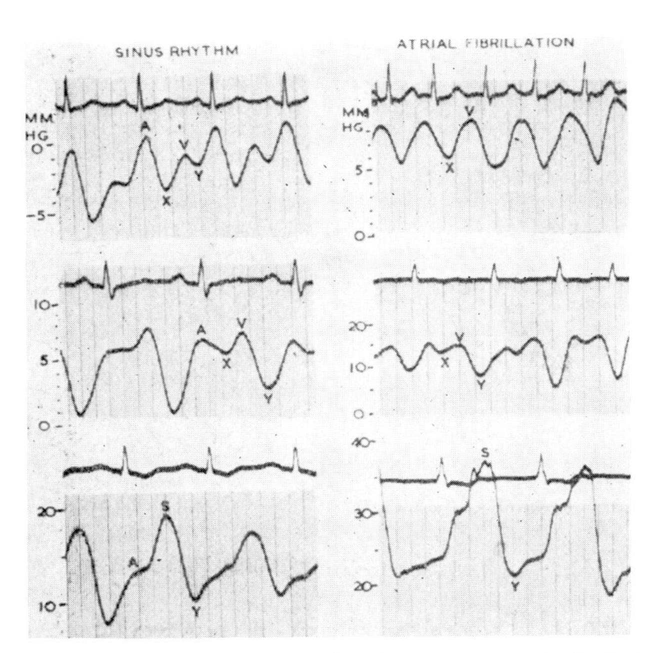

FIGURE 11-14. Right atrial pressure pulses from patients who had sinus rhythm (*left*) and atrial fibrillation (*right*). *Above:* normal x descent. *Middle:* impaired x descent. *Below:* x descent replaced by positive systolic wave s. (From McMichael and Shillingford, Brit. Med. J., *i*:537, 1957.)

v waves are encountered in patients in whom the regurgitation has developed rapidly due, for example, to ruptured chordae tendineae or to bacterial endocarditis, and in whom the right atrium has had insufficient time to enlarge greatly. Further, in patients with rightsided heart failure, atrial fibrillation and venous stasis, *v* waves may be found even in the absence of tricuspid regurgitation; thus, even with careful analysis of pressure records and inspection of the jugular venous pulse, it may be difficult to know whether regurgitation exists (Wood, 1956). The *y* descent following opening of the tricuspid valve is brisk, provided that tricuspid stenosis does not coexist.

The severity of tricuspid regurgitation may vary from moment to moment or even from beat to beat depending upon the degree of filling of the right ventricle. It is intensified by a deep inspiration (McCord and Blount, 1952). It is diminished by prolonged rest and increased by muscular exercise, which also increases the mean atrial pressure (Yu et al., 1958). Indeed, although exercise increases the total forward flow through the tricuspid valve during diastole, the increase in regurgitant flow may be so marked that the net forward flow is unchanged or even diminished (Korner and Shillingford, 1957). In patients with atrial fibrillation, the longer cardiac cycles are associated with more complete filling of the right ventricle and hence with an increased degree of regurgitation.

As previously stated, the indicator dilution technique has been applied to the detection and assessment of tricuspid regurgitation (Bajec et al., 1958; Collins et al., 1959). Mainly because of poor mixing in the right sided heart chambers, especially when they are enlarged, the accuracy of quantitative data is in some doubt.

PULMONARY VALVE DISEASE

PULMONARY STENOSIS. The systolic pressure gradient across the pulmonary valve does not exceed 5 to 10 mm. Hg in normal resting subjects. In patients with excessive levels of pulmonary blood flow resulting from large left-to-right shunts such as uncomplicated atrial septal defect, the gradient is often greater but rarely exceeds 20 mm. Hg (Kjellberg et al., 1958). Rudolph et al. (1954) however, reported gradients as high as 50 mm. Hg in the presence of a normal pulmonary valve. These gradients generally are attributed to a relative stenosis and disappear after correction of the lesion responsible for the left-to-right shunt (Blount et al., 1954). However, gradients may also be present across the pulmonary valve in patients with patent ductus arteriosus, in whom the flow through the valve is normal.

In congenital pulmonary valvular stenosis, systolic pressure gradients across the valve may be as great as 200 mm. Hg. When an extremely high pressure is recorded in the right ventricle, it is advisable to avoid passing the catheter through the pulmonary valve; otherwise, the critically small orifice may be further compromised, resulting in acute right ventricular failure or even death. The pressure pulse in the pulmonary artery is damped and distorted; the anacrotic limb is slow and often obscured by coarse vibrations, and the mean pressure is usually reduced. As the catheter is withdrawn toward the ventricle, the pressure pulse may be distorted by large negative deflections (Sobin et al., 1954). These are synchronous with the maximal intensity of the systolic murmur and result from a Venturi effect induced by the jet of blood entering the dilated pulmonary artery (Watson and Lowe, 1962). The transition to the high systolic pressure in the ventricle is abrupt as the catheter is pulled back through the valve (Fig. 11-15). The right ventricular pressure pulse has distinctive features (Harris, 1955); commonly, the ejection plateau is absent, and there is a pointed peak. In mild valvular stenosis, the right atrial pressure is normal, but with more severe obstruction, there is a prominent *a* wave, reflecting right atrial hypertrophy.

Despite the obstruction at the valve, the cardiac output is usually maintained at a normal level. Eventually, the right ventricle may fail. This is indicated by increases in right ventricular end-diastolic pressure and in

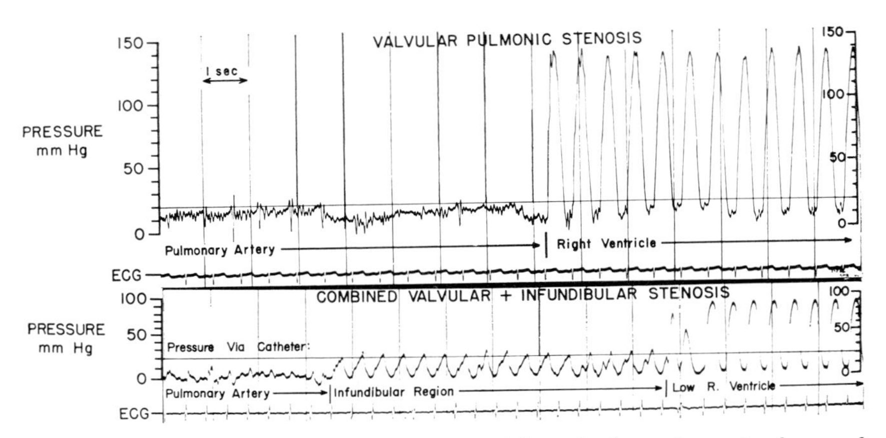

FIGURE 11-15. Pressures recorded during withdrawal of a catheter tip from pulmonary artery to low right ventricle in patients with (*above*) valvular and (*below*) valvular and infundibular pulmonary stenosis. (From Marshall, Helmholz and Wood. In: Handbook of Physiology. Section 2: Circulation, Volume 1. Washington, D.C., American Physiological Society, 1962.)

right atrial pressure. At this stage, there may be cyanosis due to increased extraction of blood from the capillaries in the skin; arterial blood is still normally saturated. Inability of the right ventricle to meet increased demands may lead to increased cyanosis, dyspnea, fatigue and syncope on exertion. If the foramen ovale is patent, right-to-left shunting of blood occurs, leading to desaturation of arterial blood and thus to further cyanosis. Further progression of right ventricular failure leads to tricuspid regurgitation.

Pulmonary stenosis has been simulated in animal experiments by constricting the pulmonary artery. In adult dogs, the right ventricle compensates fully for pressure gradients up to about 60 mm. Hg; greater gradients lead to progressive right ventricular failure (Taquini et al., 1960). Amorim et al. (1961) also found that the canine right ventricle failed when its systolic pressure was acutely increased to more than 60 mm. Hg by inflating a balloon in the pulmonary artery. Failure was attributed to overdistention of the right ventricle, and possibly to the acutely increased right atrial pressure impeding coronary venous drainage. Thus, although the right ventricle adapts well to long standing obstruction of its outflow, it has only a limited capacity to adapt to acute increases in outflow resistance.

Ikkos et al. (1966) assessed the effects of exercise on cardiac output and right ventricular pressure in 46 patients with pulmonary stenosis and intact ventricular septum (Fig. 11-16). The rate of increase of right ventricular systolic pressure was greater than in normal subjects, and it was particularly great in the patients with the most severe degrees of stenosis (pulmonary valve area less than 0.33 cm.^{2} per M.^{2}). Relative prolongation

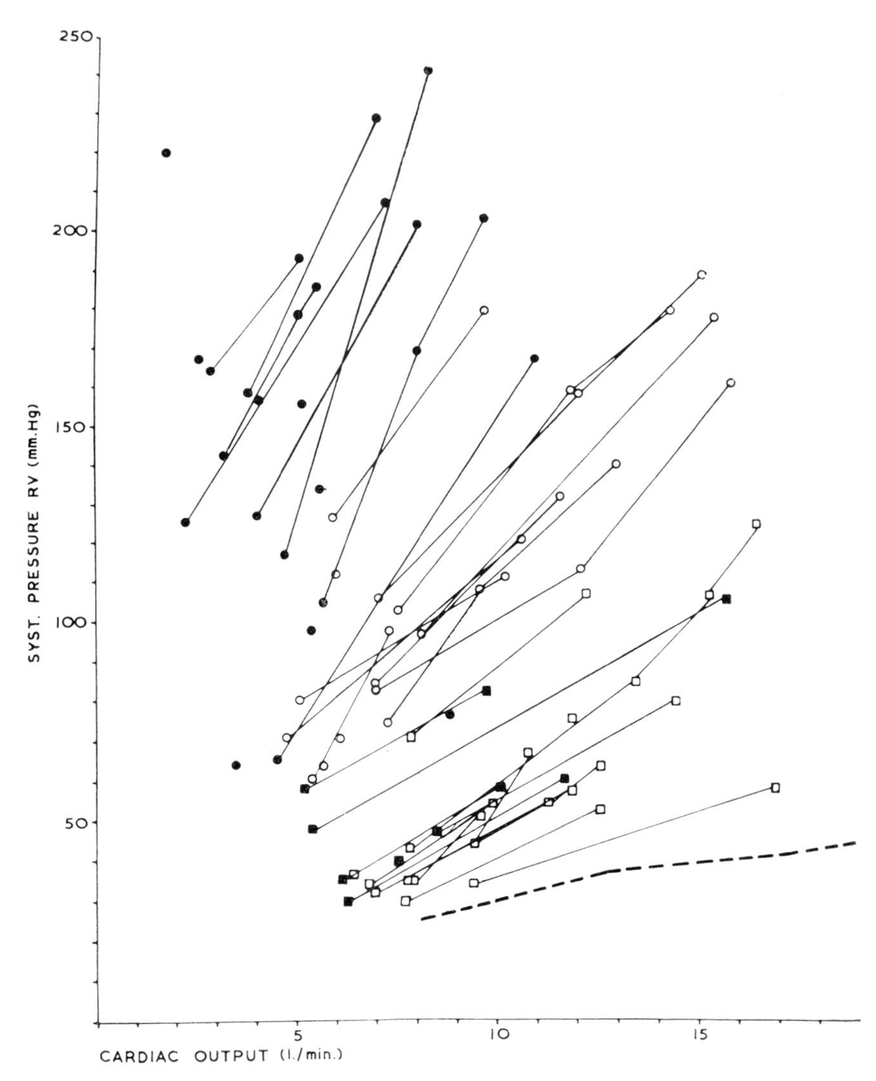

FIGURE 11-16. Systolic pressure in the right ventricle (ordinate) related to cardiac output (abscissa) at rest and during exercise in patients with isolated pulmonary valvular stenosis. The symbols indicate different degrees of stenosis, based on calculations using the Gorlin formula: ● < ·33, ○ < ·66, ■ < 1.0, □ > 1.0 cm.^{2} per M.^{2} body surface area. The interrupted line shows mean values from 33 healthy young subjects. (From Ikkos, Jonsson and Linderholm, Brit. Heart J., 28:316, 1966.)

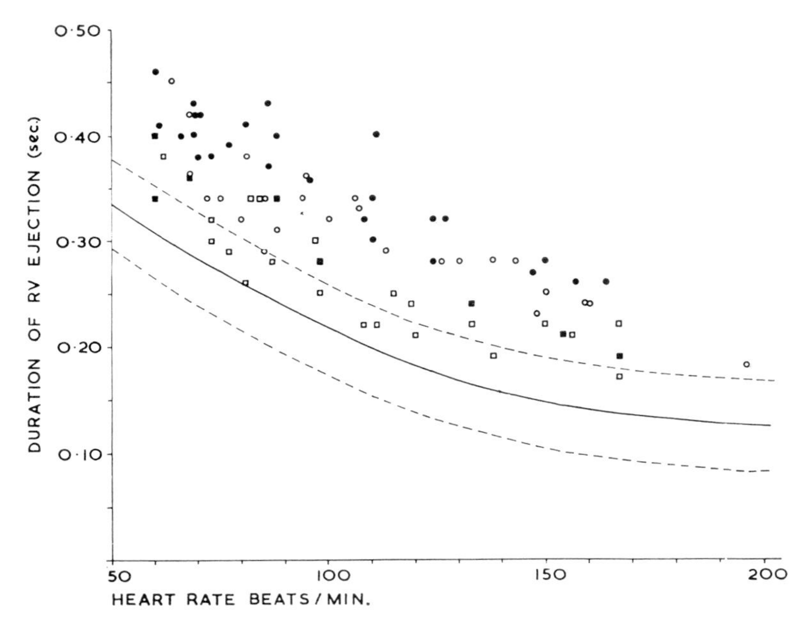

FIGURE 11-17. Duration of right ventricular ejection in relation to heart rate in patients with pulmonary stenosis. Symbols as in Figure 11-16. The continuous line shows the relationship between these parameters in 24 healthy men; the interrupted lines indicate ± 2 standard error of the mean. (From Ikkos, Jonsson and Linderholm, Brit. Heart J., 28:316, 1966.)

of systole was observed in most patients and helped to compensate for the severe impediment to ventricular ejection (Fig. 11-17). Increase in the filling pressure of the right ventricle was regarded as an additional compensatory mechanism.

Other lesions causing obstruction to the egress of blood from the right ventricle have similar hemodynamic effects. Infundibular stenosis, resulting from muscular hypertrophy, may be isolated or associated with valvular stenosis. When it is isolated, the ventricular wall is of normal thickness distal to the obstruction; proximally, it is hypertrophied in proportion to the severity of the obstruction. When valvular and infundibular obstruction coexist, two systolic pressure gradients are demonstrable on withdrawing the catheter from the pulmonary artery to the inflow region of the right ventricle. The pressure pulse in the ventricle proximal to the obstruction may differ from that seen in isolated valvular stenosis (Harris, 1955). The systolic upstroke is brisk and is followed by a more gradual slope to a peak towards the end of systole and then by an abrupt descent to the baseline.

Obstruction may also be due to anomalous muscle bundles within the right ventricle. These are sometimes accompanied by ventricular septal

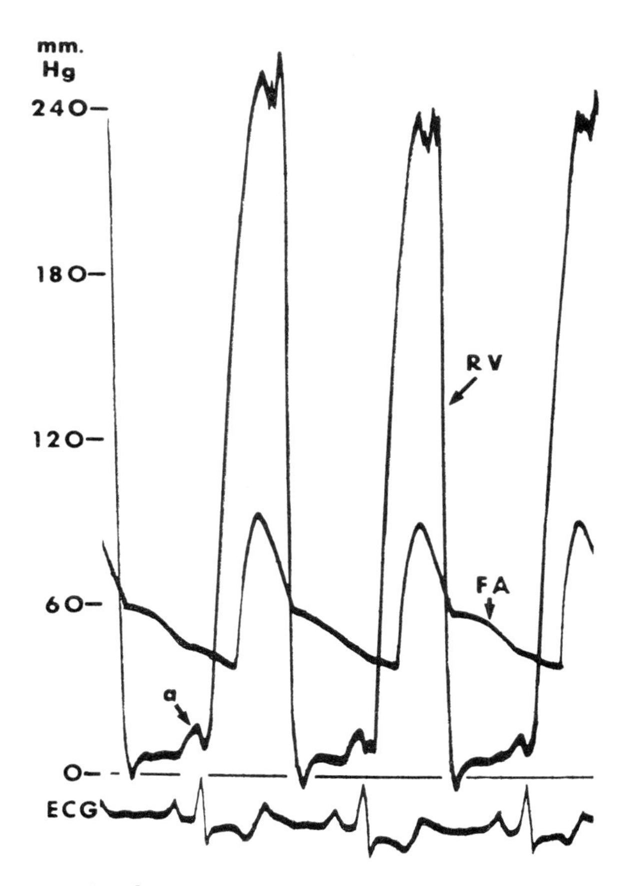

FIGURE 11-18. Simultaneous pressures from right ventricle (inflow tract) and femoral artery in patient with right ventricular obstruction from an anomalous muscle bundle. (From Lucas and Marshall. In: Intravascular Catheterization. Ed. Zimmerman. Second edition. Springfield, Thomas, 1966.)

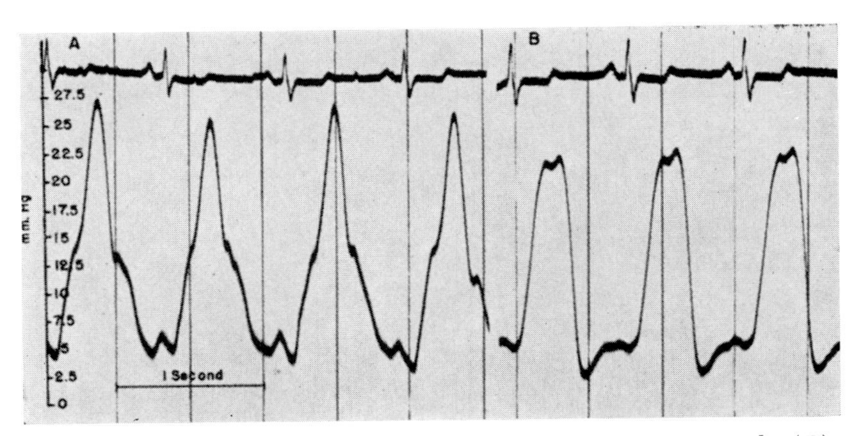

FIGURE 11-19. Pressures in pulmonary artery (*A*) and right ventricle (*B*) in patient with severe congenital pulmonary valvular regurgitation. Note the similarity of diastolic pressures. (From Kaplan. In: Intravascular Catheterization. Ed. Zimmerman. Second edition. Springfield, Thomas, 1966.)

defect (Lucas et al., 1962), but they may be present as the sole lesion or in association with additional obstruction at the pulmonary valve (Warden et al., 1966). The right ventricular systolic pressure proximal to the bundles may be as high as 240 mm. Hg (Fig. 11-18).

PULMONARY REGURGITATION. Mild regurgitation occasionally develops in patients with severe pulmonary hypertension, and is attributed to stretching of the valve ring. It may also follow operations on the pulmonary valve. More severe regurgitation, occurring as an isolated lesion, is rather uncommon and is generally well tolerated (Marshall and Jones, 1964). The diastolic pressures in the pulmonary artery and the right ventricle are almost identical (Fig. 11-19). In some animal preparations, however, gradual hypertrophy and dilatation of the right ventricle have occurred (Kay and Thomas, 1954; Fowler and Duchesne, 1958).

REFERENCES

Amorim, D. de S., Marshall, H. W., Donald, D. E., and Wood, E. H.: Effect of unilateral pulmonary artery obstruction on circulatory dynamics in dogs with chronic atrial septal defects. Circ. Research, *9*:1316, 1961.

Armelin, E., Donald, D. E., and Wood, E. H.: Comparison of dilution technics using aortic injection with upstream sampling for assessment of aortic regurgitation. Circ. Research, *15*:287, 1964.

Armelin, E., Michaels, L., Marshall, H. W., Donald, D. E., Cheesman, R. J., and Wood, E. H.: Detection and measurement of experimentally produced aortic regurgitation by means of indicator dilution curves recorded from the left ventricle. Circ. Research, *12*:269, 1963.

Arnott, W. M.: Physiologic problems in mitral stenosis. Editorial. Am. Heart J., *68*: 145, 1964.

Bajec, D. F., Birkhead, N. C., Carter, S. A., and Wood, E. H.: Localization and esti-

mation of severity of regurgitant flow at the pulmonary and tricuspid valves. Proc. Staff Meet. Mayo Clin., *33*:569, 1958.
Balchum, O. J., Gensini, G., and Blount, S. G., Jr.: The effect of hexamethonium upon the pulmonary vascular resistance in mitral stenosis. J. Lab. Clin. Med., *50*:186, 1957.
Bates, D. V., Varvis, C. J., Donevan, R. E., and Christie, R. V.: Variations in the pulmonary capillary blood volume and membrane diffusion component in health and disease. J. Clin. Invest., *39*:1401, 1960.
Becker, D. L., Burchell, H. B., and Edwards, J. E.: Pathology of the pulmonary vascular tree. II. The occurrence in mitral insufficiency of occlusive pulmonary vascular lesions. Circulation, *3*:230, 1951.
Bishop, J. M., Harris, P., Bateman, M., and Raine, J. M.: Respiratory gas exchange in mitral stenosis at three levels of inspired oxygen before and after the infusion of acetylcholine. Clin. Sci., *22*:53, 1962.
Bishop, J. M., Wade, O. L., and Donald, K. W.: Changes in jugular and renal arteriovenous oxygen content difference during exercise in heart disease. Clin. Sci., *17*:611, 1958.
Blain, J. M., Schafer, H. Siegel, A. L., and Bing, R. J.: Studies on myocardial metabolism. Myocardial metabolism in congestive failure. Am. J. Med., *20*:820, 1956.
Bloomfield, D. A., Battersby, E. J., and Sinclair-Smith, B. C.: Use of indicator dilution technique in measuring combined aortic and mitral insufficiency. Circ. Research, *18*:97, 1966.
Blount, S. G., Swan, H., Gensini, G., and McCord, M. C.: Atrial septal defect. Clinical and physiologic response to complete closure in five patients. Circulation, *9*:801, 1954.
Braunwald, E., and Awe, W. C.: The syndrome of severe mitral regurgitation with normal left atrial pressure. Circulation, *27*:29, 1963.
Braunwald, E., Goldblatt, A., Aygen, M. M., Rockoff, S. D., and Morrow, A. G.: Congenital aortic stenosis. 1. Clinical and hemodynamic findings in 100 patients. Circulation, *27*:426, 1963.
Braunwald, E., and Morrow, A. G.: A method for the detection and estimation of aortic regurgitation flow in man. Circulation, *17*:505, 1958.
Bristow, J. D., Crislip, R. L., Farrehi, C., Harris, W. E., Lewis, R. P., Sutherland, D. W., and Griswold, H. E.: Left ventricular volume measurements in man by thermodilution. J. Clin. Invest., *43*:1015, 1964.
Carleton, R. A., Levinson, G. E., and Abelmann, W. H.: Assessment of mitral regurgitation by indicator dilution: observations on the principle of Korner and Shillingford. Am. Heart J., *58*:663, 1959.
Collins, N. P., Braunwald, E., and Morrow, A. G.: Detection of pulmonic and tricuspid valvular regurgitation by means of indicator solutions. Circulation, *20*:561, 1959.
Conn, H. L., Jr.: Use of indicator-dilution curves in the evaluation of acquired heart disease. Prog. Cardiovasc. Dis., *2*:166, 1959.
Connolly, D. C., Kirklin, J. W., and Wood, E. H.: The relationship between pulmonary artery wedge pressure and left atrial pressure in man. Circ. Research, *2*:434, 1954.
Connolly, D. C., and Wood, E. H.: Hemodynamic data during rest and exercise in patients with mitral valve disease in relation to the differentiation of stenosis and insufficiency from the pulmonary artery wedge pressure pulse. J. Lab. Clin. Med., *49*:526, 1957.
Cooper, T., Braunwald, E., and Morrow, A. G.: Pulsus alternans in aortic stenosis. Circulation, *18*:64, 1958.
Daugherty, R. L.: Hydraulics. New York, McGraw-Hill, 1937.
Dexter, L., Harken, D. E., Cobb, L. A., Novack, P., Schlant, R. C., Phinney, A. O., and Haynes, F. W.: Aortic stenosis. A.M.A. Arch. Int. Med., *101*:254, 1958.
Dollery, C. T., and Hugh-Jones, P.: Distribution of gas and blood in the lungs in disease. Brit. Med. Bull., *19*:59, 1963.
Dollery, C. T., and West, J. B.: Regional uptake of radioactive oxygen, carbon monox-

ide and carbon dioxide in the lungs of patients with mitral stenosis. Circ. Research, *8*:765, 1960.

Donald, K. W.: Pulmonary vascular resistance in mitral valvular disease. In: Pulmonary Circulation. Ed. Adams and Veith. New York, Grune & Stratton, 1959.

Donald, K. W., Bishop, J. M., and Wade, O. L.: Studies of minute to minute changes of arteriovenous oxygen content difference, oxygen uptake and cardiac output and rate of achievement of steady state during exercise in rheumatic heart disease. J. Clin. Invest., *33*:1146, 1954.

Donald, K. W., Bishop, J. M., and Wade, O. L.: Changes in the oxygen content of axillary venous blood during leg exercise in patients with rheumatic heart disease. Clin. Sci., *14*:531, 1955.

Donald, K. W., Bishop, J. M., Wade, O. L., and Wormald, P. N.: Cardiorespiratory function two years after mitral valvotomy. Clin. Sci., *16*:325, 1957.

Doyle, A. E., Goodwin, J. F., Harrison, C. V., and Steiner, R. E.: Pulmonary vascular patterns in pulmonary hypertension. Brit. Heart J., *19*:353, 1957.

Dutrey, D. E., and Drake, E. H.: Pre-operative diagnosis of acquired valvular disease. Am. J. Cardiol., *8*:319, 1961.

Edwards, J. E., Tomkins, R. G., Hood, R. T., Kirklin, J. W., and Burchell, H. B.: Biopsy of the lung and cardiac catheterization studies in patients treated surgically for mitral stenosis. J. Lab. Clin. Med., *40*:795, 1952.

Eliasch, H.: Pulmonary circulation at rest and on effort in mitral stenosis. Scand. J. Clin. Lab. Invest., *4* (Suppl. 4): 1, 1952.

Ellison, R. G., Brown, W. J., Jr., Hague, E. E., and Hamilton, W. F.: Physiologic observations in experimental pulmonary insufficiency. J. Thorac. Surg., *30*:633, 1955.

Epps, R. G., and Adler, R. H.: Left atrial and pulmonary capillary venous pressures in mitral stenosis. Brit. Heart J., *15*:298, 1953.

Ferencz, C., and Dammann, J. F., Jr.: Significance of the pulmonary vascular bed in congenital heart disease. V. Lesions of the left side of the heart causing obstruction of the pulmonary venous return. Circulation, *16*:1046, 1957.

Ferguson, D. J., and Varco, R. L.: The relation of blood pressure and flow to the development and regression of experimentally induced pulmonary arteriosclerosis. Circ. Research, *3*:152, 1955.

Ferrer, M. I., Harvey, R. M., Cathcart, R. T., Cournand, A., and Richards, D. W.: Hemodynamic studies in rheumatic heart disease. Circulation, *6*:688, 1952.

Ferrer, M. I., Harvey, R. M., Kuschner, M., Richards, D. W., and Cournand, A.: Hemodynamic studies in tricuspid stenosis of rheumatic origin. Circ. Research, *1*:49, 1953.

Ferri, F., Rovati, V., Panesi, M., Romanelli, R., and Righim, E.: Su la natura riflessa della ipertensione arteriosa del piccolo circolo da ostacolato deflusso delle vene polmonari. Rass. Fisiopat. Clin. Ter., *28*:608, 1956.

Fleming, H. A., and Wood, P.: The myocardial factor in mitral valve disease. Brit. Heart J., *21*:117, 1959.

Fowler, N. O., and Duchesne, E. R.: Effect of experimental pulmonary valvular insufficiency on the circulation. J. Thorac. Surg., *35*:643, 1958.

Friedman, W. F., and Braunwald, E.: The accurate estimation of left atrial pressure without cardiac catheterization in patients with mitral valve disease. Ann. Int. Med., *64*:1151, 1966 (Abstract).

Gibson, R., and Wood, P.: The diagnosis of tricuspid stenosis. Brit. Heart J., *17*:552, 1955.

Goodale, F., Sanchez, G., Friedlich, A. C., Scannel, J. G., and Myers, G. S.: Correlation of pulmonary arteriolar resistances with pulmonary vascular changes in patients with mitral stenosis before and after valvulotomy. New Eng. J. Med., *252*:979, 1955.

Gorelick, M. M., Lenkei, S. C. M., Heimbecker, R. O., and Gunton, R. W.: Estimation of mitral regurgitation by injection of dye into left ventricle with simultaneous left atrial sampling: a clinical study of 60 confirmed cases. Am. J. Cardiol., *10*:62, 1962.

Gorlin, R., and Gorlin, S. G.: Hydraulic formula for calculation of the area of the stenotic mitral valve, other cardiac valves and central circulatory shunts. Am. Heart J., *41*:1, 1951.
Gorlin, R., Haynes, F. W., Goodale, W. T., Sawyer, C. J., Dow, J. W., and Dexter, L.: Studies of the circulatory dynamics in mitral stenosis. Altered dynamics at rest. Am. Heart J., *41*:30, 1951.
Gorlin, R., Lewis, B. M., Haynes, F. W., and Dexter, L.: Studies of the circulatory dynamics at rest in mitral valvular regurgitation with and without stenosis. Am. Heart J., *43*:357, 1952.
Gorlin, R., McMillan, I. K. R., Medd, W. E., Matthews, M. B., and Daley, R.: Dynamics of the circulation in aortic valvular disease. Am. J. Med., *18*:855, 1955.
Goyette, E. M., Farinacci, C. J., Forsee, J. H., and Blake, H. A.: Clinicopathologic correlation of lung biopsies in mitral stenosis. Am. Heart J., *47*:645, 1954.
Guidry, L. D., Wood, E. H., and Burchell, H. B.: Application of a method for detecting and estimating severity of aortic regurgitation alone or in association with mitral regurgitation. Proc. Staff Meet. Mayo Clin., *33*:596, 1958.
Haller, J. A., Jr., and Morrow, A. G.: Experimental mitral insufficiency. Surgery, *38*:518, 1955.
Hamer, J.: The pulmonary capillary bed in mitral valve disease. Brit. Heart J., *27*:319, 1965.
Hancock, E. W., and Fleming, P. R.: Aortic stenosis. Quart. J. Med., *29*:209, 1960.
Harris, P.: Some variations in the shape of the pressure curve in the human right ventricle. Brit. Heart J., *17*:173, 1955.
Harrison, C. V.: The pathology of the pulmonary vessels in pulmonary hypertension. Brit. J. Radiol. (N.S.), *31*:217, 1958.
Harvey, R. M., Ferrer, M. I., Samet, P., Bader, R. A., Bader, M. E., Cournand, A., and Richards, D. W.: Mechanical and myocardial factors in rheumatic heart disease with mitral stenosis. Circulation, *11*:531, 1955.
Heath, D., and Best, P. V.: The tunica media of the arteries of the lung in pulmonary hypertension. J. Path. Bact., *76*:165, 1958.
Henry, E. W.: Small pulmonary vessels in mitral stenosis. Brit. Heart J., *14*:406, 1952.
Hoffman, J. I. E., and Rowe, G. G.: Some factors affecting indicator dilution curves in the presence and absence of valvular incompetence. J. Clin. Invest., *38*:138, 1959.
Hugenholtz, P. G., Ryan, T. J., Stein, S. W., and Abelmann, W. H.: The spectrum of pure mitral stenosis. Hemodynamic studies in relation to clinical disability. Am. J. Cardiol., *10*:773, 1962.
Hytten, F. E., and Paintin, D. B.: Increase in plasma volume during normal pregnancy. J. Obst. Gyn. Brit. Comm., *70*:402, 1963.
Ikkos, D., Jonsson, B., and Linderholm, H.: Effect of exercise in pulmonary stenosis with intact ventricular septum. Brit. Heart J., *28*:316, 1966.
Irisawa, H., Wilson, M. F., and Rushmer, R. F.: Left ventricle as a mixing chamber. Circ. Research, *8*:183, 1960.
Jose, A. D., Taylor, R. R., and Bernstein, L.: The influence of arterial pressure on mitral incompetence in man. J. Clin. Invest., *43*:2094, 1964.
Kaplan, S.: Pressure curve analysis. In: Intravascular Catheterization. Ed. Zimmerman. Second edition. Springfield, Thomas, 1966.
Kay, J. H., and Thomas, V.: Experimental production of pulmonary insufficiency. Arch. Surg., *69*:646, 1954.
Kerley, P.: In: Shanks, S. C., and Kerley, P.: A Textbook of X-ray Diagnosis. Volume 2. Second edition. London, Lewis, 1951.
Kitchin, A., and Turner, R.: Diagnosis and treatment of tricuspid stenosis. Brit. Heart J., *26*:354, 1964.
Kjellberg, S. R., Mannheimer, E., Rudhe, U., and Jonsson, B.: Diagnosis of Congenital Heart Disease. Chicago, Year Book, 1958.
Kopelman, H., and Lee, G. de J.: Intrathoracic blood volume in mitral stenosis and left ventricular failure. Clin. Sci., *10*:383, 1951.

Korner, P. I., and Shillingford, J. P.: The quantitative estimation of valvular incompetency by dye dilution curves. Clin. Sci., *14*:553, 1955.

Korner, P. I., and Shillingford, J. P.: Further observations on the estimation of valvular incompetence from indicator dilution curves. Clin. Sci., *15*:417, 1956.

Korner, P. I., and Shillingford, J. P.: Tricuspid incompetence and right ventricular output in congestive heart failure. Brit. Heart J., *19*:1, 1957.

Larrabee, W. F., Parker, R. L., and Edwards, J. E.: Pathology of intrapulmonary arteries and arterioles in mitral stenosis. Proc. Staff Meet. Mayo Clin., *24*:316, 1949.

Leach, J. K., Friedlich, A. L., Myers, G. S., Sanders, C. A., and Scannell, J. G.: Usefulness and limitation of left heart catheterization in mitral disease. Am. J. Cardiol., *10*:57, 1962.

Levinson, G. E., Stein, S. W., Carleton, R. A., and Abelmann, W. H.: Measurement of mitral regurgitation in man from simultaneous atrial and arterial dilution curves after ventricular injection. Circulation, *24*:720, 1961.

Lewis, B. M., Gorlin, R., Houssay, H. E., Haynes, F. W., and Dexter, L.: Clinical and physiological correlations in patients with mitral stenosis. Am. Heart J., *43*:2, 1952.

Lewis, Sir T.: Diseases of the Heart. London, Macmillan, 1946.

Libanoff, A. J., and Rodbard, S.: Evaluation of the severity of mitral stenosis and regurgitation. Circulation, *33*:218, 1966.

Liu, C. K., Piccirillo, R. T., and Ellestad, M.: Distensibility of the post mortem human left atrium in nonrheumatic and rheumatic heart disease. Am. J. Cardiol., *13*:232, 1964.

Lombardo, T. A., Rose, L., Taeschler, M., Tuluy, S., and Bing, R. J.: The effect of exercise on coronary blood flow, myocardial oxygen consumption and cardiac efficiency in man. Circulation, *7*:71, 1953.

Lottenbach, C., and Shillingford, J. P.: Functional tricuspid incompetence in relation to the venous pressure. Brit. Heart J., *19*:395, 1957.

Lucas, R. V., Jr., and Marshall, R. J.: Congenital heart disease—non-cyanotic. In: Intravascular Catheterization. Ed. Zimmerman. Second Edition. Springfield, Ill., Thomas, 1966.

Lucas, R. V., Jr., Varco, R. L., Lillehei, C. W., Adams, P., Jr., Anderson, R. C., and Edwards, J. E.: Anomalous muscle bundle of the right ventricle. Hemodynamic consequences and surgical considerations. Circulation, *25*:443, 1962.

Mackenzie, J.: Quoted by McMichael, J., and Shillingford, J. P.: The role of valvular incompetence in heart failure. Brit. Med. J., *i*:537, 1957.

Mackinnon, J., Vickers, C. F. H., and Wade, E. G.: The effects of adrenergic-blocking agents on the pulmonary circulation in man. Brit. Heart J., *18*:442, 1956.

Marshall, H. W., Helmholz, H. F., Jr., and Wood, E. H.: Physiological consequences of congenital heart disease. In: Handbook of Physiology. Section 2: Circulation, Volume 1, Washington, D.C., American Physiological Society, 1962.

Marshall, H. W., Woodward, E., Jr., and Wood, E. H.: Hemodynamic methods for differentiation of mitral stenosis and regurgitation. Am. J. Cardiol., *2*:24, 1958.

Marshall, R., McIlroy, M. B., and Christie, R. V.: The work of breathing in mitral stenosis. Clin. Sci., *13*:137, 1954.

Marshall, R. J., and Jones, J. E.: Isolated pulmonary valvular regurgitation complicated by thyrotoxicosis. Brit. Heart J., *26*:572, 1964.

Marshall, R. J., and Shepherd, J. T.: Interpretation of changes in "central" blood volume and slope volume during exercise in man. J. Clin. Invest., *40*:375, 1961.

Mason, D. T., Braunwald, E., Ross, J., Jr., and Morrow, A. G.: Diagnostic value of the first and second derivatives of the arterial pressure pulse in aortic valve disease and in hypertrophic subaortic stenosis. Circulation, *30*:90, 1964.

McCord, M. C., and Blount, S. G., Jr.: The hemodynamic pattern in tricuspid valve disease. Am. Heart J., *44*:671, 1952.

McCord, M. C., Swan, H., and Blount, S. G., Jr.: Tricuspid stenosis. Clinical and physiologic evaluation. Am. Heart J., *48*:405, 1954.

McCredie, R. M.: The diffusing characteristics and pressure-volume relationships of

the pulmonary capillary bed in mitral valve disease. J. Clin. Invest., *43*:2279, 1964.
McDonald, L., Dealy, J. B., Jr., Rabinowitz, M., and Dexter, L.: Clinical, physiological and pathological findings in mitral stenosis and regurgitation. Medicine, *36*:237, 1957.
McGaff, C. J., Roveti, G. C., Glassman, E., and Milnor, W. R.: The pulmonary blood volume in rheumatic heart disease and its alteration by isoproterenol. Circulation, *27*:77, 1963.
McMichael, J., and Shillingford, J. P.: The role of valvular incompetence in heart failure. Brit. Med. J., *i*:537, 1957.
Morrow, A. G., Brawley, R. K., and Braunwald, E.: Effects of aortic regurgitation on left ventricular performance. Direct determinations of aortic blood flow before and after valve replacement. Circulation, *31* (Suppl. 1):80, 1965.
Newcombe, C. P., Sinclair, J. D., Donald, D. E., and Wood, E. H.: Detection and assessment of mitral regurgitation by left atrial indicator dilution curves. Circ. Research, *9*:1196, 1961.
Nixon, P. G. F., and Wooler, G. H.: Left ventricular filling pressure gradient in mitral incompetence. Brit. Heart J., *25*:382, 1963.
Owen, S. G., and Wood, P.: A new method of determining the degree or absence of mitral obstruction: An analysis of the diastolic part of indirect left atrial pressure tracings. Brit. Heart J., *17*:41, 1955.
Pantridge, J. F., and Marshall, R. J.: Tricuspid stenosis. Lancet, *i*:1319, 1957.
Parker, F., and Weiss, S.: The nature and significance of the structural changes in the lungs in mitral stenosis. Am. J. Path., *12*:573, 1936.
Paul, M. H., and Rudolph, A. M.: Pulmonary valve obstruction during cardiac catheterization. Circulation, *18*:53, 1958.
Radner, S.: Suprasternal pressure curves in mitral insufficiency. Acta Med. Scand., *152*:1, 1955.
Raine, J. M., and Bishop, J. M.: The distribution of alveolar ventilation in mitral stenosis at rest and after exercise. Clin. Sci., *24*:63, 1963.
Rapaport, E., Kuida, H., Haynes, F. W., and Dexter, L.: The pulmonary blood volume in mitral stenosis. J. Clin. Invest., *35*:1393, 1956.
Reale, A., Goldberg, H., Likoff, W., and Denton, C.: Rheumatic tricuspid stenosis. Am. J. Med., *21*:47, 1956.
Regan, T. J., de Fazio, V., Binak, K., and Hellems, H. K.: Norepinephrine induced pulmonary congestion in patients with aortic valve regurgitation. J. Clin. Invest., *38*:1564, 1959.
Roberts, W. C., Braunwald, E., and Morrow, A. G.: Acute severe mitral regurgitation secondary to ruptured chordae tendinae. Clinical, hemodynamic, and pathologic considerations. Circulation, *33*:58, 1966.
Rodrigo, F. A., and Snellen, H.: Estimation of valve area and valvular resistance. Am. Heart J., *45*:1, 1953.
Rossall, R. E., and Gunning, A. J.: Basal horizontal lines on chest radiographs. Significance in heart disease. Lancet, *i*:604, 1956.
Rowe, G. G., Afonso, S., Castillo, C. A., and McKenna, D. H.: The mechanism of the production of Duroziez's murmur. New Eng. J. Med., *272*:1207, 1965.
Rudolph, A. M., Nadas, A. S., and Goodale, W. T.: Intracardiac left-to-right shunt with pulmonic stenosis. Am. Heart J., *48*:808, 1954.
Rushmer, R. F.: Cardiovascular Dynamics. Second edition. Philadelphia, Saunders, 1961.
Sancetta, S. M., and Kleinerman, J.: Effect of mild steady state exercise on total pulmonary resistance of normal subjects and those with isolated aortic valvular lesions. Am. Heart J., *53*:404, 1957.
Sanders, C. A., Hawthorne, J. W., DeSanctis, R. W., and Austen, W. G.: Tricuspid stenosis: a difficult diagnosis in the presence of atrial fibrillation. Circulation, *33*:26, 1966.
Sandler, H., Dodge, H. T., Hay, R. E., and Rackley, C. E.: Quantitation of valvular insufficiency in man by angiocardiography. Am. Heart J., *65*:501, 1963.

Sarnoff, S. J., Braunwald, E., Welch, G. H., Jr., Case, R. B., Stainsby, W. N., and Macruz, R.: Hemodynamic determinants of oxygen consumption of the heart with special reference to the tension-time index. Am. J. Physiol., *192*:148, 1958.

Schenk, W. G., Jr., Menno, A. D., and Martin, J. W.: Hemodynamics of chronic experimental aortic insufficiency. Ann. Surg., *154*:295, 1961.

Schreiner, B. F., Jr., Murphy, G. W., Glick, G., and Yu, P. N.: Effect of exercise on the pulmonary blood volume in patients with acquired heart disease. Circulation, *27*:559, 1963.

Scott, R. C., Kaplan, S., and Stiles, W. J.: Observations on the effects of tetraethylammonium chloride on the pulmonary vascular resistance in mitral stenosis. Am. Heart J., *50*:720, 1955.

Semler, H. J., Shepherd, J. T., and Wood, E. H.: The role of vessel tone in maintaining pulmonary vascular resistance in patients with mitral stenosis. Circulation, *19*:386, 1959.

Skinner, N. S., Mitchell, J. H., Wallace, A. G., and Sarnoff, S. J.: Hemodynamic consequences of atrial fibrillation at constant ventricular rates. Am. J. Med., *36*:342, 1964.

Sobin, S. S., Carson, M. M., Johnson, J. L., and Baker, C. R.: Pulmonary valvular stenosis with intact ventricular septum: Isolated valvular stenosis and valvular stenosis associated with interatrial shunt. Am. Heart J., *48*:416, 1954.

Spencer, M. P., and Dennison, A. B., Jr.: Pulsatile blood flow in the vascular system. In: Handbook of Physiology. Section 2: Circulation, Volume 2. Washington, D.C., American Physiological Society, 1963.

Steiner, R. E.: Radiological appearances of the pulmonary vessels in pulmonary hypertension. Brit. J. Radiol., *31*:188, 1958.

Swan, H. J. C., and Beck, W.: Ventricular non-mixing as a source of error in the estimation of ventricular volume by the indicator dilution technic. Circ. Research, *8*:989, 1960.

Taquini, A. C., Fermoso, J. D., and Aramendia, P.: Behavior of the right ventricle following acute constriction of the pulmonary artery. Circ. Research, *8*:315, 1960.

Taquini, A. C., Lozada, B. B., Donaldson, R. J., D'Aiutolo, R. E. H., and Ballina, E. S.: Mitral stenosis and cor pulmonale. Am. Heart J., *46*:639, 1953.

VanWassbergen, G. P. W.: Het microscopische Aspect der perifere Longlymfvaten bij Veranderingen in de kleine Bloedsomloop. Thesis, Leiden, 1961.

Wade, O. L., and Bishop, J. M.: Cardiac Output and Regional Blood Flow. Oxford, Blackwell, 1962.

Wagenvoort, C. A.: The morphology of certain vascular lesions in pulmonary hypertension. J. Path. Bact., *78*:503, 1959.

Wagenvoort, C. A., Health, D., and Edwards, J. E.: The pathology of the pulmonary vasculature. Springfield, Ill., Thomas, 1964.

Walters, W. A. W., MacGregor, W. G., and Hills, M.: Cardiac output at rest during pregnancy and the puerperium. Clin. Sci., *30*:1, 1966.

Warden, H. E., Lucas, R. V., Jr., and Varco, R. L.: Right ventricular obstruction resulting from anomalous muscle bundles. J. Thorac. Cardiovasc. Surg., *51*:53, 1966.

Warner, H. R.: Analysis of the role of indicator technics in quantitation of valvular regurgitation. In: Symposium on use of indicator dilution technics in the study of the circulation. New York, American Heart Association, Inc., 1962.

Warner, H. R., and Toronto, A. F.: Quantitation of backflow in patients with aortic insufficiency using an indicator technic. Circ. Research, *6*:29, 1958.

Watson, H., and Lowe, K. G.: Severe tricuspid stenosis revealed after aortic valvotomy. Brit. Heart J., *24*:241, 1962.

Watson, H., and Lowe, K. G.: Ventricular pressure flow relationships in isolated valvular stenosis. Brit. Heart J., *24*:431, 1962.

Werkö, L., Varnauskas, E., Eliasch, H., Lagerlöf, H., Senning, A., and Thomasson, B.: Further evidence that the pulmonary capillary venous pressure pulse in man reflects cyclic pressure changes in the left atrium. Circ. Research, *1*:337, 1953.

West, J. B., and Dollery, C. T.: Distribution of blood flow and the pressure-flow relations of the whole lung. J. Appl. Physiol., *20*:175, 1965.
White, P. D.: Heart Disease. Third edition. New York, Macmillan, 1944.
Williams, M. H., Jr.: Pulmonary function studies in mitral stenosis before and after commissurotomy. J. Clin. Invest., *32*:1094, 1953.
Wilson, W. S., Brandt, R. L., Judge, R. D., Morris, J. D., and Clifford, M. E.: An appraisal of the double indicator dilution method for the estimation of mitral regurgitation in human subjects. Circulation, *23*:64, 1961.
Wood, E. H., Sturm, R. E., and Sanders, J. J.: Data processing in cardiovascular physiology with particular reference to roentgen videodensitometry. Mayo Clin. Proc., *39*:849, 1964.
Wood, P.: An appreciation of mitral stenosis. Brit. Med. J., *i*:1051, 1954.
Wood, P.: Diseases of the Heart and Circulation. Second edition. Philadelphia, Lippincott, 1956.
Wood, P., Besterman, E. M., Towers, M. K., and McIlroy, M. B.: The effect of acetylcholine on pulmonary vascular resistance and left atrial pressure in mitral stenosis. Brit. Heart J., *19*:279, 1957.
Woodward, E., Jr., Burchell, H. B., and Wood, E. H.: Dilution curves associated with valvular regurgitation. Proc. Staff Meet. Mayo Clin., *32*:518, 1957A.
Woodward, E., Jr., Swan, H. J. C., and Wood, E. H.: Evaluation of a method for detection of mitral regurgitation from indicator dilution curves recorded from the left atrium. Proc. Staff Meet. Mayo Clin., *32*:525, 1957B.
Wright, J. L., and Wood, E. H.: Value of central and peripheral intraarterial pressures and pulse contours in cardiovascular diagnosis. Minnesota Med., *41*:215, 1958.
Yu, P. N., Harken, D. E., Lovejoy, F. W., Jr., Nye, R. E., Jr., and Mahoney, E. B.: Clinical and hemodynamic studies of tricuspid stenosis. Circulation, *13*:680, 1956.
Yu, P. N., Nye, R. E., Jr., Lovejoy, F. W., Jr., Schreiner, B. F., and Yim, B. J. B.: Studies of pulmonary hypertension. IX. The effects of intravenous hexamethonium on pulmonary circulation in patients with mitral stenosis. J. Clin. Invest., *37*:194, 1958.

Chapter 12

EFFECTS OF SURGERYIN CHRONIC VALVULAR DISEASE

- Closed and Open Operations
- Prosthetic Devices
- Cardiac Function Following Mitral Valve Replacement
- Cardiac Function Following Aortic Valve Replacement
- Effects of Multiple Valve Replacement

In chronic acquired valvular disease, the patient's disability is determined mainly by the hemodynamic effects of the valve deformities, although such other factors as rheumatic myocardial disease, arteriosclerosis of the coronary arteries and systemic arterial hypertension may be contributory. Therefore, the chief aim of surgery is the correction of the mechanical valvular defects.

CLOSED AND OPEN OPERATIONS

Closed operations continue to be performed by many surgeons for the relief of mitral stenosis (Hoeksema et al., 1966). Initial satisfactory results, based on clinical assessment, may be expected in about 80 per cent of suitably selected cases (Ellis et al., 1950; Ellis et al., 1959). Corresponding hemodynamic improvement may be demonstrated by comparing the results of preoperative and postoperative cardiac catheterization studies. Thus, Morrow and Braunwald (1961) found a reduction in the mean pressure difference across the mitral valve during diastole from 16 to 6 mm. Hg in a group of patients who had had closed transventricular mitral valvotomy. In other patients, clinical improvement is not accompanied by objective evidence of improved valvular function. In such cases, it may be assumed that the operation to relieve the stenosis was inadequate, and that the clinical improvement resulted from more adequate medical treatment, greater restriction of physical activity or psychic factors.

Long term follow-up studies have shown that an increasing number of patients deteriorate following initially satisfactory operations (Baker and Hancock, 1960). Deterioration may occur because of the development of restenosis or of regurgitation, or because of progression of myocardial disease (rheumatic or ischemic). It may also occur because the operation to relieve the stenosis was less than optimal. For this reason, there is increasing support for the view that all operations for mitral stenosis should be performed using an open technique, which allows more meticulous correction of the valvular deformity and, if necessary, replacement of the valve by a prosthetic device. An open technique is mandatory in certain situations, including the presence of heavy calcification of the valve, an unsatisfactory previous operation, or disease of one or more of the other valves.

In acquired valvular lesions other than mitral stenosis, the results of closed operations have been unsatisfactory, and open heart techniques are now routinely used. Annuloplasty (Merendino et al., 1959) and valvuloplasty (McGoon, 1960) sometimes confer considerable benefit, assessed by both clinical and hemodynamic criteria, in mitral regurgitation. However, for most cases of mitral regurgitation and for all cases of aortic valve disease, replacement of the damaged valve is the operation of choice.

PROSTHETIC DEVICES

A number of prosthetic devices have been developed for the replacement of diseased valves. The most widely used of these is the Starr-Edwards caged ball-valve prosthesis (Starr and Edwards, 1961). Although its efficacy has been repeatedly confirmed, it provides greater resistance to blood flow than does the normal mammalian leaflet valve.

The normal mitral valve area of up to 5 cm.^{2} during diastole is greater than the cross sectional area of 1.65 to 3.1 cm.^{2} provided by Starr-Edwards prostheses. In addition, Kezdi et al. (1964), who carried out studies using Starr-Edwards prostheses in a mechanical pulse duplicator, found that their effective orifices were 11 to 17 per cent less than their measured orifices (Fig. 12-1). Consequently, at normal levels of cardiac output, a pressure difference is to be anticipated across a ball-valve.

Since the prosthesis, like a stenosed valve, maintains its rigid orifice at high rates of flow, the pressure difference increases during muscular exercise. Because of the parabolic relationship between pressure and flow (Fig. 12-1), a pressure difference that is of little hemodynamic significance during rest may become highly significant during exercise.

Pressure differences also exist with valves, such as the University of Cape Town lenticular prosthesis (Beck et al., 1965) and the full flow orifice valve (McHenry et al., 1965), that have larger areas. This suggests that factors other than the area of the valve orifice, such as the presence of the rigid metallic ring in the valve annulus may play a role.

Inertia of the ball at the onset of systole leads to a slight delay in closure of the valve. In a mechanical system, this caused a significant de-

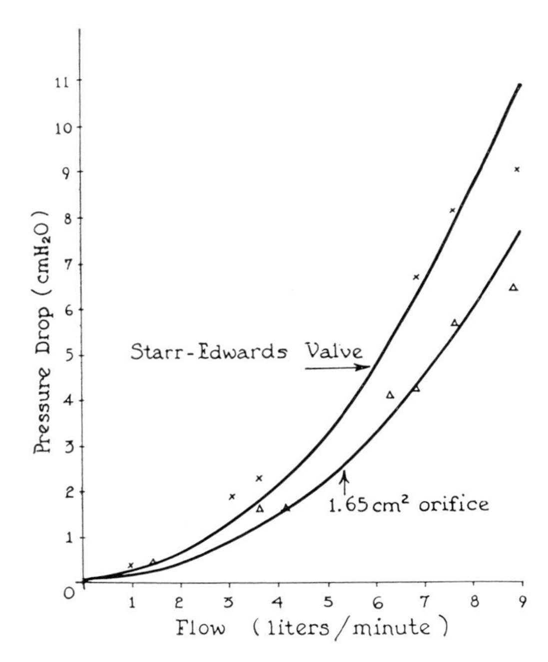

FIGURE 12-1. Pressure-flow relationships in a mechanical pulse duplicator across a Starr-Edwards ball-valve prosthesis (×) and a circular orifice with an identical area (△). The ball-valve prosthesis caused a greater resistance to flow. (From Kezdi, Head and Buck, Circulation, *30*:55, 1964.)

gree of regurgitation (Kezdi et al., 1964). However, angiocardiographic studies in patients whose mitral valves had been replaced by Starr-Edwards prostheses showed only minimal regurgitation of opaque medium from ventricle to atrium (Rockoff et al., 1966), probably because the similar densities of blood and of the ball minimized inertia. This contrasted with more severe degrees of regurgitation around the ring in patients whose prostheses had become partially detached from the annulus.

The left ventricle is enlarged in hearts with mitral regurgitation, and bulky devices such as the Starr-Edwards valve do not compromise the cavity. In isolated mitral stenosis, however, the left ventricle is generally normal in size. Roberts and Morrow (1966) described six patients who had had stenosed mitral valves replaced by Starr-Edwards prostheses, and in whom signs of a progressive decrease in cardiac output preceded death. At autopsy, the left ventricular cavities were normal or nearly normal in size. In each, the muscular septum protruded into the cage, preventing full descent of the ball during diastole and hence impeding emptying of the left atrium.

Intravascular hemolysis and hemoglobinuria occurring during or soon after open heart surgery results from mechanical trauma to the erythrocytes. It is most commonly due to damaged plastic tubing in the pump oxygenator (Keith et al., 1961) or to excessive trauma to cells returned from the coronary perfusion system (Roper, 1963). Chronic hemolysis may also become apparent later in the postoperative period in patients with malfunctioning prosthetic devices (Stevenson and Baker, 1964; Sears and Crosby, 1965). It probably results from trauma to erythrocytes because of increased turbulence of blood flow around leaking prostheses, although in some cases an autoimmune process may also be involved (Pirofsky, 1965). Lesser degrees of hemolysis may occur in all patients with prosthetic valves and in many patients with valvular disease who have had no cardiac operations (Brodeur et al., 1965; Gehrmann et al., 1966; Veneziale et al., 1966). The onset of anemia may be delayed for many months because of the presence of available iron stores in the body.

CARDIAC FUNCTION FOLLOWING MITRAL VALVE REPLACEMENT

The effect of a mitral valvular prosthesis on the function of an otherwise normal heart has been studied in dogs. Rastelli et al. (1967) inserted Starr-Edwards ball-valve prostheses: in one group, all leaflets and chordae tendineae were removed; in a second group, only the anterior leaflet and its chordae were removed; and in a third group, all leaflets and chordae were preserved. In the immediate postoperative period, values for cardiac output (Fig. 12-2) and left atrial pressure were identical with those in a

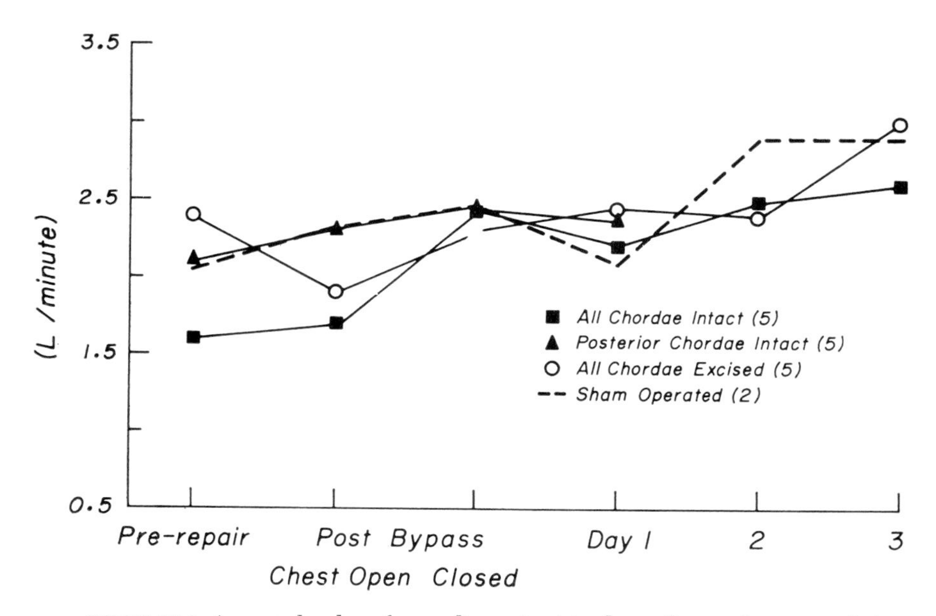

FIGURE 12-2. Averaged values for cardiac output in dogs after replacement of the mitral valve by a No. 1-M Starr-Edwards prosthesis. Note that the values were similar in the three groups of dogs (chordae preserved, partially excised or totally excised) and in dogs submitted to a sham operation. (From Rastelli, Tsakiris, Frye and Kirklin, Circulation, *35* [Suppl. I]:34, 1967.)

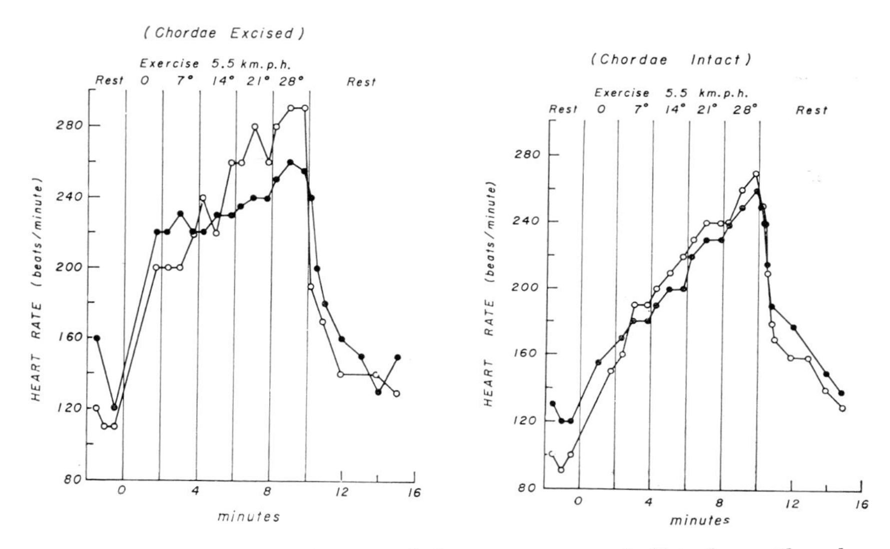

FIGURE 12-3. Heart rate during graded exercise on a treadmill in dogs with replacement of the mitral valve by a Starr-Edwards prosthesis. *Left panel:* two dogs with chordae excised, two months after operation. *Right panel:* two dogs with chordae intact, four months after operation. Note the normal stepwise increase in heart rate and the rapid recovery at the end of exercise. (From Rastelli, Tsakiris, Frye and Kirklin, Circulation, 35 [Suppl. I]:34, 1967.)

group of sham operated dogs. More detailed hemodynamic measurements were made at an average of two months after operation. Values for cardiac output both at rest and during infusion of acetylcholine were identical in the surgically treated dogs and in a group of normal dogs. Heart rates were somewhat higher, and stroke volumes therefore lower, in the animals with Starr-Edwards valves. In the control state, left atrial pressures were normal, and there was no end-diastolic pressure difference across the valves. During the infusion of acetylcholine, when cardiac output was increased and the heart rate was rapid, left atrial pressures averaged 13 mm. Hg compared with 1 mm. Hg in the normal dogs. The mean diastolic pressure difference across the valve averaged 12 and 11 mm. Hg in dogs with intact and excised chordae, respectively, whereas there was no pressure difference in normal dogs. During graded exercise, the response of the heart rate was similar to that of normal animals, and the decrease of heart rate after exercise ended was equally rapid (Fig. 12-3). Thus, in otherwise normal animals, there is only slight impairment of cardiac performance associated with the insertion of a Starr-Edwards prosthesis, whether or not the chordae are preserved.

Rastelli and Kirklin (1966) also studied the hemodynamic effects of prosthetic replacement of diseased mitral valves in the immediate postoperative period in man, because of the clinical observation that the early and late results of mitral valve replacement were less satisfactory than those of aortic valve replacement (Ellis et al., 1965). Cardiac output, stroke volume, and pressures in right atrium, pulmonary artery, left ventricle and systemic arteries were measured before, during and at intervals up to 48 hours after operation for replacement of the mitral valve with a Starr-Edwards prosthesis. Cardiac output generally reached its lowest value (average 1.7 liters per $M.^2$ per minute between three and six hours after operation. The ventricular filling pressures were high, there was no significant diastolic pressure difference across the prosthesis, and there was no pressure difference across the left ventricular outflow tract. Blood gas tensions and pH were satisfactory. Also, there was no reason to suspect that tricuspid valve regurgitation was a major determinant of the reduced cardiac output. It was concluded that impaired performance of the left ventricle, possibly related to the prolonged period of induced ventricular fibrillation during perfusion (Race et al., 1964; Stoney and Roe, 1964), contributed significantly to the low cardiac output. Other mechanical factors such as the effects of cutting of all the chordae tendineae (Lillehei et al., 1964) and fixation of the valve annulus by the rigid ring of the prosthesis might have contributed.

An end-diastolic pressure difference was present at rest in six of 12 patients one year after replacement of the mitral valve by a Starr-Edwards prosthesis, and it increased during exercise. In the other patients, no pressure difference was demonstrable at rest, but it occurred during exercise. The mean pressure in the pulmonary artery was less after operation than before, but it did not return to normal levels, mainly because of a persistent increase in left atrial pressure. Pulmonary vascular resistance was decreased. In the majority of cases, the right atrial pressure was greater after operation than before, despite the decrease in pulmonary arterial pressure. This suggested that the right ventricle was not functioning normally (Morgan, 1967).

Wang et al. (1966) also studied the response to exercise in 23 patients one year after insertion of a Starr-Edwards prosthesis. The exercise was accompanied by approximately a threefold increase in oxygen consumption. Patients who had had mitral stenosis had an average increase of cardiac index from 2.7 to 4.0 liters per $M.^2$ per minute and an average increase in left atrial or pulmonary artery wedge pressure from 11 to 18 mm. Hg. Those who had had mitral regurgitation had an average increase of cardiac index from 2.8 to 4.1 liters per $M.^2$ per minute and in left atrial or pulmonary artery wedge pressure from 12 to 17 mm. Hg. All had a small end-diastolic pressure difference at rest that increased with exercise.

The behavior of the pulmonary vascular bed was assessed by Braunwald et al. (1965) in 31 patients shortly before and two to 20 months after replacement of the mitral valve with a Starr-Edwards prosthesis. Fourteen had dominant stenosis and 17 dominant regurgitation. The preoperative

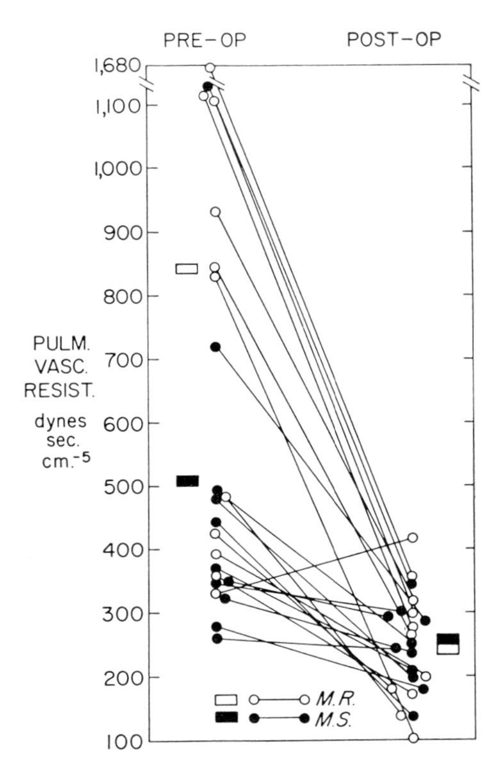

FIGURE 12-4. Values for pulmonary vascular resistance before and after replacement of the mitral valve by a Starr-Edwards prosthesis in patients with mitral regurgitation and mitral stenosis. (From Braunwald, Braunwald, Ross and Morrow, New Eng. J. Med., *273*:509, 1965.)

systolic pressure in the pulmonary artery equaled or exceeded 50 mm. Hg in all. Operation decreased this pressure from 75 to 39 mm. Hg, decreased the mean pressure difference from pulmonary artery to left atrium from 23 to 15 mm. Hg, and increased the cardiac index from 2.0 to 3.0 liters per $M.^2$ per minute (average values). Pulmonary vascular resistance decreased on the average from 8 to 3 units, the result being similar in those with dominant stenosis and those with dominant regurgitation (Fig. 12-4). Serial studies in one patient showed a progressive decrease in pulmonary arterial pressure and vascular resistance. It was concluded that the most impressive results from mitral valve replacement are to be expected in patients with serious mitral valve disease and advanced pulmonary vascular disease.

Dalen et al. (1967) performed daily hemodynamic studies for eight to ten days following replacement of the mitral valve with a compact discoid prosthesis in five consecutive patients with severe pulmonary hypertension. The mean left atrial pressure decreased from 28 mm. Hg before surgery to 10 mm. Hg 24 hours after surgery, and the mean pulmonary artery pressure decreased from 71 mm. Hg before surgery to 47 mm. Hg after 24 hours and to 35 mm. Hg at the end of the study (averaged values). The cardiac index increased from 1.7 liters per M.^{2} per minute before surgery to 2.6 liters per M.^{2} per minute after 24 hours and to 4.0 liters per M.^{2} per minute at the end of the study; this contrasted with the decrease soon after surgery in the patients of Rastelli and Kirklin (1966) who had had caged ball prostheses inserted. Pulmonary vascular resistance decreased from 15 units before surgery to 6 units four days after surgery. These striking early changes suggested that pulmonary arteriolar vasoconstriction secondary to increased pressure in the left atrium, pulmonary veins or pulmonary capillaries may be the most important factor in the pathogenesis of pulmonary vascular disease in patients with mitral valve disease. If the results are confirmed by others, there will be important implications for the treatment of patients with severe pulmonary hypertension complicating mitral valve disease, and particularly for the choice of prosthetic device.

CARDIAC FUNCTION FOLLOWING AORTIC VALVE REPLACEMENT

The average cardiac output of 18 patients with prosthetic replacement of the aortic valve was within the normal range by the second day after operation (Kloster et al., 1966). Only three patients had values less than 2.5 liters per M.^{2} per minute, and they had had prolonged heart failure prior to operation. Patients with replacement of mitral or of mitral and aortic valves had, on the whole, less initial improvement in cardiac output. The main reason for this appeared to be the presence of residual (uncorrected) valve defects, such as mild to moderate aortic lesions in those who had mitral valve replacement only, and tricuspid regurgitation in those who had replacement of both mitral and aortic valves. The presence of tricuspid regurgitation was associated with marked impairment of cardiac function, even though it appeared mild at the time of surgery.

Factors other than residual valve lesions that contributed to decreased cardiac output in the early postoperative period included tachyarrhythmias and hypovolemia. Correction of hypovolemia rapidly increased the cardiac output towards normal values, except in some patients with residual valve lesions or severe myocardial disease. Kirklin and Theye (1963) also found an increase in output after rapid infusion of blood following cardiopulmonary bypass; the most likely mechanism was thought to be augmented diastolic filling of the ventricles.

Judson et al. (1964) demonstrated improved left ventricular function in the late postoperative period in patients who had stenosed or incompetent aortic valves replaced by Starr-Edwards prostheses. Persistent small transvalvar systolic pressure differences did not exceed 25 mm. Hg and were well tolerated. Figure 12-5 shows that an infusion of isoproterenol

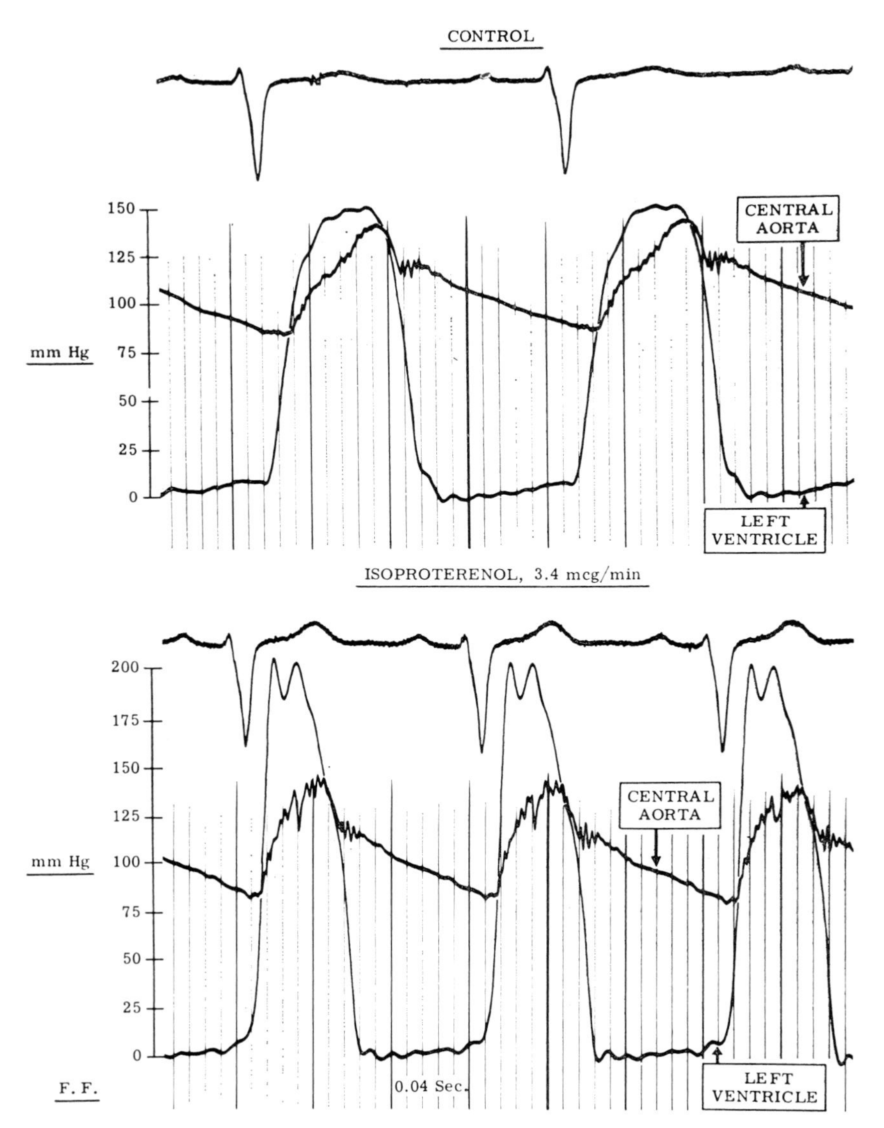

FIGURE 12-5. Pressure pulses from left ventricle and central aorta in a patient with a Starr-Edwards prosthesis replacing the aortic valve. The mean systolic pressure difference across the valve increased from 21 to 57 mm. Hg during an infusion of isoproterenol. (From Judson, Ardaiz, Strach and Jennings, Circulation, 29 [Suppl. 1]: 14, 1964.)

increased the mean systolic pressure difference between left ventricle and aorta from 21 to 57 mm. Hg.

Bristow et al. (1964A) also found small differences in systolic pressure, from 14 to 30 mm. Hg, across Starr-Edwards valves. With one exception, the pressure difference did not increase during exercise. In all their patients, left atrial and left ventricular end-diastolic pressures decreased to normal levels, indicative of enhanced left ventricular function. However, exercise was sometimes accompanied by a smaller increase in cardiac output than in normal subjects. Since the resistance to outflow from the left ventricle was slight, the impaired response to exercise must have been due to persistent effects of long-standing valve disease upon left ventricular function. It is unlikely that a ventricle, subjected for years to the stress of severe aortic stenosis or regurgitation, can ever fully recover. Whether continued hemodynamic improvement will occur over a period of years remains to be seen.

The effects of mild muscular exercise (oxygen consumption about three times that at rest) were assessed by Ross et al. (1966) in 14 patients with satisfactory clinical results following replacement of the aortic valve by a Starr-Edwards prosthesis. The increase of cardiac output in relation to oxygen consumption was normal or only slightly reduced. Eight patients, however, had an abnormal increase (greater than 3 mm. Hg) in left ventricular end-diastolic pressure. In three of these, there was a concordant increase in stroke volume, which may have resulted from operation of the Frank-Starling mechanism or of a positive inotropic influence. In the remaining five, an unchanged or decreased stroke volume was thought to indicate depressed ventricular performance. As in the patients of Bristow et al. (1964A), exercise of this degree did not lead to an increase in the peak or mean systolic pressure difference across the prosthesis. It is likely, however, that the systolic pressure differences would increase with harder work.

Cardiac function was assessed by Hubis et al. (1966) in patients four to 10 months after replacement of either the aortic (group A) or mitral (group B) valve by a Starr-Edwards prosthesis. In the patients of group B, all papillary muscles were excised. The average age in each group was 48 years. In group A, the resting cardiac index was 3.2 liters per M.^{2} per minute, and the pulmonary artery and pulmonary artery wedge pressure were normal. During exercise, the pressures did not increase, despite a 68 per cent increase in cardiac output. In group B, the resting cardiac index was 2.5 liters per M.^{2} per minute; during identical exercise, mean pressures in the pulmonary artery and wedge increased to 40 and 19 mm. Hg, respectively, despite an increase of only 27 per cent in cardiac output. The difference in response could not be related to valve obstruction, atrial fibrillation or age. On the assumption that myocardial damage was similar in the two groups, these authors concluded that absence of papillary muscle function may have accounted for the impaired responses to exercise in group B.

EFFECTS OF MULTIPLE VALVE REPLACEMENT

Resting values for cardiac output, left ventricular end-diastolic pressure and pulmonary arterial pressure were restored to normal or nearly to normal following replacement of both aortic and mitral valves by Starr-Edwards prostheses (Morrow et al., 1967). The mean diastolic pressure difference across the mitral prosthesis increased from 4 to 9 mm. Hg with mild exercise, whereas the peak systolic pressure difference across the aortic prosthesis was unchanged at 10 mm. Hg (average values). In contrast with the responses in normal subjects, exercise was accompanied by a decrease in stroke volume and an increase of 6 mm. Hg in left ventricular end-diastolic pressure. This suggested that myocardial performance was less efficient than in patients with prosthetic replacement of only one valve.

Eight patients with lesions of aortic, mitral and tricuspid valves had distinct increases in pressure in both atria prior to surgery and marked decreases in resting levels of cardiac output (Bristow et al., 1966). Four had severe pulmonary hypertension. Four to 10 months after replacement of all three valves by Starr-Edwards prostheses, there were consistent decreases in right ventricular systolic pressure and in right and left atrial pressures, while the cardiac output had improved. Failure of the cardiac output to attain normal resting values or to increase by the predicted amount during exercise could have been related to persistent impairment of myocardial function. However, a less than optimal result should be attributed to faulty muscle only after the possibility of a mechanical defect (such as a leak around a prosthetic valve) has been eliminated by angiocardiography or other means.

Although tricuspid regurgitation may be due to deformities of the valve cusps or supporting structures resulting from rheumatic damage, it is more commonly due to dilatation of the annulus resulting from right ventricular hypertension and failure. Twenty eight patients, prior to prosthetic replacement of the mitral valve, had clinical and hemodynamic evidence of associated tricuspid regurgitation. The mean right atrial pressure averaged 11 mm. Hg, and the pulmonary arterial systolic pressure averaged 75 mm. Hg. One to four years later, evidence for tricuspid regurgitation had diminished or disappeared; the right atrial pressure averaged 5 mm. Hg, and the pulmonary arterial systolic pressure averaged 39 mm. Hg. Thus, prosthetic replacement of the tricuspid valve should rarely be necessary in the management of tricuspid regurgitation (Braunwald et al., 1967).

A small proportion of patients fail to improve, and even deteriorate following prosthetic replacement of one or more valves (Peterson et al.,

1967). In some of these, regurgitation through defects at the suture line is responsible. In others, obstruction to blood flow is caused by deposition of thrombus on the annulus or struts of the metal cage of the prosthesis, or by swelling or deformity of the Silastic ball. Additional causes include the presence of uncorrected lesions at other valves and extensive myocardial disease. The heart rate may also be a factor limiting cardiac performance. Boicourt et al. (1967) measured the diastolic filling period of the ventricles by recording the opening and closing sounds of mitral and tricuspid Starr-Edwards prostheses. Extrapolation of the lines correlating heart rate and diastolic filling period gave estimates of the heart rates at which filling would be severely compromised in resting subjects. These rates were of the order of 150 to 190 beats per minute. The results indicate the importance of maintaining the ventricular rate within the physiological range.

REFERENCES

Baker, C., and Hancock, W. E.: Deterioration after mitral valvotomy. Brit. Heart J., *22*:281, 1960.

Beck, W., Fergusson, D. J. G., Barnard, C. N., and Schrire, V.: Hemodynamic findings following replacement of the mitral valve with the University of Cape Town prosthesis. Circulation, *32*:721, 1965.

Boicourt, O. W., Bristow, J. D., Griswold, H. E., and Starr, A.: Effect of heart rate on performance of Starr-Edwards prosthetic valves. Circulation, *32* (Suppl. II): 54, 1967.

Braunwald, E., Braunwald, N. S., Ross, J., Jr., and Morrow, A. G.: Effects of mitral-valve replacement on the pulmonary vascular dynamics of patients with pulmonary hypertension. New Eng. J. Med., *273*:509, 1965.

Braunwald, N. S., Ross, J., Jr., and Morrow, A. G.: Conservative management of tricuspid regurgitation in patients undergoing mitral valve replacement. Circulation, *35* (Suppl. I):63, 1967.

Bristow, J. D., Kloster, F. E., Herr, R., Starr, A., McCord, C. W., and Griswold, H. E.: Cardiac catheterization studies after combined tricuspid, mitral and aortic valve replacement. Circulation, *34*:437, 1966.

Bristow, J. D., McCord, C. W., Starr, A., Ritzmann, L. W., and Griswold, H. E.: Clinical and hemodynamic results of aortic valvular replacement with a ball-valve prosthesis. Circulation, *29* (Suppl. 1):36, 1964A.

Brodeur, M. T. H., Sutherland, D. W., Koler, R. D., Starr, A., Kinsey, J. A., and Griswold, H. E.: Red blood cell survival in patients with aortic valvular disease and ball-valve prosthesis. Circulation, *32*:570, 1965.

Dalen, J. E., Matloff, J. M., Evans, G. L., Hoppin, F. C., Jr., Bhardwaj, P. Harken, D. E., and Dexter, L.: Early reduction of pulmonary vascular resistance after mitral-valve replacement. New Eng. J. Med., *277*:387, 1967.

Ellis, F. H., Jr., Callahan, J. A., McGoon, D. C., and Kirklin, J. W.: Results of open operation for acquired mitral-valve disease. New Eng. J. Med., *272*:869, 1965.

Ellis, F. H., Jr., Connolly, D. C., Kirklin, J. W., and Parker, R. L.: Results of mitral commissurotomy. Follow-up of three and one-half to seven years. A.M.A. Arch. Int. Med., *102*:928, 1950.

Ellis, L. B., Harken, D. E., and Black, H.: A clinical study of 1000 consecutive cases of mitral stenosis two to nine years after mitral valvuloplasty. Circulation, *19*:803, 1959.

Gehrmann, G., Bleifeld, W., and Kaulen, D.: Herzklappenfehler and Hämolyse. Klin. Wschr., *44*:1, 1966.

Hoeksema, T. D., Wallace, R. B., and Kirklin, J. W.: Closed mitral commissurotomy. Recent results in 291 cases. Am. J. Cardiol., *17*:825, 1966.

Hubis, H. J., Hultgren, H. N., and Shumway, N. E.: Cardiac function following prosthetic replacement of the aortic valve. Circulation, *34* (Suppl. III):131, 1966 (Abstract).

Judson, W. E., Ardaiz, J., Strach, T. B. J., and Jennings, R. S.: Post-operative evaluation of prosthetic replacement of aortic and mitral valves. Circulation, *29* (Suppl. I):14, 1964.

Keith, H. B., Ginn, E., Williams, G. R., and Campbell, G. S.: Massive hemolysis in extracorporeal circulation. J. Thorac. Cardiovasc. Surg., *41*:404, 1961.

Kezdi, P., Head, L. R., and Buck, B. A.: Mitral ball-valve prosthesis. Dynamic and clinical evaluation. Circulation, *30*:55, 1964.

Kirklin, J. W., and Theye, R. A.: Cardiac performance after open intracardiac surgery. Circulation, *28*:1061, 1963.

Kloster, F. E., Bristow, J. D., Starr, A., McCord, C. W., and Griswold, H. E.: Serial cardiac output and blood volume studies following cardiac valve replacement. Circulation, *33*:528, 1966.

Lillehei, C. W., Levy, M. J., and Bonnabeau, R. C., Jr.: Mitral valve replacement with preservation of papillary muscles and chordae tendineae. J. Thorac. Cardiovasc. Surg., *47*:532, 1964.

McGoon, D. C.: Repair of mitral insufficiency due to ruptured chordae tendineae. J. Thorac. Cardiovasc. Surg., *39*:357, 1960.

McHenry, M. M., Smeloff, E. A., Davey, T. B., Kaufman, B., and Fong, W. Y.: Hemodynamic results with full-flow orifice prosthetic valves. Circulation, *35* (Suppl. I):24, 1967.

Merendino, K. A., Thomas, G. I., Jesseph, J. E., Herron, P. W., Winterscheid, L. C., and Vetto, R. R.: The open correction of rheumatic mitral regurgitation and/or stenosis, with special reference to regurgitation treated by posteromedial annuloplasty using a pump-oxygenator. Ann. Surg., *150*:5, 1959.

Morgan, J. J.: Hemodynamics one year following mitral replacement. Am. J. Cardiol., *19*:189, 1967.

Morrow, A. G., and Braunwald, N. S.: Transventricular mitral commissurotomy. Surgical technique and a hemodynamic evaluation of the method. J. Thorac. Cardiovasc. Surg., *41*:225, 1961.

Morrow, A. G., Mason, D. T., Ross, J., Jr., and Braunwald, E.: Combined prosthetic replacement of the mitral and aortic valves. Preoperative and postoperative hemodynamic studies at rest and the left ventricular response to muscular exercise. Circulation, *35* (Suppl. I):15, 1967.

Peterson, C. R., Herr, R., Crisera, R. V., Starr, A., Bristow, J. D., and Griswold, H. E.: The failure of hemodynamic improvement after valve replacement surgery. Etiology, diagnosis, and treatment. Ann. Int. Med., *66*:1, 1967.

Pirofsky, B.: Aortic valve surgery and autoimmune hemolytic anemia. Am. Heart J., *70*:426, 1965.

Race, D., Stirling, G. R., and Morris, K. N.: Induced ventricular fibrillation in open-heart surgery. J. Thorac. Cardiovasc. Surg., *47*:271, 1964.

Rastelli, G. C., and Kirklin, J. W.: Hemodynamic state early after prosthetic replacement of mitral valve. Circulation, *34*:448, 1966.

Rastelli, G. C., Tsakiris, A. G., Frye, R. L., and Kirklin, J. W.: Exercise tolerance and hemodynamic studies after replacement of canine mitral valve with and without preservation of chordae tendineae. Circulation, *35* (Suppl. I):34, 1967.

Roberts, W. C., and Morrow, A. G.: Low cardiac output and left atrial thrombosis following mitral valvular replacement: the small left ventricle syndrome. Am. J. Cardiol., *17*:135, 1966 (Abstract).

Rockoff, S. D., Ross, J., Jr., Oldham, N. N., Jr., Mason, D. T., Morrow, A. G., and Braunwald, E.: Ventriculo-atrial regurgitation following prosthetic replacement of the mitral valve. Angiocardiographic and hemodynamic findings. Am. J. Cardiol., *17*:817, 1966.

Roper, C.: Clinicopathologic conference. Complications of open heart surgery. Am. J. Med., *35*:842, 1963.
Ross, J., Jr., Morrow, A. G., Mason, D. T., and Braunwald, E.: Left ventricular function following replacement of the aortic valve. Hemodynamic responses to muscular exercise. Circulation, *33*:507, 1966.
Sears, D. A., and Crosby, W. H.: Intravascular hemolysis due to intracardiac prosthetic devices. Diurnal variations related to activity. Am. J. Med., *39*:341, 1965.
Starr, A., and Edwards, M. L.: Mitral valve replacement. The shielded ball valve prosthesis. J. Thorac. Cardiovasc. Surg., *42*:673, 1961.
Stevenson, T. D., and Baker, H. J.: Haemolytic anaemia following insertion of Starr-Edwards ball valve prosthesis. Lancet, *ii*:982, 1964.
Stoney, R. J. and Roe, B. B.: Ventricular function after induced, intermittently ischemic ventricular fibrillation. Effect of moderate hypothermia. J. Thorac. Cardiovasc. Surg., *48*:838, 1964.
Veneziale, C. M., McGuckin, W. F., Hermans, P. E., and Mankin, H. T.: Hypohaptoglobinemia and valvular heart disease: association with hemolysis after insertion of valvular prostheses and in cases in which operation had not been performed. Mayo Clin. Proc., *41*:657, 1966.
Wang, Y., Schloff, L., and Lillehei, C. W.: Hemodynamics at rest and supine exercise one year following mitral valve replacement by a Starr-Edwards prosthesis. Circulation, *34* (Suppl. III):234, 1966 (Abstract).

Chapter 13

CARDIOMYOPATHY

- Cardiomyopathy With Congestive Features
- Cardiomyopathy With Restrictive Features
- Obstructive Cardiomyopathy
- Cardiomyopathy Without Congestive, Restrictive or Obstructive Features
- Specific Varieties of Cardiomyopathy

congestive
restrictive
obstructive

Myocardial function may become impaired through its being involved in a variety of infectious, ischemic, infiltrative, nutritional, metabolic and other disorders of more obscure origin. The term cardiomyopathy could legitimately be applied to any or all of these conditions, since it literally means *disease of heart muscle*. However, such an all inclusive application would be so broad as to have little practical value. Hence, it is customary to exclude from consideration common conditions such as ischemic, hypertensive, rheumatic and syphilitic heart disease, cor pulmonale and congenital heart disease. In all of these, although damage to heart muscle may play a role, involvement of other tissues in the heart and elsewhere is also important and often dominant. Even after exclusion of these common and well defined entities, the classification of the different forms of cardiomyopathy presents many problems and, to some extent, must be arbitrary. Indeed, it is not possible to formulate a classification that will at the same time satisfy clinical, pathological and physiological criteria.

Goodwin et al. (1961), from careful collation of clinical and hemodynamic data, concluded that three general patterns emerged: (1) presentation with congestive heart failure and often atrioventricular valvular regurgitation, frequently simulating the effects of severe ischemic heart disease; (2) simulating constrictive pericarditis; and (3) causing obstruction to the egress of blood from the ventricles, more generally the left ventricle.

A fourth pattern is exemplified by those cases with unexplained cardiac hypertrophy who have features of neither congestive failure, constriction nor obstruction (Braunwald and Aygen, 1963).

Distinct and consistent lines of demarcation between these four groups do not exist. Some patients may have features of both congestion and constriction at the same time. In others, over months or years, one pattern may merge into another. However, for purposes of description, the classification into congestive, restrictive, obstructive and non-obstructive groups is convenient and will be followed here.

CARDIOMYOPATHY WITH CONGESTIVE FEATURES

Clinical and hemodynamic findings have been described in detail by a number of authors, including Goodwin et al. (1961) and Fowler et al. (1961). The hearts are moderately or severely dilated and show diminished pulsation on fluoroscopy. The heart sounds are often muffled, suggesting the presence of pericardial effusion. Third heart sounds are frequently present, and the coincidence of third and fourth heart sounds may give rise to summation gallop; these sounds as a rule disappear following intensive treatment of heart failure only to recur with the next episode of decompensation. Pansystolic murmurs, depending on their location, radiation and variation with the phases of respiration, indicate the presence of mitral or tricuspid valve regurgitation or both. The jugular venous pressure is increased, characteristically showing a positive systolic wave with a rapid *y* descent due to tricuspid regurgitation, and peripheral edema is present. The arterial pulse has a decreased volume. Atrial fibrillation is frequent. The diffuse nature of the myocardial disease is reflected in the electrocardiogram which commonly shows low voltage, abnormal *T* waves, evidence of biventricular hypertrophy, atrioventricular or intraventricular conduction defects and various arrhythmias. At autopsy, the myocardium, especially that of the left ventricle, is extensively diseased, pale and often flaccid.

In the 18 cases reviewed by Fowler et al. (1961), the hearts weighed up to 825 g., and in 11 cases, there was dilatation of all four chambers. An abnormal accumulation of pericardial fluid was present in only three. Four cases had been catheterized. Values for cardiac output were 1.1 to 1.6 liters per $M.^2$ per minute, for arteriovenous difference in oxygen content 6.8 to 7.9 ml. per 100 ml., for right atrial pressure 2 to 18 mm. Hg and for pulmonary artery wedge pressure 17 to 27 mm. Hg. Thus, all four had left ventricular decompensation at the time of the study; three of them had also right ventricular decompensation.

Yu et al. (1966) performed combined left and rightsided cardiac catheterization in six patients with idiopathic congestive cardiomyopathy. In two who subsequently died, autopsy confirmed the absence of coronary artery disease and of rheumatic valvular disease. All had a prominent left ventricular impulse and radiographic evidence of left ventricular, left atrial and usually right ventricular enlargement; five had apical systolic murmurs, and three had protodiastolic gallop rhythm. Hemodynamic data are shown in Table 13-1. All had increased pressures in the left atrium, and two had systemic venous congestion. There was no significant dif-

TABLE 13-1. Hemodynamic Data in Patients with Idiopathic Congestive Cardiomyopathy*

CASE	O_2 UPTAKE (ML./M.^{2}/MIN.)	A-V O_2 DIFFERENCE (ML./100 ML.)	CARDIAC INDEX (L.M.^{2}/MIN.)	STROKE INDEX (ML./M^2)	PRESSURES (MM. HG)			
					RA	RV	LA	LV
1	–	–	1.5	21	4	56/3	23	120/22
2	149	6.4	2.3	20	3	40/6	24	131/32
3	145	5.9	2.5	26	1	40/5	24	–
4	135	8.4	1.6	25	15	65/15	26	–
5	138	8.2	1.7	17	8	55/8	31	82/30
6	113	5.4	2.1	26	4	28/4	15	110/20

* Adapted from Yu, Schreiner, Cohen and Murphy, Am. Heart J., *71*:330, 1966.

ference in systolic pressure across the outflow tract of either right or left ventricle. Left ventricular stroke volume and stroke work were uniformly decreased.

Studies were repeated in three of these patients following intravenous administration of acetylstrophanthidin or ouabain. This resulted in slowing of the heart, increased stroke work and stroke volume, augmented maximal rate of pressure development in the left ventricle and reduction of left ventricular end-diastolic pressure towards normal levels. Pulmonary blood volume was decreased. Thus, the acute administration of digitalis glycosides temporarily reversed the left ventricular failure. Despite this, long term management of these patients with a strict cardiac regimen failed to prevent progressive deterioration.

The majority of the patients studied by Massumi et al. (1965) had histories of chronic alcoholism and malnutrition, and these factors were thought to be responsible for the cardiomyopathy. Cases with sinus rhythm had prominent *a* waves in the jugular venous pulse both during congestive heart failure and after treatment. Prominent *v* waves, with a rapid *y* descent, were present during failure, due to tricuspid regurgitation. Mitral and tricuspid systolic murmurs, and in one case a pulmonary diastolic murmur, disappeared when compensation was regained. Fifteen of 18 patients catheterized while in congestive failure had decreased cardiac outputs (0.9 to 3.2 liters per M.^{2} per minute), while three had increased outputs (4.0, 5.0 and 7.3 liters per M.^{2}). The administration of ouabain to five patients with decreased outputs who had not previously received digitalis resulted in restoration of their outputs towards more nearly normal values. Systolic and diastolic pressures were commonly increased in both ventricles. The presence of tricuspid regurgitation was demonstrated by the indicator dilution technique in eight of nine cases.

Although the hemodynamic features were predominantly those of congestive cardiomyopathy, the ventricular pressure pulses showed pronounced dips in early diastole, a feature more characteristic of patients with restrictive cardiomyopathy. However, this contour was not present in the compensated cases, and it disappeared after administration of ouabain in four of five decompensated cases. Massumi et al. (1965) felt, therefore, that the early diastolic dip was related to loss of compliance secondary to the overdistention of failure, rather than to permanent restrictive myocardial changes.

CARDIOMYOPATHY WITH RESTRICTIVE FEATURES

This variety of presentation is characteristic of conditions such as diffuse myocardial fibrosis (Robin and Burwell, 1957; Nye et al., 1957; Goodwin et al., 1961) and amyloidosis (Hetzel et al., 1953; Brigden, 1957) that lead to diminished elasticity of the myocardium. In some cases, coexistent endocardial sclerosis or pericardial thickening may contribute to the loss of compliance of the chambers. In addition, endocardial fibroelastosis (Lynfield et al., 1960) and endomyocardial fibrosis (Shillingford and Somers, 1961) may be present with features of restrictive cardiomyopathy.

The common denominator of these conditions appears to be the rigid ventricular wall that fails to relax adequately during diastole, thus simulating the effects of constrictive pericarditis. However, the distinction between congestive and restrictive cardiomyopathy is not absolute since certain patients show, at the same time, clinical or hemodynamic features of both groups (Goodwin et al., 1961).

Robin and Burwell (1957) studied 11 patients with intractable right and leftsided heart failure due to diffuse myocardial fibrosis, the etiology of which was unknown in most cases. The cardiac output was decreased (1.1 to 2.9, mean 2.1 liters per M.^{2} per minute), and the oxygen content of mixed venous blood was low. The right atrial pressures varied from 14 to 40 mm. Hg, the right ventricular pressures from 25/13 to 70/40 mm. Hg and the mean pulmonary artery wedge pressures from 13 to 40 mm. Hg. In eight of the nine cases in which a right ventricular pressure pulse was obtained, an early diastolic dip was recorded. The physiological derangements resembled those of constrictive pericarditis and endocardial fibroelastosis; they were thought to be due to interference with both diastolic filling and systolic emptying of the ventricles.

In the cases of restrictive cardiomyopathy described by Nye et al. (1957), the right atrial and the right ventricular end-diastolic pressures were usually less high, and the respiratory variations in right atrial pressures were usually more pronounced than in constrictive pericarditis. Also, the early dip in diastolic pressure reached 0 mm. Hg more frequently. However, there was no absolute distinction on hemodynamic grounds, and in some instances, the correct diagnosis could be made only by inspection of the heart at thoracotomy. Yu et al. (1966) also showed that there is an early diastolic dip followed by an abrupt plateau in pressure pulses from the left ventricle. Acute treatment with digitalis in two patients had little effect on cardiac output or on left ventricular diastolic, left atrial or pulmonary artery pressures; this contrasted with the obvious hemodynamic improvement in patients with congestive features.

Gottsegen and Romoda (1964) found that, although other hemodynamic features were similar or identical, the systolic upstroke time of the right ventricle was more prolonged (sometimes exceeding 0.20 second) in restrictive cardiomyopathy than in constrictive pericarditis.

Diffuse myocardial fibrosis and amyloidosis characteristically involve the entire heart, resulting in marked alterations of the volume and distensibility characteristics of both ventricles (Yu et al., 1964). Pressure differences between the two atria are small. When the lesion predominantly affects the left ventricle, as in most cases of endocardial fibroelastosis and some cases of endomyocardial fibrosis, left ventricular end-diastolic, left atrial and pulmonary artery pressures are increased, whereas right ventricular end-diastolic and right atrial pressures may be normal. Thus, Lynfield et al. (1960) found right atrial and right ventricular end-diastolic pressures to be 6 mm. Hg or less in all but one of their studies of children with endocardial fibroelastosis, and Lambert and Vlad (1958) found left atrial pressures 9 and 13 mm. Hg higher than those in the right atrium in two of their patients. More extensive involvement of the right ventricle, however, leads to increased end-diastolic pressure, to a dip and plateau contour, and to a considerable increase in mean right atrial pressure.

OBSTRUCTIVE CARDIOMYOPATHY

For many years, isolated descriptions appeared in the literature of hearts that showed diffuse or localized hypertrophy of muscle, involving especially the outflow tract of the left ventricle, in the absence of any demonstrable cause. Braunwald et al. (1964), in their monograph on this condition, drew attention to the paper of Schmincke (1907) who described two such hearts. Schmincke suggested that the muscular hypertrophy, by obstructing the passage of blood from the left ventricle, could lead to additional hypertrophy and, in turn, to further obstruction to outflow. The reports of Brock (1957, 1959), the pathological description by Teare (1958) and the development of refinements in techniques for physiological and radiographic studies of the left side of the heart stimulated great interest in this and related disorders. Many clinical, physiological, pharmacological and pathological reports have been published. The underlying nature of the disorder remains uncertain. Indeed, it is not clear whether all cases are examples of a single disease, or whether they represent similar end results of a number of separate entities. Uncertainty as to etiology has led to the use of many descriptive terms, including aortic subvalvular stenosis (Brock, 1957), asymmetrical hypertrophy of the heart in young adults (Teare, 1958), muscular subaortic stenosis (Brent et al., 1960; Menges et al., 1961; Wigle et al., 1962), obstructive cardiomyopathy (Goodwin et al., 1960), idiopathic hypertrophic subaortic stenosis (Braunwald et al., 1964) and functional subaortic stenosis (Brachfeld and Gorlin, 1961). All these terms imply that a cardinal manifestation of the condition is the presence of a significant obstruction to the egress of blood from the left ventricle to the aorta. The validity of this implication, however, has recently been debated (Criley et al., 1965; Burchell, 1966; Ross et al., 1966A).

THE NATURE OF THE MUSCULAR HYPERTROPHY. Although the anatomical changes described vary from case to case and from series to series, the dominant finding is extreme hypertrophy of the interventricular septum, particularly its upper portion adjacent to the anterior cusp of the mitral valve (Teare, 1958; Paré et al., 1961). While the free walls of the ventricle may also be hypertrophied, the changes are less striking. Thus, Menges et al. (1961) found that the ratio of thickness of the septum to the free wall averaged 0.45 in normal hearts and 0.98 in hearts hypertrophied from causes other than obstructive cardiomyopathy, whereas in three cases of the latter, it was 1.55 to 1.76. The papillary muscles and columnae carneae are also hypertrophied. The hypertrophied septum bulges into the lumen of the left ventricular outflow tract. In addition, Björk et al. (1961) showed that in some cases, abnormal insertion of the anterior cusp of the mitral valve into the septum may contribute to the narrowing of the outflow tract. The septum may also bulge into the outflow tract of the right ventricle, compromising the cavity of this chamber (Brent et al., 1960). The cavity of the left ventricle is reduced. Thus, Klein et al. (1964) found a mean end-diastolic volume of 71 ml. per $M.^2$ in six cases, compared with mean values of 96 and 148 ml. per $M.^2$ in normal subjects and patients with valvular aortic stenosis, respectively.

The muscle fibers in the areas of hypertrophy are generally thickened, with abnormal nuclei, and the muscle bundles are arranged in bizarre patterns. Electron microscopy of the muscle fibers reveals certain similarities to sinuatrial nodal cells and atrial muscle (Pearse, 1964). There is proliferation of sympathetic nerve fibers and of connective tissue.

HEMODYNAMICS DURING REST. In typical cases, there are many features that permit differentiation from aortic valvular stenosis, even before cardiac catheterization and angiocardiography are performed. There is a double apical impulse (Wigle et al., 1962); the first impulse can be shown by apex cardiography to be a presystolic expansion wave, or *a* wave, and the second is the customary systolic outward thrust (Braunwald et al., 1964). The systolic murmur and thrill, most prominent at the lower left sternal border and apex, are related to the outflow obstruction and, in some cases, to associated mitral regurgitation. The *a* wave is prominent

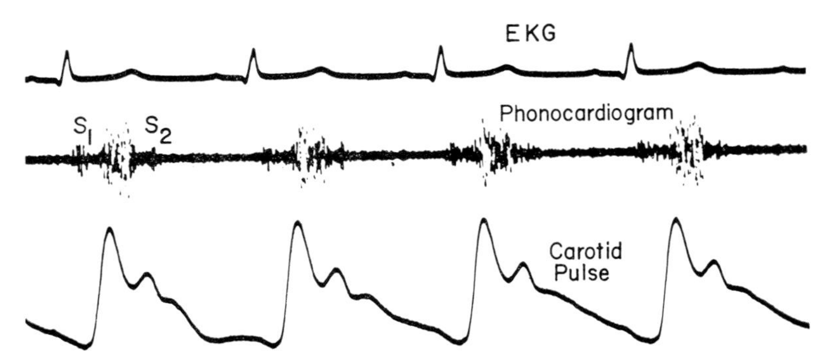

FIGURE 13-1. Electrocardiogram (lead II), phonocardiogram (third intercostal space along left sternal border) and indirect carotid arterial pulse pressure. Note the systolic ejection murmur and the bisferiens contour of the pressure pulse. (From Whalen, Cohen, Sumner and McIntosh, Am. J. Cardiol., *11*:8, 1963.)

in the jugular venous pulse. The peripheral arterial pulses are characteristically sharp, in contrast with the slowly rising pulses when valvular stenosis is present. Indirectly recorded carotid pulses or intra-arterial pressure tracings show characteristic contours (Soulié et al., 1959; Brachfeld and Gorlin, 1959; Whalen et al., 1963; Braunwald et al., 1964; Fig. 13-1). The systolic upstroke is rapid, with no anacrotic notch, and attains a sharp peak; it declines from this, to rise again more slowly during the latter part of systole and ends in a sharply defined dicrotic notch. The rapidity of the initial component was confirmed by measurement of its first derivative (Mason et al., 1964), which averaged 1092 ± 372 mm. Hg per second, as compared with 811 ± 185 and 358 ± 85 mm. Hg per second in normal subjects and patients with aortic valvular stenosis, respectively. Calculation of the second derivative permitted better separation between normal subjects and patients with obstructive cardiomyopathy. The duration of systolic upstroke is less than in normal persons (Boiteau et al., 1963; Wigle, 1963).

Brachfeld and Gorlin (1959) provided an explanation for the characteristic pressure pulse of obstructive cardiomyopathy, which has since been confirmed by direct measurement of the velocity of blood flow. The sharp initial percussion wave is due to the rapid ejection of an initial volume of blood; contraction of the hypertrophied muscle then severely impairs further ejection. Normal subjects eject 57 per cent of their stroke volume during the first half of systole, whereas patients with obstructive cardiomyopathy eject 70 to 85 per cent in the same period (Hernandez et al., 1964) (Fig. 13-2). Similar findings were reported by Pierce et al. (1964) who measured the volume of aortic blood flow by an electromagnetic flowmeter at thoracotomy. The delayed secondary or tidal wave in late systole may represent a rapid deceleration phenomenon, or perhaps a reflected wave. The total duration of systole, measured from the indirect carotid arterial pulse and corrected for the RR interval, averaged 0.33 second in patients with obstructive cardiomyopathy (Braunwald et al., 1964), as compared with 0.30 second in normal subjects (Benchimol et al., 1960).

Detailed hemodynamic measurements in 64 patients were reported by Braunwald et al. (1964). The mean left atrial pressure often exceeded 12 mm. Hg, the upper limit of normal, and the *a* wave was prominent. In 47 patients, the left ventricular end-diastolic pressure exceeded 12 mm. Hg, reflecting diminished ventricular distensibility rather than cardiac failure in its customary sense. The maximal peak systolic pressure differences between the left ventricle and the brachial artery in resting subjects varied from 0 to 174 mm. Hg; in 14, the difference exceeded 100 mm. Hg; in 21, it was between 50 and 100 mm. Hg, and in 15 it was between 10 and 50 mm. Hg. The remaining 14 patients had insignificant differences but eight

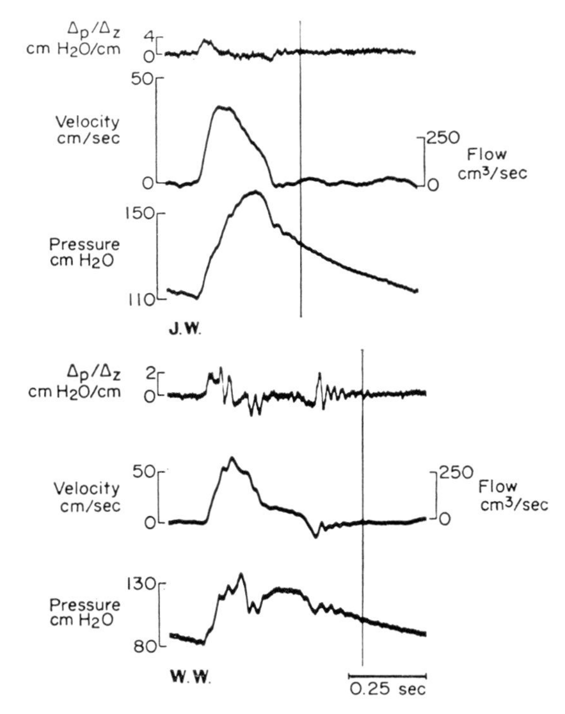

FIGURE 13-2. The upper three tracings, *from above down*, show the pressure gradient, the computed phasic blood flow and velocity, estimated by the pressure gradient technique, and the pressure recorded from the ascending aorta of a normal subject. The flow accelerated to a peak of 400 ml. per second early in systole and gradually decelerated so that 58 per cent of the total stroke volume was ejected during the first half of systole. The lower panel shows data from a patient with obstructive cardiomyopathy in whom both acceleration and deceleration of flow were rapid; 79 per cent of the stroke volume was ejected during the first half of systole. (From Hernandez, Greenfield and McCall, J. Clin. Invest., *43*:401, 1964.)

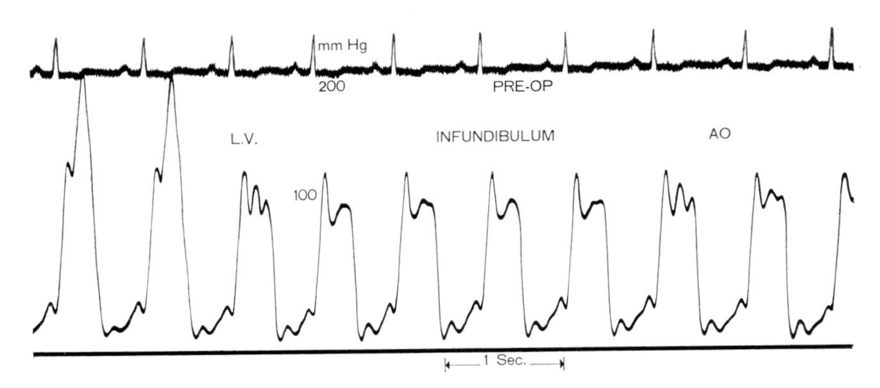

FIGURE 13-3. Pressure record during withdrawal of catheter tip across hypertrophic infundibulum. Note the striking anacrotic notch in the cavity of the left ventricle. (From Sousa, Zerbini, Jatene, Fontes, Magalhães and Filho, Am. J. Cardiol., *15*:801, 1965.)

of them developed differences during provocative tests. These findings were similar to those of other reported series. A notch was frequently noted on the ascending limb of the left ventricular pressure pulse (Fig. 13-3). Withdrawal of a catheter tip from the cavity of the left ventricle towards the aorta revealed a sudden decrease in systolic pressure to the level of that in the aorta at a site usually 2 to 4 cm. below the level of the aortic valve (Fig. 13-4).

Nine of 59 patients had pulmonary arterial systolic pressures exceeding 40 mm. Hg and other authors have also reported the occurrence of moderate pulmonary hypertension (Goodwin et al., 1960; Wigle et al., 1962). Ten patients had pressure differences ranging from 10 to 62 mm. Hg across the right ventricular outflow tract (Fig. 13-5). Goodwin et al. (1961) and Grosse-Brockhoff and Loogen (1962) confirmed the presence of obstruction to the outflow tract of the right ventricle by the hypertrophied septum at operation in patients in whom large pressure differences had previously been recorded. The mean right atrial pressure was usually normal, but the *a* wave was prominent and gave rise to an end-diastolic kick in the right ventricular pressure pulse.

Resting values for cardiac output have usually been within the normal range or even above normal except for those with Class IV disability (criteria of New York Heart Association) (Bevegård et al., 1962; Wigle et al., 1962; Braunwald et al., 1964).

LABILITY OF HEMODYNAMICS. The magnitude of pressure differences across the left ventricular outflow tract often differed considerably, not only on repeated studies, but also during the course of a single study (Krasnow et al., 1963; Braunwald et al., 1964). This contrasts with the relative constancy of pressure differences across anatomically fixed areas of

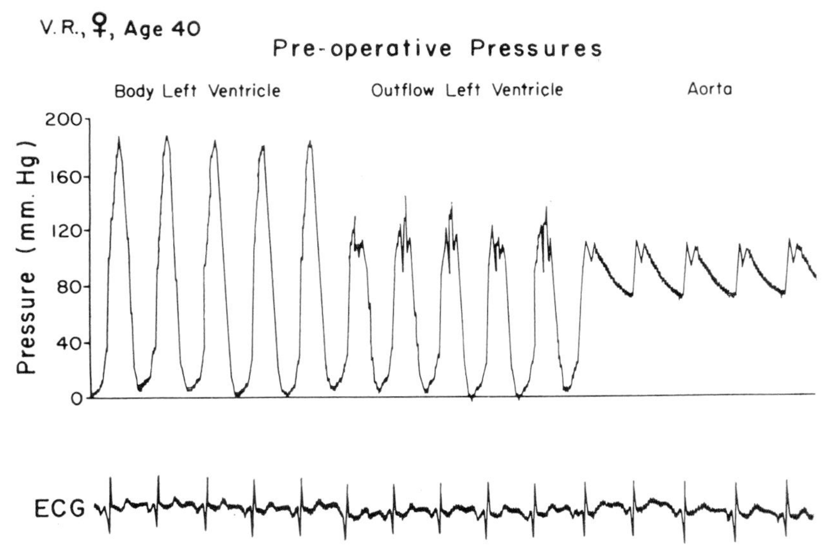

FIGURE 13-4. Progression of changes in pressure tracing in left ventricular outflow tract and aorta, demonstrating presence of subaortic stenosis. This was subsequently shown to be due to muscular hypertrophy rather than to a fibrous diaphragm. (From Julian and Javid, Med. Clin. N. Amer., *50*:309, 1966.)

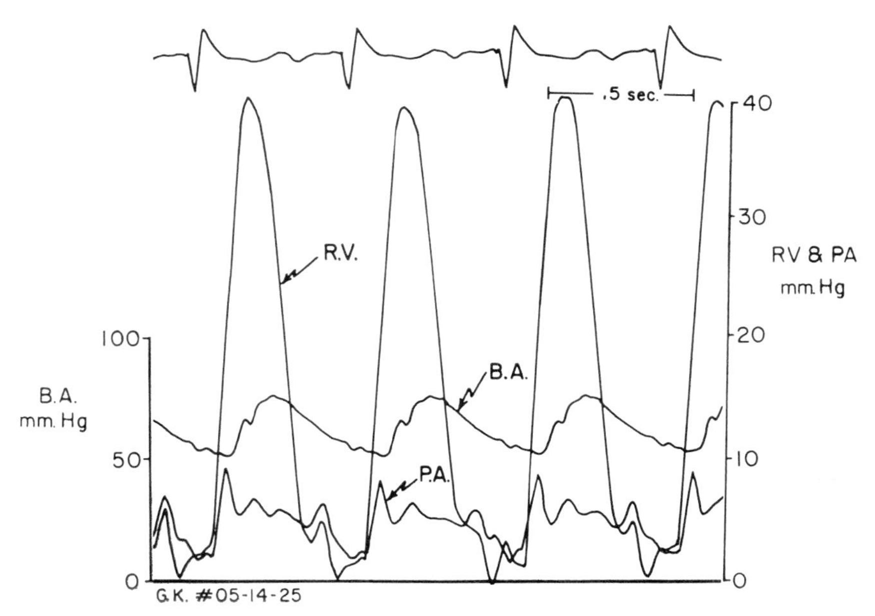

FIGURE 13-5. Pressure pulses from brachial artery (BA), right ventricle (RV) and pulmonary artery (PA) in a patient with obstruction of outflow from both ventricles. Note the systolic pressure difference between RV and PA. (From Braunwald, Lambrew, Rockoff, Ross and Morrow, Circulation, *30*[Suppl. IV]:3, 1964.)

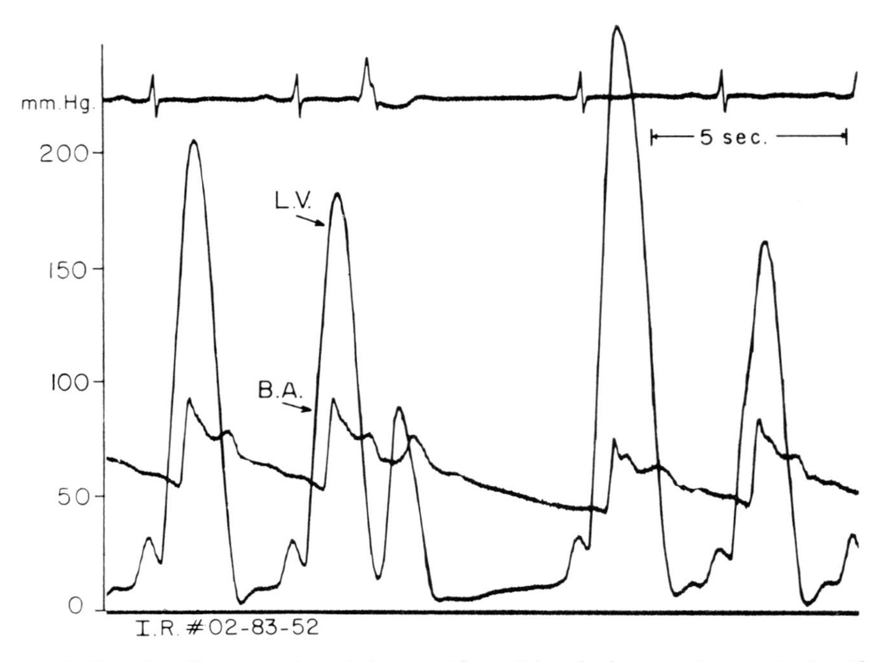

FIGURE 13-6. Pressures from left ventricle and brachial artery in a patient with obstructive cardiomyopathy. Note the diminished pulse pressure in the brachial artery during the post-extrasystolic beat. (From Braunwald, Lambrew, Rockoff, Ross and Morrow, Circulation, *30*[Suppl. IV]:3, 1964.)

stenosis, such as aortic or pulmonary valvular stenosis or discrete membranous subaortic stenosis, and suggests that the degree of obstruction from muscular hypertrophy is affected by a variety of changes in the physiological state of the subjects. Lability of pressure differences has also been induced, by many different investigators, through the use of physical, physiological and pharmacological stimuli, as will be discussed below. It appears that the effects of these various stimuli are due mainly to the alterations that they induce in the force of contraction of the ventricular myocardium (Krasnow et al., 1963) or in the volume of blood in the left ventricle (Braunwald and Ebert, 1962).

PHYSICAL AND PHYSIOLOGICAL STIMULI. Brockenbrough et al. (1961) described characteristic effects of a ventricular premature contraction on the pulse pressure of the subsequent normal beat. In normal subjects and most patients with discrete obstructive lesions, the peripheral arterial pulse pressure in the post-extrasystolic beat was increased. In patients with obstructive cardiomyopathy, it was usually either unchanged or diminished (Fig. 13-6), an abnormality that may be accentuated when measurements are made during the administration of an inotropic agent such as isoproterenol (Whalen et al., 1963). Gault et al. (1966) showed that the peripheral blood flow associated with the postextrasystolic beat, and hence presumably its stroke volume, was diminished in obstructive cardiomyopathy, whereas it was increased in normal subjects. The probable explanation is that enhanced myocardial contractility following the extrasystole increases the force of contracion of the hypertrophied muscle and thereby renders the obstruction more complete.

Mason et al. (1966) found that the pressure difference across the hypertrophied left ventricular outflow tract was increased by an average of 35 mm. Hg during tilting to the 45 degree head up position, and the postextrasystolic decrease in arterial pulse pressure was more prominent. Tilting to a 20 degree head down position reduced the difference in pressure, as did raising the lower limbs. They concluded that the effects resulted from changes in left ventricular volume secondary to changes in venous return.

During the Valsalva maneuver, the reduction in left ventricular stroke volume results in a diminished pressure difference across discrete obstructive lesions, such as aortic valvular stenosis. In obstructive cardiomyopathy, the pressure difference between left ventricle and aorta increases, because the extremely small ventricular volume results in relatively more severe obstruction (Braunwald et al., 1964; Marcus and Jones, 1965; Fig. 13-7). Following release of the strain, increased filling of the left ventricle may result in diminution or abolition of the pressure difference. The effect of the Valsalva maneuver is intensified by simultaneous administration of isoproterenol.

Abnormalities of left ventricular function, manifested by a frequent decrease in stroke volume and stroke work and by an invariable increase in

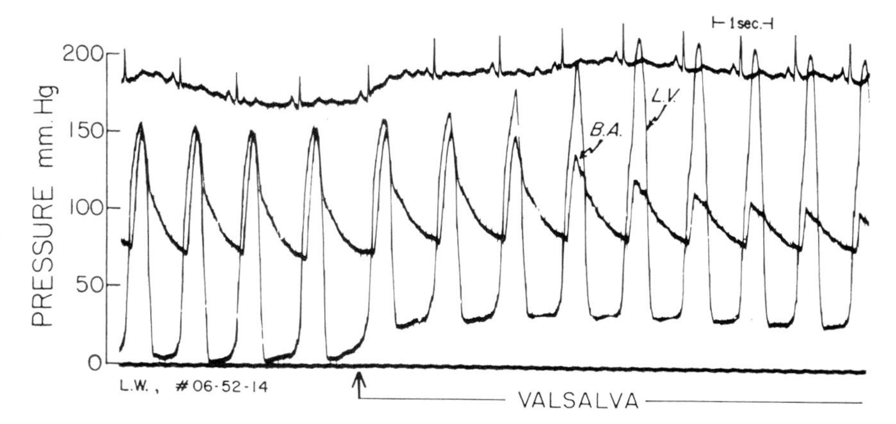

FIGURE 13-7. Effect of Valsalva maneuver in a patient with obstructive cardiomyopathy who had no resting systolic pressure difference between left ventricle and brachial artery. A progressively greater pressure difference developed during the strain. (From Ross, Braunwald, Gault, Mason and Morrow, Circulation, *34*:558, 1966.)

end-diastolic pressure, occurred during leg exercise performed in the supine position (Braunwald et al., 1964). The pressure difference across the outflow tract increased in some but not all patients; it tended to be greater shortly after than during exercise. In some patients, a pressure difference, absent during rest, became manifest with exercise (Whalen et al., 1963).

Ross et al. (1966B) studied the effects of tachycardia induced by the use of atropine. Although this reduced the mean systolic pressure differences in patients with discrete (non-muscular) obstructions above, at or below the aortic valve, it increased the pressure difference in patients with muscular obstruction.

PHARMACOLOGICAL STIMULI. Digitalis, through its positive inotropic effect, intensifies the outflow obstruction and increases the systolic pressure difference (Braunwald et al., 1964; Taylor et al., 1964). The left ventricular end-diastolic pressure may increase. Catecholamines such as isoproterenol that stimulate beta adrenergic receptors in the myocardium may have an even more striking effect than digitalis glycosides. They both increase the force of contraction and diminish left ventricular volume (Harrison et al., 1964). Their use in obstructive cardiomyopathy is accompanied by increases in left ventricular end-diastolic pressure and by the development of mitral valve regurgitation (Whalen et al., 1963) in patients in whom the valve was previously competent. These effects of isoproterenol may be prevented by prior beta adrenergic receptor blockade.

Catecholamines that stimulate alpha adrenergic receptors only, such as methoxamine and phenylephrine, have effects opposite to those of isoproterenol. They induce systemic arterial vasoconstriction, increase the volume of the left ventricle, do not increase myocardial contractility and abolish the pressure difference across the left ventricular outflow tract (Harrison et al., 1964; Goodwin et al., 1964).

General anesthesia may also abolish the pressure difference (Braunwald et al., 1964) by diminishing cardiac contractility and possibly increasing the ventricular volume or reducing stroke volume. This may explain the absence of a measurable pressure difference at the time of operation in patients who previously had evidence of severe obstruction.

The effects of nitroglycerin (Braunwald et al., 1964) and amyl nitrite (Wigle et al., 1963B; Goodwin et al., 1964; Marcus et al., 1964; Hancock and Fowkes, 1966) have also been studied. Nitroglycerin, like isoproterenol, reduces the size of the left ventricular cavity and accentuates the severity of the muscular obstruction of the outflow tract. Amyl nitrite increases cardiac output (Perloff et al., 1963) and probably decreases the left ventricular volume; its effects on the pressure difference across the muscular obstruction resemble those of nitroglycerin.

TRUE OR FALSE OBSTRUCTION? That there is a true localized obstruction to the egress of blood from the left ventricle due to hypertrophic muscle is implicit in the term obstructive cardiomyopathy. The concept of obstruction has been accepted by most workers on the basis of the hemodynamic evidence that has been summarized above, together with supportive evidence at angiocardiography and surgery. However, the authenticity of the obstruction has been questioned (Criley et al., 1965, 1966).

Under certain conditions, systolic pressure differences may be demonstrated in the ventricles of animals. Gauer (1950) found such differences during late systole within the left ventricles of dogs subjected to hemorrhagic shock; they were accentuated by epinephrine. Martin et al. (1963) also found pressure differences during hemorrhagic shock, and Krasnow et al. (1963) induced reversible obstruction by infusion of isoproterenol. Morrow et al. (1965) concluded that the pressure differences in these and other situations were factitious, due to the fact that the catheter tip was impacted between trabecula and therefore was measuring intramyocardial rather than intraluminal pressure. White et al. (1966) confirmed this. In their studies, isoproterenol induced apparent differences in systolic pressure of 30 to 146 (mean 77) mm. Hg in seven dogs. Cinéangiography showed no obstruction in the outflow tract but demonstrated systolic obliteration of the apex of the ventricle in which the tip of the catheter was situated. The pressure difference resulted from the recording of pressure in the isometrically contracting apical muscle about the tip of the catheter.

These observations understandably warranted consideration of the possibility that some of the pressure differences recorded in man might be artifactual. Criley et al. (1965) showed that, in their angiocardiograms, the outflow tract of the ventricle was narrowed but insufficiently to account for recorded pressure differences; the predicted total obstruction in late systole (Pierce et al., 1964) never occurred. On the other hand, on all occasions on which a high pressure was recorded, their catheter tips were situated among the trabecula or in the apex of the ventricle, situations at which there was complete obliteration of the cavity during the latter half of systole (Fig. 13-8). In their view, the effects of many of the physiological and pharmacological interventions discussed previously could be explained equally readily by differences in the completeness of systolic obliteration of the apical portion of the left ventricle. They suggested hypertrophic hyperkinetic cardiomyopathy as a more apt physiological title for the lesion.

Ross et al. (1966A) and Wigle et al. (1967) subsequently marshalled impressive evidence that, although factitious pressure differences can certainly occur from cavity obliteration, true outflow tract obstruction is usually the basis for the difference. Thus, at operation, the surgeon's finger can feel firm constriction in the outflow tract but not in the body of the ventricle; the operations of myomectomy or myotomy are generally followed by reduction or abolition of the pressure gradient (Wigle et al.,

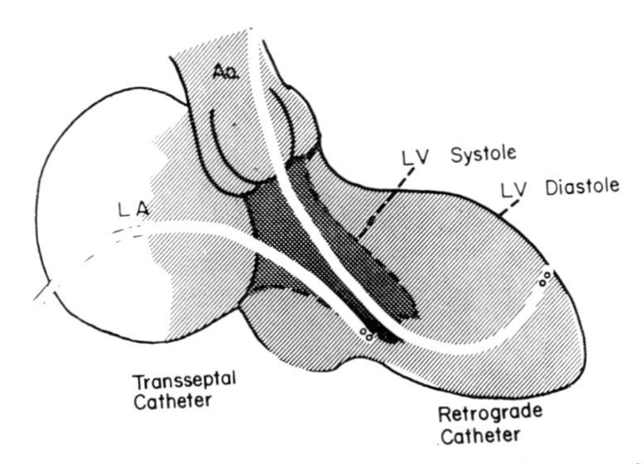

FIGURE 13-8. Superimposed systolic and diastolic frames of a left ventricular cinéangiocardiogram from a patient with a 133 mm. Hg systolic pressure difference in the left ventricle. Note extremely small systolic ventricular size (dark crosshatching) and absence of obstruction at any site in the left ventricle. The retrograde catheter was free in the left ventricular cavity during diastole (light gray shading) but completely enfolded by myocardium during systole. The transseptal catheter was in an intertrabecular recess. Both ventricular catheters recorded equally high ventricular pressures. The retrograde catheter was slowly withdrawn during the cinéangiogram, and a fall in pressure was noted as it entered the area representing systolic chamber size on the diagram. The catheters were not penetrating the myocardium during systole but were completely enfolded by contracting muscle. (From Criley, Lewis, White and Ross, Circulation, 32:881, 1965.)

1963A; Morrow et al., 1964; Bentall et al., 1965; Frye et al., 1965); and in some cases, at angiography, the catheter tip was clearly in an unobliterated portion of the ventricle at a time when it was recording a high pressure.

Krasnow et al. (1963) suggested that patients with obstructive cardiomyopathy may have an abnormal sensitivity to catecholamine stimulation. The demonstration by Pearse (1964) of excessive quantities of adrenergic type fibers in portions of resected muscle from patients with obstructive cardiomyopathy adds further speculation to such a possible relationship.

CARDIOMYOPATHY WITHOUT CONGESTIVE, RESTRICTIVE OR OBSTRUCTIVE FEATURES

Braunwald and Aygen (1963) reported 14 patients with left ventricular hypertrophy who either had no symptoms or had had non-progressive symptoms for periods of several years. None had congestive heart failure, cardiac dilatation, arrhythmias or a history of embolism. Their physical signs and angiocardiographic features resembled those in patients with obstructive cardiomyopathy. Mean right atrial and left atrial pressures were usually within normal limits. In some patients, a prominent left atrial *a* wave resulted in increased left ventricular end-diastolic pressure. There was no pressure difference across the left ventricular outflow tract or across any of the four cardiac valves. However, mild differences (30 to 40 mm. Hg) appeared across the outflow tract in three of five patients during intravenous infusion of isoproterenol.

It is not clear whether such cases constitute a separate entity, or whether, in the course of time, they will develop definitive obstructive features. One possibility is that the presence or absence of a pressure difference in patients with idiopathic left ventricular hypertrophy depends upon the precise location of the hypertrophied muscle.

Six of the patients reported by Yu et al. (1966) had comparable clinical and hemodynamic features. There was no evidence of such possible underlying diseases as hypertension, coronary arteriosclerosis, or congenital or valvular heart lesions. The cardiac outputs were 2.8 to 4.5 (mean 3.8) liters per M.^{2} per minute, the stroke volumes 34 to 60 (mean 50) ml. per M.^{2} per minute and the end-diastolic pressures in the right and left ventricles 3 to 8 (mean 5) and 10 to 13 (mean 11) mm. Hg, respectively. During a follow up period of at least two years, none developed features of left ventricular outflow obstruction, congestion or restriction. Long term repeated examinations will be required before the natural course of the heart disease becomes apparent.

IDIOPATHIC HYPERKINETIC STATE. Brachfeld and Gorlin (1960) described eight patients, referred because of precordial systolic ejection murmurs, who had striking increases in resting values for cardiac output in the absence of any demonstrable underlying disease. Moderate exercise, sufficient to increase the cardiac output in control subjects by over 3 liters per M.^{2} per minute, increased the output in the patients by only about 1 liter. In two of three subjects, the administration of reserpine restored the resting cardiac output and stroke volume to normal levels.

Snyder et al. (1966) described 16 patients with resting values for cardiac output of up to 11.2 liters per M.^{2} per minute, brachial arterial systolic pressures of 148 to 194 mm. Hg and left ventricular ejection rates of 238 to 451 ml. per M.^{2} per second. Frohlich et al. (1966) described two similar cases in whom the administration of beta adrenergic blocking drugs reversed the hyperkinetic features. They suggested that these patients had excess beta adrenergic activity during rest. Harris (1966) studied a group of psychotic patients with persistent sinus tachycardia and increased resting levels of cardiac output and of free fatty acids in the plasma. Beta adrenergic receptor blockade reversed all these features, again suggesting that the hyperkinetic circulation may result from chronically excessive stimulation of beta adrenergic receptors in the heart.

SPECIFIC VARIETIES OF CARDIOMYOPATHY

FAMILIAL CARDIOMYOPATHY. There can be a familial incidence of cardiomyopathy (Evans, 1949; Treger and Blount, 1965). An autosomal dominant type of inheritance has been demonstrated in the larger families, but in a few instances a recessive inheritance has been reported. The pathological findings have been variable. In some cases, there is diffuse or asymmetrical hypertrophy of the myocardium; others are characterized by varying degrees of fibrosis, accumulation of glycogen (Gaunt and Lecutier, 1956) or other polysaccharides (Barry and Hall, 1962), infiltration with chronic inflammatory cells, or thickening of the media and intima of small coronary vessels (Battersby and Glenner, 1961; Treger and Blount, 1965).

The physiological changes likewise vary. Cases with muscular hypertrophy have evidence of obstruction to the outflow tract of the left (and sometimes right) ventricle, either during rest or provoked by infusion of inotropic drugs. Others without demonstrable obstruction have normal intracardiac pressures and levels of blood flow early in the disease, or they may have an increased left atrial pressure and an impaired response of the cardiac output to muscular exercise (Treger and Blount, 1965). In more advanced stages of the disease, the features are characteristic of congestive cardiomyopathy. There is a not infrequent association with the pre-excitation syndrome (Schiebler et al., 1959), paroxysmal arrhythmias and sudden death (Evans, 1949).

CARDIOMYOPATHY ASSOCIATED WITH ALCOHOLISM. Excessive consumption of alcohol may cause direct injury to the heart, leading to alcoholic cardiomyopathy (Burch and Walsh, 1960; Evans, 1961; Brigden and Robinson, 1964).

Beriberi results from vitamin B_1 deficiency and may occur in alcoholic patients who stop eating. It differs from alcoholic cardiomyopathy in that it responds to treatment with vitamin B_1. Blacket and Palmer (1960) studied 19 patients with thiamine sensitive beriberi associated with chronic alcoholism. The cardiac output (4.2 to 15.5, mean 7.1 liters per $M.^2$ per minute), and oxygen consumption (mean 156 ml. per $M.^2$ per minute) were increased, and the arteriovenous difference in oxygen content was reduced (1.0 to 4.0, mean 2.65 ml. per 100 ml.). The right ventricular end-diastolic and pulmonary artery wedge pressures were increased. Systemic vascular resistance was low, averaging 760 dynes sec. $cm.^{-5}$. Forearm blood flow was about three times normal levels. These changes were all reversed following treatment with thiamine. Blacket and Palmer (1960) concluded that beriberi primarily causes vasodilatation in skeletal muscle, with a consequent decrease in systemic vascular resistance and an increase in cardiac output.

Akbarian et al. (1966) also found tachycardia (106 beats per minute), increased cardiac output (6.0 liters per $M.^2$ per minute), increased stroke volume (58 ml. per $M.^2$ per minute), increased right and left ventricular filling pressures, increased blood volume, reduced systemic vascular resistance (770 dynes sec. $cm.^5$) and reduced arteriovenous difference in oxygen content (3.25 ml. per 100 ml.) in four patients with congestive failure due to beriberi. In one patient, there was a marked increase in peripheral resistance and a decrease in cardiac output 37 minutes after an intravenous dose of thiamine. In another, methoxamine failed to increase peripheral resistance; this attested to the severity of the peripheral vasodilatation. Long term treatment with thiamine restored the hemodynamic measurements to normal.

REFERENCES

Akbarian, M., Yankopoulous, N. A., and Abelmann, W. H.: Hemodynamic studies in beriberi heart disease. Am. J. Med., *41*:197, 1966.

Barry, M., and Hall, M.: Familial cardiomyopathy. Brit. Heart J., *24*:613, 1962.

Battersby, E. J., and Glenner, G. G.: Familial cardiomyopathy. Am. J. Med., *30*:382, 1961.

Benchimol, A., Dimond, E. G., and Shen, Y.: Ejection time in aortic stenosis and mitral stenosis. Am. J. Cardiol., *6*:728, 1960.

Bentall, H. H., Cleland, W. P., Oakley, C. M., Shah, P. M., Steiner, R. E., and Goodwin, J. F.: Surgical treatment and postoperative haemodynamic studies in hypertrophic obstructive cardiomyopathy. Brit. Heart J., *27*:585, 1965.

Bevegård, S., Jonsson, B., and Karlöf, I.: Low subvalvular aortic and pulmonic stenosis caused by asymmetrical hypertrophy and derangement of muscle bundles of the ventricular wall. Acta Med. Scand., *172*:269, 1962.

Björk, V. O., Hultquist, G., and Lodin, H.: Subaortic stenosis produced by an abnormally placed anterior mitral leaflet. J. Thorac. Cardiovasc. Surg., *41*:659, 1961.

Blacket, R. B., and Palmer, A. J.: Haemodynamic studies in high output beri-beri. Brit. Heart J., *22*:483, 1960.

Boiteau, G. M., Bourassa, M. G., and Allenstein, B. J.: Upstroke time ratio. A new concept in differentiating valvular and subvalvular aortic stenosis. Am. J. Cardiol., *11*:319, 1963.

Brachfeld, N., and Gorlin, R.: Subaortic stenosis. A revised concept of the disease. Medicine, *38*:415, 1959.

Brachfeld, N., and Gorlin, R.: Idiopathic hyperkinetic state. A new clinical syndrome. Brit. Heart J., *22*:353, 1960.

Brachfeld, N., and Gorlin, R.: Functional subaortic stenosis. Ann. Int. Med., *54*:1, 1961.

Braunwald, E., and Aygen, M. M.: Idiopathic myocardial hypertrophy without congestive heart failure or obstruction to blood flow. Clinical hemodynamic and angiocardiographic studies in fourteen patients. Am. J. Med., *35*:7, 1963.

Braunwald, E., and Ebert, P. A.: Hemodynamic alterations in idiopathic hypertrophic subaortic stenosis induced by sympathomimetic drugs. Am. J. Cardiol., *10*:489, 1962.

Braunwald, E., Lambrew, C. T., Rockoff, S. D., Ross, J., Jr., and Morrow, A. G.: Idiopathic hypertrophic subaortic stenosis: 1. A description of the disease based upon an analysis of 64 patients. Circulation, *30* (Suppl. IV):3, 1964.

Brent, L. B., Aburano, A., Fisher, D. L., Moran, T. J., Myers, J. D., and Taylor, W. J.: Familial muscular subaortic stenosis. An unrecognized form of "idiopathic heart disease," with clinical and autopsy observations. Circulation, *21*:167, 1960.

Brigden, W.: Uncommon myocardial diseases: the non-coronary cardiomyopathies. Lancet, *ii*:1179 and 1243, 1957.

Brigden, W., and Robinson, J.: Alcoholic heart disease. Brit. Med. J., *ii*:1283, 1964.

Brock, R.: Functional obstruction of the left ventricle (acquired aortic subvalvar stenosis). Guy's Hosp. Rep., *106*:221, 1957.

Brock, R.: Functional obstruction of the left ventricle (acquired aortic subvalvar stenosis). Guy's Hosp. Rep., *108*:126, 1959.

Brockenbrough, E. C., Braunwald, E., and Morrow, A. G.: A hemodynamic technic for the detection of hypertrophic subaortic stenosis. Circulation, *23*:189, 1961.

Burch, G. E., and Walsh, J. J.: Cardiac insufficiency in chronic alcoholism. Am. J. Cardiol., *6*:864, 1960.

Burchell, H. B.: Pressure differences and obstruction of left ventricular outflow. Editorial. Circulation, *34*:556, 1966.

Cohen, J., Effat, H., Goodwin, J. F., Oakley, C. M., and Steiner, R. E.: Hypertrophic obstructive cardiomyopathy. Brit. Heart J., *26*:16, 1964.

Criley, J. M., Lewis, K. B., White, R. I., Jr., and Ross, R. S.: Pressure gradients without obstruction. A new concept of "hypertrophic subaortic stenosis." Circulation, *32*:881, 1965.

Criley, J. M., Wilson, W. S., and Ross, R. S.: Left ventricular emptying in outflow tract obstruction. J. Clin. Invest., *45*:999, 1966 (Abstract).

Evans, W.: Familial cardiomegaly. Brit. Heart J., *11*:68, 1949.

Evans, W.: Alcoholic cardiomyopathy. Am. Heart J., *61*:556, 1961.

Fowler, N. O.: Gueron, M., and Rowlands, D. T.: Primary myocardial disease. Circulation, *23*:498, 1961.

Frohlich, E. D., Dustan, H. P., and Page, I. H.: Hyperdynamic beta-adrenergic circulatory state. A.M.A. Arch. Int. Med., *117*:614, 1966.

Frye, R. L., Kinkaid, O. W., Swan, H. J. C., and Kirklin, J. W.: Results of surgical treatment of patients with diffuse subvalvular aortic stenosis. Circulation, *32*:52, 1965.

Gauer, O. H.: Evidence in circulatory shock of an isometric phase of ventricular contraction following ejection. Fed. Proc., *9*:47, 1950 (Abstract).

Gault, J. H., Ross, J., Jr., and Mason, D. T.: Patterns of brachial arterial blood flow in conscious subjects with and without cardiac dysfunction. Circulation, *34*:833, 1966.

Gaunt, R. T., and Lecutier, M. A.: Familial cardiomegaly. Brit. Heart J., *18*:251, 1956.

Goodwin, J. F., Gordon, H., Hollman, A., and Bishop, M. B.: Clinical aspects of cardiomyopathy. Brit. Med. J., *i*:69, 1961.

Goodwin, J. F., Hollman, A., Cleland, W. P., and Teare, D.: Obstructive cardiomyopathy simulating aortic stenosis. Brit. Heart J., *22*:403, 1960.

Goodwin, J. F., Shah, P. M., Oakley, C. M., Cohen, J., Yipintsoi, T., and Pocock, W.: Clinical pharmacology of hypertrophic obstructive cardiomyopathy. In: Ciba Foundation Symposium on Cardiomyopathies. Boston, Little, Brown, 1964.

Gottsegen, G., and Romoda, T.: Hemodynamic patterns of constrictive pericarditis and diffuse myocardial fibrosis. Cor et Vasa (Praha), *6*:194, 1964.

Grosse-Brockhoff, F., and Loogen, F.: Infundibular pulmonary stenosis in chronic left ventricular cardiopathy. Deutsche Med. Wchnschr., *87*:525, 1962.

Hancock, E. W., and Fowkes, W. C.: Effects of amyl nitrite in aortic valvular and muscular subaortic stenosis. Circulation, *33*:383, 1966.

Harris, W. S.: Excessive cardiac adrenergic activity: cause of a hyperkinetic circulatory state in psychotic patients. Circulation, *34* (Suppl. III):123, 1966 (Abstract).

Harrison, D. C., Glick, G., Goldblatt, A., and Braunwald, E.: Studies on cardiac dimensions in intact, unanesthetized man. IV. Effects of isoproterenol and methoxamine. Circulation, *29*:186, 1964.

Hernandez, R. R., Greenfield, J. C., Jr., and McCall, B. W.: Pressure-flow studies in hypertrophic subaortic stenosis. J. Clin. Invest., *43*:401, 1964.

Hetzel, P. S., Wood, E. H., and Burchell, H. B.: Pressure pulses in the right side of the heart in a case of amyloid disease and in a case of idiopathic heart failure simulating constrictive pericarditis. Proc. Staff Meet. Mayo Clin. *28*:107, 1953.

Julian, O. C., and Javid, H.: Left ventricular outflow obstruction: Surgical indications and treatment. Med. Clin. N. Amer., *50*:309, 1966.

Klein, M. D., Lane, F. J., and Gorlin, R.: Unusual characteristics of the left ventricular chamber in subaortic stenosis. Clin. Res., *12*:186, 1964 (Abstract).

Krasnow, N., Rolett, E., Hood, W. B., Jr., Yurchak, P. M., and Gorlin, R.: Reversible obstruction of the ventricular outflow tract. Am. J. Cardiol., *11*:1, 1963.

Lambert, E. C., and Vlad, P.: Primary endomyocardial disease. Ped. Clin. N. Amer., *5*:1057, 1958.

Lynfield, J., Gasul, B. M., Luan, L. L., and Dillon, R. F.: Right and left heart

catheterization and angiocardiographic findings in idiopathic cardiac hypertrophy with endocardial fibroelastosis. Circulation, *21*:386, 1960.
Marcus, F. I., and Jones, R. C.: The use of the Valsalva maneuver to differentiate fixed-orifice aortic stenosis from muscular subaortic stenosis. Am. Heart J., *69*:473, 1965.
Marcus, F. I., Perloff, J. K., and DeLeon, A. C.: The use of amyl nitrite in the hemodynamic assessment of aortic valvular and muscular subaortic stenosis. Am. Heart J., *68*:468, 1964.
Martin, A. M., Hackel, D. B., and Sieker, H. O.: Intraventricular pressure changes in dogs during hemorrhagic shock. Fed. Proc., *22*:252, 1963 (Abstract).
Mason, D. T., Braunwald, E., and Ross, J., Jr.: Effects of changes in body position on the severity of obstruction to left ventricular outflow in idiopathic hypertrophic subaortic stenosis. Circulation, *33*:374, 1966.
Mason, D. T., Braunwald, E., Ross, J., Jr., and Morrow, A. G.: Diagnostic value of the first and second derivatives of the arterial pressure pulse in aortic valve disease and in hypertrophic subaortic stenosis. Circulation, *30*:90, 1964.
Massumi, R. A., Rios, J. C., Gooch, A. S., Nutter, D., DeVita, V. T., and Datlow, D. W.: Primary myocardial disease. Report of fifty cases and review of the subject. Circulation, *31*:19, 1965.
Menges, H., Jr., Brandenburg, R. O., and Brown, A. L., Jr.: The clinical, hemodynamic, and pathologic diagnosis of muscular subvalvular aortic stenosis. Circulation, *24*:1126, 1961.
Morrow, A. G., Lambrew, C. T., and Braunwald, E.: Idiopathic hypertrophic subaortic stenosis. II. Operative treatment and the results of pre- and postoperative hemodynamic evaluations. Circulation, *30* (Suppl. IV):120, 1964.
Morrow, A. G., Vasko, J. S., Henney, R. P., and Brawley, R. K.: Can outflow obstruction be induced within the normal left ventricle? Am. J. Cardiol., *16*:540, 1965.
Nye, R. E., Jr., Lovejoy, F. W., Jr., and Yu, P. N.: Clinical and hemodynamic studies of myocardial fibrosis. Circulation, *16*:332, 1957.
Paré, J. A. P., Fraser, R. G., Pirozynski, W. J., Shanks, J. A., and Stubington, D.: Hereditary cardiovascular dysplasia. A form of familial cardiomyopathy. Am. J. Med., *31*:37, 1961.
Pearse, A. G. E.: The histochemistry and electron microscopy of obstructive cardiomyopathy. In: Ciba Foundation Symposium on Cardiomyopathies. Boston, Little, Brown, 1964.
Perloff, J. K., Calvin, J., DeLeon, A. C., and Bowen, P.: Systemic hemodynamic effects of amyl nitrite in normal man. Am. Heart J., *66*:460, 1963.
Pierce, G. E., Morrow, A. G., and Braunwald, E.: Idiopathic hypertrophic subaortic stenosis. III. Intraoperative studies of the mechanism of obstruction and its hemodynamic consequences. Circulation, *30* (Suppl. IV):152, 1964.
Robin, E. D., and Burwell, C. S.: Hemodynamic aspects of diffuse myocardial fibrosis. Circulation, *16*:730, 1957.
Ross, J., Jr., Braunwald, E., Gault, J. H., Mason, D. T., and Morrow, A. G.: The mechanism of the intraventricular pressure gradient in idiopathic subaortic stenosis. Circulation, *34*:558, 1966A.
Ross, J., Jr., Mason, D. T., Cohn, L. H., and Braunwald, E.: Effects of changes in heart rate on the severity of obstruction to left ventricular outflow in idiopathic hypertrophic subaortic stenosis. Circulation, *34* (Suppl. III):202, 1966B (Abstract).
Schiebler, G. L., Adams, P., and Anderson, R. C.: Familial cardiomegaly in association with Wolff-Parkinson-White syndrome. Am. Heart J., *58*:113, 1959.
Schmincke, A.: Ueber linkseitige muskolöse Conusstenosen. Deutsche Med. Wchnschr., *33*:2082, 1907.
Shillingford, J. P., and Somers, K.: Clinical and hemodynamic patterns in endomyocardial fibrosis. Brit. Heart J., *23*:433, 1961.
Snyder, D., Brest, A. N., and Novack, P.: Systolic hypertension. A presenting finding in the hyperkinetic heart syndrome. Circulation, *31* (Suppl. II):199, 1966 (Abstract).

Soulié, P., Degeorges, M., Joly, F., Caramanian, M., and Carlotti, J.: Une cause de'erreur dans le diagnostic hémodynamique des rétrécissements aortiques. Arch. Mal. Coeur, 52:1002, 1959.

Sousa, J. E. M. R., Zerbini, E. de J., Jatene, A. D., Fontes, V. F., Magalhães, H. M., and Filho, C. M. C.: Transaortic infundibulectomy for hypertrophic subaortic stenosis. Am. J. Cardiol., *15*:801, 1965.

Taylor, R. R., Bernstein, L., and Jose, A. D.: Obstructive phenomena in ventricular hypertrophy. Brit. Heart J., *26*:193, 1964.

Teare, D.: Asymmetrical hypertrophy of the heart in young adults. Brit. Heart J., *20*:1, 1958.

Treger, A., and Blount, S. G.: Familial cardiomyopathy. Am. Heart J., *70*:40, 1965.

Whalen, R. E., Cohen, A. I., Sumner, R. G., and McIntosh, H. D.: Demonstration of the dynamic nature of idiopathic hypertrophic subaortic stenosis. Am. J. Cardiol., *11*:8, 1963.

White, R. I., Jr., Lewis, K. B., and Criley, J. M.: Nonobstructive nature of isoproterenol-induced left ventricular pressure gradients in dogs. Circulation, *32* (Suppl. II):219, 1966 (Abstract).

Wigle, E. D.: The arterial pressure pulse in muscular subaortic stenosis. Brit. Heart J., *25*:97, 1963.

Wigle, E. D., Chrysohou, A., and Bigelow, W. G.: Results of ventriculomyotomy in muscular subaortic stenosis. Am. J. Cardiol., *11*:572, 1963A.

Wigle, E. D., Heimbecker, R. O., and Gunton, R. W.: Idiopathic ventricular septal hypertrophy causing muscular subaortic stenosis. Circulation, *26*:325, 1962.

Wigle, E. D., Lenkei, S. C. M., Chrysohou, A., and Wilson, D. R.: Muscular subaortic stenosis. The effect of peripheral vasodilatation. Canad. Med. Ass. J., *89*:896, 1963B.

Wigle, E. D., Marquis, Y., and Auger, P.: Muscular subaortic stenosis. Initial left ventricular inflow tract pressure in the assessment of intraventricular pressure differences in man. Circulation, *35*:1100, 1967.

Yu, P. N., Cohen, J., Schreiner, B. F., Jr., and Murphy, G. W.: Hemodynamic alterations in primary myocardial disease. Prog. Cardiovasc. Dis., *7*:125, 1964.

Yu, P. N., Schreiner, B. F., Jr., Cohen, J., and Murphy, G. W.: Idiopathic cardiomyopathy. A study of left ventricular function and pulmonary circulation in 15 patients. Am. Heart J., *71*:330, 1966.

Chapter 14

PERICARDIAL DISEASE

- Pericardial Effusion
- Constrictive Pericarditis
- Defects of the Pericardium

PERICARDIAL EFFUSION

The normal pericardial sac contains 5 to 30 ml. of clear serous fluid (Hall, 1948). Up to 100 ml. additional fluid may accumulate within a short time without causing any increase in intrapericardial pressure or any sign of compression of the heart. With further rapid increases in volume, the pressure increases slowly. Finally, a stage is reached at which the pericardial sac is so distended that any small addition of volume leads to a large increase in pressure within the sac.

The hemodynamic effects of acute cardiac tamponade were studied by Isaacs et al. (1954) who made rapid injections of 130 ml. air into the pericardial sac in anesthetized dogs with open chests. The intrapericardial pressure increased from 1 to 13 mm. Hg, the right atrial pressure from 7 to 15 mm. Hg and the left atrial pressure from 8 to 16 mm. Hg. Although there was an absolute increase in the atrial pressures, the effective filling pressures (atrial minus intrapericardial) decreased. Mean pressures in the aorta and pulmonary artery decreased from 150 to 60 and from 24 to 18 mm. Hg, respectively. Systemic blood flow, measured by a Potter electroturbinometer, decreased from 3.1 to 1.2 liters per minute. After removal of the air, pressures and flows rapidly returned to previous levels.

Biplane cinéangiography was used to study rapidly occurring changes in the left ventricular volume of dogs before and after the induction of tamponade. Tamponade resulted in increases of left ventricular end-diastolic and intrapericardial pressures and decreases in aortic blood pressure and cardiac output. Left ventricular end-diastolic volume fell from 28 to 19 ml., end-systolic volume from 12 to 10 ml. and the ejection fraction from 59 to 45 per cent (mean values). The rate of ventricular emptying during systole decreased from 117 to 58 ml. per second. Thus, decreases in the ejection fraction and in the rate of ventricular emptying, in addition to the well known impairment of diastolic filling, contribute to the altered dynamics of pericardial tamponade (Craig et al., 1966).

In man, acute effusions that produce distention of the pericardium are also accompanied by increased venous pressure, diminished systemic arterial pressure and decreased cardiac output. With each inspiration, there is a further transient increase in jugular venous and a decrease in systemic arterial pressure. Inspiration is accompanied by descent of the diaphragm, which results in a more negative intrathoracic pressure and a more positive intraabdominal pressure, changes that facilitate increased filling of the right atrium. In pericardial effusion, filling of the right atrium is impeded, so that the great veins become distended at the time of maximal venous return.

Inspiratory decrease in systemic arterial pressure was termed pulsus paradoxus by Kussmaul (1873). This term has led to misunderstanding, since it implies that the pulse changes in a direction opposite to the normal. In fact, the arterial pressure decreases during inspiration in normal subjects, but the decrease is by less than 10 mm. Hg. The intrathoracic pressure changes during the respiratory cycle do not affect left atrial and pulmonary venous pressures equally, so that there is a small reduction in the gradient between pulmonary venous and left atrial pressure during inspiration. This would decrease left atrial and left ventricular filling and would explain the slight reduction in left ventricular ejection and systemic arterial pressure observed during inspiration in normal conditions (Katz and Gauchat, 1924; Golinko et al., 1963).

In pericardial effusion, the inspiratory decrease in arterial pressure is much more pronounced, sometimes to the extent that peripheral pulses become impalpable. Pulsus paradoxus also occurs in chronic constrictive pericarditis. However, it is not pathognomonic of pericardial disease. It also occurs in chronic obstructive disease of the airways, such as asthma and severe emphysema, because of the unusually wide swings of pressure during respiration. Dornhorst et al. (1952) felt that increased filling of the right atrium during inspiration, by further raising intrapericardial pressure, impeded left ventricular filling. Wood (1956) and Dock (1961) suggested that the diaphragm, descending during inspiration, tightens the pericardium, raises intrapericardial pressure and impedes filling of the left ventricle. In the dogs with closed chests studied by Golinko et al. (1963), the cardiac output during acutely induced tamponade decreased from 4.7 to 1.7 liters per minute, and the decrease in systemic arterial systolic pressure during inspiration averaged 15 to 22 mm. Hg. Prior to tamponade, there was a small pressure gradient from pulmonary veins to left atrium throughout the respiratory cycle; during tamponade, the gradient persisted with expiration but was annulled or even reversed during inspiration. Retrograde passage of iodinated oil from left atrium to pulmonary vein during inspiration was demonstrated in cinéangiograms. In these studies, an altered pulmonary venous–left atrial pressure gradient was mainly responsible for the pulsus paradoxus.

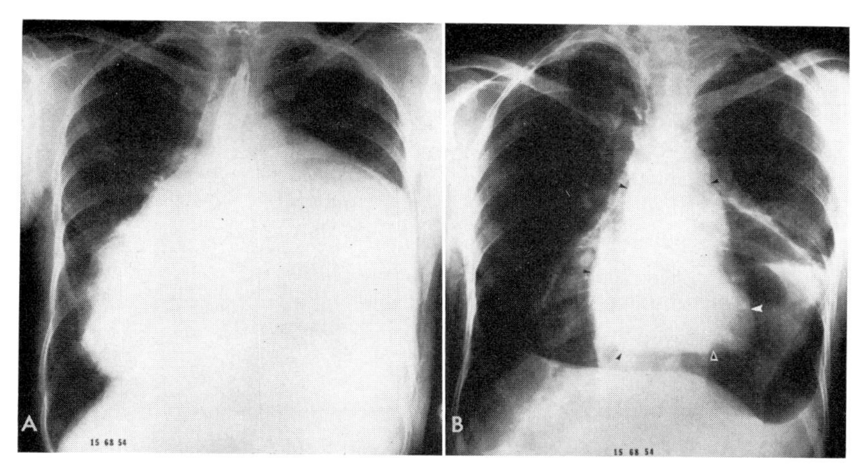

FIGURE 14-1. Posteroanterior x-ray films of the chest in a patient with chronic pericardial effusion. *A:* Before aspiration. *B:* After aspiration of 3.5 liters of cholesterol laden fluid and injection of 1.5 liters air. Note the thickened pericardium and the small cardiac silhouette.

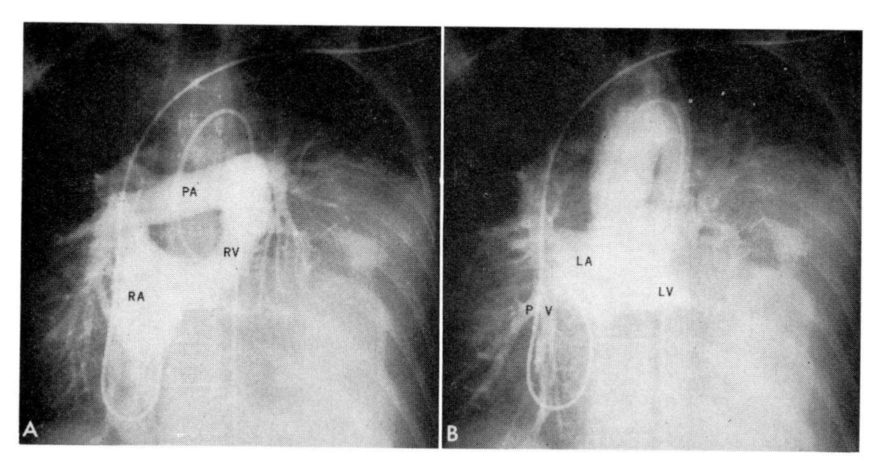

FIGURE 14-2. Angiocardiograms in the patient with chronic pericardial effusion prior to aspiration of the fluid, illustrating the small size of the heart chambers. *A:* rightsided structures. *B:* Leftsided structures. RA, Right atrium; RV, right ventricle; PA, pulmonary artery; PV, pulmonary veins; LA, left atrium; LV, left ventricle.

In contrast with acute tamponade, the pericardium can become adapted to a greatly increased content of fluid when this accumulates more slowly. Thus, if the intrapericardial and systemic venous pressures have been acutely increased by the accumulation of fluid, the gradual addition of further fluid is necessary if the increase of venous pressure is to be maintained (Foulger and Foulger, 1932). An extreme example of this adaptation is provided by those patients who have chronic pericarditis with effusion of 2 liters or more, but who have few symptoms and normal systemic venous pressures. Figure 14-1 shows x-ray films of a woman before and after aspiration from her pericardial sac of 3.5 liters of cholesterol laden fluid (seven per cent of her body weight). She had distention of the neck veins because of compression of the superior vena cava, but she did not have pulsus paradoxus. Figure 14-2 shows the remarkable degree of compression of the cardiac chambers to which she had become adapted.

CONSTRICTIVE PERICARDITIS

Constrictive pericarditis exists when adequate diastolic filling of the ventricles is hampered by a thick rigid fibrotic pericardium. The signs and symptoms are in large part caused by the increased venous pressures in both pulmonary and systemic circulations. The systemic venous pulse characteristically has a steep y descent and a deep y trough (Fig. 14-3*A*);

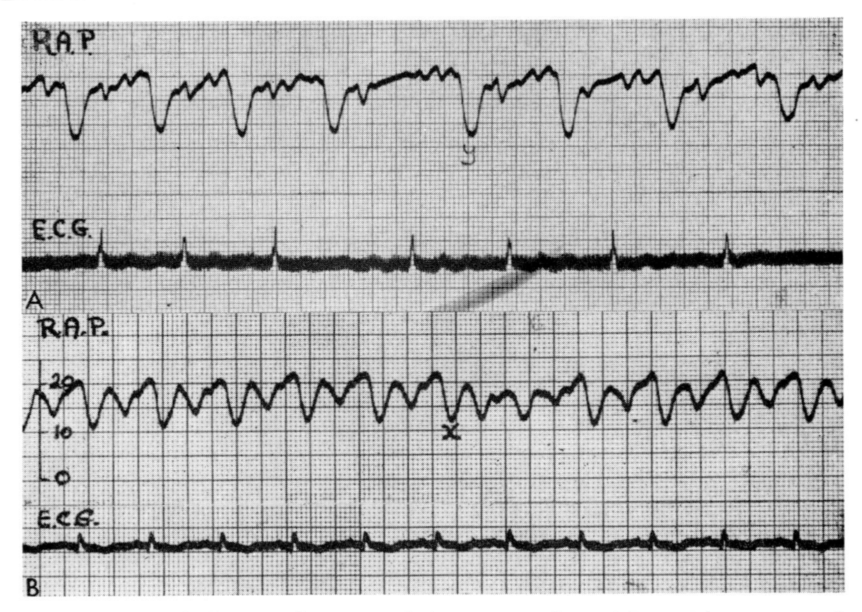

FIGURE 14-3. *A:* Steep y descent and deep y trough in right atrial pressure pulse in patient with constrictive pericarditis. *B:* Steep x descent in right atrial pressure pulse in a second patient. (From Wood, Am. J. Cardiol., 7:48, 1961.)

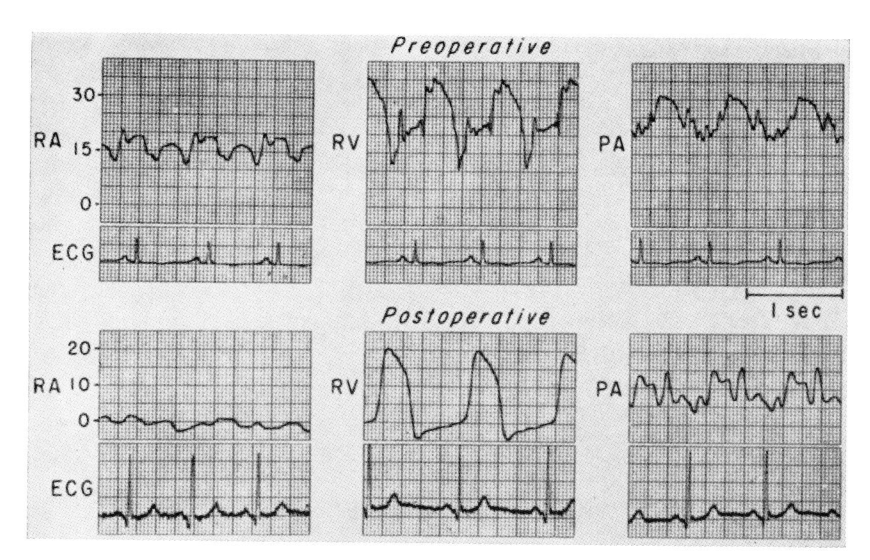

FIGURE 14-4. Before resection of the constrictive pericardium, the right atrial pressure was considerably increased, the right ventricular pressure showed an early diastolic dip with an elevated mid and late diastolic plateau and the pulmonary arterial pressure was moderately increased. After resection, the levels of pressure and the contours of the pressure pulses were restored to normal. (From Kloster, Crislip, Bristow, Herr, Ritzmann, and Griswold, Circulation, *32*:415, 1965.)

this results from the high atrial pressure, the sudden release of pressure as the tricuspid valve opens and the sudden rise of pressure as further diastolic filling is prevented by the rigid pericardium. This is an important finding in that it excludes the possibility of tricuspid stenosis which in many other respects may simulate constrictive pericarditis. Because of the small orifice of the valve, decompression of the right atrium is slow in tricuspid stenosis, and a y descent is not seen. In some cases, there is also a prominent x descent (Gibson, 1959), with the result that the right atrial pressure pulse has a W or M shaped contour (Fig. 14-3*B*).

As in pericardial tamponade, pressures in both atria characteristically increase during inspiration. The inspiratory increase in right atrial pressure is readily demonstrable in the veins of the neck; the increase in left atrial pressure has been demonstrated during cardiac catheterization (Sawyer et al., 1952; Wood, 1961). The systolic pressure in the right ventricle is normal or slightly increased. There is a prominent early diastolic dip in pressure followed by rapid rise to attain a plateau for about the remaining two thirds of diastole (square root sign) (Fig. 14-4). The terminal portion of the early diastolic dip corresponds in time with the prominent sharp third heart sound which is due to the sudden cessation of ventricular inflow resulting from the rigid pericardium. Neither the early diastolic dip nor the third heart sound is present in pericardial effusion (Fowler, 1962;

Lange et al., 1966). The pulse pressure in the pulmonary artery is small, and the difference between mean pressures in right atrium and pulmonary artery is less than in normal persons.

The systemic arterial pulse pressure is often though not always diminished and, as in pericardial tamponade, pulsus paradoxus may be noted. The response of the arterial pressure pulse to the Valsalva maneuver is generally of the square wave type. The cardiac output during rest is normal or low (Wood, 1961), and, characteristically, there is little increase in output with exercise (Wade and Bishop, 1962). However, McHenry et al. (1965) described two patients with clinical and hemodynamic evidence of severe constriction who were able to undertake strenuous exercise, with a sixfold increase in oxygen consumption and with increases in cardiac output from 5.5 to 17.7 and 4.6 to 14.6 liters per minute, respectively. Johansson (1958) suggested that an increase in the stroke volume during rest may be the best evidence of a successful surgical result. Failure of a low cardiac output to return to normal following a technically successful operation for resection of the pericardium is presumptive evidence of myocardial atrophy (Dines et al., 1958) or of fibrocalcific changes in the myocardium.

The hemodynamic changes that have been described are characteristic but not pathognomonic of constrictive pericarditis. Similar findings may occur in such conditions as idiopathic cardiomyopathy (Burwell and Robin, 1954), myocardial fibrosis (McKusick, 1952), obesity (Lange et al., 1966) and cardiac amyloidosis (Hetzel et al., 1953). Differential features are discussed by Yu et al. (1953), Wilson et al. (1954) and Wood (1961).

Patients with complete surgical decortication of the ventricles subsequently had normal pressures in the right side of the heart both at rest and during moderate exercise (Fig. 14-4). Those with less complete freeing of the ventricles had persistent mild increases in rightsided pressures and inadequate increases in cardiac output with exercise. Decortication of the atria and venae cavae made no difference to the postoperative findings (Kloster et al., 1965).

DEFECTS OF THE PERICARDIUM

Congenital absence of the parietal pericardium is an occasional finding at necropsy in persons who died of some totally unrelated cause (Beck, 1931; Ellis et al., 1959) and who had no history of cardiac disability. Partial or total pericardiectomy has no effect on the heart size in resting dogs (Mazzone, 1912), although van Liere and Grisler (1930) found that vagal stimulation caused more cardiac dilatation after pericardiectomy than in intact animals. Vigorous exercise is well tolerated (Beck and Moore, 1925). The racing times of a greyhound were similar before and after removal of the pericardium (Donald et al., 1964)

Holt et al. (1960) found that in hypervolemic dogs, removal of the pericardium resulted in considerable distention of the heart, with high transmural pressures throughout the cardiac cycle. They concluded that the intact pericardium protects the heart from overdistention in ventricular diastole. In the absence of hypervolemia, pericardiectomy does not lead to overdistention of the heart (Grant, 1926) or other impairment of cardiac function (Moore and Shumacker, 1953). Mitral and tricuspid valve regurgitation develop more readily in the absence of the pericardium, when the heart is subjected to increased filling pressure (Berglund et al., 1955). Bartle et al. (1966), using biplane angiocardiography, found that the end-diastolic and end-systolic volumes of the left ventricle increased to a significantly greater extent after an acute volume load of saline or blood in pericardiectomized dogs than in sham operated dogs. There was no significant difference between the two groups in intravascular pressures, the maximal rate of increase of left ventricular pressure, stroke volume, stroke work or ejection time, values for all of which increased.

Partial defects of the pericardium are potentially more serious, since they may permit herniation of portions of the heart. These herniations are usually asymptomatic (Chang and Leigh, 1961), but incarceration and strangulation may be caused by the hernial ring of the defect and may lead to syncope and sudden death (Sunderland and Wright-Smith, 1944).

REFERENCES

Bartle, S. H., Hermann, H. J., Cavo, J. W., Moore, R. A., and Costenbader, J. M.: Effect of the pericardium on left ventricular volume and function in acute hypervolemia. Circulation, *34* (Suppl. III):50, 1966 (Abstract).

Beck, C. S.: Congenital deficiency of the pericardium. The function of the pericardium. A.M.A. Arch. Surg., *22*:282, 1931.

Beck, C. S., and Moore, R. L.: The significance of the pericardium in relation to surgery of heart. A.M.A. Arch. Surg., *11*:550, 1925.

Berglund, E., Sarnoff, S. J., and Isaacs, J. P.: Ventricular function. Role of the pericardium in regulation of cardiovascular hemodynamics. Circ. Research, *3*:133, 1955.

Burwell, C. S., and Robin, E. D.: Some points in the diagnosis of myocardial fibrosis. Trans. Assoc. Amer. Physicians, *67*:67, 1954.

Chang, C. H., and Leigh, T. F.: Congenital partial defect of the pericardium associated with herniation of the left atrial appendage. Am. J. Roent., Rad. Ther. & Nuc. Med., *86*:517, 1961.

Craig, R. J., Whalen, R. E., Behar, V. S., Thompson, H. K., Jr., and McIntosh, H. D.: Ventricular volume changes in acute pericardial tamponade. Circulation, *34* (Suppl. III):80, 1966 (Abstract).

Dines, D. E., Edwards, J. E., and Burchell, H. B.: Myocardial atrophy in constrictive pericarditis. Proc. Staff Meet. Mayo Clin., *33*:93, 1958.

Dock, W.: Inspiratory traction on the pericardium: the cause of pulsus paradoxus in pericardial disease. A.M.A. Arch. Int. Med., *108*:837, 1961.

Donald, D. E., Milburn, S. E., and Shepherd, J. T.: Effect of cardiac denervation on the maximal capacity for exercise in the racing greyhound. J. Appl. Physiol., *19*:849, 1964.

Dornhorst, A. C., Howard, P., and Leathart, G. L.: Pulsus paradoxus. Lancet, *i*:746, 1952.

Ellis, K., Leeds, N. E., and Himmelstein, A.: Congenital deficiencies in parietal pericardium; review with 2 new cases including successful diagnosis by plain roentgenography. Am. J. Roent., Rad. Ther. & Nuc. Med., *82*:125, 1959.

Foulger, M., and Foulger, J. H.: The blood pressure and electrocardiogram in pericardial effusion. Am. Heart J., *7*:744, 1932.

Fowler, N. O.: Physical Diagnosis of Heart Disease. New York, Macmillan, 1962.

Gibson, R.: Atypical constrictive pericarditis. Brit. Heart J., *21*:583, 1959.

Golinko, R. J., Kaplan, N., and Rudolph, A. M.: The mechanism of pulsus paradoxus during acute pericardial tamponade. J. Clin. Invest., *42*:249, 1963.

Grant, R. T.: Congenital pericardial deficiency. An observation on the function of the pericardium. Heart, *13*:371, 1926.

Hall, E. M.: The heart. In: Anderson, W. A. D.: Pathology. St. Louis, Mosby, 1948.

Hetzel, P. S., Wood, E. H., and Burchell, H. B.: Pressure pulses in the right side of the heart in a case of amyloid disease and in a case of idiopathic heart failure simulating constrictive pericarditis. Proc. Staff Meet. Mayo Clin., *28*:107, 1953.

Holt, J. P., Rhode, E. A., and Kines, H.: Pericardial and ventricular pressure. Circ. Research, *8*:1171, 1960.

Isaacs, J. P., Berglund, E., and Sarnoff, S. J.: Ventricular function. III. The pathologic physiology of acute cardiac tamponade studied by means of ventricular function curves. Am. Heart J., *48*:66, 1954.

Johansson, L.: Surgical Treatment of Chronic Constrictive Pericarditis. A Clinical Study of 38 Cases, with Special Reference to the Value of the Left Transpleural Approach. Diss. Med., Stockholm, Karolinska Institutet, 1958.

Katz, L. N., and Gauchat, H. W.: Pulsus paradoxus (with special reference to pericardial effusions): II. Experimental. A.M.A. Arch. Int. Med., *33*:371, 1924.

Kloster, F. E., Crislip, R. L., Bristow, J. D., Herr, R. H., Ritzmann, L. W., and Griswold, H. E.: Hemodynamic studies following pericardiectomy for constrictive pericarditis. Circulation, *32*:415, 1965.

Kussmaul, A.: Über schwielige Mediastino-Pericarditis und den paradoxen Puls. Klin. Wschr., *10*:443, 1873.

Lange, R. L., Botticelli, J. T., Tsagiris, T. J., Walker, J. A., Gani, M., and Bustamente, R. A.: Diagnostic signs in compressive cardiac disorders. Constrictive pericarditis, pericardial effusion, and tamponade. Circulation, *33*:763, 1966.

Mazzone, F.: Contributo sperimentale alla pericardiectomia. Zentralblatt f. Chir., *39*:1046, 1912.

McHenry, M. M., Ord, J. W., Johnston, R. R., and Shoener, J. A.: Exercise performance and stroke volume changes in two patients with constrictive pericarditis. Am. Heart J., *70*:180, 1965.

McKusick, V. A.: Chronic constrictive pericarditis. 1. Some clinical and laboratory observations. Bull. Johns Hopkins Hosp., *90*:3, 1952.

Moore, T. C., and Shumacker, H. B., Jr.: Congenital and experimentally produced pericardial defects. Angiology, *4*:1, 1953.

Sawyer, C. G., Burwell, C. S., Dexter, L., Eppinger, E. C., Goodale, W. T., Gorlin, R., Harken, D. E., and Haynes, F. W.: Chronic constrictive pericarditis: further consideration of the pathologic physiology of the disease. Am. Heart J., *44*:207, 1952.

Sunderland, S., and Wright-Smith, R. J.: Congenital pericardial defects. Brit. Heart J., *6*:167, 1944.

van Liere, E. J., and Grisler, G.: The influence of the pericardium on acute cardiac dilatation produced by vagal stimulation. Am. J. Physiol., *94*:162, 1930.

Wade, O. L., and Bishop, J. M.: Cardiac Output and Regional Blood Flow. Oxford, Blackwell, 1962.

Wilson, R. H., Hoseth, W., Sadoff, C., and Dempsey, M. E.: Pathologic physiology and diagnostic significance of the pressure pulse tracings in the heart in patients with constrictive pericarditis and pericardial effusion. Am. Heart J., *48*:671, 1954.

Wood, P.: Diseases of the Heart and Circulation. Second edition. London, Eyre and Spottiswood, 1956.
Wood, P.: Chronic constrictive pericarditis. Am. J. Cardiol., 7:48, 1961.
Yu, P. N. G., Lovejoy, F. W., Joos, H. A., Nye, R. E., and Mahoney, E. B.: Right auricular and ventricular pressure patterns in constrictive pericarditis. Circulation, 7:102, 1953.

Chapter 15

INTRACARDIAC AND INTERVASCULAR SHUNTS

- Detection and Quantitation of Shunts
- Left-to-Right Shunts
- Right-to-Left Shunts

The presence of abnormal communications between chambers of the left and right sides of the heart, or between the great vessels, results in the shunting of blood. The magnitude and direction of the shunt in any particular case are determined by the nature of the anatomical and pathological changes. The shunt may be exclusively arteriovenous (left to right), resulting in the abnormal recirculation of blood through the pulmonary circulation; it may be exclusively venoarterial (right to left), resulting in diversion of blood away from the pulmonary circulation and in desaturation of blood in the systemic arteries; or it may be bi-directional. Most shunts are congenital.

In addition, shunts may be acquired between adjacent arteries and veins in more peripheral parts of the body. When these are sufficiently large, they result in a pronounced decrease in peripheral vascular resistance and in a chronically increased cardiac output.

DETECTION AND QUANTITATION OF SHUNTS

During cardiac catheterization, several techniques are of value in detecting or confirming the site of a shunt and in assessing its magnitude and direction.

UNUSUAL COURSE TAKEN BY CARDIAC CATHETER. The cardiac catheter often traverses the defect responsible for the shunt. For example, when a secundum variety of atrial septal defect is present, it may pass from the high portion of the right atrium in a leftward direction to enter the left atrium and the left ventricle or a pulmonary vein. When a patent ductus arteriosus is the responsible lesion, the catheter may pass through this to enter the descending aorta. The course taken by the catheter is usually sufficiently characteristic to enable the experienced operator to recognize the site and nature of the defect (Fig. 15-1).

MEASUREMENT OF OXYGEN SATURATION. This is of particular value in the case of arteriovenous shunts. The diagnosis is based upon the demonstration of increased saturation in the rightsided chamber or vessel with which the defect communicates. If the shunt is large, its location can be established with confidence. However, two possible sources of confusion exist. First, more than one shunt is occasionally present. Second, the coexistence of valvular regurgitation may result in shunted blood being detected in a chamber proximal to that into which the shunt occurs. For example, the combination of ventricular septal defect with tricuspid regurgitation may lead to an erroneous conclusion that a shunt is present at atrial level.

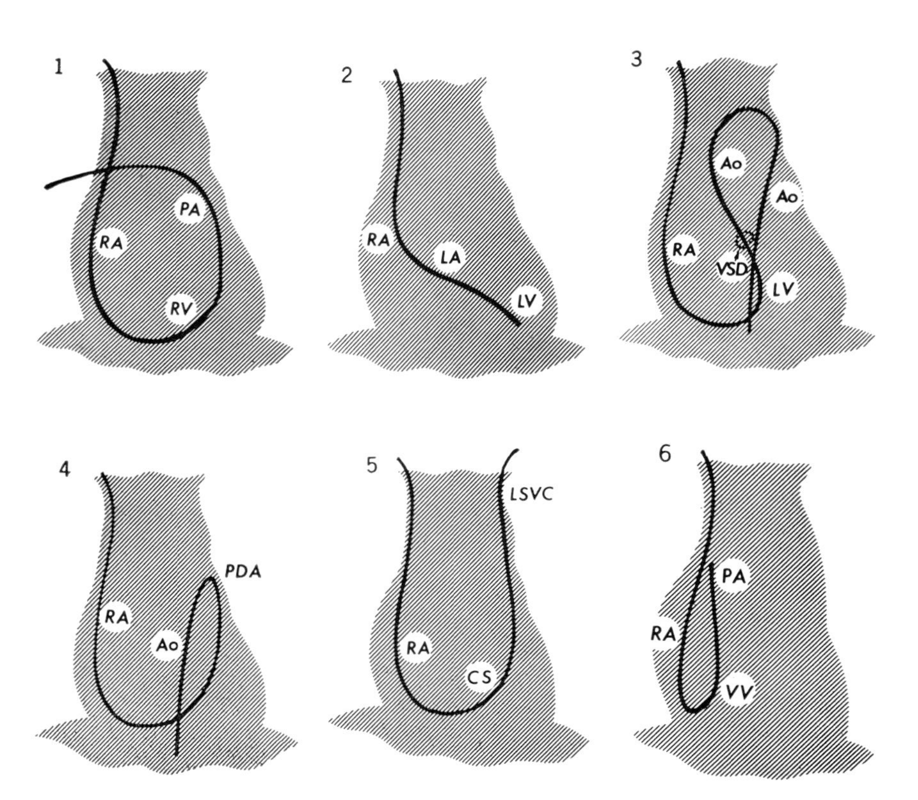

FIGURE 15-1. Characteristic directions taken by catheters in a normal heart and in various congenital cardiac defects. 1. Normal heart. 2. Septum secundum variety of atrial septal defect. 3. Ventricular septal defect. 4. Patent ductus arteriosus. 5. Persistent left superior vena cava. 6. Congenitally corrected transposition of the great vessels. RA, Right atrium; RV, right ventricle; PA, pulmonary artery; LA, left atrium; LV, left ventricle; VSD, ventricular septal defect; Ao, aorta; PDA, patent ductus arteriosus; CS, coronary sinus; LSVC, left superior vena cava; VV, venous ventricle.

Increased precision in the detection of small arteriovenous shunts is possible through the availability of the cuvette type of transmission oximeter that permits rapid sequential sampling with reinfusion of the blood into the patient (Wood et al., 1960). Alternative methods include reflection oximetry (Bossina et al., 1960) and the use of fiberoptic catheters (Gamble et al., 1965). The last of these is particularly suited for continuous monitoring of the oxygen saturation of either arterial or venous blood (Harrison et al., 1965).

Nevertheless, if the shunt is small, there may be difficulty in proving its existence by oximetric techniques alone. This is especially so if it is occurring at the level of the great veins or the right atrium. The reason is that even in normal subjects, streamlining of venous blood occurs in the right atrium with resultant inhomogeneity of saturation (see Chapter 1). In subjects who are apprehensive, moment to moment alterations in systemic blood flow may also make difficult the interpretation of minor increases in saturation. When the subject is in a steady state, relatively small increases in saturation (three to four per cent) may be significant, particularly if the increase in saturation is consistently found in several series of measurements taken in rapid succession.

The approximate magnitude of pulmonary and systemic flow and of the flow through shunts may be calculated from saturation data. The equations for pulmonary (O_p) and systemic (O_s) blood flow are:

$$Q_p = \frac{V_{O_2}}{C_{pvO_2} - C_{paO_2}}$$

and

$$Q_s = \frac{V_{O_2}}{C_{saO_2} - C_{mvO_2}}$$

where V_{O_2} is the total oxygen consumption per minute, C_{pvO_2} and C_{paO_2} are the oxygen contents of blood in the pulmonary veins and pulmonary artery, and C_{saO_2} and C_{mvO_2} are the oxygen contents of blood in systemic arteries and of mixed venous blood, respectively. The value for mixed venous blood is commonly taken as the averaged saturation of samples from the superior and inferior venae cavae.

If it is not possible to obtain a sample from the pulmonary veins (or left atrium), the content of systemic arterial blood may be substituted in the equation for pulmonary blood flow. Because of venous admixture in the leftsided heart chambers, the saturation of blood in systemic arteries is normally one to three per cent less than that in pulmonary veins; therefore, this substitution leads to a slight overestimate of pulmonary blood flow.

Several other factors reduce the absolute accuracy in the calculation of blood flow in patients with shunts:

1. When the lesion is a high ventricular septal defect, blood in the

pulmonary artery may not be completely mixed, and when it is a patent ductus arteriosus, mixing is certainly incomplete. This will affect the calculation of pulmonary blood flow.

2. When there is a very large left-to-right shunt, the difference in oxygen content between pulmonary artery and pulmonary veins is small. Therefore, minor inaccuracies in the measurement of oxygen content may account for substantial errors in the calculated level of pulmonary blood flow. This is best illustrated by an example.

Normal patient: $V_{O_2} = 240$ ml. per minute; C_{pvO_2} and $C_{paO_2} = 150$ and 190 ml. per liter; $Q_p = 240/190 - 150 = 240/40 = 6.0$ liters per minute. If the margin of error in measuring the oxygen content is $\pm$ 2 ml. per liter, then the maximal and minimal values for Q_p are $240/188 - 152 = 240/36 = 6.67$ liters per minute and $240/192 - 148 = 240/44 = 5.45$ liters per minute, respectively. Thus, the potential variability of results is $6.67 - 5.45$ or 1.22 liters per minute (20 per cent of the true value of 6.0 liters per minute.).

Patient with large left-to-right shunt: $V_{O_2} = 240$ ml. per minute; C_{pvO_2} and $C_{paO_2} = 180$ and 190 ml. per liter; $Q_p = 240/190 - 180 = 240/10 = 24.0$ liters per minute. Assuming the same margins of error, maximal and minimal values for Q_p are $240/188 - 182 = 240/6 = 40.0$ liters per minute and $240/192 - 178 = 240/14 = 17.1$ liters per minute. In this instance, the potential variability is $40.0 - 17.1$ or 22.9 liters per minute (95 per cent of the true value of 24.0 liters per minute).

Clearly, when very large left-to-right shunts are present, values calculated for pulmonary blood flow should be regarded as orders of magnitude rather than as precise values. As a corollary, values derived from this flow, such as pulmonary vascular resistance, should also be regarded as approximations.

3. For the valid application of the direct Fick principle, samples of mixed venous and arterial blood must be drawn simultaneously. When shunts are present, simultaneous sampling of blood from all the requisite sites for the measurement of both pulmonary and systemic flow is usually not possible, for technical reasons. If the patient is in a steady state, the inaccuracy due to asynchronous sampling may be small; otherwise, especially in infants and children, it may be considerable.

4. In the case of right-to-left shunts, it is often not possible to obtain samples of blood from the pulmonary veins or from a leftsided chamber proximal to the entry of the shunted blood. Therefore, one must assume that pulmonary venous blood is 98 per cent saturated with oxygen. In the presence of chronic lung disease, severe pulmonary venous congestion or alveolar hypoventilation from heavy sedation, this assumption is unwarranted; if it is made, the magnitude of the right-to-left shunt will be overestimated.

Volumes of flow through shunts (Q_{sh}) are readily derived when pulmonary and systemic flows are known. Thus, for a left-to-right shunt:

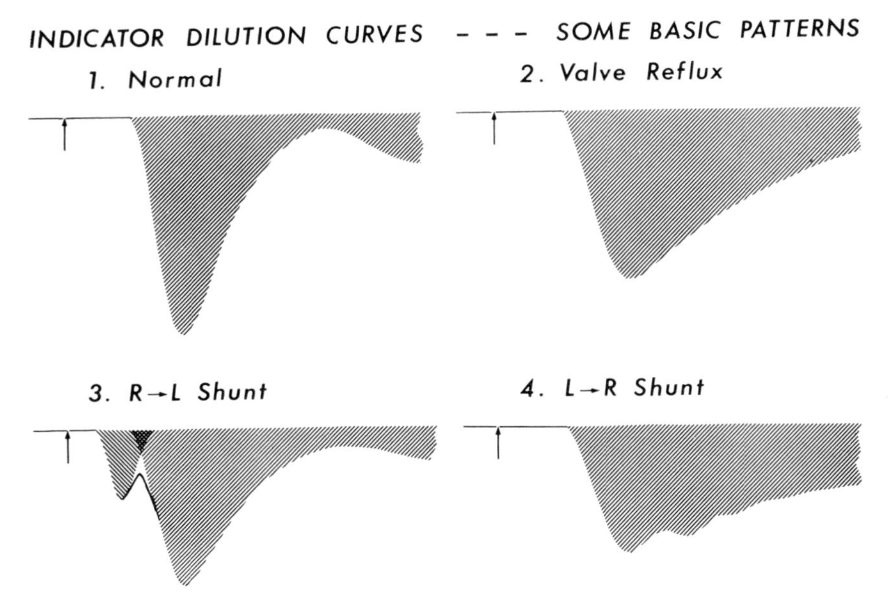

FIGURE 15-2. Some basic patterns of dilution curves recorded from systemic arteries following injection of indicator into sites in the right side of the heart. For descriptions, see text.

$Q_{sh} = Q_p - Q_s$. The shunt flow may also be expressed as a percentage of total pulmonary flow: Q_{sh} (%) $= 100\ (Q_p - Q_s)/Q_p$. For a right-to-left shunt: $Q_{sh} = Q_s - Q_p$. The shunt flow may be expressed as a percentage of total systemic flow: Q_{sh} (%) $= 100\ (Q_s - Q_p)/Q_s$. When a shunt is bidirectional, the situation is much more complex. Although formulae have been devised for estimating the flow in each direction (Dexter et al., 1947), so many assumptions have to be made that their value is doubtful.

DYE DILUTION CURVES. A variety of dilution techniques, involving the use of different indicators, are now available for the detection and quantitation of shunts. Details of their application are beyond the scope of this book and are available in several reviews (Fox, 1966; Marshall and Wood, 1966; Kaplan et al., 1966). This discussion will be concerned with basic principles. Most attention will be paid to techniques involving the use of colored dyes such as indocyanine green, since these are most widely used. The application of other types of indicators will be considered more briefly.

Figure 15-2 shows some basic patterns of dilution curves recorded by continuous sampling of blood from a peripheral artery through a densitometer, following injection of indocyanine green dye into the right atrium. The polarity is such that increasing concentration is recorded in a downward direction. In the normal curve, there is a delay following the injection before the first appearance of dye at the sampling site (appearance time).

The concentration then increases rapidly to a rounded peak and declines more slowly (disappearance slope) to attain a minimal value (least concentration) as recirculation commences.

When a right-to-left shunt is present distal to the site of injection, a fraction of dye traverses it, thereby bypassing the pulmonary circulation and appearing early at the sampling site. In the third curve, the early appearing dye accounts for the initial small triangle. The main portion of the curve (second large triangle) is inscribed by dye taking a normal course. The fraction of dye that is shunted is equal to the area of the initial triangle divided by the combined area of both triangular components of the curve. The right-to-left shunt may be expressed as a percentage of total systemic blood flow by multiplying this fraction by 100. These calculations are valid, however, only if the injected dye has become adequately mixed with venous blood before it reaches the site of the shunt. Otherwise, spuriously high values may be obtained in consequence of preferential shunting of inadequately mixed dye across the defect. In practice, unless the sampling site is in a central location just distal to the shunt (for example, the root of the aorta) and blood is sampled rapidly through the densitometer, or unless a fiberoptic catheter is used, the two triangular components of the curve will be so smeared that they cannot be separated. The calculation may then be made from measurement of the forward portions of the two triangles, as described by Swan et al. (1953) (Fig. 15-3). In infants with right-to-left shunts, the extremely short pulmonary circulation time occasionally results in such smearing that identification of an early component, let alone its quantitation, may be difficult.

The site in the heart or great vessels at which the right-to-left shunt is occurring may be localized by recording a series of dilution curves fol-

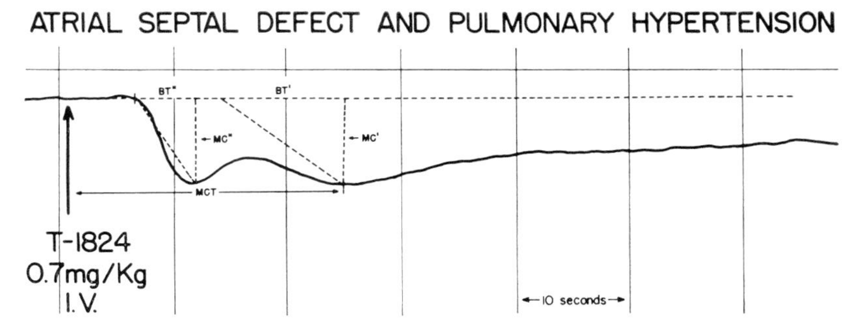

FIGURE 15-3. Forward triangle method for calculation of the magnitude of a right-to-left shunt. The formula is 100 (BT″ x MC″) ÷ (BT″ x MC″) + BT′ x MC′). BT′ is taken as 46 per cent of MCT (based on measurements by Hetzel et al. [1958] of the time components of normal dilution curves). In this example, the shunt was 32 per cent of total systemic flow, and the oxygen saturation of arterial blood was 81 percent. (From Marshall and Wood. In: Intravascular Cathetherization. Ed. Zimmerman. Second edition. Springfield, Thomas, 1966.)

lowing injection of dye successively into pulmonary artery, right ventricle and right atrium. Injection into a vessel or chamber distal to the site of the shunt results in no early appearance of dye, whereas injection at or proximal to its site results in demonstration of early appearing dye.

In Figure 15-2, the fourth curve shows the characteristic alteration in contour of an arterial dilution curve when a moderately large left-to-right shunt is present. The appearance time is normal. The magnitude of the initial peak is reduced in proportion to the size of the shunt. The disappearance slope is prolonged and distorted due to repeated pulmonary recirculation of an exponentially diminishing fraction of the injected dye. Although there is some similarity between the contours of such a curve and that of valvular regurgitation (Fig. 15-2, second curve), the disappearance slope of the former generally shows gentle undulations whereas that of the latter is perfectly smooth.

Small left-to-right shunts are less readily demonstrable in arterial dilution curves than are small right-to-left shunts. The reason is that the latter cause deflections from the level baseline preceding the portion of the curve due to normally circulating dye, whereas the deflections due to small left-to-right shunts are blended in the disappearance slope. Thus, right-to-left shunts as small as two or three per cent of the systemic blood flow can be detected, whereas left-to-right shunts of up to 20 per cent of the pulmonary blood flow may fail to distort conventionally recorded curves sufficiently to permit a diagnosis to be made with confidence (Broadbent and Wood, 1954). This was also demonstrated by Castillo et al. (1966) who simulated the effects of different sizes of shunts by injecting appropriate fractions of dye at appropriate times into different sites in the hearts of normal dogs.

With increasingly large left-to-right shunts, the peak concentration of the initial portion of the arterial dilution curve becomes progressively less, whereas the distortion of the disappearance slope becomes progressively greater. Therefore, the ratio of the peak concentration to the concentration at one or more points on the disappearance slope should have an inverse relationship to the magnitude of the shunt. Empirical formulae were derived by Carter et al. (1960) for estimation of the shunt as a percentage of total pulmonary blood flow (Fig. 15-4). Since factors other than the magnitude of the shunt may also influence the contours and time components of indicator dilution curves (Marshall, 1962), the calculated value is an approximation. Clearly, if valvular regurgitation coexists, the size of the shunt will be overestimated, since regurgitation also decreases peak concentration and increases the distortion during the disappearance phase. Also, the formulae were derived from analysis of curves obtained from a peripheral artery, following injection into the right side of the heart. They cannot be applied to the analysis of curves resulting from other combinations of injection and sampling sites. Finally, the formulae are of little value in the presence of extremely small left-to-right shunts.

Prior to the introduction of indocyanine green dye, dilution curves could not be recorded from the venous side of the circulation, since the spectral absorption peaks of the blue dyes such as T-1824 that were then in use coincided with the maximal spectral absorption of reduced hemoglobin. The absorption peak of indocyanine green, in contrast, is at 800 mμ, a point at which oxyhemoglobin and reduced hemoglobin transmit light equally. Therefore, curves recorded with this dye as the indicator are relatively unaffected by variations in the oxygen saturation of hemoglobin (Fox et al., 1957). A number of consequent refinements of technique have permitted more certain identification of small left-to-right shunts and have facilitated their localization.

1. The venous sampling technique consists of injecting dye into a distal pulmonary artery and sampling, in succession, from the main pulmonary artery, high and low positions in the right ventricle, right atrium and superior vena cava. The presence of early appearing dye in a curve implies that there is a left-to-right shunt at or proximal to the sampling site. Although this is a precise method for the detection and localization of very small left-to-right shunts, it has the disadvantage that it entails the introduction of two venous catheters.

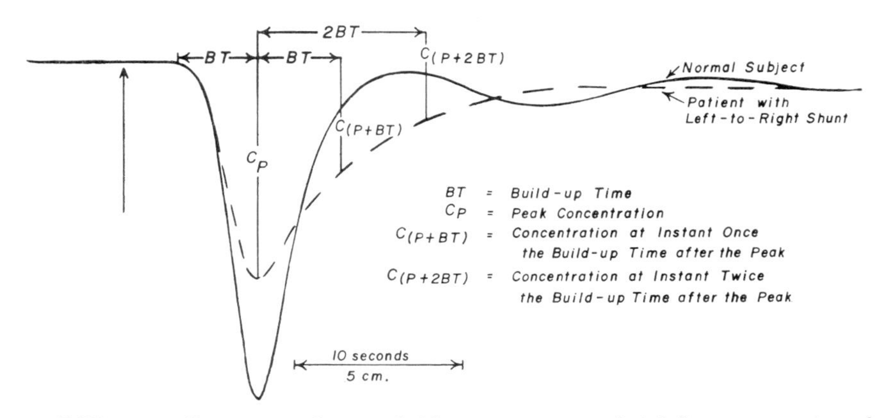

FIGURE 15-4. Superimposed arterial dilution curve recorded following injection of dye into the right side of the heart in a normal subject and a patient with a left-to-right shunt. Note that the peak concentration (C_p) is less and the concentration at specfiic points on the disappearance slope—$C_{(P+BT)}$ and $C_{(P+2BT)}$—is greater in the patient with the shunt. The shunt, expressed as a percentage of pulmonary blood flow, is calculated as the average of the following expressions:

$$141 \times C_{(P+BT)}/C_p - 42$$

and

$$135 \times C_{(P+2BT)}/C_p - 14$$

(From Marshall and Wood. In: Intravascular Catheterization. Ed. Zimmerman. Second edition. Springfield, Thomas, 1966.)

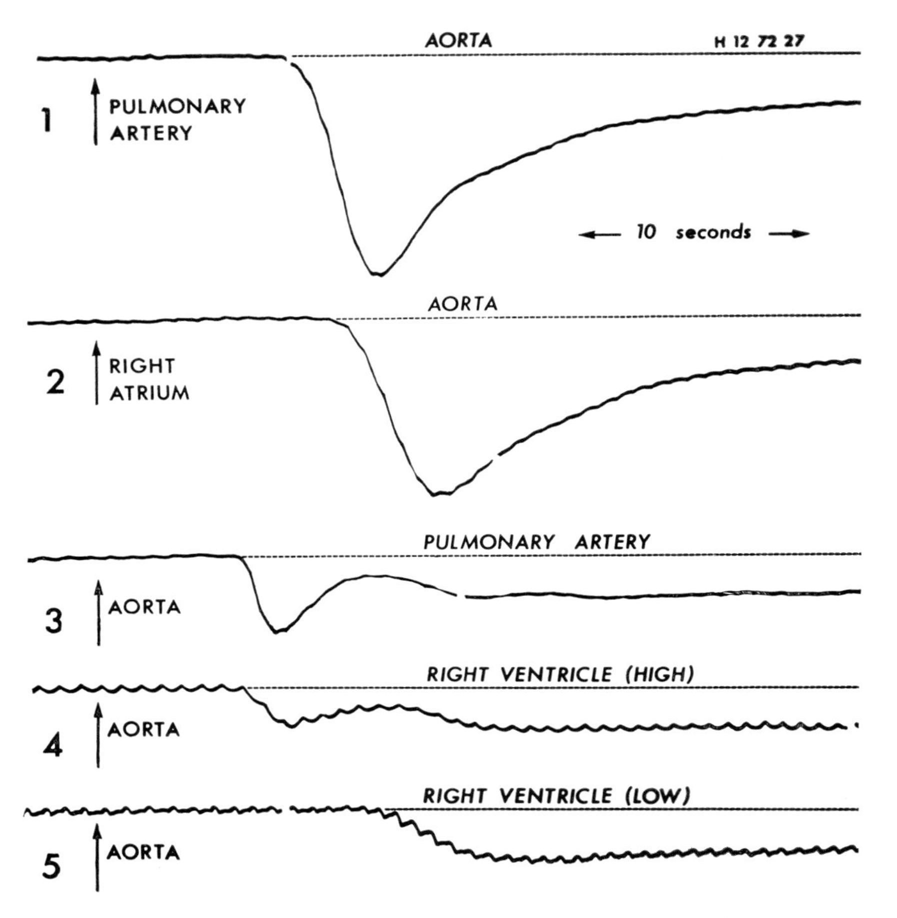

FIGURE 15-5. Localization of small left-to-right shunt by the use of two catheters. The upper pair of curves were obtained by sampling from the aortic root following injection of dye into the pulmonary artery and right atrium, respectively. They show prolongation of the disappearance slope due to the effects of a left-to-right shunt or valvular regurgitation or both. The lower three curves were recorded following injection of dye into the aortic root. Early appearing dye was detected in the high right ventricle but not in the low right ventricle. The diagnosis of a small high ventricular septal defect associated with aortic regurgitation due to a prolapsed valve cusp and with infundibular pulmonary stenosis was made by angiocardiography and confirmed by subsequent operation.

2. Simultaneous leftsided cardiac catheterization enables dye to be injected in the left atrium, left ventricle, aortic root and aortic arch, while dilution curves are recorded, in turn, from various sites in the rightsided chambers and great vessels. An example of this application is shown in Fig. 15-5.

OTHER INDICATOR DILUTION METHODS. Many types of indicator substances other than colored dyes are now available. They include nitrous oxide, radioactive ethyl or methyl iodide (Case et al., 1958), radioactive krypton (Kr^{85}), helium followed by oxygen (Amplatz et al., 1961), Freon, hydrogen, chemical reducing agents such as sodium ascorbate, and gamma emitting radioisotopes detectable by precordial scanning.

Gaseous indicators are particularly suited for the detection of left-to-right shunts, since they are rapidly introduced to the left side of the heart by inhalation. The nitrous oxide method (Sanders et al., 1959; Bernstein and Jose, 1962) has the disadvantage that the determination of levels of the gas in arterial and venous samples is time consuming, and results are not immediately available. Krypton-85 is the gas most widely used at present. Before its inhalation, a sample of blood is obtained for a background count of radioactivity. A mixture of Krypton-85 and air is then inhaled for 30 seconds. Between the tenth and thirtieth seconds, simultaneous samples are obtained from a cardiac catheter in an appropriate chamber or vessel in the venous side of the circulation and from a systemic artery. After correction for background count, the ratio of venous to arterial count is obtained. Braunwald et al. (1962) found ratios of 13 to 113 per cent in 161 patients subsequently proved to have left-to-right shunts, and of 0 to 12 per cent in 162 patients without shunts.

The method employing inhaled hydrogen as indicator and intravascular platinum electrodes as detectors has comparable sensitivity (Clark and Bargeron, 1959). For the detection of left-to-right shunts, one electrode is placed in the aorta and the other at various sites in the right side of the heart. Potentials from the two electrodes are recorded following the inhalation of a single breath of hydrogen. The transit time of hydrogen between the two electrodes identifies the shunt. Vogel et al. (1962) used a catheter with electrodes 10 cm. apart to permit the recording of dilution curves from adjacent chambers. For right-to-left shunts, hydrogen dissolved in physiological saline solution is injected into various sites in the right side of the heart and its early appearance detected in the aorta or peripheral arteries. The hydrogen method has the disadvantage that the gas is flammable. Further attempts at quantitation of the demonstrated shunts have not been successful (Hyman, 1961), and there may be false positive results in the presence of pulmonary disease (Clark et al., 1960).

Amplatz (1966) has recently introduced the use of Freon, a relatively inert non-toxic gas that is used in the refrigerator industry for the detection of leaks. In the presence of a left-to-right shunt, the gas is immediately detected in blood drawn via a catheter from the right side of the heart following a single inhalation of Freon 12 or Freon 22. Since Freon is rapidly eliminated from the blood, several curves may be obtained in rapid succession.

Ascorbic acid may also be used as an indicator. A small platinum electrode polarized as an anode, mounted on the catheter tip, has been

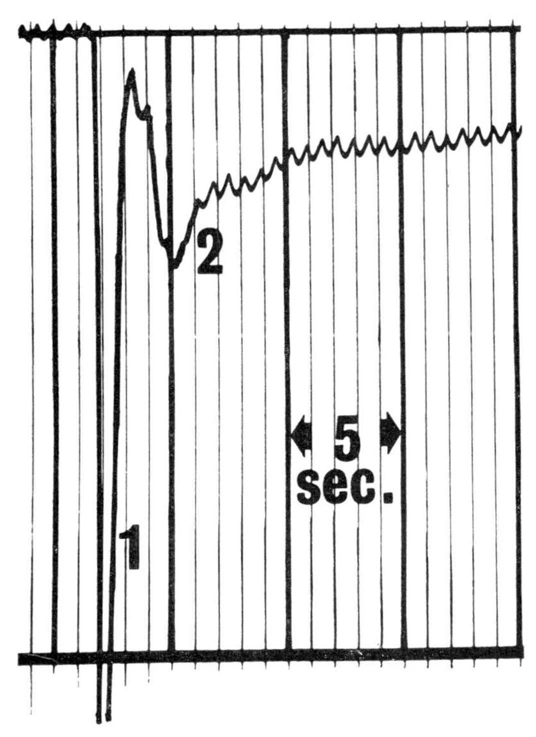

FIGURE 15-6. Dilution curve obtained from a platinum electrode polarized as an anode in the pulmonary artery following injection of sodium ascorbate into the right ventricle. Deflection 1 was caused by the ascorbate initially flowing past the electrode, whereas deflection 2 resulted from early pulmonary recirculation due to a large left-to-right shunt at atrial level. The dynamic response of the instrument is apparent from the suddenness of the initial deflection. (From Kaplan, Clark and Bargeron. In: Intravascular Catheterization. Ed. Zimmerman. Second edition. Springfield, Thomas, 1966.)

used as a detecting device for left-to-right shunts (Clark and Bargeron, 1959). When the acid is injected through the catheter, it is immediately detected. As it leaves the site of the injection, the tracing rapidly falls towards the baseline. When a left-to-right shunt is present, a second peak occurs two to four seconds later (Fig. 15-6). When a shunt is not present, the second peak is delayed and corresponds with systemic recirculation of the acid. Aortic or arterial electrodes may also be used to detect both left-to-right and right-to-left shunts.

ANGIOCARDIOGRAPHY. Continuous improvements in equipment and techniques during the past two decades have led to the pre-eminent role of angiocardiography in the localization of shunts in all areas of the circulation. These have included the development of catheters to permit selective injections, of power injectors, of contrast media with increased radiopacity, reduced viscosity and fewer side effects, of improved biplane angiographs and ciné techniques, of image intensification fluoroscopy, and of electronic circuits to permit triggering of the injection at predetermined times during the cardiac cycle. The anatomical information provided by selective angiocardiography supplements the physiological information provided by pressure measurements, oximetry and indicator dilution techniques in the assessment of the effects of shunts. Angiocardiography, in a sense, is itself an indicator dilution technique, since it provides information concerning the temporal dispersal of an indicator (the contrast medium). This is emphasized by the development of roentgen videodensitometric techniques that may in the future, when combined with computer techniques, make possible the measurement of blood flow in individual vessels of healthy subjects or patients (Wood et al., 1964).

LEFT-TO-RIGHT SHUNTS

The physiological effects of left-to-right shunts are partly dependent on their location. In this discussion, the effects of shunts between low pressure vessels and chambers (the great veins and the atria) will be considered separately from the effects of those between the ventricles or between the great arteries (pulmonary artery and aorta). The secundum variety of atrial septal defect will be taken as the prototype of the former and ventricular septal defect as the prototype of the latter.

SHUNTS IN LOW PRESSURE AREAS. In patients without heart disease, the mean left atrial pressure averages 8 mm. Hg and the mean right atrial pressure 4 mm. Hg; thus, there is a mean difference of 4 mm. Hg from left to right atrium (Braunwald et al., 1961). When an atrial septal defect is small, there is still a small pressure difference (Dexter, 1956) during most of the cardiac cycle (Little et al., 1949). This ensures that the blood will shunt in a left-to-right direction. With large defects, there is little or no difference. Maintenance of an exclusively or predominantly left-to-right shunt is then due to the greater distensibility of the right atrium and to the lesser resistance to filling of the right ventricle as compared with the leftsided chambers.

There is often a small right-to-left component in the shunt, even in patients in whom the pulmonary artery pressure is normal or only slightly increased. This component is more readily demonstrable when dye is injected into the inferior vena cava, and represents persistent streamlining of flow that occurs to a more marked degree as a necessary component of the circulation in the fetus. In these patients, the amount of venous admixture is too small to have much effect on the oxygen saturation of systemic arterial blood, which is in the range of 94 to 97 per cent.

The magnitude of the left-to-right shunt is dependent upon the size of the defect and upon the relative resistances to filling of the right ventricle and the pulmonary circulation on the one hand, and of the left ventricle

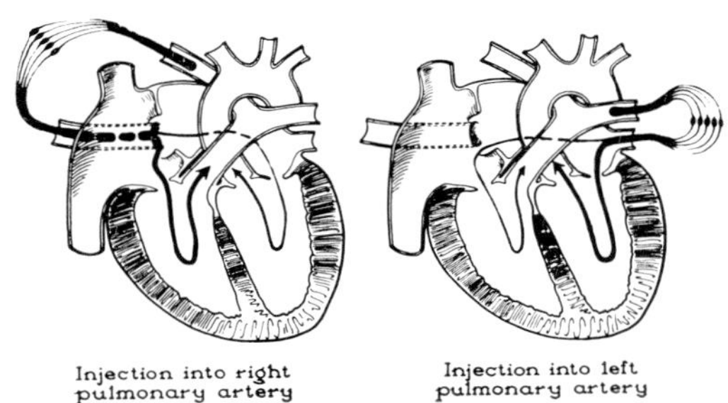

FIGURE 15-7. Diagram of paths taken by indicator following its injection into the right and left pulmonary arteries in a patient with atrial septal defect. Note that the right pulmonary veins are situated close to the defect, and hence most of the indicator injected into the right lung shunts across the defect. In contrast, there is preferential streaming through the mitral valve of indicator injected into the left lung. (From Swan, Hetzel, Burchell and Wood, Circulation, *14*:200, 1956.)

and the systemic circulation on the other. The low resistance of normal pulmonary vessels may permit a fourfold increase in pulmonary blood flow, while systemic blood flow remains normal. Values of the order of 25 liters per minute for pulmonary blood flow are not infrequent. Since the resting heart rate is within the normal range, the right ventricular stroke volume may be up to 400 ml. Such a large stroke volume affects the function of the heart in several ways. The right ventricle is greatly enlarged to accommodate this volume in addition to the end-systolic volume. The rate of ejection of blood into the pulmonary artery is increased, and this is the basis for the early systolic murmur commonly heard along the upper left border of the sternum. The increased rate of flow may lead to a systolic pressure gradient of up to 25 mm. Hg across the pulmonary valve; in normal subjects, the gradient does not exceed 5 mm. Hg. The duration of right ventricular ejection is prolonged, and this leads to delayed closure of the pulmonary valve and hence to wide separation of the aortic and pulmonary components of the second heart sound. In normal subjects, the degree of splitting of the second heart sound varies during the respiratory cycle; it is widest during inspiration, since this augments systemic venous return and increases the filling of the right side of the heart. In patients with atrial septal defect, the atria are in free communication. Therefore, the inspiratory increase in venous return no longer affects solely the rightsided chambers; also, it is a small increase in relation to the total volume of the right ventricle. The right atrium and the pulmonary arteries are also greatly enlarged in order to accommodate the increased flow of blood, whereas the left atrium is usually normal in size, since it is effectively decompressed by the defect. The tricuspid valve remains competent for many years, even in the presence of a very large left-to-right shunt. The increased rate of flow through this valve orifice may give rise to a diastolic murmur. However, if complications such as pulmonary hypertension or atrial fibrillation occur, further dilatation of the right atrium and ventricle and stretching of the tricuspid valve ring lead to tricuspid regurgitation.

Swan et al. (1956A) showed that there is usually preferential shunting of blood returning from the right lung. The reason is that the ostia of the right pulmonary veins are situated close to the edge of the defect, whereas those of the left pulmonary veins are situated at a distance (Fig. 15-7).

The Valsalva maneuver may be used to illustrate alterations in the central circulation in atrial septal defect. During the latter part of the strain there is, in normal persons, a marked decrease in effective arterial

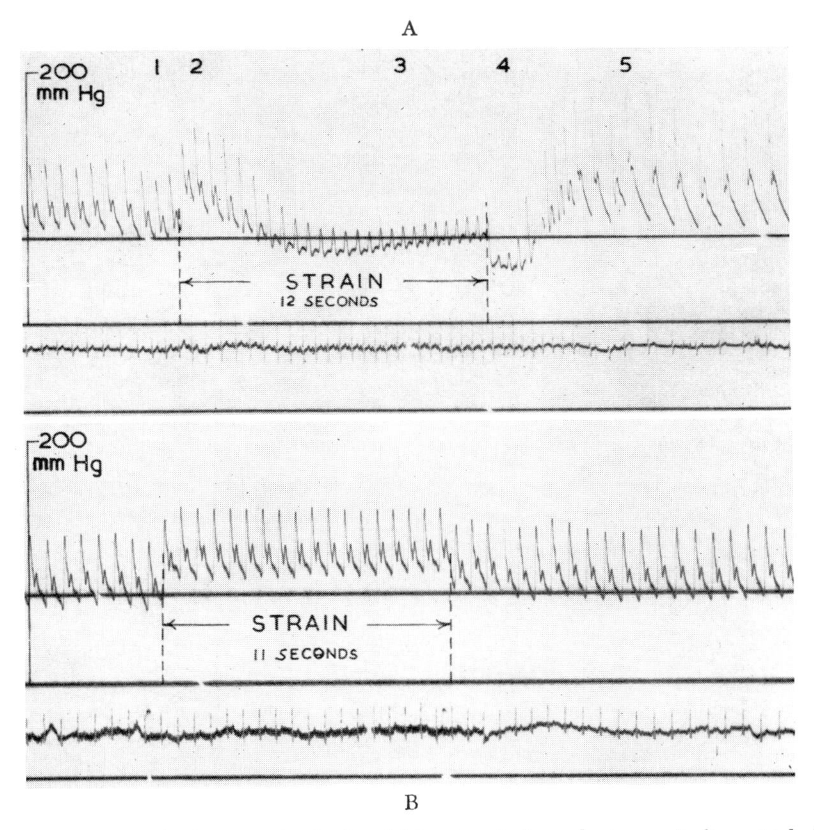

FIGURE 15-8. *A:* Pressure in the brachial artery before, during and after a Valsalva maneuver in a normal subject. Note the rapid decrease in arterial pressure and the increase in heart rate as the strain is continued, and the overshoot of arterial pressure and reflex bradycardia soon after release of the strain. *B:* Pressure in the brachial artery in a patient with a large uncomplicated septal defect. The response is of the square wave type, with no alteration in either effective blood pressure or heart rate, similar to the response in patients with left ventricular failure. (From Hancock, Oliver, Swanson and Hultgren, Am. Heart J., *65*:50, 1963.)

systolic, diastolic and pulse pressures and an increase in heart rate. These changes are due to depletion of the reservoir of blood in the pulmonary circulation and to a consequent decrease in left ventricular output. Immediately after release of the strain, the arterial pressures are low, but they rapidly increase and overshoot the control level, owing to a combination of peripheral vasoconstriction and rapid repletion of the pulmonary circulation from the surge of systemic venous return. The rapid increase in arterial pressure during the overshoot phase stimulates the arterial baroreceptors and may result in bradycardia. Lee and Gimlette (1957) found a response to the Valsalva maneuver of the square wave type, similar to that characteristic of heart failure, in two patients with atrial septal defect. Hancock et al. (1963) also found square wave responses in the majority of the patients with atrial septal defect whom they studied (Fig. 15-8). The exceptions were patients with small left-to-right shunts and with only slightly enlarged hearts. The square wave response is due to the greatly increased volume of blood in the rightsided heart chambers and lungs that ensures an adequate supply of blood for left ventricular filling for the total duration of the strain.

Additional effects of the Valsalva maneuver may be demonstrated by arterial oximetry (McIlroy, 1959) and indicator dilution curves. In patients with a bidirectional shunt at atrial level, the arterial saturation may increase during a Valsalva maneuver, because of diminution or abolition of the right-to-left component of the shunt; following release of the strain, there may be a sudden decrease in arterial saturation, due to the transient increase in the right-to-left component of the shunt occasioned by sudden overfilling of the right atrium by the surge of desaturated venous blood.

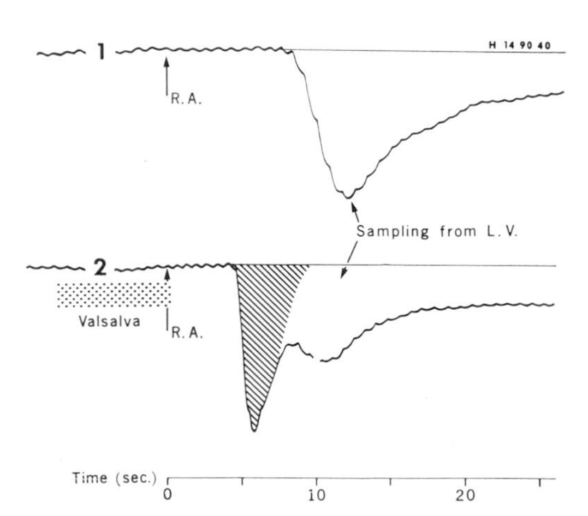

FIGURE 15-9. Demonstration of large transient right-to-left shunt in a patient with atrial septal defect and valvular pulmonary stenosis. *Above:* A control curve shows no right-to-left shunt and a small left-to-right shunt. *Below:* The shaded area indicates the approximate magnitude of the right-to-left shunt that was demonstrated by injecting indicator into the right atrium just before the release of a Valsalva maneuver.

Indicator dilution techniques may also be used to demonstrate the occurrence of right-to-left shunting following release of the strain. This is most readily shown in the presence of an increased resistance to outflow from the right ventricle, due to pulmonary hypertension or pulmonary stenosis (Fig. 15-9).

The pulmonary artery pressure is normal or only slightly increased in the majority of patients with atrial septal defect and in almost all those under 21 years of age. Thus, the pulmonary vascular resistance is usually decreased. In some patients, however, pulmonary vascular resistance increases, due to hypertrophy of the media and secondary thickening of the intima of the pulmonary arteries and arterioles. This leads to pulmonary hypertension, to additional hypertrophy and reduced distensibility of the right ventricle and to a decrease in the magnitude of the left-to-right shunt. Weidman et al. (1957) found that, in those patients whose mean pulmonary arterial pressures exceeded 30 mm. Hg, there was an inverse relationship between pressure and flow. Shunting at the atrial level becomes bidirectional and eventually, when the right ventricle has become less distensible than the left, it may be predominantly or exclusively in the right-to-left direction. It is not clear why this sequence of events occurs in some patients and not in others with equally large shunts.

Although the increased pulmonary vascular resistance is mainly due to organic changes in the walls of the resistance vessels, vasoconstriction may be a contributory factor. Thus, the inhalation of 100 per cent oxygen

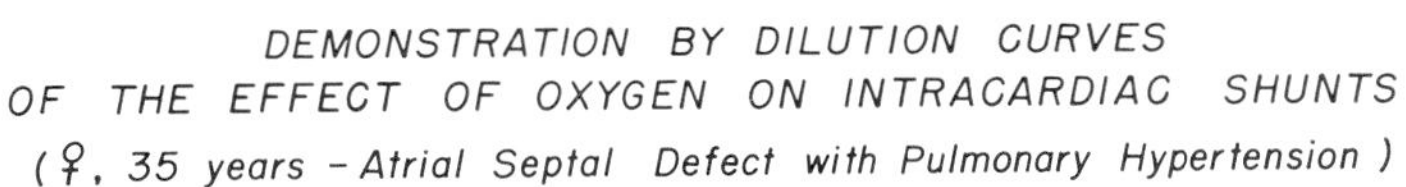

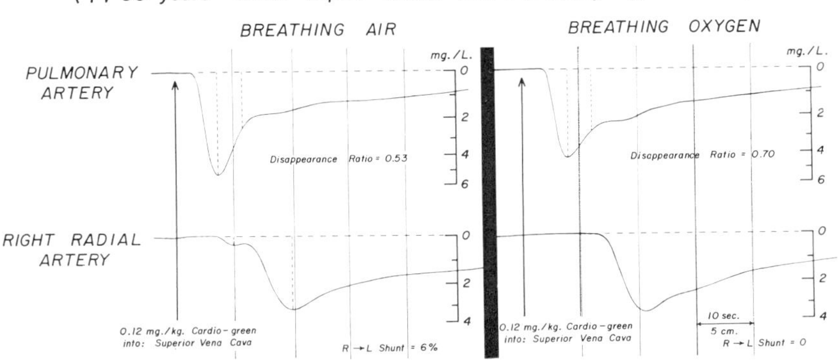

FIGURE 15-10. Effect of inhalation of air and of 100 per cent oxygen on the shunt in a patient with atrial septal defect and moderate pulmonary hypertension. The left-to-right shunt, shown best in the disappearance slopes of the curves recorded from the pulmonary artery, was increased during the breathing of oxygen, while the small right-to-left shunt, shown in the curve recorded from the radial artery, was abolished. (From Swan, Burchell and Wood, Circulation, *20*:66, 1959.)

in place of air often leads to a decrease of up to 50 per cent in calculated values for pulmonary vascular resistance. The magnitude of the left-to-right shunt may be increased, and the right-to-left component of the shunt abolished (Fig. 15-10). Also, acetylcholine chloride, when infused into the pulmonary artery, may slightly reduce pulmonary arterial pressure, increase blood flow, or both (Shepherd et al., 1959).

The hemodynamic effects of atrial septal defects may be greatly modified by the coexistence of valvular lesions such as pulmonary stenosis and mitral stenosis, or of other shunts. When two or more congenital defects coexist, the hemodynamic effects are mainly determined by the more severe lesion. Thus, when there is mild pulmonary valve stenosis, with a right ventricular systolic pressure in the range of 50 to 80 mm. Hg, the flow through a large atrial septal defect is predominantly in the left-to-right direction. However, it is not as great as it would be through an identical septal defect in the absence of valvular obstruction, and reversal of the flow can be readily demonstrated by the Valsalva maneuver (Fig. 15-9). When the pulmonary stenosis is severe, there is a further increase in the resistance to filling of the hypertrophied right ventricle, and the shunt through the atrial defect may be balanced or predominantly in the right-to-left direction.

When atrial septal defect coexists with mitral valve disease, the hemodynamic effects again are determined by the relative severity of the two lesions. Thus, severe mitral stenosis or mitral atresia is accompanied by a high left atrial pressure. If the interatrial communication is small, there is a continuous pressure gradient between the atria which results in continuous left-to-right shunting and sometimes in a continuous murmur (Ross et al., 1963). If the obstruction at the valve is severe and the interatrial communication is large, then the left-to-right shunt is enhanced; further, the increased left atrial pressure is transmitted to the right atrium, so that systemic venous pressure is increased. Both mitral stenosis and mitral regurgitation may, at times, result in such stretching of the walls of the left atrium that a left-to-right shunt occurs through the gradual development of incompetence of the foramen ovale (Marshall and Warden, 1964).

SHUNTS IN HIGH PRESSURE AREAS. The effects of ventricular septal defects are determined mainly by their size and by the state of the pulmonary vascular bed. Small defects provide resistance to flow between the ventricles, so that a pressure difference is maintained. Large defects, with cross sectional areas equal to or greater than that of the aortic valve ring, or greater than 1 $cm.^2$ per $M.^2$ body surface area cause very little resistance to flow, so that pressures in the two ventricles are equal (Fig. 15-11). When the resistance in the pulmonary circulation is low, pulmonary blood flow is increased by up to three or even four times normal (hyperkinetic pulmonary hypertension). When it is high, pulmonary blood flow is normal or decreased (obstructive pulmonary hypertension). In many

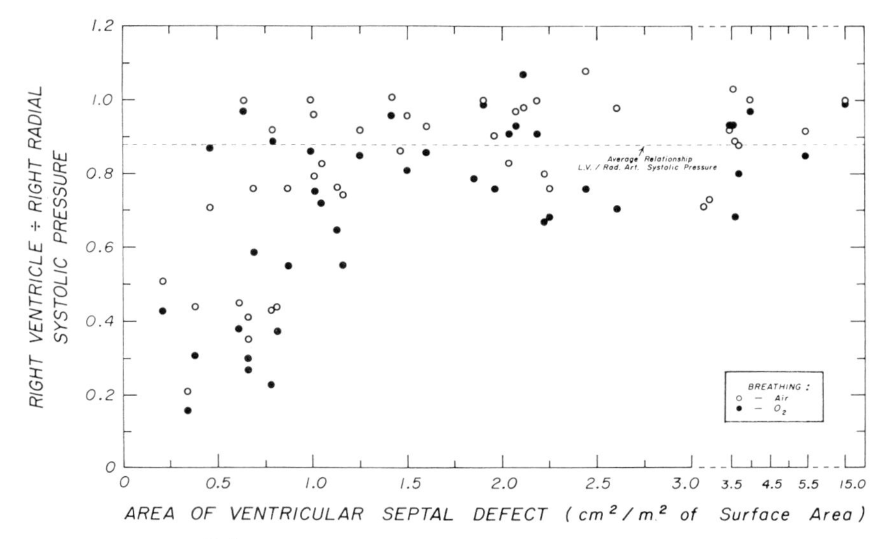

FIGURE 15-11. Relation between right ventricular and systemic arterial systolic pressures and the area of ventricular septal defects. The horizontal line indicates the average ratio of left ventricular to peripheral arterial systolic pressures. It would be anticipated that, in patients with equal systolic pressures in the two ventricles, values for right ventricular/systemic arterial systolic pressures would cluster about this line. Note that this does occur when the area of the defect is greater than 1 cm.^{2} per M.^{2} (From Marshall, Helmholz and Wood. In: Handbook of Physiology. Section 2: Circulation, Volume 1. Washington, D.C., American Physiological Society, 1962.)

instances, the situation is intermediate, since increased flow coexists with increased vascular resistance (Lucas et al., 1961).

Small ventricular septal defects result in small left-to-right shunts and only slight increases in pressure in the right ventricle and pulmonary artery. The pulmonary vascular resistance remains within normal limits. Some close spontaneously during infancy (Evans et al., 1960; Nadas et al., 1961). The remainder are well tolerated. Serial hemodynamic studies have shown that pulmonary vascular resistance remains normal over the years (Lucas et al., 1961; Mudd et al., 1964; Kidd et al., 1965). Reversal of the shunt does not occur.

The effects of large ventricular septal defects are partly dependent on the patient's age. In the newborn, the presence of the fetal pattern of pulmonary vessels (Wagenvoort et al., 1961) is responsible for the persistence of a high level of pulmonary vascular resistance. This limits the size of the left-to-right shunt. With the passage of time, the pulmonary vascular bed may mature at the normal rate, resulting in a marked decrease in vascular resistance and hence in a marked increase in the left-to-right shunt and in pulmonary blood flow. Left ventricular failure and death may occur in the first year of life.

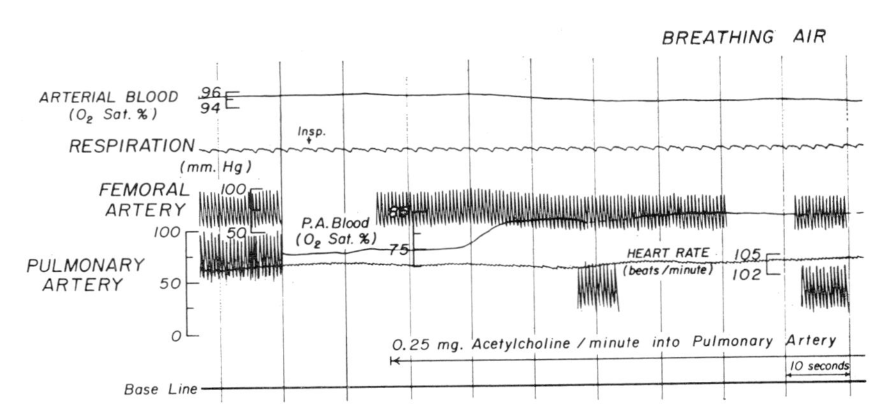

FIGURE 15-12. Effects of infusion of acetylcholine into the pulmonary artery of an eight year old boy with a large ventricular septal defect. In the control period, pressures in the femoral and pulmonary arteries were almost identical. During the infusion, the pulmonary arterial systolic pressure decreased from 95 to 65 mm. Hg, the pulmonary blood flow increased (note the increase from 75 to 83 per cent in saturation of blood in the pulmonary artery), and pulmonary vascular resistance decreased from 1620 to 510 dynes sec. cm.$^{-5}$. The changes were due to a direct action of acetylcholine on the pulmonary vessels. The absence of any change in heart rate or respiration rate indicates that the acetylcholine was inactivated before it could reach the systemic circulation. (From Shepherd, Semler, Helmholz and Wood, Circulation, *20*:381, 1959.)

On the other hand, many patients with very large left-to-right shunts survive, perhaps because resolution of the fetal pattern of pulmonary vessels has been delayed or less complete. Some of these, despite recurrent episodes of congestive heart failure, do not appear to develop progressive pulmonary vascular disease over a period of several to many years (Lucas et al., 1961; Stanton and Fyler, 1961). In others, gradual changes occur in the pulmonary arterioles, leading to increased pulmonary vascular resistance (Weidman et al., 1963; Auld et al., 1963) and hence to a decrease in the left-to-right shunt and in the pulmonary blood flow.

Theoretically, a similar situation could occur if the pulmonary vascular bed failed to undergo any maturation from the fetal state (Edwards, 1957; Dammann and Ferencz, 1956). The studies of Kidd et al. (1965) suggest that this must be uncommon. Thus, 78 per cent of the children whom they studied under two years of age had a pulmonary blood flow at least twice the systemic flow, and none had reversal of the shunt (Eisenmenger reaction). The proportion of children between two and 16 years of age with such a large pulmonary/systemic flow ratio was less, and cases with unequivocal reversal of the shunt were found.

As in atrial septal defect complicated by pulmonary hypertension, increased vasomotor tone may play a minor role, at least in some cases. Thus, the infusion of acetylcholine (Fig. 15-12) or inhalation of oxygen enriched gas mixtures (Fig. 15-13) may decrease pulmonary artery pressure, increase pulmonary blood flow, or both. In some cases, these maneuvers result in the development of a pressure gradient between the right and left ventricles where none was present previously. The effect of oxygen is relatively less pronounced in the patients with the greatest increases in pulmonary vascular resistance. Similarly, in patients with idiopathic pulmonary hypertension, the extremely high vascular resistance is little affected by inhaling oxygen (Shepherd et al., 1957). The blood vessels in such cases presumably have the pathological changes of the high resistance–low reserve system of Edwards (1957).

An additional factor limiting the size of the left-to-right shunt in ventricular septal defect is the development of localized muscular hypertrophy of the outflow tract of the right ventricle (Gasul et al., 1957; Watson and Lowe, 1965). Serial catheterization has occasionally led to proof of gradually increasing obstruction. Vogel and Blount (1965) showed that in some patients, the presence of outflow tract obstruction, not otherwise apparent, may be demonstrated following the administration of Priscoline, a pulmonary vasodilator drug.

Reliable measurements of changes in pulmonary and systemic blood flow during exercise are difficult to obtain in patients with left-to-right shunts, because of the need to obtain blood samples simultaneously from several sites (Bruce and John, 1957; Swan et al., 1958; Davies and Gazetopoulos, 1966).

ARTERIOVENOUS FISTULAE. Direct communications between ar-

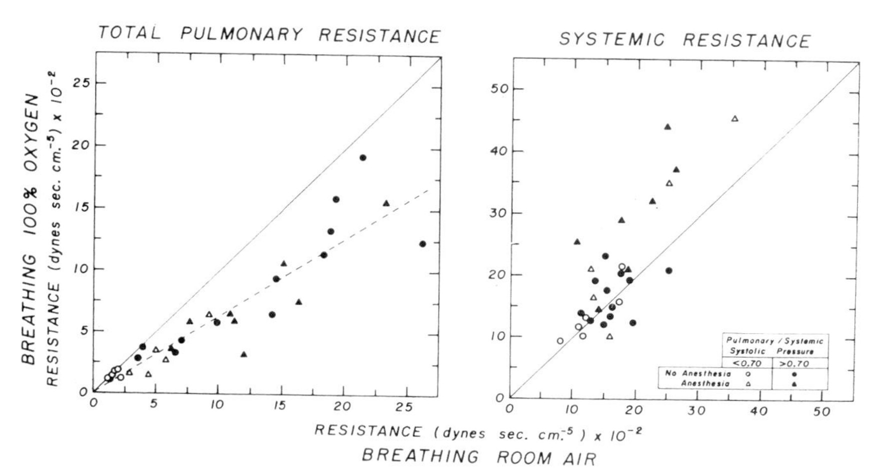

FIGURE 15-13. Relation of pulmonary vascular resistance (*left panel*) and of systemic vascular resistance (*right panel*) while breathing 100 per cent oxygen to that while breathing air in 31 patients with ventricular septal defect. Note the uniform decrease (mean value, dotted line,–36 per cent) in pulmonary resistance and the less uniform increase in systemic resistance while breathing oxygen. (From Marshall, Swan, Burchell and Wood, Circulation, 23:241, 1961.)

teries and veins result in the shunting of arterial blood into the venous system. The extent of the hemodynamic alterations is dependent upon their size and, to some extent, upon their location. Congenital arteriovenous fistulae may occur in various sites, but they are particularly common in the heart and great vessels and in the brain. Fistulae involving the coronary arteries, such as coronary artery–coronary sinus communications, have effects similar to those elsewhere in the body, but in addition, they may cause myocardial ischemia, owing to diversion of blood away from the myocardial capillary bed. Thus, their effect on the heart is greater than that of more peripherally located fistulae with comparable levels of flow. For example, Steinberg et al. (1958), in a study of cases of coronary arteriovenous fistulae coming to autopsy, found a mean cardiac weight of 700 g. and individual cardiac weights up to 1800 g.

The hemodynamic effects of more peripheral arteriovenous fistulae have been extensively studied. Warren et al. (1947A) assessed the cardiac output by the ballistocardiograph in 47 patients with traumatic fistulae. In 22, the cardiac output was increased by less than 25 per cent over that measured subsequently, after surgical repair of the fistula. In the remaining 25, the output was increased by 25 to 127 per cent. In individual cases, values as high as 24 liters per $M.^2$ per minute have been recorded (Binak et al., 1960). Warren et al. (1947B) found increases in total blood volume ranging from 200 to 1,060 ml. per $M.^2$ in 44 per cent of their patients. The increase tended to be greater in patients with larger fistulae. The fistulae, which are often aneurysmally dilated, accommodate some but probably not all of the increase in blood volume; part may represent the increased volume in normal vascular beds characteristic of incipient heart failure. Within a few days of closure of the fistula, the blood volume decreases to normal (Holman, 1965).

Cardiac failure eventually develops in most patients with large fistulae. It may occur as early as three months after development of the fistula, or it may be delayed for fifty years or more (Dorney, 1957). With the onset of failure, the cardiac output decreases but still remains well above normal values (Spurny and Pierce, 1961). Following repair of the fistula and recovery from congestive heart failure, cardiac output returns to normal levels.

The response to muscular exercise has been investigated. In two of seven patients studied by Binak et al. (1960), there was a disproportionately large increase in cardiac output. In three others, none of whom had cardiac failure, the output during exercise actually decreased, possibly because the contracting muscles of the thighs compressed or occluded the fistula. Muenster et al. (1959) found a normal increase in cardiac output during exercise in two patients with recently acquired fistulae, and a decrease in output during exercise in two patients who were in cardiac failure. In them, following surgical correction of the fistula, cardiac compensation was restored and the response to exercise became normal. Muenster et al. (1959) also pointed out that the hypervolemia associated with arteriovenous fistulae helps to maintain an adequate systemic arterial blood pressure; however, when decompensation ensues, the hypervolemia contributes an additional burden to the failing heart.

Fistulae may be detrimental to the local circulation, since part of the normal blood flow to the tissues distal to the shunt may be diverted. This has already been referred to in the case of coronary arteriovenous fistulae. The occurrence of severe ischemia and gangrene in the distal part of a limb has been recorded. Also, Maldonado et al. (1964) showed that renal arteriovenous fistulae, by diverting blood away from the normal vascular bed of the kidney, may result in renal ischemia, with consequent diastolic hypertension.

Abrupt changes in the circulation follow acute compression or obliteration of a fistula. The most striking finding is a decrease in heart rate (Nicoladoni-Branham sign). A marked change in rate occurs in the space of one or two heart beats (Burchell, 1958; Fig. 15-14). At the same time, there is a prompt increase in arterial blood pressure. The bradycardia may be blocked by prior treatment with atropine (Lewis and Drury, 1923; Nickerson et al., 1947), indicating that it is mediated by the vagus nerve.

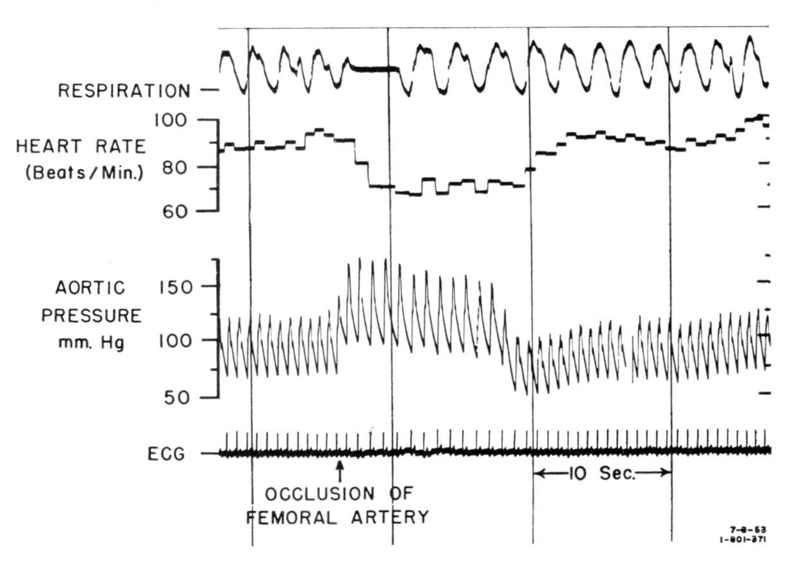

FIGURE 15-14. Effects of sudden compression of the femoral artery. There is an immediate increase in arterial blood pressure and a reflex decrease in heart rate. (From Burchell, Med. Clin. N. Amer., *42*:1029, 1958.)

Most likely, the reflex is triggered by the sudden increase in arterial pressure. Compression of the fistula does not alter the right atrial pressure. The cardiac output and the stroke volume decrease during compression or occlusion of the fistula.

RIGHT-TO-LEFT SHUNTS

These result in desaturation of arterial blood. Small right-to-left shunts may be detected only by use of special techniques, such as indicator dilution curves and selective angiocardiography, but larger shunts become manifest through the occurrence of cyanosis.

Cyanosis becomes visible when the capillaries in the skin contain an average of 5 g. of reduced hemoglobin per 100 ml. blood (Lundsgaard and Van Slyke, 1923). The content of reduced hemoglobin of capillary blood is generally taken as the average of the contents of arterial and venous blood. In a normal resting subject, with 15 g. hemoglobin per 100 ml. blood, the arterial blood is about 95 per cent saturated and thus contains only 0.75 g. reduced hemoglobin. The venous blood is about 75 per cent saturated and thus contains 3.75 g. reduced hemoglobin. Therefore, capillary blood contains, on the average, about 2.25 g. reduced hemoglobin, or less than half the amount required to cause cyanosis.

Two of the factors that facilitate the occurrence of cyanosis are the degree of venous admixture of arterial blood and the increased total content of hemoglobin resulting from secondary polycythemia. A patient with 20 g. hemoglobin per 100 ml. blood and an arterial oxygen saturation of 80 per cent has 4.0 g. reduced hemoglobin in the arterial blood. If venous blood has an oxygen saturation of 60 per cent, its content of reduced hemoglobin is 8.0 g. Therefore, capillary blood contains, on the average, about 6.0 g. reduced hemoglobin, sufficient to lead to mild cyanosis.

The extent of arterial desaturation is dependent not only on the absolute magnitude of the right-to-left shunt, but also on the ratio between this and the pulmonary blood flow. For example, patients with tetralogy of Fallot have greatly reduced pulmonary blood flow and therefore characteristically have low values for the saturation of systemic arterial blood. Thus, admixture of a pulmonary venous blood flow of 2.0 liters per $M.^2$ per minute at 98 per cent saturation with a right-to-left shunt of 1.25 liters per $M.^2$ per minute at 50 per cent saturation will result in a systemic arterial blood flow of 3.25 liters per $M.^2$ per minute at 79 per cent saturation.

In contrast, patients with total pulmonary venous connection to the right atrium, resulting in complete admixture of pulmonary and systemic venous blood in this chamber, do not appear cyanosed, provided that their pulmonary blood flow is increased at least twofold. Thus, complete admixture of a pulmonary venous blood flow of 10.5 liters per $M.^2$ per minute at 98 per cent saturation with a systemic blood flow of 3.5 liters per $M.^2$ per minute at 65 per cent would result in a saturation of 90 per cent. The 5 liters of this mixed blood shunting in the right-to-left direction across the atrial septal defect to sustain the systemic circulation would consist of 3.75 liters derived from pulmonary veins and 1.25 liters derived from systemic veins. Clearly, a reduction in the magnitude of pulmonary blood flow, due for example to progressive pulmonary vascular disease, would result in more marked desaturation of systemic arterial blood (Swan et al., 1956B).

In addition to the factors just discussed, the occurrence of cyanosis is dependent on the content of reduced hemoglobin in the capillaries of the skin and mucous membranes rather than on the average content of hemoglobin in all capillaries. Thus, when the blood flow through the skin becomes greatly increased in relation to its metabolic needs, as after a hot bath, cyanosis of the skin may become less marked or even disappear, although the mucous membranes may remain dusky.

In contrast, when flow through skin is reduced, cyanosis is intensified because of more complete extraction of oxygen from capillary blood. Cyanosis also becomes intensified during exercise, for several possible reasons. Exercise, by reducing the resistance of the systemic vascular bed, increases the size of the right-to-left shunt; the tissues extract more oxygen from each volume of blood; and, because of redistribution of flow in the systemic circulation to meet the demands of the exercising muscles, the blood supply to the skin may be reduced and the rate of extraction of oxygen therefore increased (Muth et al., 1958).

Cyanosis may also occur in patients with normal arterial oxygen saturation, if the systemic blood flow is sufficiently low. For example, a patient with severe mitral valvular disease may have an arterial saturation of 95 per cent, whereas the saturation of mixed venous blood is 45 per cent. If the blood contains 15 g. hemoglobin per 100 ml., then the average content of mixed capillary blood is 5.25 g. reduced hemoglobin. Since such a patient would probably have a disproportionate reduction in skin blood flow, the content of reduced hemoglobin in skin capillaries would be even greater.

Cyanosis becomes more intense when the total content of blood in a given area of skin is increased through dilatation of capillaries, even though there is no change in the absolute amount of reduced hemoglobin per 100 ml. capillary blood. It is more readily detected in blond subjects and cannot be recognized in the skin of darkly pigmented races.

For these various reasons, although there is a qualitative correlation between the arterial oxygen saturation and the intensity of cyanosis when average values are considered, marked variability exists when individual values are compared (Geraci and Wood, 1951).

Although cyanosis in congenital heart disease is usually detectable in

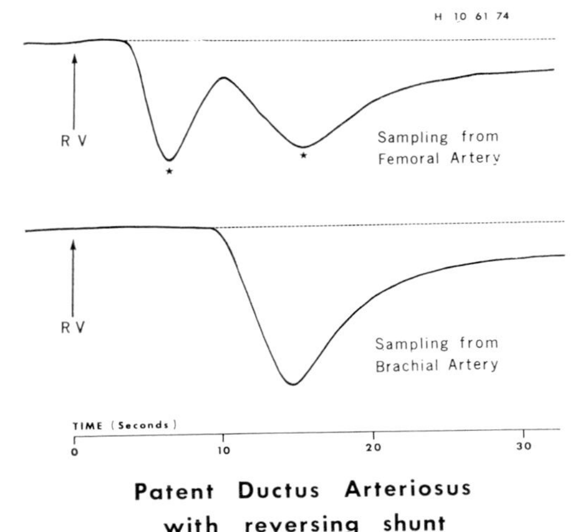

FIGURE 15-15. Dilution curves recorded from the femoral and right brachial arteries following injection of indicator dye into the right ventricle in a patient with patent ductus arteriosus and reversal of the shunt due to severe pulmonary hypertension. Note the large right-to-left shunt detected at the former site and its absence at the latter. The patient had cyanosis and clubbing of the feet but not of the right hand.

all areas of the body surface, occasionally anatomical features of the shunt result in its being more intense in or even confined to either the upper or the lower half of the body. For example, when patent ductus arteriosus is complicated by severe pulmonary hypertension, the shunt occurs in the right-to-left direction into the upper descending aorta; the feet are cyanosed, the right hand is pink and the left hand may be intermediate in color, owing to the relative proximity of the origins of the left subclavian artery and the patent ductus (Fig. 15-15). The combination of interruption of the aortic arch with complete transposition of the great vessels leads to the reverse situation, since desaturated blood from the venous ventricle perfuses the aortic arch, while the descending aorta is perfused by more highly saturated blood from the arterial ventricle via a patent ductus arteriosus.

Polycythemia is another consequence of the desaturation of arterial blood. It results from stimulation of the bone marrow by the low oxygen tension of blood and is analogous with the polycythemia of chronic pulmonary disease or high altitude. Polycythemia, by increasing the oxygen carrying capacity of the blood, is a useful adaptation. In patients with moderate cyanosis, the hematocrit is increased to between 50 and 60 per cent. With proportionately larger right-to-left shunts, as in such conditions as tetralogy of Fallot and pulmonary valve atresia, it may be as high as 80 per cent. At this level, the benefit resulting from the increased capacity is annulled by the greatly increased viscosity (Fig. 15-16) which adds to the work of the heart and to the risk of developing thrombosis in arteries and veins. Arterial hypoxemia appears to be responsible for thrombocytopenia, an occasional cause of bleeding in patients with severe cyanotic congenital heart disease (Hartmann, 1952; Paul et al., 1961).

Clubbing of the digits is a further consequence of arterial hypoxemia. With the exception of the color, the appearance of the affected digits is similar to that in clubbing from other causes, such as chronic suppurative infections. Clubbed fingers have increased numbers of capillaries and numerous arteriovenous shunts that permit a high rate of blood flow (Mendlowitz, 1942). Lovell (1950) showed that clubbed fingers associated with cyanotic congenital heart disease had a greater content of blood, particularly in veins, than those associated with chronic bronchopulmonary disease. Only rarely does clubbing progress to true hypertrophic osteoarthropathy in patients with right-to-left shunts.

The hemodynamic changes associated with squatting after exercise in such conditions as the tetralogy of Fallot and pulmonary stenosis with right-to-left shunt at atrial level have been examined. It is well known

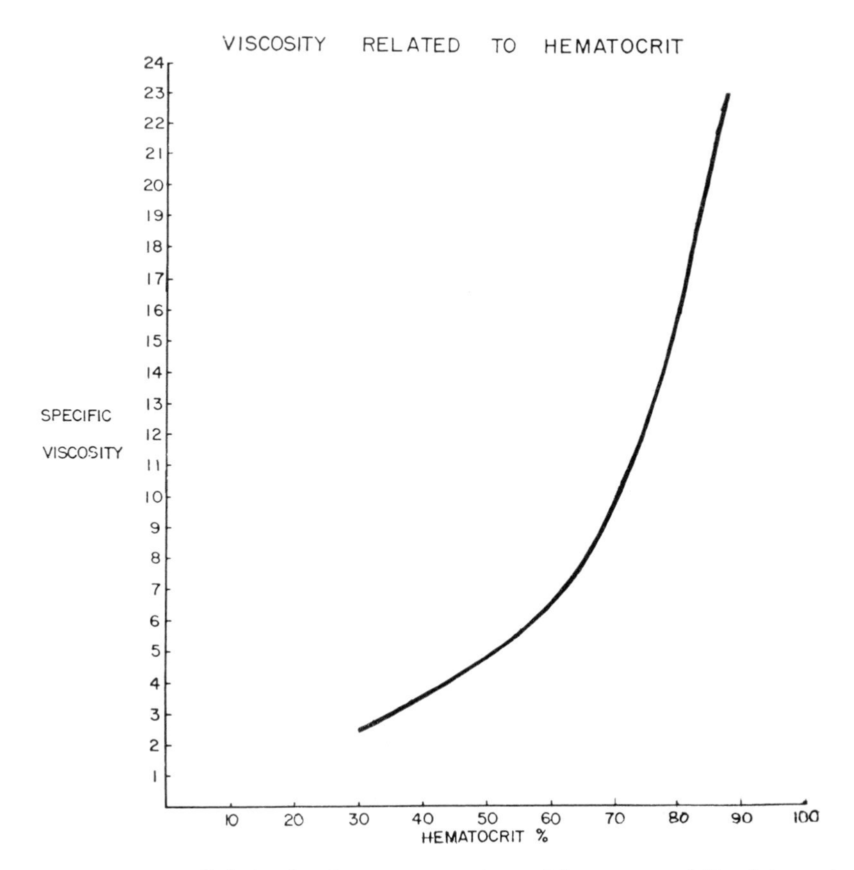

FIGURE 15-16. Relationship between viscosity and hematocrit of blood in patients with cyanotic heart disease. (From Rudolph, Nadas and Borges, Pediatrics, *11*:454, 1953.)

that the oxygen saturation of arterial blood returns to its customary level more rapidly after exercise when the subject squats (Lurie, 1953). When patients with cyanotic congenital heart disease exercise their legs, the oxygen content of the femoral venous blood is rapidly and greatly decreased. Consequently, the blood which is shunted into the systemic arteries has a lower oxygen content, and in turn, the oxygen saturation of arterial blood is reduced. Squatting causes kinking of the femoral vessels in the groin and the popliteal vessels in the popliteal fossa, so that the blood flow to the legs is decreased (Brotmacher, 1957). When patients with tetralogy squat immediately after exercise, the oxygen content of the femoral venous blood is still very low. With the reduction in leg blood flow, the oxygen content of the blood in the right side of the heart is increased, and the systemic arterial saturation is improved, even if there were no change in the volume of the right-to-left shunt. By reducing the blood flow to the legs, squatting prolongs the recovery period for the active muscles and allows a more gradual repayment of the oxygen debt.

Since the shunt in tetralogy of Fallot is usually from the right ventricle to the aorta, and since the total systemic vascular resistance is increased by squatting, the right-to-left shunt is decreased. This contributes to the increased arterial oxygen saturation. Squatting, like recumbency, removes the force of gravity on the circulation below heart level, so that the volume of blood in the legs is decreased, and the thoracic blood volume is increased. This may increase the common ventricular filling pressure and hence increase the pulmonary blood flow (O'Donnell and McIlroy, 1962).

A few conditions resulting in right-to-left shunts are characterized by normal or nearly normal intracardiac pressures. These include anomalous systemic venous return to the left atrium (Meadows et al., 1961), pulmonary arteriovenous fistula (Friedlich et al., 1950) and Ebstein's malformation of the tricuspid valve. In the majority of cases, the direction of the shunt results from an impediment to outflow of blood from the right side of the heart, due either to obstructive lesions within the heart itself or to obstructive or obliterative changes in the pulmonary vascular bed. The effects on cardiac function depend upon the precise nature of the anatomical defect or defects in any particular case.

REFERENCES

Amplatz, K.: New simple shunt detector. Circulation, *34* (Suppl. III):43, 1966 (Abstract).

Amplatz, K., Wang, Y., and Adams, P., Jr.: Helium-oxygen inhalation test: A simple test for identification of small left-to-right shunts. Circulation, *24*:877, 1961 (Abstract).

Auld, P. A., Johnson, A. L., Gibbons, J. E., and McGregor, M.: Changes in pulmonary vascular resistance in infants and children with left-to-right intracardiac shunts. Circulation, *27*:257, 1963.

Bernstein, L., and Jose, A. D.: Experience with the foreign gas method for the detection of left-to-right intracardiac shunts. Australas. Ann. Med., *11*:176, 1962.
Binak, K., Regan, T. J., Christensen, R. C., and Hellems, H. K.: Arteriovenous fistula: hemodynamic effects of occlusion and exercise. Am. Heart J., *60*:495, 1960.
Bossina, K. K., Mook, G. A., and Zijlstra, W. G.: Direct-reflection oximetry in routine cardiac catheterization. Circulation, *22*:908, 1960.
Braunwald, E., Brockenbrough, E. C., Frahm, C. J., and Ross, J., Jr.: Left atrial and left ventricular pressure in subjects without cardiovascular disease. Observations in eighteen patients studied by transseptal left heart catheterization. Circulation, *24*:267, 1961.
Braunwald, E., Goldblatt, A., Long, R. T. L., and Morrow, A. G.: The Krypton^{85} inhalation test for the detection of left-to-right shunts. Brit. Heart J., *24*:47, 1962.
Broadbent, J. C., and Wood, E. H.: Indicator-dilution curves in acyanotic congenital heart disease. Circulation, *9*:890, 1954.
Brotmacher, L.: Haemodynamic effects of squatting during recovery from exertion. Brit. Heart J., *19*:567, 1957.
Bruce, R. A., and John, G. G.: Effects of upright posture and exercise on pulmonary hemodynamics in patients with central cardiovascular shunts. Circulation, *16*: 776, 1957.
Burchell, H. B.: Observations on bradycardia produced by occlusion of an artery proximal to an arteriovenous fistula (Nicoladoni-Branham Sign). Med. Clin. N. Amer., *42*:1029, 1958.
Carter, S. A., Bajec, D. F., Yannicelli, E., and Wood, E. H.: Estimation of left-to-right shunt from arterial dilution curves. J. Lab. Clin. Med., *55*:77, 1960.
Case, R. B., Hurley, H. W., Keating, R. P., Sachs, H. L., and Loeffler, E. E.: Detection of circulatory shunts by use of a radioactive gas. Pros. Soc. Exp. Biol. Med., 97:4, 1958.
Castillo, C. A., Kyle, J. C., Gilson, W. E., and Rowe, G. G.: Simulated shunt curves. Am. J. Cardiol., *17*:691, 1966.
Clark, L. C., Jr., and Bargeron, L. M., Jr.: Left-to-right shunt detection by an intravascular electrode with hydrogen as an indicator. Science, *130*:709, 1959.
Clark, L. C., Jr., Bargeron, L. M., Jr., Lyons, C., Bradley, M. N., and MacArthur, K. T.: Detection of right-to-left shunts with an arterial potentiometric electrode. Circulation, *22*:949, 1960.
Dammann, J. F., Jr., and Ferencz, C.: Significance of the pulmonary vascular bed in congenital heart disease; defects between ventricles or great vessels in which both increased pressure and blood flow may act upon the lungs and in which there is common ejectile force. Am. Heart J., *52*:210, 1956.
Davies, H., and Gazetopoulos, N.: Haemodynamic changes on exercise in patients with left-to-right shunts. Brit. Heart J., *28*:579, 1966.
Dexter, L.: Atrial septal defect. Brit. Heart J., *18*:209, 1956.
Dexter, L., Haynes, F. W., Burwell, C. S., Eppinger, E. C., Seibel, R. E., and Evans, J. M.: Studies of congenital heart disease. 1. Technique of venous catheterization as a diagnostic procedure. J. Clin. Invest., *26*:547, 1947.
Dorney, E. R.: Peripheral A-V fistula of fifty-seven years' duration with refractory heart failure. Am. Heart J., *54*:778, 1957.
Edwards, J. E.: Functional pathology of the pulmonary vascular tree in congenital cardiac disease. Circulation, *15*:164, 1957.
Evans, J. R., Rowe, R. D., and Keith, J. D.: Spontaneous closure of ventricular septal defects. Circulation, *22*:1044, 1960.
Fox, I. J.: Indicators and detectors for dilution studies in the circulation and their application to organ or regional blood-flow measurement. In: Intravascular Catheterization. Ed. Zimmerman. Second edition. Springfield, Thomas, 1966.
Fox, I. J., Brooker, L. G., Heseltine, D. W., Essex, H. E., and Wood, E. H.: A tricarbocyanine dye for continuous recording of dilution curves in whole blood independent of variations in blood oxygen saturation. Proc. Staff Meet. Mayo Clin., *32*:478, 1957.

Friedlich, A. L., Bing, R. T., and Blount, S. C., Jr.: Physiological studies in congenital heart disease; circulatory dynamics in anomalies of venous return to heart including pulmonary arteriovenous fistula. Bull. Johns Hopkins Hosp., *86*:20, 1950.

Gamble, W. J., Hugenholtz, P. G., Monroe, R. G., Polanyi, M., and Nadas, A. S.: The use of fiber-optics in clinical cardiac catheterization. 1. Intracardiac oximetry. Circulation, *31*:328, 1965.

Gasul, B. M., Dillon, R. F., Vrla, V., and Hait, G.: Ventricular septal defects. Their natural transformation into those with infundibular stenosis or into cyanotic or non-cyanotic type of tetralogy of Fallot. J.A.M.A., *164*:847, 1957.

Geraci, J. E., and Wood, E. H.: The relationship of arterial oxygen saturation to cyanosis. Med. Clin. N. Amer., *35*:1185, 1951.

Hancock, E. W., Oliver, G. C., Swanson, M. J., and Hultgren, H. N.: Valsalva's maneuver in atrial septal defect. Am. Heart J., *65*:50, 1963.

Harrison, D. C., Kapany, N. S., Miller, H. A., Silbertrust, N., and Drake, R. P.: Fiberoptics for in vivo monitoring of oxygen saturation and hemodynamics. Circulation, *32* (Suppl. II):108, 1965 (Abstract).

Hartmann, R. C.: Hemorrhagic disorder occurring in patients with cyanotic congenital heart disease. Bull. Johns Hopkins Hosp., *91*:49, 1952.

Holman, E.: Abnormal arteriovenous communications. Great variability of effects with particular reference to delayed development of cardiac failure. Circulation, *32*:1001, 1965.

Hyman, E. S.: Linear system for quantitating hydrogen at a platinum electrode. Circ. Research, *9*:1093, 1961.

Kaplan, S., Clark, L. C., Jr., and Bargeron, L. M., Jr.: Intravascular polarographic and potentiometric electrodes. In: Intravascular Catheterization. Ed. Zimmerman. Second edition. Springfield, Thomas, 1966.

Kidd, L., Rose, V., Collins, G., and Keith, J.: The hemodynamics in ventricular septal defect in childhood. Am. Heart J., *70*:732, 1965.

Lee, G. de J., and Gimlette, T. M. D.: A simple test for interatrial communication. Brit. Med. J., *i*:1278, 1957.

Lewis, T., and Drury, A. N.: Observations relating to arteriovenous aneurysm: Circulatory manifestations in clinical cases with particular reference to arterial phenomena of aortic regurgitation. Heart, *10*:301, 1923.

Little, R. C., Opdyke, D. F., and Hawley, J. G.: Dynamics of experimental atrial septal defects. Am. J. Physiol., *158*:241, 1949.

Lovell, R. R. H.: Observations on the structure of clubbed fingers. Clin. Sci., *9*:299, 1950.

Lucas, R. V., Jr., Adams, P., Jr., Anderson, R. C., Meyne, N. G., Lillehei, C. W., and Varco, R. L.: The natural history of isolated ventricular septal defect: A serial physiologic study. Circulation, *24*:1372, 1961.

Lundsgaard, C., and Van Slyke, D. D.: Cyanosis. Medicine, *2*:1, 1923.

Lurie, P. R.: Postural effects in tetralogy of Fallot. Am. J. Med., *15*:297, 1953.

Maldonado, J. E., Sheps, S. G., Bernatz, P. E., DeWeerd, J. H., and Harrison, E. G.: Renal arterio-venous fistula. A reversible cause of hypertension and heart failure. Am. J. Med., *37*:499, 1964.

Marshall, H. W., Helmholz, H. F., Jr., and Wood, E. H.: Physiological consequences of congenital heart disease. In: Handbook of Physiology. Section 2: Circulation, Volume 1. Washington, D.C., American Physiological Society, 1962.

Marshall, H. W., Swan, H. J. C., Burchell, H. B., and Wood, E. H.: Effect of breathing oxygen on pulmonary artery pressure and pulmonary vascular resistance in patients with ventricular septal defect. Circulation, *23*:241, 1961.

Marshall, H. W., and Wood, E. H.: Diagnostic applications of indicator dilution technics in congenital and acquired heart disease. In: Intravascular Catheterization. Ed. Zimmerman. Second edition. Springfield, Thomas, 1966.

Marshall, R. J.: Factors modifying the contours of indicator-dilution curves. Circ. Research, *10*:123, 1962.

Marshall, R. J., and Warden, H. E.: Mitral valve disease complicated by left-to-right shunt at atrial level. Circulation, *29*:432, 1964.

McIlroy, M. B.: The clinical use of oximetry. Brit. Heart J., *21*:293, 1959.
Meadows, W. R., Bergstrand, I., and Sharp, J. T.: Isolated anomalous connection of a great vein to the left atrium. The syndrome of cyanosis and clubbing, "normal" heart, and left ventricular hypertrophy on electrocardiogram. Circulation, *24*:669, 1961.
Mendlowitz, M.: Clubbing and hypertrophic osteoarthropathy. Medicine, *21*:269, 1942.
Mudd, J. G., Aykent, Y., Fagan, L., Shields, J. B., Davis, M., Donahoe, J., and Hanlon, C. R.: Untreated, low-pressure ventricular septal defect. Repeated cardiac catheterization. A.M.A. Arch. Surg., *89*:126, 1964.
Muenster, J. J., Graettinger, J. S., and Campbell, J. A.: Correlation of clinical and hemodynamic findings in patients with systemic arteriovenous fistulas. Circulation, *20*:1079, 1959.
Muth, H. A. V., Wormald, P. N., Bishop, J. M., and Donald, K. W.: Further studies of blood flow in the resting arm during supine leg exercise. Clin. Sci., *17*:603, 1958.
Nadas, A. S., Scott, L. P., Hauck, A. J., and Rudolph, A. M.: Spontaneous functional closing of ventricular septal defects. New Eng. J. Med., *264*:309, 1961.
Nickerson, J. L., Elkin, D. C., and Warren, J. V.: Effect of temporary occlusion of arteriovenous fistulas on heart rate, stroke volume and cardiac output. J. Clin. Invest., *30*:215, 1947.
O'Donnell, T. V., and McIlroy, M. B.: The circulatory effects of squatting. Am. Heart J., *64*:347, 1962.
Paul, M. H., Currimbhoy, Z., Miller, R. A., and Schulman, I.: Thrombocytopenia in cyanotic congenital heart disease. Circulation, *24*:1013, 1961 (Abstract).
Ramirez de Arellano, A. A., Hetzel, P. S., and Wood, E. H.: Measurement of pulmonary blood flow using the indicator-dilution technic in patients with a central arteriovenous shunt. Circ. Research, *4*:400, 1956.
Ross, J., Jr., Braunwald, E., Mason, D. T., Braunwald, N. S., and Morrow, A. G.: Interatrial communication and left atrial hypertension. A cause of continuous murmur. Circulation, *28*:853, 1963.
Rudolph, A. M., Nadas, A. S., and Borges, W. H.: Hematologic adjustments to cyanotic congenital heart disease. Pediatrics, *11*:454, 1953.
Sanders, R. J., Cooper, T., and Morrow, A. G.: An evaluation of the nitrous oxide method for the quantification of left-to-right shunts. Circulation, *19*:898, 1959.
Shepherd, J. T., Edwards, J. E., Burchell, H. B., Swan, H. J. C., and Wood, E. H.: Clinical, physiological, and pathological considerations in idiopathic pulmonary hypertension. Brit. Heart J., *19*:70, 1957.
Shepherd, J. T., Semler, H. J., Helmholz, H. F., Jr., and Wood, E. H.: Effects of infusion of acetylcholine on pulmonary vascular resistance in patients with pulmonary hypertension and congenital heart disease. Circulation, *20*:381, 1959.
Spurny, O. M., and Pierce, J. A.: Cardiac output in systemic arteriovenous fistulas complicated by heart failure. Am. Heart J., *61*:21, 1961.
Stanton, R. E., and Fyler, D. C.: The natural history of pulmonary hypertension in children with ventricular septal defects assessed by serial right-heart catheterization. Pediatrics, *27*:621, 1961.
Steinberg, I., Baldwin, J. S., and Dotter, C. T.: Coronary arteriovenous fistula. Circulation, *17*:372, 1958.
Swan, H. J. C., Burchell, H. B., and Wood, E. H.: Effect of oxygen on pulmonary vascular resistance in patients with pulmonary hypertension associated with atrial septal defect. Circulation, *20*:66, 1959.
Swan, H. J. C., Hetzel, P. S., Burchell, H. B., and Wood, E. H.: Relative contribution of blood from each lung to the left-to-right shunt in atrial septal defect: Demonstration by indicator-dilution technics. Circulation, *14*:200, 1956A.
Swan, H. J. C., Marshall, H. W., and Wood, E. H.: The effect of exercise in the supine position on pulmonary vascular dynamics in patients with left-to-right shunts. J. Clin. Invest., *37*:202, 1958.
Swan, H. J. C., Toscano-Barboza, E., and Wood, E. H.: Hemodynamic findings in

total anomalous pulmonary venous drainage. Proc. Staff Meet. Mayo Clin., *31*:177 1956B.

Swan, H. J. C., Zapata-Diaz, J., and Wood, E. H.: Dye dilution curves in cyanotic congenital heart disease. Circulation, *8*:80, 1953.

Vogel, J. H., and Blount, S. G.: Masked infundibular pulmonary obstruction in ventricular septal defect with pulmonary hypertension. Circulation, *31*:876, 1965.

Vogel, J. H. K., Grover, R. F., and Blount, S. G., Jr.: Detection of the small intracardiac shunt with the hydrogen electrode. A highly sensitive and simple technique. Am. Heart J., *64*:13, 1962.

Wagenvoort, C. A., Neufeld, H. N., and Edwards, J. E.: The structure of the pulmonary arterial tree in fetal and early postnatal life. Lab. Invest., *10*:751, 1961.

Warren, J. V., Nickerson, J. L., and Elkin, D. C.: The cardiac output in patients with arteriovenous fistulas. J. Clin. Invest., *30*:210, 1947A.

Warren, J. V., Elkin, D. C., and Nickerson, J. L.: The blood volume in patients with arteriovenous fistulas. J. Clin. Invest., *30*:220, 1947B.

Watson, H., and Lowe, K. G.: Functional adaptations of the right ventricular outflow tract in congenital heart disease. Brit. Heart J., *27*:408, 1965.

Weidman, W. H., DuShane, J. W., and Kincaid, O. W.: Observations concerning progressive pulmonary vascular obstruction in children with ventricular septal defects. Am. Heart J., *65*:148, 1963.

Weidman, W. H., Swan, H. J. C., DuShane, J. W., and Wood, E. H.: A hemodynamic study of atrial septal defect and associated anomalies involving the atrial septum. J. Lab. Clin. Med., *50*:165, 1957.

Wood, E. H., Sturm, R. E., and Sanders, J. J.: Data processing in cardiovascular physiology with particular reference to roentgen videodensitometry. Mayo Clin. Proc., *39*:849, 1964.

Wood, E. H., Sutterer, W. F., and Cronin, L.: Oximetry. In: Medical Physics. Volume 3. Ed. Glasser. Chicago, Year Book, 1960.

Chapter 16

CARDIAC EFFECTS OF PULMONARY DISEASE

THE NORMAL PULMONARY CIRCULATION

PRESSURE-FLOW RELATIONSHIPS. The normal pulmonary vascular bed has a low resistance to blood flow and is highly distensible. The difference in mean pressure between the pulmonary artery and the pulmonary veins is about 10 mm. Hg, or approximately 10 per cent of the corresponding difference in the systemic circulation. The low resistance of the pulmonary arterioles is evident from the pulsatile pattern of pulmonary capillary blood flow (Lee and Dubois 1955; Fig. 16-1). Considerable increases in blood flow are accompanied by only moderate increases in this pressure difference. When either the right or the left pulmonary artery in man is completely occluded by a balloon tipped catheter (Brofman et al., 1957), the total pulmonary blood flow remains unchanged, so that the rate of flow through the unoccluded lung is doubled. The mean pulmonary arterial pressure increases by about 5 mm. Hg, the pulmonary venous pressure is unchanged, and pulmonary vascular resistance is decreased.

Although there are some conflicts in data for pressure-flow relationships during exercise in man (Riley et al., 1948; Hickam and Cargill, 1948; Donald et al., 1955; Barratt-Boyes and Wood, 1957; Cournand, 1958), the more common finding is a slight increase in mean pulmonary arterial pressure during moderate exercise (Fig. 2-5, Chapter 2). Pulmonary vascular resistance is decreased, probably through dilatation of patent vessels and the opening of previously closed vessels.

PULMONARY VASOMOTOR ACTIVITY. The resistance vessels in the lung have the ability to constrict and dilate and hence to regulate total or regional pulmonary blood flow. In acute experiments, inhalation

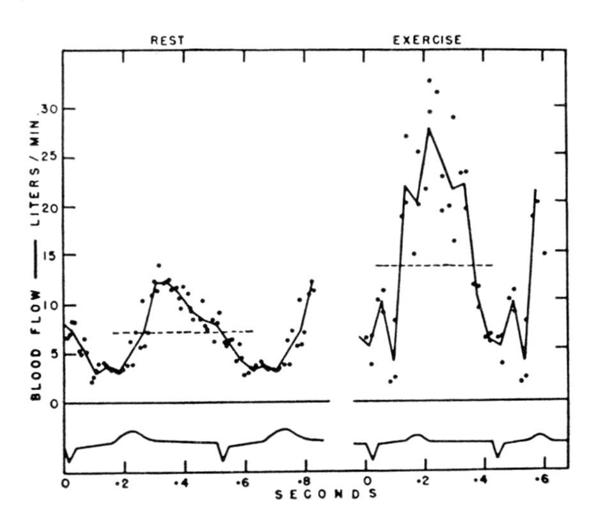

FIGURE 16-1. Instantaneous pulmonary capillary flow rates at rest and after exercise. The dots indicate instantaneous flow rates at each 0.04 sec. from four consecutive cycles. Continuous lines: average instantaneous flow rates. Interrupted lines: mean flow rates (liters per minute). (From Lee and DuBois, J. Clin. Invest., *34*:1380, 1955.)

of oxygen in low concentration (under 12 per cent) causes an increase of a few mm. in pulmonary arterial pressure. Since there is no change in left atrial pressure or pulmonary blood volume and only a slight increase in pulmonary blood flow (Asmussen and Nielsen, 1955), the most likely mechanism is a modest vasoconstriction. Although there is conflicting evidence about the site of the constriction, both the precapillary and postcapillary small vessels may be involved (Fishman, 1961); it is unlikely that constriction of muscle at the junctions between pulmonary veins and left atrium (Nathan and Eliakim, 1966) plays a role. Although the means whereby hypoxia constricts vascular smooth muscle is unknown, it appears to act locally or via an intrapulmonary reflex rather than via an extrapulmonary control system (Aviado et al., 1957; Duke, 1957). By contrast, the resistance vessels of the systemic circulation, in the absence of autonomic nervous reflexes, dilate when the oxygen tension of the blood perfusing them is reduced.

Liljestrand (1958) showed that an increase in the hydrogen ion concentration of the blood is associated with constriction of small pulmonary vessels. This has been confirmed by other observers (Bergofsky et al., 1961; Enson et al., 1964; Downing et al., 1965; Rudolph and Yuan, 1966). In animal studies, the infusion of fixed acids and the breathing of carbon dioxide caused the same increase in pulmonary vascular resistance for equivalent increases in hydrogen ion concentration, even though the increments in carbon dioxide tension of the blood were very small during the acid infusions and very large during the carbon dioxide breathing.

Thus, acute hypercapnia seems to elicit pulmonary vasoconstriction through the acidosis it produces (Bergofsky et al., 1962). This would explain the conflicting reports of the effects of hypercapnia on the pulmonary circulation: in normal humans, carbon dioxide breathing is without discernible effect, since the accompanying increase in minute ventilation minimizes the change in hydrogen ion concentration; whereas when ventilation is controlled so that hydrogen ion concentration increases, pulmonary vascular resistance increases.

An additional factor contributing to the rise in pulmonary artery pressure accompanying the increase in hydrogen ion concentration may be augmented aggregation and rigidity of the red cells (Dintenfass and Burnard, 1966). Since the pulmonary blood volume does not increase in patients receiving infusions of hydrochloric acid, a shift of blood from the systemic veins to the lungs is not a contributory factor (Harvey et al., 1967).

Liljestrand (1958) suggested that increased hydrogen ion concentration may be responsible for the pressor effect of hypoxia as a consequence of a local release of lactic acid. Others, however, have claimed that alveolar hypoxia can cause pulmonary vasoconstriction independently of changes in hydrogen ion or lactate concentration (Duke et al., 1960; Bergofsky et al., 1962; Fig. 16-2). An increase in blood hydrogen ion concentration can, however, potentiate and a decrease can attenuate the response to hypoxia. This conclusion is based on animal experiments and upon the demonstration that in patients with chronic obstructive lung disease, a fall in blood hydrogen ion concentration caused by the administration of alkali is associated with pulmonary vasodilatation in the presence of severe hypoxia (Enson et al., 1964).

Hypoxia caused a reversible loss of potassium and gain in sodium in isolated strips of pulmonary arteries. This did not occur in strips from pulmonary veins or systemic arteries. In view of this, Bergofsky and Holtzman (1967) suggested that one of the actions of hypoxia on the small pulmonary vessels is to cause reversible depolarization of the smooth muscle so that the resting negative intracellular potential moves closer to zero and therefore to its excitatory threshold.

Chronic hypoxia occurs at high altitudes. Its effects on the pulmonary and systemic circulations have been discussed in Chapter 3. Although vasoconstriction probably plays a role, the major factor is muscular hypertrophy of the small arteries and arterioles (Arias-Stella and Saldaña, 1963).

The short term inhalation of pure oxygen has no measurable effect on pulmonary vascular pressures in normal subjects. However, the pressure difference across the normal lung is so low that it is difficult to assess the effects of vasodilator agents. In patients with pulmonary hypertension associated with hypoxemia, the inhalation of enriched oxygen mixtures

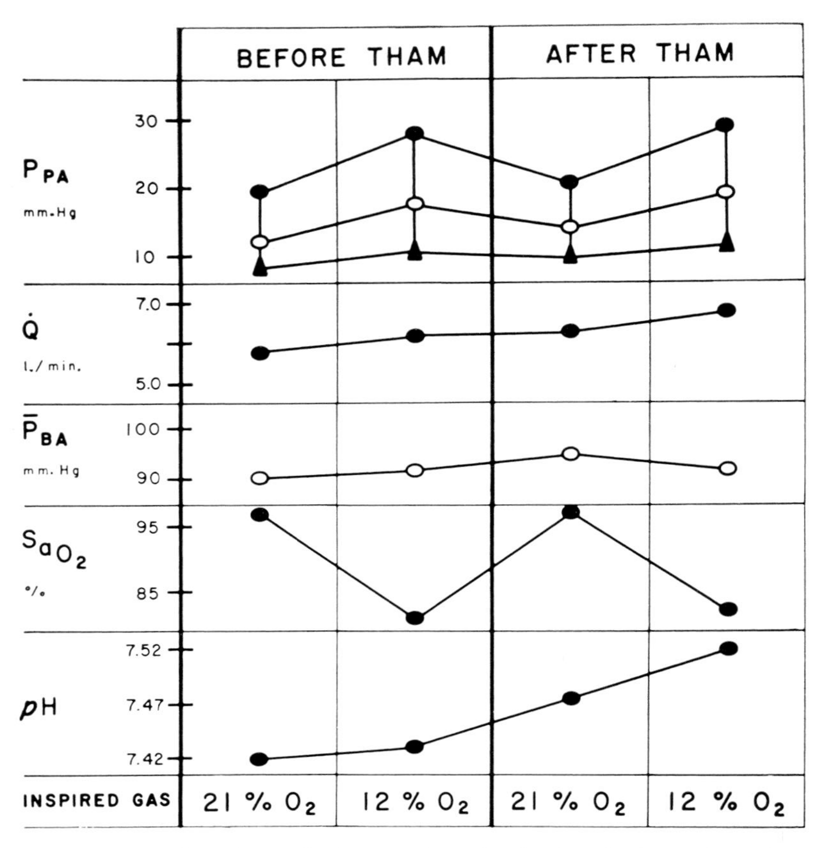

FIGURE 16-2. The effects of infusion of tris buffer (THAM) on the pulmonary arterial pressor response to hypoxia in man (mean results from five persons). Note that THAM did not prevent the rise in pressure. (From Bergofsky, Lehr, Tuller, Rigatto and Fishman, Ann. N.Y. Acad. Sci., 92:627, 1961.)

decreases pulmonary vascular resistance, as it does also in some patients with pulmonary hypertension associated with congenital heart disease.

Numerous drugs have been used in efforts to study the reactivity of the pulmonary circulation (Aviado, 1960). There are several difficulties inherent in their use: (1) most drugs affect both the pulmonary and systemic circulations; therefore, it is difficult to be certain whether a given effect on the pulmonary vessels is direct or is secondary to changes in the systemic circulation; (2) some drugs in appropriate concentrations also modify bronchomotor tone; this, rather than a direct effect on pulmonary vessels, may alter pulmonary vascular resistance; and (3) as was previously pointed out in relation to the effect of oxygen, the low values for pressure and resistance in the normal pulmonary circulation frustrate efforts to demonstrate vasodilatation. Therefore, the most definitive studies have been those carried out in patients with pulmonary hypertension.

The most useful drug has been acetylcholine. When infused into the pulmonary artery in concentrations too low to cause bronchial constriction or to affect the systemic circulation or the pattern of respiration, it causes a significant decrease in pulmonary arterial pressure and pulmonary vascular resistance in many cases of pulmonary hypertension due to hypoxia (Fritts et al., 1958), congenital heart disease (Shepherd et al., 1959), emphysema (Chidsey et al., 1960) and mitral stenosis (Söderholm and Werkö, 1959). Since it is effective in totally sympathectomized subjects, it must act directly rather than through release of reflex vasoconstriction.

Although epinephrine and norepinephrine can be shown to constrict pulmonary blood vessels in special animal preparations, their effect on the pulmonary circulation in man is predominantly secondary to an increase in left atrial pressure (Harris and Heath, 1962).

COR PULMONALE

Many forms of pulmonary disease may eventually affect the function of the heart. The term cor pulmonale is often applied to these situations, although it lacks specificity. Ferrer and Harvey (1958) defined it as "cardiac enlargement or failure in association with a disease process known to attack primarily the lungs or some aspect of the act of breathing and in so doing to compromise right ventricular function."

One important etiological category consists of those forms of pulmonary disease, such as acute massive pulmonary embolism, recurrent pulmonary embolism or idiopathic pulmonary hypertension, that cause extensive anatomical reduction of the vascular bed. A second category includes chronic obstructive pulmonary disease, particularly pulmonary emphysema, which may lead to cor pulmonale through a combination of several mechanisms among which alveolar hypoventilation is pre-eminent. In addition, a number of conditions in which movement of the chest wall is severely restricted may eventually compromise the function of the right side of the heart.

Conditions leading to left ventricular failure, such as aortic stenosis or ischemic heart disease, and conditions such as mitral stenosis that also cause chronic pulmonary hypertension, may in time cause rightsided heart failure. However, the term cor pulmonale is most useful when it is confined to the sequelae of primary disease of the lung vessels, lungs or chest wall, and in this discussion, the use of the term will be so restricted.

ACUTE PULMONARY HYPERTENSION

The most common cause of acute pulmonary hypertension is pulmonary embolism. Although occlusion of one of the two pulmonary arteries by inflation of a balloon results in little hemodynamic disturbance, the effects of major pulmonary embolism upon the right side of the heart are dramatic. This contrast has caused debate as to whether the effects of embolism can be attributed solely to a more complete mechanical obstruction of the pulmonary vascular bed, or whether vasoconstriction plays a role. Much experimental work has been performed in animals, but it has not led to a definitive conclusion.

The possible role of vasoactive substances released from impacted blood clots, such as 5-hydroxytryptamine, or from lung tissue, such as histamine, has also been investigated. Although 5-hydroxytryptamine is a potent constrictor of pulmonary vessels (Aviado, 1960), evidence that it may be a factor is contradictory (Cobb and Nanson, 1960; Halmagyi and Colebatch, 1961; Hyman et al., 1964). Release of 5-hydroxytryptamine from platelets, however, may be responsible for bronchoconstriction adjacent to the site of the embolus (Thomas and Gurewich, 1965). Histamine probably does not contribute (Halmagyi and Colebatch, 1961).

Acute massive pulmonary embolism in man imposes a sudden pressure load on the right ventricle, leading to dilatation of this chamber. The right ventricular end-diastolic, right atrial and systemic venous pressures increase, and the tricuspid valve may become incompetent. Stretching of the walls of the right atrium together with reversal of the normal pressure gradient between left and right atria provides an opportunity for paradoxical embolism to occur in those individuals in whom the margins of the foramen ovale are not sealed. The cardiac output decreases precipitously, mixed venous blood is excessively desaturated, and there is profound arterial hypotension. The concentration of lactate and pyruvate in the blood increases (Bradley et al., 1966). Precordial pain may be due to acute dilatation of the pulmonary artery (Gorham, 1961). Alternatively, it may be related to myocardial ischemia. Scherf and Schönbrunner (1937) proposed that there is a pulmonocoronary reflex inducing vasoconstriction. However, bilateral cervical vagotomy failed to alter the electrocardiographic changes in experimental pulmonary embolism (Malinow et al., 1946). As Katz (1945) pointed out, the combination of arterial hypotension, increased right atrial pressure and reduced cardiac output, together with the increased cardiac work, is sufficient to account for myocardial ischemia without the necessity of invoking reflex vasoconstriction.

In patients who survive the acute episode, the pulmonary artery pressure decreases, due to a combination of factors including lysis of thrombotic material and peripheral migration of thrombus.

Marshall and Allison (1962) showed that the injection of 60 to 80 ml. small clots of autologous blood into the pulmonary arteries of dogs decreased the diffusing capacity for carbon monoxide and increased the pulmonary arterial pressure. One week later, the pressures and diffusing capacity had returned to normal. Such small clots undergo fibrinolysis through the action of the proteolytic enzyme, plasmin; they contain high concentrations of plasminogen, and plasminogen activators are released when blood vessel walls (Kwaan and McFadzean, 1956) or lung tissue (Lincoln et al., 1957) are damaged. Organization of embolic material proceeds simultaneously with fibrinolysis.

In man, fibrinolysis occurs more slowly and less completely than in other species (Niewiarowski and Latallo, 1959), and old partially organized emboli and thrombi are frequently found in the pulmonary arteries at autopsy. Some patients slowly and insidiously develop chronic pulmonary hypertension and, eventually, rightsided cardiac failure from recurrent pulmonary embolism.

Infarction does not occur following ligation of arteries in normal lungs and does not usually occur following experimental embolization of normal animals (Kjellberg and Olsson, 1960). Increased collateral flow from bronchial arteries to the lung distal to the occlusion can be demonstrated within 24 hours (Steinberg and Mundy, 1936), although several months are required for full development of bronchopulmonary anastomotic channels (Bloomer et al., 1949). The bronchial circulation is sufficient to maintain viability of lung tissue. Emboli arising from organized thrombi frequently do not completely occlude the vessels in which they become impacted, but permit some blood to pass through (Smith et al., 1964). However, when embolism occurs in association with pulmonary venous congestion, low cardiac output or other conditions, such as pneumonic consolidation, bronchial obstruction or atelectasis, the collateral circulation is inadequate to maintain viability, and infarction results.

IDIOPATHIC PULMONARY HYPERTENSION

For many years, cases of hypertrophy of the right ventricle associated with narrowing or occlusion of the small arteries and arterioles throughout the lung in the absence of any apparent causative lesion have been recognized at autopsy. The techniques of cardiac catheterization and angiocardiography have permitted fuller documentation of such cases, and the term primary pulmonary hypertension was applied to them by Dresdale et al. (1951). It is uncertain whether primary, or idiopathic, hypertension is a specific entity (Wade and Ball, 1957), and even at autopsy, there may be difficulty in distinguishing it from chronic thromboembolic disease (Rosenberg, 1964). On clinical and laboratory examination, the diagnosis is necessarily one of exclusion. Thus, one must show that the pulmonary hypertension is not related to obstructive lesions distal to the lungs (such as stenosis of the pulmonary veins, mitral stenosis or conditions leading to left ventricular failure), to intrinsic pulmonary disease or to the presence of shunts. The first of these possibilities can be excluded by recording a normal left atrial or pulmonary artery wedge pressure, although the latter is often difficult to obtain; the second, by demonstrating normal pulmonary function tests, x-ray films and other supportive data; and the third, by recording normal indicator dilution curves (Shepherd et al., 1957). Angiocardiography is of value in excluding the presence of obstructive lesions in larger pulmonary arteries that could have resulted from major emboli or thrombi, or from multiple congenital arterial stenoses.

In most cases, the history suggests that the condition is acquired in childhood or early adult life. According to Edwards and Heath (1960), the arrangement of the elastic tissue in the main pulmonary artery supports the belief that the condition is not congenital. The histological changes in the small arteries and arterioles, which include progressive hypertrophy of the media, local dilatation lesions, fibrous intimal proliferation and plexiform lesions, resemble those in pulmonary hypertension complicating congenital defects (Heath and Edwards, 1958). Necrotizing arteritis is more frequently seen, however, possibly because of a more rapid progression of the pulmonary hypertension.

In the 28 cases collected from the literature by Wade and Bishop (1962), the mean pulmonary artery pressure was moderately to greatly increased, varying from 35 to 115 mm. Hg with an average of 67 mm. Hg. The values were similar for patients with and without congestive failure. The mean value for cardiac output was 2.1 liters per $M.^2$ per minute, for stroke volume 27 ml. per $M.^2$, and for oxygen saturation of arterial blood 93.4 per cent. The response to exercise was severely impaired; the oxygen saturation of arterial blood tended to fall, and in seven of eight patients, the stroke volume decreased.

The increased pressure work of the right ventricle is reflected in the electrocardiogram and in the heaving left parasternal impulse. The right atrial and systemic venous pressure pulses show prominent *a* waves, as in pulmonary valvular stenosis. Eventually, right ventricular failure occurs.

Patients with severe idiopathic pulmonary hypertension have cyanosis due to the reduced cardiac output. Right-to-left shunting may occur, due to the development of incompetence of the foramen ovale secondary to dilatation of the right atrium; this may augment the cyanosis. When a patient is first studied at this stage of the disease, it is difficult to decide whether the right-to-left shunt at atrial level resulted from rightsided failure due to idiopathic pulmonary hypertension, or whether the basic lesion was an atrial septal defect that eventually was complicated by secondary pulmonary hypertension and reversal of the shunt. Indeed, the distinction may be difficult even at autopsy.

Desaturation of systemic arterial blood could also be explained by interstitial thickening of the pulmonary parenchyma, with resulting impairment of diffusion. Also, if the development of bronchopulmonary anastomotic channels is a feature, as Wade and Ball (1957) suggested, drainage of bronchial venous blood to the left atrium in the presence of right ventricular failure (Liebow et al., 1959) could account for mild arterial desaturation. Arterial desaturation is sometimes sufficient to account for polycythemia, as in the cases of Kuida et al. (1957).

Although anatomical changes in the small arteries and arterioles are of paramount importance in the development of the hypertension and the eventual rightsided failure, there is evidence that, at least in some patients, and in the earlier stages of the disease, vasoconstriction plays a subsidiary role. Thus, infusion of drugs such as Priscoline (Gardiner, 1954), reserpine (Halmagyi et al., 1957), isoproterenol (Lee et al., 1963) and acetylcholine have resulted in decreases in pulmonary vascular resistance. Figure 16-3 shows intravascular pressures and saturation of arterial and mixed venous blood in a patient before and during infusion of acetylcholine into the pulmonary artery. The pulmonary blood flow was unchanged (4.4 to 4.6 liters per minute); the mean pulmonary artery pressure decreased from 56 to 25 mm. Hg and the total pulmonary resistance from 1020 to 435 dynes sec. cm.$^{-5}$ As the disease advances, responsiveness to vasodilator

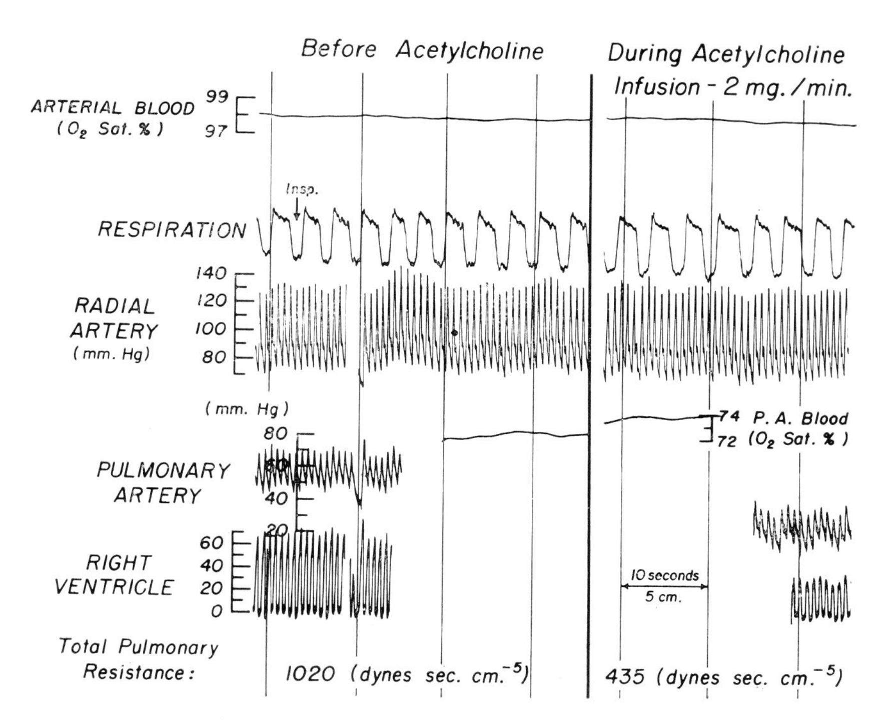

FIGURE 16-3. Effect of infusion of acetylcholine into the pulmonary artery in a patient with idiopathic pulmonary hypertension. There was no change in respiration rate, heart rate or systemic blood pressure, whereas pulmonary arterial pressure and total pulmonary resistance were markedly decreased. (From Marshall, Helmholz and Shepherd, Circulation, *20*:391, 1959.)

drugs is lost. Thus, Samet et al. (1960) studied a patient in whom acetylcholine reduced pulmonary vascular resistance from 2000 to 1500 dynes sec. cm.$^{-5}$ during rest and from 2000 to 1110 dynes sec. cm.$^{-5}$ during exercise. Three years later, the resistance during rest had increased to approximately 3500 dynes sec. cm.$^{-5}$, and no decrease occurred with acetylcholine (Samet and Bernstein, 1963). Sleeper et al. (1962) performed serial catheterization on five patients; three had a progressive increase in pulmonary arterial pressure and pulmonary vascular resistance and a decrease in cardiac output.

Loss of consciousness on exertion is common in idiopathic pulmonary hypertension. Howarth and Lowe (1953) obtained blood pressure records in such patients during induced syncope after exertion. Blood pressure fell gradually, and not precipitously, after exercise. Sinus bradycardia and loss of consciousness occurred when the systemic pressure reached low levels. A syncopal attack was induced during cardiac catheterization in a patient with idiopathic pulmonary hypertension. As the systemic pressure fell, the pulse pressure in the right ventricle decreased with a rise in the diastolic pressure. These results are compatible with acute failure of the right ventricle.

CHRONIC OBSTRUCTIVE PULMONARY DISEASE

The changes in the circulation in association with chronic obstructive pulmonary disease, most commonly emphysema with or without chronic bronchitis, result from a number of functional derangements.

1. Because of the progressive stretching and obliteration of the alveolar septa, the extent of the pulmonary capillary bed is reduced. Additional obliteration of small vessels may result from associated lesions such as chronic bronchitis and pulmonary fibrosis. With the ultimate advent of pulmonary hypertension, a vicious cycle may become established, since the hypertension may lead to fibrotic thickening of the remaining small arteries. Deformity and compression of branches of the pulmonary artery by adacent emphysematous spaces may increase vascular resistance.

Despite these changes, the reserve of the normal pulmonary vascular bed is so great that the pulmonary artery pressure may remain normal or, at most, show only a slight increase during rest. However, with the stress of exercise, the reserve is inadequate, and increasing rates of pulmonary blood flow are accompanied by disproportionate increases in pulmonary arterial pressure, even when there are no problems with gas exchange. The majority of patients with emphysema behave like this. Only a minority have markedly increased pressures during rest. Many die from chronic respiratory failure without ever having had rightsided cardiac failure.

Increased pulmonary vasomotor tone may play a role in some cases. Parker et al. (1966) found that an infusion of aminophylline in patients with cor pulmonale reduced mean pulmonary artery pressure from 39 to 25 mm. Hg, right ventricular end-diastolic pressure from 9 to 2 mm. Hg, left ventricular end-diastolic pressure from 8 to 3 mm. Hg and brachial arterial mean pressure from 95 to 86 mm. Hg. The heart rate and oxygen consumption increased and the cardiac index was unchanged. Thus, aminophylline appeared to reduce pulmonary arteriolar tone.

2. Hyperinflation and decreased elasticity of the lungs alter the mechanics of respiration, and the work of breathing in increased. In some cases, there is a mechanical impediment in the return of venous blood to the chest. Thus, Nakhjavan et al. (1966) showed that in normal subjects and in many persons with chronic pulmonary disease, blood flows into the thorax continually during the respiratory cycle, with a greater velocity during inspiration. In some patients with severe hyperinflation of the lungs and depression of the diaphragm, flow was reduced or arrested during inspiration. This phenomenon could account for the occurrence of peripheral edema in certain patients who have emphysema without pulmonary hypertension or cardiac enlargement.

3. Inspired air is unevenly and inefficiently distributed to the alveoli. The distribution of blood to the different segments of the lung is also uneven. Thus, poorly perfused alveoli may be overventilated, whereas adequately perfused alveoli may be underventilated. In addition, many alveolar capillaries are attenuated or obliterated. The net result is that mixed pulmonary venous blood and hence systemic arterial blood is inadequately oxygenated. Since carbon dioxide diffuses much more readily than oxygen across the alveolar membrane, the first serious effect of the alveolar hypoventilation is arterial hypoxemia. As is true of normal persons (Peñaloza et al., 1963) and animals (Grover et al., 1963) at high altitudes (Chapter 3), there is a direct relationship between the severity of the hypoxemia and the pulmonary arterial pressure (Table 16-1). Hypoxemia contributes to the pulmonary hypertension in several ways. It may increase cardiac output. If sufficiently severe, it causes compensatory polycythemia and increased blood viscosity (Motley, 1958). It leads to pulmonary vasoconstriction. Thus, with improvement in the condition of a patient with severe

TABLE 16-1. Pulmonary Vascular Pressures and Blood Gas Tensions and pH in Four Patients with Chronic Bronchitis and Emphysema*

	PA PRESSURES (MM. HG)				ARTERIAL BLOOD		
PATIENT	SYST.	DIAST.	MEAN	WEDGE	O_2 SAT. %	pCO_2 (MM. HG.)	pH (UNITS)
1	27	11	19	5	94	34	7.47
2	30	14	21	0	90	40	7.44
3	55	25	37	6	77	57	7.39
4	67	30	44	5	72	54	7.38

* Reproduced from 7th Conf. Res. in Emphysema, Aspen, 1964; Med. Thorac. 22:108-117 (Karger, Basel/New York 1965).

TABLE 16-2. Effect of Decreased, Normal and Increased Alveolar Ventilation on the Composition of Arterial Blood†

VENTILATION	ALVEOLAR VENTILATION (L./MIN.)	GAS TENSIONS (MM. HG)		ARTERIAL GAS CONTENTS		ARTERIAL pH (UNITS)
		ARTERIAL O_2	ARTERIAL AND ALVEOLAR CO_2	O_2 (% SAT.)	MM./L. CO_2	
Decreased	2.50	67	69	88.5	27.2	7.24
Normal	4.27	104	40	97.4	21.9	7.40
Increased	7.50	122	23	98.8	17.5	7.56

* Assuming in each case a respiratory quotient of 0.8 and an O_2 consumption of 250 ml./min.

† From The Lung, 2nd edition, by Julius H. Comroe, Jr., et al. Copyright 1962, Year Book Medical Publishers, Inc. used by permission of Year Book Medical Publishers.

emphysema, an increase in the oxygen saturation of arterial blood and a reduction of pressure in the pulmonary artery go hand in hand.

In more advanced cases, carbon dioxide diffusion becomes inadequate, and hypercapnia occurs. As was mentioned earlier, it is the accompanying acidosis rather than the hypercapnia per se that contributes to the pulmonary hypertension (Table 16-2).

The pulmonary artery wedge pressure is characteristically normal in patients with chronic obstructive emphysema (Dexter et al., 1951). Therefore, pulmonary venous hypertension does not normally contribute to the increase in pulmonary artery pressure in man. Boyd et al. (1966) compared the response of the left ventricle to increased afterload, produced by infusion of methoxamine, in patients with emphysema and in normal subjects. Increases in stroke work, stroke power and left ventricular end-diastolic pressure were almost identical in the two groups. Therefore, there was no apparent impairment of left ventricular function in emphysema. Ježek et al. (1964) found that in patients with chronic pulmonary disease without pulmonary hypertension at rest and in those with compensated cor pulmonale, the dynamics of contraction of both right and left ventricles were normal.

McMichael (1948) suggested that congestive failure associated with emphysema was a form of high output failure. However, there have been few subsequent data to support this. The cardiac output, measured by the direct Fick method, was significantly higher in 79 patients with cor pulmonale from emphysema (mean 3.3 liters per $M.^2$ per minute) than in 43 patients with hypertensive and ischemic heart disease (mean 2.6 liters) (Harvey et al., 1965). The difference was more pronounced in those studied between 1942 and 1949 than in those studied between 1950 and 1960. During the latter era, the arterial oxygen saturation was six per cent greater and the hematocrit six per cent less (mean values). It was felt that improved medical management of the underlying lung disease had reduced the number of patients encountered with abnormally high outputs (exceeding 4.0 liter per $M.^2$ per minute).

That hypoxemia is the most important factor accounting for the relatively high cardiac ouput during rest in some cases of decompensated cor pulmonale is suggested by the observation that the output decreases when compensation is regained (Harvey, 1964). Alternatively, the increased work of breathing during failure (Hammond, 1961) could account for this difference. In failure due to ischemic and other forms of heart disease, the output increases as compensation is regained. However, Wade and Bishop (1962), reviewing data from many sources, found no consistent change in cardiac output after recovery from failure secondary to emphysema. The mean cardiac index during failure was 3.7 liters per $M.^2$ per minute, and after recovery, it was 3.9 liters.

Wade and Bishop (1962) discussed the alterations in the distribution of systemic blood flow in emphysema. The renal blood flow averaged 18 per cent of the cardiac output in patients free from congestive heart failure, whereas in the presence of congestive failure, it was reduced to nine per cent. The mechanism of the renal vasoconstriction is unknown. Cerebral blood flow is increased in proportion to the increase in arterial levels of pCO_2 (Patterson et al., 1952). The resting coronary blood flow is within normal limits.

Shaw et al. (1965) measured cardiac output, intravascular pressures and blood gases at rest and during exercise in 44 patients with chronic irreversible obstructive airway disease and compared the results with those in normal subjects. During rest, the mean arteriovenous differences in oxygen content were 4.5 and 4.0 ml. per 100 ml., respectively. In most of the emphysematous patients, the cardiac output increased to a normal degree during exercise in both the upright and supine positions (Fig. 16-4). Pulmo-

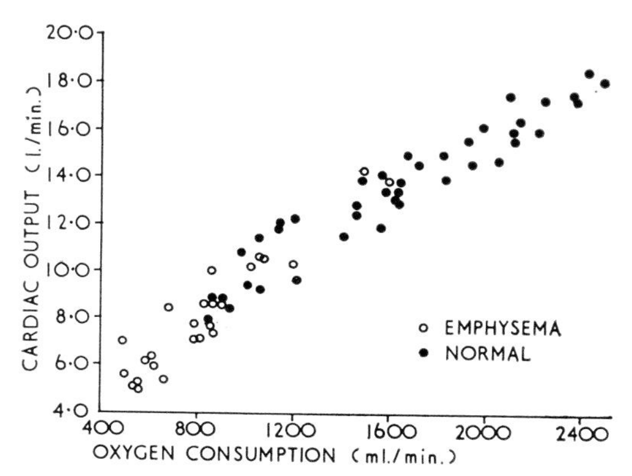

FIGURE 16-4. Relationship of cardiac output to oxygen consumption in 18 patients with emphysema (25 estimations) and 10 normal subjects (41 estima- (From Shaw, Grover, Reeves and Blount, Brit. Heart J., 27:674, tions) during treadmill exercise. 1965.)

nary hypertension was not responsible for the relatively low cardiac output in some of the patients; however, the output tended to be lower in the more severely hypoxemic patients.

Auscultatory signs suggesting the presence of tricuspid valve regurgitation are relatively common in rightsided failure secondary to chronic pulmonary disease (Verel et al., 1962). However, only one of 70 patients with cor pulmonale had a right atrial pressure tracing indicative of tricuspid regurgitation (Sherman et al., 1965). It is possible that a more sensitive technique, such as the use of indicator dilution curves, would reveal a higher incidence than is suggested by the contours of pressure pulses.

Although the hematocrit is often slightly increased in patients with chronic bronchitis and emphysema who have arterial desaturation (Vanier et al., 1963), substantial degrees of polycythemia are uncommon. In a highly selected and severely disabled group of 15 patients with chronic bronchitis complicated by polycythemia and increased blood viscosity, the mean pulmonary artery pressures were increased (28 to 60, average 47 mm. Hg), and the cardiac outputs were normal (2.3 to 4.3, average 3.3 liters per $M.^2$ per minute) in the resting state. During mild exercise, corresponding with an average oxygen consumption of 403 ml. per $M.^2$ per minute, the pulmonary artery pressures increased considerably, whereas the response of the cardiac output was impaired (Segel and Bishop, 1966). After repeated phlebotomy had restored the hematocrit and blood viscosity to normal, the mean pulmonary artery pressure decreased by an average of only 4 mm. Hg; in individual patients, there was a positive correlation between pulmonary artery pressure and total blood volume. In another group of patients with chronic bronchitis and no polycythemia, a rapid infusion of serum albumin increased the pulmonary arterial pressure. It was concluded that an increase in the total blood volume contributes importantly to the pulmonary hypertension in certain patients with chronic bronchitis, whereas an increase in blood viscosity per se has little effect.

OTHER CAUSES OF ALVEOLAR HYPOVENTILATION

Although alveolar hypoventilation with consequent development of cor pulmonale is most frequently the result of intrinsic pulmonary disease, a number of other conditions in which movement of the chest wall is restricted or in which the lungs are prevented from expanding adequately also result in alveolar hypoventilation. Some examples of these are shown in Table 16-3. Of these, kyphoscoliosis and severe obesity not infrequently progress to the development of cor pulmonale.

Kyphoscoliosis results from bending and rotation of the thoracic portion of the vertebral column and leads to shortening and distortion of the thoracic cage and to severe compression of the lungs (Hanley et al., 1958;

TABLE 16-3. Some Additional Causes of Alveolar Hypoventilation

BASIC DEFECT	EXAMPLES
1. Limitation of movement of entire thoracic wall	Kyphoscoliosis Severe obesity
2. Weakness or paralysis of muscles of respiration	Poliomyelitis Muscular dystrophy
3. Primary depression of the respiratory center	General anesthesia Cerebral hypoxia
4. Extrinsic limitation of lung movement	Pleural effusion Pneumothorax

Bergofsky et al., 1959; Caro and DuBois, 1961). The compliance of the chest wall is greatly diminished, and the work of breathing is increased. Respirations are rapid and shallow, probably because this pattern of breathing involves the least expenditure of effort. As a result, even though the total minute ventilation is normal or increased, alveolar hypoventilation is present and leads to hypoxemia and eventually to carbon dioxide retention. Additional deleterious factors include diminution in compliance of the lungs and disturbances in ventilation-perfusion relationships due to collapse of lung tissue or to uneven ventilation from regional changes in distensibility (Turino et al., 1965).

In less severe cases of kyphoscoliosis, the pulmonary arterial pressure is normal during rest, but during exercise, it increases out of proportion to the increase in cardiac output. In more advanced cases, owing to a combination of vasoconstriction from the effects of hypoxia, mechanical compression of some vessels and medial hypertrophy or intimal fibrosis in the smaller arteries and arterioles, the pulmonary artery pressure is abnormally high at rest. An inverse linear correlation has been demonstrated between pulmonary arterial pressure and the oxygen saturation of systemic arterial blood (Fig. 16-5). Correction of hypoxemia by the inhalation of 100 per cent oxygen reduces the pulmonary artery pressure even when, through depression of the respiratory center, hypoventilation results in a further increase in arterial pCO_2 and in increased acidosis. When the abnormal levels of pCO_2 and pH are corrected in addition to the pO_2, through treatment with a mechanical respirator, there is an additional decrease in the pulmonary artery pressure (Turino et al., 1965).

Hanley et al. (1958) found values of 66 to 71 per cent for arterial oxygen saturation and 65 to 74 mm. Hg for arterial pCO_2 in three patients with heart failure secondary to kyphoscoliosis. Corresponding values for 10 patients who had recovered from failure were 71 to 93 per cent and 33 to 64 mm. Hg. Bergofsky et al. (1959) found normal values for pulmonary blood flow during rest (2.8 to 3.7 liters per $M.^2$ per minute) in 13 subjects whose mean pulmonary artery pressures ranged from 10 to 33 mm. Hg.

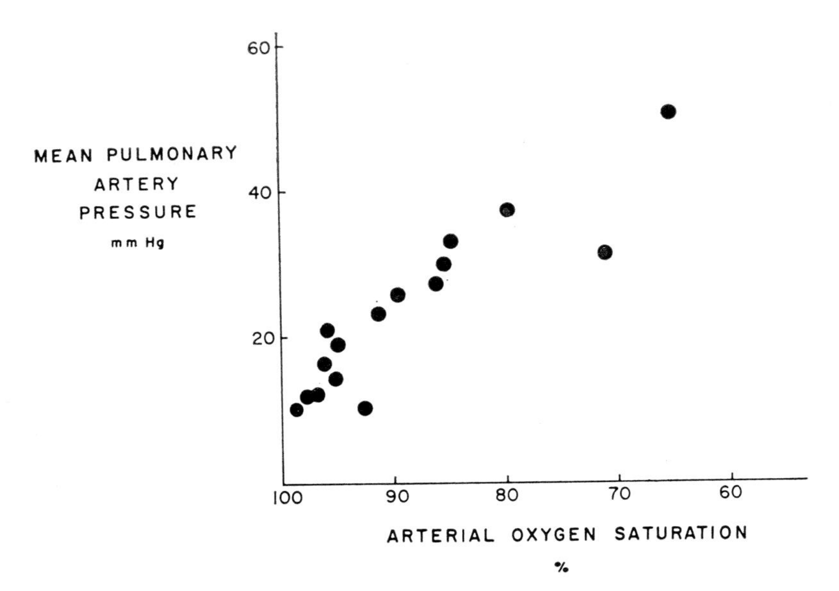

FIGURE 16-5. Relation between mean pulmonary artery pressure and systemic arterial oxygen saturation in patients with kyphoscoliosis. (From Turino, Goldring and Fishman, Bull. N.Y. Acad. Med., *41*:959, 1965.)

The pulmonary blood flow increased normally during exercise, with the increment averaging 700 ml. flow per 100 ml. additional oxygen consumption, but there was a disproportionate increase in pulmonary artery pressure. Thus, the enlargement of the right side of the heart in severe kyphoscoliosis is mainly determined by the increased pressure work associated with chronic pulmonary hypertension.

Cor pulmonale has also occurred in patients many years following thoracoplasty (Zimmerman, 1951), even when the contralateral lung was apparently healthy. Another condition that often results in gross distortion of the posteroanterior diameter of the thorax and displaces the heart and mediastinum is pectus excavatum. Although the distance between the lower end of the sternum and the vertebral column may be as short as one inch, there is little or no impairment of pulmonary function (Van Buchem and Nieveen, 1963). The heart appears enlarged in the anteroposterior projection, due to compression, but its total volume is not increased. Resting values for cardiac output and stroke volume are normal in both the supine and sitting positions. However, during exercise in the sitting position, the increase in stroke volume is less than usual, possibly because of impaired ventricular filling (Bevegård, 1962; Gattiker and Bühlman, 1966). Cor pulmonale does not occur.

Like pectus excavatum, the straight back syndrome is associated with a decreased diameter of the thorax, with apparent but not genuine cardiac enlargement, and with functional murmurs and other auscultatory phenomena (DeLeon et al., 1965). However, pulmonary and cardiac function again are quite normal, at least during rest.

Severe obesity (see Chapter 4) is associated with excessive deposition of adipose tissue over the chest wall and the abdomen. This may so limit movement of the thorax that even in the presence of a normal heart and lungs, alveolar hypoventilation leads to the occurrence of severe degrees of hypoxemia and hypercapnia (Sieker et al., 1955; Auchincloss et al., 1955; Burwell et al., 1956). Some patients develop increasing lethargy, drowsiness, periodic breathing and eventually unconsciousness, the so-called Pickwickian syndrome.

The oxygen cost of breathing in severe obesity is increased (Fig. 16-6). Naimark and Cherniack (1960) showed that the mean compliance of the total respiratory system (lungs and chest wall) was 0.119 liters per cm. H_2O in normal subjects but was only 0.052 liters per cm. H_2O in obese subjects. Since the compliances of the lungs were similar, the difference was due to a reduced compliance of the chest wall (0.077 liters per cm. H_2O in the obese, as compared with 0.224 liters per cm. H_2O in the normal group). The difference was further accentuated when measurements were made during recumbency. In addition to the decreased compliance of the chest wall, the high position of the diaphragm results in a reduced vital capacity. As with emphysema and kyphoscoliosis, the hypoxia and hyper-

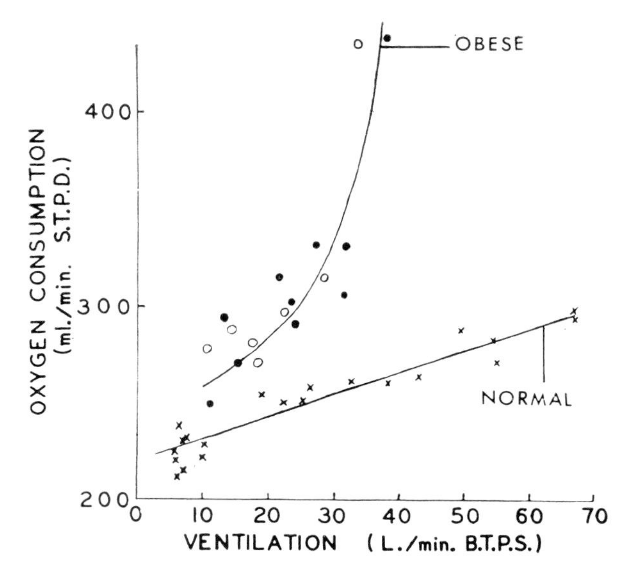

FIGURE 16-6. The change in oxygen consumption at increasing rates of minute ventilation in a normal and an obese subject. (From Cherniack, Canad. Med. Ass. J., *80*:613, 1959.)

TABLE 16-4. Changes in Arterial Gases and pH in a Patient with Alveolar Hypoventilation Due to Severe Obesity and Myxedema

DATE	pH (UNITS)	pCO_2 (MM. HG)	pO_2 (MM. HG)	O_2 SAT. (%)
10:14 (a)	7.39	65.5	33	65
10:20 (b)	7.17	>100	31	61
(c)	7.35	64	109	98
10:27	7.46	52	46	81
11:7 (d)	7.41	62	42	78

(a) On admission: weight 143 Kg.; height 153 cm.; protein-bound iodine 0.6 μg per 100 ml.; cyanosed, somnolent, with periods of apnea.
(b) Deeply comatose.
(c) Following mechanical ventilation with inhalation of oxygen.
(d) Alert and responsive. Weight 124 Kg.

capnia lead to an increase in pulmonary vascular resistance, and this is contributed to by the associated polycythemia. Intercurrent infections such as acute bronchitis and pneumonia lead to a further increase in the work of breathing and may precipitate decompensation. In advanced stages of the disease, right ventricular hypertrophy and congestive heart failure may occur. Cor pulmonale due to extreme obesity is reversible, provided the patient can be persuaded to lose sufficient weight. With progressive loss in weight, the hypoxemia and hypercapnia improve, and the polycythemia disappears.

Myxedema may also be associated with alveolar hypoventilation, and the unusual combination of severe obesity with myxedema is particularly liable to cause severe degrees of hypoxemia, hypercapnia and carbon dioxide narcosis. Blood gas values from such a case are shown in Table 16-4.

The other causes of alveolar hypoventilation listed in Table 16-3 less commonly progress to cor pulmonale. Five of 40 patients with chronic poliomyelitis studied by Cherniack et al. (1957) were found to have hemoglobin levels of 16.8 to 18.2 g. per 100 ml., hematocrits of 52 to 59 per cent and erythrocyte counts of 5.9 to 6.5 millions per c.mm. All had alveolar hypoventilation secondary to weakness of the respiratory muscles. Improvement in the blood counts followed an adequate period of treatment with intermittent mechanically aided respiration.

Grant and Arnold (1965) have drawn attention to the occasional occurrence of severe hypoventilation without apparent cause in persons who have no detectable abnormality of the lungs or chest wall. Arterial hypoxemia and hypercapnia are present. Voluntary overbreathing corrects the hypoxemia and the hypercapnia. The patients may develop the manifestations of carbon dioxide narcosis; they may also develop pulmonary hypertension and rightsided cardiac failure.

REFERENCES

Arias-Stella, J., and Saldaña, M.: Terminal portion of the pulmonary arterial tree in people native to high altitudes. Circulation, *28*:915, 1963.

Asmussen, E., and Nielsen, M.: The cardiac output in rest and work at low and high oxygen pressures. Acta Physiol. Scand., *35*:73, 1955.

Auchincloss, J. H., Jr., Cook, E., and Renzetti, A. D.: Clinical and physiologic aspects of a case of obesity, polycythemia and alveolar hyperventilation. J. Clin. Invest., *34*:1537, 1955.

Aviado, D. M., Jr.: The pharmacology of the pulmonary circulation. Pharm. Rev., *12*:159, 1960.

Aviado, D. M., Jr., Ling, J. S., and Schmidt, C. F.: Effects of anoxia in pulmonary circulation: reflex pulmonary vasoconstriction. Am. J. Physiol., *189*:253, 1957.

Barratt-Boyes, B. G., and Wood, E. H.: Hemodynamic response of healthy subjects to exercise in the supine position while breathing oxygen. J. Appl. Physiol., *11*:129, 1957.

Bergofsky, E. H., and Holtzman, S.: A study of the mechanisms involved in the pulmonary arterial pressor response to hypoxia. Circ. Research, *20*:506, 1967.

Bergofsky, E. H., Lehr, D. E., and Fishman, A. P.: The effect of changes in hydrogen ion concentration on the pulmonary circulation. J. Clin. Invest., *41*:1492, 1962.

Bergofsky, E. H., Lehr, D. E., Tuller, M. A., Rigatto, M., and Fishman, A. P.: The effects of acute alkalosis and acidosis on the pulmonary circulation. Ann. N. Y. Acad. Sci., *92*:627, 1961.

Bergofsky, E. H., Turino, G. M., and Fishman, A. P.: Cardiorespiratory failure in kyphoscoliosis. Medicine, *38*:263, 1959.

Bevegård, S.: Postural circulatory changes at rest and during exercise in patients with funnel chest, with special reference to factors affecting the stroke volume. Acta Med. Scand., *171*:695, 1962.

Bloomer, W. E., Harrison, W., Lindskog, G. E., and Liebow, A. A.: Respiratory function and blood flow in bronchial artery after ligation of pulmonary artery. Am. J. Physiol., *157*:317, 1949.

Boyd, D. L., Childress, R. H., Higgs, L. M., and Williams, J. F., Jr.: Left ventricular function in patients with chronic obstructive pulmonary disease. Circulation, *34* (Suppl. III):63, 1966 (Abstract).

Bradley, E. C., Adachi, R. T., and Weil, M. H.: Hemodynamic studies on clinical shock following pulmonary embolization. Clin. Res., *14*:122, 1966.

Brofman, B. L., Charms, B. L., Kohn, P. M., Elder, J., Newman, R., and Rizika, M.: Unilateral pulmonary artery occlusion in man. Control studies. J. Thorac. Cardiovasc. Surg., *34*:206, 1957.

Burwell, C. S., Robin, E. D., Whaley, R. D., and Bickelmann, A. G.: Extreme obesity associated with alveolar hypoventilation—a Pickwickian syndrome. Am. J. Med., *21*:819, 1956.

Caro, C. G., and Dubois, A. B.: Pulmonary function in kyphoscoliosis. Thorax, *16*:282, 1961.

Cherniack, R. M.: Respiratory effects of obesity. Canad. Med. Assoc. J., *80*:613,1959.

Cherniack, R. M., Ewart, W. B., and Hildes, J. A.: Polycythemia secondary to respiratory disturbances in poliomyelitis. Ann. Int. Med., *46*:720, 1957.

Chidsey, C. A., III, Fritts, H. W., Jr., Zocche, G. P., Himmelstein, A., and Cournand, A.: Effect of acetylcholine on the distribution of pulmonary blood flow in patients with chronic pulmonary emphysema. Mal. Cardiovasc., *1*:15, 1960.

Cobb, B., and Nanson, E. M.: Further studies with serotonin and experimental pulmonary embolism. Ann. Surg., *151*:501, 1960.

Comroe, J. H., Jr., Forster, R. E., II, DuBois, A. B., Briscoe, W. A., and Carlsen, A.: The Lung: Clinical Physiology and Pulmonary Function Tests. Second edition. Chicago, Year Book, 1962.

Cournand, A.: Control of the pulmonary circulation in normal man. In: Proceedings of the Harvey Tercentenary Congress. Ed. McMichael. Oxford, Blackwell, 1958.

DeLeon, A. C., Jr., Perloff, J. K., Twigg, H., and Majd, M.: The straight back syndrome. Clinical cardiovascular manifestations. Circulation, *32*:193, 1965.
Dexter, L., Whittenberger, J. L., Gorlin, R., Lewis, B. M., Haynes, F. W., and Spiegl, R. J.: The effect of chronic pulmonary disease (cor pulmonale and hypoxia) on the dynamics of the circulation in man. Trans. Assoc. Amer. Physicians, *64*:226, 1951.
Dintenfass, L., and Burnard, E. D.: Effect of hydrogen ion concentration on the in-vitro viscosity of packed red cells and blood at high hematocrits. Med. J. Australia, *1*:1072, 1966.
Donald, K. W., Bishop, J. M., Cumming, G., and Wade, O. L.: Effect of exercise on the cardiac output and circulatory dynamics of normal subjects. Clin. Sci., *14*:37, 1955.
Downing, S. E., Talner, N. S., and Gardner, T. H.: Cardiovascular responses to metabolic acidosis. Am. J. Physiol., *208*:237, 1965.
Dresdale, D. T., Schultz, M., and Michtom, R. J.: Primary pulmonary hypertension. I. Clinical and hemodynamic study. Am. J. Med., *11*:686, 1951.
Duke, H. N.: Observations of the effect of hypoxia on the pulmonary vascular bed. J. Physiol., *135*:45, 1957.
Duke, H. N., Killick, E. M., and Marchant, J. V.: Changes in pH of the perfusate during hypoxia in isolated perfused cat lungs. J. Physiol., *153*:413, 1960.
Edwards, J. E., and Heath, D.: Configuration of elastic tissue of pulmonary trunk in idiopathic pulmonary hypertension. Circulation, *21*:59, 1960.
Enson, Y., Giuntini, C., Lewis, M. L., Morris, T. Q., Ferrer, M. I., and Harvey, R. M.: The influence of hydrogen ion concentration and hypoxia on the pulmonary circulation. J. Clin. Invest., *43*:1146, 1964.
Ferrer, M. I., and Harvey, R. M.: Decompensated pulmonary heart disease with a note on the effect of digitalis. In: Pulmonary Circulation. Eds. Adams and Veith. New York, Grune & Stratton, 1958.
Fishman, A. P.: Respiratory gases in the regulation of the pulmonary circulation. Physiol. Rev., *41*:214, 1961.
Fritts, H. W., Jr., Harris, P., Clauss, R. H., Odell, J. E., and Cournand, A.: The effect of acetylcholine on the human pulmonary circulation under normal and hypoxic conditions. J. Clin. Invest., *36*:99, 1958.
Gardiner, J. M.: The effect of "priscol" in pulmonary hypertension. Australas. Ann. Med., *3*:59, 1954.
Gattiker, H., and Bühlmann, A.: Cardiopulmonary function and exercise tolerance in supine and sitting position in patients with pectus excavatum. Helv. Med. Acta, *33*:122, 1966.
Gorham, I. W.: A study of pulmonary embolism. III. The mechanism of pain; based on a clinico-pathological investigation of 100 cases of minor and 100 cases of massive embolism of the pulmonary artery. A.M.A. Arch. Int. Med., *108*:418, 1961.
Grant, J. L., and Arnold, W., Jr.: Idiopathic hypoventilation. J.A.M.A., *194*:119, 1965.
Grover, R. F., Reeves, J. T., Will, D. H., and Blount, S. G., Jr.: Pulmonary vasoconstriction in steers at high altitude. J. Appl. Physiol., *18*:567, 1963.
Halmagyi, D. F. J., and Colebatch, H. J. H.: Cardiorespiratory effects of experimental lung embolism. J. Clin. Invest., *40*:1785, 1961.
Halmagyi, D. F. J., Felkai, B., Czipott, Z., and Kovacs, G.: The effect of Serpasil in pulmonary hypertension. Brit. Heart J., *19*:375, 1957.
Hammond, J. D. S.: The work of breathing in patients with chronic cor pulmonale. Clin. Sci., *20*:107, 1961.
Hanley, T., Platts, M. M., Clifton, M., and Morris, T. L.: Heart failure of the hunchback. Quart. J. Med., *27*:155, 1958.
Harris, P., and Heath, D.: The Human Pulmonary Circulation. Its Form and Function in Health and Disease. Edinburgh, Livingstone, 1962.
Harvey, R. M. In: Herzinsuffizienz. Hämodynamik, und Stoffwechsel. Internationales Symposion. Stuttgart, Thieme, 1964.

Harvey, R. M.: The influence of hydrogen ion in the control of pulmonary artery pressures in patients with obstructive disease of the lungs. Medicina Thorac., *22*:108, 1965.
Harvey, R. M., Enson, Y., Betti, R., Lewis, M. L., Rochester, D. F., and Ferrer, M. I.: Further observations on the effect of hydrogen ion on the pulmonary circulation. Circulation, *35*:1019, 1967.
Harvey, R. M., Enson, Y., Cournand, A., and Ferrer, M. I.: Cardiac output in cor pulmonale. Arch. Kreislaufforsch., *46*:7,1965.
Heath, D., and Edwards, J. E.: The pathology of hypertensive pulmonary vascular disease. Description of six grades of structural changes in the pulmonary arteries with special reference to congenital cardiac septal defects. Circulation, *18*:533, 1958.
Hickam, J. B., and Cargill, W. H.: Effect of exercise on cardiac output and pulmonary arterial pressure in normal persons and in patients with cardiovascular disease and pulmonary emphysema. J. Clin. Invest., *27*:10, 1948.
Howarth, S., and Lowe, J. B.: The mechanism of effort syncope in primary pulmonary hypertension and cyanotic congenital heart disease. Brit. Heart J., *15*:47, 1953.
Hyman, A. L., Myers, W. D., and Meyer, A.: The effect of acute pulmonary embolus upon cardiopulmonary hemodynamics. Am. Heart J., *67*:313, 1964.
Ježek, V., Daum, S., and Šerf, B.: Heart contraction in chronic cor pulmonale. Cor et Vasa (Praha), *6*:86, 1964.
Katz, L. N.: Pulmonary embolism. Dis. Chest, *11*:249, 1945.
Kjellberg, S. R., and Olsson, S. E.: Roentgenological studies of experimental pulmonary embolism without complicating infarction in dogs. Acta Radiol., *33*:507, 1950.
Kuida, H., Dammin, G. J., Haynes, F. W., Rapaport, E., and Dexter, L.: Primary pulmonary hypertension. Am. J. Med., *23*:166, 1957.
Kwaan, H. C., and McFadzean, A. J. S.: On plasma fibrinolytic activity induced by ischaemia. Clin. Sci., *15*:245, 1956.
Lee, G. de J., and DuBois, A. B.: Pulmonary capillary blood flow in man. J. Clin. Invest., *34*:1380, 1955.
Lee, T. D., Jr., Roveti, G. C., and Ross, R. S.: The hemodynamic effects of isoproterenol on pulmonary hypertension in man. Am. Heart J., *65*:361, 1963.
Liebow, A. A., Hales, M. R., and Bloomer, W.: In: Pulmonary Circulation. Eds. Adams and Veith. New York, Grune & Stratton, 1959.
Liljestrand, G.: Chemical control of the distribution of the pulmonary blood flow. Acta Physiol. Scand., *44*:216, 1958.
Lincoln, A. F., Moorman, J. A., and Schultz, R. L.: Fibrinolysis following thoracic surgery. Surg. Gyn. Obst., *105*:541, 1957.
Malinow, M. R., Katz, L. N., and Kondo, B.: Is there a vagal pulmonocoronary reflex in pulmonary embolism? Am. Heart J., *31*:702, 1946.
Marshall, R., and Allison, P. R.: Pulmonary embolism by small bood clots. Thorax, *17*:289, 1962.
Marshall, R. J., Helmholz, H. F., and Shepherd, J. T.: Effect of acetylcholine on pulmonary vascular resistance in a patient with idiopathic pulmonary hypertension. Circulation, *20*:391, 1959.
McMichael, J.: Pulmonary heart disease acute and chronic. Brit. Heart J., *10*:80, 1948.
Motley, H. L.: The mechanisms of chronic pulmonary heart disease (cor pulmonale), with and without arterial hypoxemia. Prog. Cardiovasc. Dis., *1*:326, 1958.
Naimark, A., and Cherniack, R. M.: Compliance of the respiratory system and its components in health and obesity. J. Appl. Physiol., *15*:377, 1960.
Nakhjavan, F. K., Palmer, W. H., and McGregor, M.: Influence of respiration on venous return in pulmonary emphysema. Circulation, *33*:8,1966.
Nathan, H., and Eliakim, M.: The junction between the left atrium and the pulmonary veins. An anatomic study of human hearts. Circulation, *34*:412, 1966.
Niewiarowski, S., and Latallo, Z.: Comparative studies of the fibrinolytic system of sera of various vertebrates. Thromb. Diath. Haem., *3*:404, 1959.

Parker, J. O., Kelkar, K., and West, R. O.: Hemodynamic effects of aminophylline in cor pulmonale. Circulation, *33*:17, 1966.

Patterson, J. L., Heyman, A., and Duke, T. W.: Cerebral circulation and metabolism in chronic pulmonary emphysema, with observations on effects of inhalation of oxygen. Am. J. Med., *12*:382, 1952.

Peñaloza, D., Sime, F., Banchero, N., Gamboa, R., Cruz, J., and Marticorena, E.: Pulmonary hypertension in healthy men born and living at high altitudes. Am. J. Cardiol., *11*:150, 1963.

Riley, R. L., Himmelstein, A., Motley, H. L., Weiner, H. M., and Cournand, A.: Studies of the pulmonary circulation at rest and during exercise in normal individuals and in patients with chronic pulmonary disease. Am. J. Physiol., *152*:372, 1948.

Rosenberg, S. A.: A study of the etiological basis of primary pulmonary hypertension. Am. Heart J., *68*:484, 1964.

Rudolph, A. M., and Yuan, S.: Response of the pulmonary vasculature to hypoxia and H^+ ion concentration changes. J. Clin. Invest., *45*:399, 1966.

Samet, P., and Bernstein, W. H.: Loss of reactivity of the pulmonary vascular bed in primary pulmonary hypertension. Am. Heart J., *66*:197, 1963.

Samet, P., Bernstein, W. H., and Widrich, J.: Intracardiac infusion of acetylcholine in primary pulmonary hypertension. Am. Heart J., *60*:433, 1960.

Scherf, D., and Schönbrunner, E.: Über den pulmocoronaren Reflex bei Lungenembolien. Klin. Wcschr., *16*:340, 1937.

Segel, N., and Bishop, J. M.: The circulation in patients with chronic bronchitis and emphysema at rest and during exercise, with special reference to the influence of changes in blood viscosity and blood volume on the pulmonary circulation. J. Clin. Invest., *45*:1555, 1966.

Shaw, D. B., Grover, R. F., Reeves, J. T., and Blount, G., Jr.: Pulmonary circulation in chronic bronchitis and emphysema. Brit. Heart J., *27*:674, 1965.

Shepherd, J. T., Edwards, J. E., Burchell, H. B., Swan, H. J. C., and Wood, E. H.: Clinical, physiological and pathological considerations in patients with idiopathic pulmonary hypertension. Brit. Heart J., *19*:70, 1957.

Shepherd, J. T., Semler, H. J., Helmholz, H. F., Jr., and Wood, E. H.: Effects of infusion of acetylcholine on pulmonary vascular resistance in patients with pulmonary hypertension and congenital heart disease. Circulation, *20*:381, 1959.

Sherman, W. T., Ferrer, M. I., and Harvey, R. M.: Competence of the tricuspid valve in pulmonary heart disease (cor pulmonale). Circulation, *31*:517, 1965.

Sieker, H. O., Estes, E. H., Jr., Kelser, G. A., and McIntosh, H. D.: A cardiopulmonary syndrome associated with extreme obesity. J. Clin. Invest., *34*:916, 1955 (Abstract).

Sleeper, J. C., Orgain, E. S., and McIntosh, H. D.: Primary pulmonary hypertension. Review of clinical features and pathologic physiology with a report of pulmonary hemodynamics derived from repeated catheterization. Circulation, *26*: 1358, 1962.

Smith, G. T., Dammin, G. J., and Dexter, L.: Postmortem arteriographic studies of the human lung in pulmonary embolization. J.A.M.A., *188*:143, 1964.

Söderholm, B., and Werkö, L.: Acetylcholine and the pulmonary circulation in mitral valvular disease. Brit. Heart J., *21*:1, 1959.

Steinberg, B., and Mundy, C. S.: Experimental pulmonary embolism and infarction. Arch. Path., *22*:529, 1936.

Thomas, D. P., and Gurewich, V.: Role of platelets in sudden death induced by experimental pulmonary emboli. Circulation, *32* (Suppl. II):207, 1965 (Abstract).

Turino, G. M., Goldring, R. M., and Fishman, A. P.: Cor pulmonale in musculoskeletal abnormalities of the thorax. Ann. N.Y. Acad. Med., *41*:959, 1965.

Van Buchem, F. S. P., and Nieveen, J.: Pectus excavatum. Acta Med. Scand., *174*:657, 1963.

Vanier, T., Dulfano, M. J., Wu, C., and Desforges, J. F.: Emphysema, hypoxia and the polycythemic response. New Eng. J. Med., *269*:169, 1963.

Verel, D., Sandler, G., and Mazurkie, S. J.: Tricuspid incompetence in cor pulmonale. Brit. Heart J., *24*:441, 1962.
Wade, G., and Ball, J.: Unexplained pulmonary hypertension. Quart. J. Med., *26*:83, 1957.
Wade, O. L., and Bishop, J. M.: Cardiac Output and Regional Blood Flow. Oxford, Blackwell, 1962.
Zimmerman, H. A.: Hemodynamic studies on a group of patients who developed cor pulmonale following thoracoplasty. J. Thorac. Cardiovasc. Surg., *22*:94, 1951.

INDEX